THEORETICAL EVALUATION
OF CHEMICAL PROPELLANTS

PRENTICE-HALL INTERNATIONAL SERIES IN SPACE TECHNOLOGY
C. W. Besserer and Floyd E. Nixon, Editors

PRENTICE-HALL, INC.
PRENTICE-HALL INTERNATIONAL, UNITED KINGDOM AND EIRE
PRENTICE-HALL OF CANADA, LTD., CANADA

ALEXANDER AND BAILEY *Systems Engineering Mathematics*
BAZOVSKY *Reliability Theory and Practice*
ELLIS AND LUDWIG *Systems Philosophy*
FOGEL *Biotechnology: Concepts and Applications*
GERATHEWOHL *Principles of Bioastronautics*
KOLK *Modern Flight Dynamics*
LINDEN *Printed Circuits in Space Technology*
LLOYD AND LIPOW *Reliability: Management, Methods and Mathematics*
LOH *Dynamics and Thermodynamics of Planetary Entry*
MACKAY *Design of Space Power Plants*
MACOMBER AND FERNANDEZ *Inertial Guidance Engineering*
NELSON AND LOFT *Space Mechanics*
ORDWAY, GARDNER, AND SHARPE *Basic Astronautics*
ORDWAY, GARDNER, SHARPE AND WAKEFORD *Applied Astronautics*
SAMARAS *Applications of Ion Flow Dynamics*
SAMARAS *Theory of Ion Flow Dynamics*
SANDLER *System Reliability Engineering*
SCHLESINGER, ET AL. *Principles of Electronic Warfare*
SLAGER *Space Medicine*
STEARNS *Navigation and Guidance in Space*
STILTZ (ED.) *Aerospace Telemetry*
WILKINS *Theoretical Evaluation of Chemical Propellants*

PRENTICE-HALL INTERNATIONAL, INC., *London*
PRENTICE-HALL OF AUSTRALIA, PTY., LTD., *Sydney*
PRENTICE-HALL OF CANADA, LTD., *Toronto*
PRENTICE-HALL FRANCE, S.A.R.L., *Paris*
PRENTICE-HALL OF JAPAN, INC., *Tokyo*
PRENTICE-HALL DE MEXICO, S.A., *Mexico City*

THEORETICAL EVALUATION
OF CHEMICAL PROPELLANTS

ROGER LAWRENCE WILKINS

Member of the Technical Staff
AEROSPACE CORPORATION

PRENTICE-HALL, INC.
Englewood Cliffs, N.J.

To NASIRA, who gave up her career in physics
for the more difficult task of being a mother

PREFACE

There are a number of texts which describe from an elementary viewpoint the theoretical performance evaluation of chemical propellants. Many of these books assume that the reader can obtain from the published literature the necessary thermodynamic data required to make performance calculations for propellant systems that produce multi-phase combustion species characterized by complex chemical equilibria. In many instances the required data are not available. Furthermore, the thermodynamic data used in many texts are compiled from various sources, and very few details are given to explain how the original data were calculated.

This book is written for those readers who wish to learn how to calculate thermodynamic data of multi-phase species and how to use the results of such calculations to compute the equilibrium composition of complex systems. Once the reader has developed these skills, he can apply the results of such calculations to a wide range of combustion problems.

The reader will find that a broad knowledge of theoretical chemistry is not essential for the reading of this text, although a knowledge of thermodynamics is assumed. Theoretical chemical information is included in the text whenever it is required for purposes of the discussion. Reference sources are presented where more detailed information may be obtained on the topics discussed in this text. For the more difficult sections of the text, illustrative examples are presented.

The first chapter discusses several methods of computing thermodynamic properties of substances in the ideal gas state from molecular structure data. Methods are described which can be used to estimate thermodynamic data from scanty experimental data. A review is given of the pertinent literature available on spectra data of compounds of elements in the first three rows of the periodic chart. Chapter Two presents a brief outline of a method for computing the thermodynamic functions of a solid from spectroscopic data and several methods for estimating the frequency spectrum of a solid from experimental data. A brief outline is presented of a procedure that has been used for computing thermodynamic properties of normal liquids using a partition function. A review is given of the relevant literature on the thermodynamic properties of solids and liquids for compounds of elements in the first three rows of the periodic chart. Chapter Three treats theoretical methods of estimating thermochemical properties of chemical compounds. A discussion is given of the pertinent literature on thermochemical properties of compounds of elements in the first three rows of the periodic chart.

In Chapter Four the results of the first three chapters are used to calculate equilibrium coefficients for individual chemical species. The methods described in this chapter for computing chemical equilibria are quite general and are not restricted by the chemical nature of the system. They can be applied to systems consisting of a gas phase which may be, but not necessarily, in equilibrium with one or more condensed phases.

The material presented in the first four chapters of this text can be used for a variety of combustion problems, such as calculating the values of theoretical parameters behind normal shock waves, detonation velocities, thermodynamic properties of plasmas, thermodynamic properties of any chemical system, and in calculating the theoretical performance of rocket propellants. Chapter Five applies the results of the first four chapters to a discussion of the performance of chemical propellants for rocket engines. Theoretical data are given for propellants systems containing hydrogen, oxygen, carbon, nitrogen, fluorine, and chlorine. Typical results obtained with metallized propellants such as lithium, boron, beryllium, aluminum, and magnesium are also presented.

Finally, the appendices are composed of series of tables that are useful in working many types of combustion problems. Using the Appendix 1 tables, the reader can compute thermodynamic data that includes anharmonic corrections. Appendices 2–4 list newly computed tables for the thermodynamic properties of over two hundred chemical species.

Useful criticisms of parts of the text have been made by Mr. Howard Myers, Mrs. Nasira Wilkins, and Dr. N. A. Gokcen.

For essential help with the typing, I am greatly obliged to Klara Toyama, Carol Giles, Gail DiBenedetto, and Mary Abell. To my wife, Nasira, I wish to express my thanks for her generously given labor in proofreading the manuscript and for offering many valuable suggestions.

ROGER L. WILKINS

CONTENTS

THEORETICAL EVALUATION
OF CHEMICAL PROPELLANTS

1

CALCULATION OF THERMO-DYNAMIC FUNCTIONS FOR IDEAL GASES

1.1. DEFINITIONS AND UNITS

1.1.1. Introduction

It is usually very difficult, often tedious, and sometimes impossible to determine experimentally the heat capacity of gases at elevated temperatures. However, molecular data obtained from spectra can be used to predict thermodynamic functions such as heat capacity, heat content, and entropy of gases. Frequently, thermodynamic functions calculated from spectroscopic data are more accurate than those determined by thermal measurements. This chapter presents some of the more important techniques of numerical calculation of thermodynamic functions of ideal gases from spectroscopic data.

1.1.2. Physical constants

At least three different sets of values of the fundamental constants have appeared in the last decade.[1] DuMond and Cohen[2,3] have prepared the most

[1] J. W. M. DuMond and E. R. Cohen, *Revs. Modern Phys.*, **25** (1953), 691; **27** (1955), 363.

[2] J. W. M. DuMond and E. R. Cohen, *Revs. Modern Phys.*, **27** (1955), 363.

[3] J. W. M. DuMond and E. R. Cohen, *Present Sources of Precise Information on the Universal Physical Constants* (Bologna, Italy: Nicola Zanichelli Editore, 1957).

recent review of the constants, which we have adopted. The fundamental constants in the reviews by DuMond and Cohen[3, 4] are tabulated in terms of the *physical mole* rather than the *chemical mole*[5] and must be corrected for use in chemical calculations. This has been done with the conversion factor 1.000272.[3] The following additional conversion factors also apply.

1 thermochemical calorie = 4.1840 joules (Ref. 6)
1 atmosphere = 1.01325×10^6 dyne/cm^2 (Ref. 6)
1 electron volt = $(1.60206 \pm 0.00003) \times 10^{-12}$ ergs (Ref. 3)

The molecular constants used in this chapter are listed below.

Avogadro's number	N	6.02322×10^{23} molecules/mole
Planck's constant	h	6.62517×10^{-27} erg-sec
velocity of light	c	2.99793×10^{10} cm/sec
Boltzmann's constant	k	1.38044×10^{-16} erg/deg
second radiation constant	hc/k	1.43880 cm-deg
gas constant per mole	$\begin{cases} R \\ R \end{cases}$	8.31469×10^7 erg/mole-deg$\quad 1.98725$ cal/mole-deg

1.1.3. Partition function

In statistical mechanics[7] the function

$$Q = \sum_K g_K \exp\left(-\frac{\epsilon_K}{kT}\right) \tag{1.1}$$

plays a well-known and important part. Q is called the *total partition function* or the *sum-over-states*. The energy of the system in energy state K is ϵ_K, and T is the absolute temperature in degrees Kelvin. The permitted energy states, or quantum states, K, are determined from quantum mechanics, while the energies of the permitted energy states or quantum states are determined from spectroscopic measurements. An energy level is said to be *degenerate* if more than one energy state has the same energy level ϵ_K. Degenerate levels are given a *statistical weight*, g_K, representing the number of quantum states with identical energy level ϵ_K. The terms *degeneracy* and *statistical weight* are used interchangeably. All thermodynamic properties of interest can be calculated from this partition function, Q.

An *ideal gas* is a gas dilute enough so that the interaction between particles

[4] J. W. M. DuMond and E. R. Cohen, *Revs. Modern Phys.*, **25** (1953), 691.

[5] The *physical mole* is based on 16 as the assigned exact mass of oxygen O^{16}. The *chemical mole* is based on the mass of 16 assigned to a mixture of three isotopes of oxygen, O^{16}, O^{17}, and O^{18}, in their naturally occurring abundance ratios.

[6] G. Herzberg, *Spectra of Diatomic Molecules* (Princeton, N.J.: D. Van Nostrand Co., Inc., 1950).

[7] See, for example, J. E. Mayer and M. G. Mayer, *Statistical Mechanics* (New York: John Wiley & Sons, Inc., 1940).

of the gas can be neglected. The total energy of an ideal gas can be written as the sum of its translational and internal energy

$$\epsilon = \epsilon_t + \epsilon_i \tag{1.2}$$

The subscript K is omitted for convenience in writing the subsequent expressions. The subscripts t and i stand for translational and internal, respectively. Consequently, ϵ_t is the translational energy and ϵ_i is the internal energy of the system. Since it is shown in quantum mechanics[8] that the translational and internal motions are independent of each other, it follows that the total partition function for an ideal gas is the product of its translational and internal partition functions

$$Q = Q_t Q_i \tag{1.3}$$

Using Eqs. (1.3) and (1.1) it is clear that the total statistical weight, g, can be written as a product

$$g = g_t g_i \tag{1.4}$$

According to Eq. (1.1) the translational partition function is given by the relation

$$Q_t = \sum_t g_t \exp \left(\frac{-\epsilon_t}{kT} \right) \tag{1.5}$$

and the internal partition function is given by the relation

$$Q_i = \sum_i g_i \exp \left(\frac{-\epsilon_i}{kT} \right) \tag{1.6}$$

The translational partition function Q_t for an ideal gas is derived in standard texts on statistical mechanics, and is given by

$$Q_t = \left[\frac{(2\pi mkT)^{3/2} V}{h^3} \right] \tag{1.7}$$

where V is the volume, m is the absolute mass of the atom or molecule, and the other symbols have their usual meaning.

We can calculate the internal partition function Q_i after g_i and ϵ_i are determined from either spectroscopic measurements or quantum mechanics. The internal energy ϵ_i of a molecule is the sum of vibrational, rotational, electronic, rotation-vibration interaction, vibration-electronic interaction, and so on

$$\epsilon_i = \epsilon_v + \epsilon_r + \epsilon_{el} + \epsilon_{v,r} + \epsilon_{r,el} + \cdots \tag{1.8}$$

where subscript v is for vibration, r is for rotation, el is for electronic. A subscript with double symbols is used to denote interaction between two different degrees of freedom. For example, double subscript v,r denotes vibration-rotation interaction. If the various motions of the system are

---

[8] See, for example, J. L. Powell and B. Crasemann, *Quantum Mechanics* (Reading, Mass.: Addison-Wesley Publishing Co., Inc., 1961).

uncoupled, then the total statistical weight is the product of the vibrational, rotational, electronic, and other statistical weights. For most polyatomic molecules the electronic energy can be neglected, since the population of molecules in excited states are negligible compared to the population of molecules in the ground state. The exceptions are molecules with low-lying energy states (for example, ClO_2, CCl, CF, and other free radicals). If we neglect the electronic, and other interactions (except vibration-rotation interaction) which the molecule may experience as a result of coupling or interaction between various degrees of freedom, we write for the internal energy of a molecule

$$\epsilon_i = \epsilon_v + \epsilon_r + \epsilon_{v,r} \tag{1.9}$$

and for the internal statistical weight

$$g_i = g_v g_r \tag{1.10}$$

where g_v is the statistical weight of the vibrational levels without rotation and g_r is the statistical weight of the rotational levels without vibration. If Eqs. (1.9) and (1.10) are substituted into Eq. (1.6), we obtain

$$Q_i = \sum_v g_v \exp\left(\frac{-\epsilon_v}{kT}\right) \sum_r g_r \exp\left(\frac{-(\epsilon_r + \epsilon_{v,r})}{kT}\right) \tag{1.11}$$

where for each vibrational level one must sum over all rotational levels.

It is very tedious to evaluate Q_i by *direct summation* according to Eq. (1.11). If interaction between vibration and rotation is neglected, one writes for molecules

$$Q_i = Q_v \cdot Q_r \tag{1.12}$$

where

$$Q_v = \sum_v g_v \exp\left(\frac{-\epsilon_v}{kT}\right) \tag{1.13}$$

and

$$Q_r = \sum_r g_r \exp\left(\frac{-\epsilon_r}{kT}\right) \tag{1.14}$$

Each factor in Eqs. (1.13) and (1.14) can be evaluated separately. In Secs. 1.3 and 1.4 we will discuss the use of partition functions to calculate thermodynamic functions for diatomic and polyatomic molecules.

The monatomic gas has only translational, electronic, and nuclear degrees of freedom. The internal energy, ϵ_i, of a monatomic gas is the sum of electronic and nuclear contributions

$$\epsilon_i = \epsilon_{el} + \epsilon_n \tag{1.15}$$

Since these energies are independent of each other for dilute gases, we write the internal statistical weight g_i for a monatomic gas as a product of the electronic and nuclear statistical weights

$$g_i = g_{el} g_n \tag{1.16}$$

It can be shown by substituting Eqs. (1.15) and (1.16) into Eq. (1.1) that the internal partition function for a monatomic gas is

$$Q_i = Q_{el}Q_n \qquad (1.17)$$

where from Eq. (1.1)

$$Q_{el} = \sum_{el} g_{el} \exp\left(\frac{-\epsilon_{el}}{kT}\right) \qquad (1.18)$$

and

$$Q_n = \sum_{n} g_n \exp\left(\frac{-\epsilon_n}{kT}\right) \qquad (1.19)$$

We write for the *molar partition function* for a monatomic gas according to standard texts on statistical mechanics [9] that

$$Q = \frac{(Q_iQ_{el}Q_n)^N}{N!} = \frac{(Q_i)^N}{N!}(Q_{el}Q_n)^N \qquad (1.20)$$

The computation of the thermodynamic functions for a monatomic gas from the molar partition function in Eq. (1.20) will be discussed in Sec. 1.2.

It is convenient to evaluate the following four thermodynamic functions of a given substance in the ideal gaseous reference state of unit pressure:

C_p^0, the heat capacity at constant pressure, cal/mole °K
$H_T^0 - H_0^0$, the heat content, kcal/mole
$-(F_T^0 - H_0^0)/T$, the free energy function, cal/mole °K
S_T^0, the entropy, cal/mole °K.

In the thermodynamic functions, the superscript zero denotes the ideal gaseous reference state and subscript zero denotes the absolute zero of temperature. These thermodynamic functions usually are tabulated in tables in the literature in the units listed. These four thermodynamic functions are expressed in texts on statistical mechanics or physical chemistry [10] in terms of the total molar partition function, Q, as

$$\frac{C_P^0}{R} = \frac{d}{dT}T\left(\frac{d\ln Q}{d\ln T}\right) \qquad (1.21)$$

$$\frac{(H_T^0 - H_0^0)}{RT} = \left(\frac{d\ln Q}{d\ln T}\right) \qquad (1.22)$$

$$\frac{-(F_T^0 - H_0^0)}{RT} = \ln Q \qquad (1.23)$$

$$\frac{S_T^0}{R} = \ln Q + \left(\frac{d\ln Q}{d\ln T}\right) \qquad (1.24)$$

[9] See, for example, J. E. Mayer and M. G. Mayer, *Statistical Mechanics* (New York: John Wiley & Sons, Inc., 1940).
[10] See, for example, W. J. Moore, *Physical Chemistry* (Englewood Cliffs, N.J.: Prentice-Hall, Inc., 1955).

1.2. THERMODYNAMIC FUNCTIONS FOR ATOMS

1.2.1. Introduction

The atom does not have vibrational or rotational degrees of freedom. Consequently, the energy of the atom is the sum of terms corresponding to translational, electronic, and nuclear energy. We write

$$\epsilon = \epsilon_t + \epsilon_{el} + \epsilon_n \tag{1.25}$$

and the statistical weight

$$g = g_t g_{el} g_n \tag{1.26}$$

If one substitutes Eqs. (1.7), (1.18), and (1.19) into Eq. (1.20) one obtains for the molar partition function for a monatomic gas

$$Q = \frac{1}{N!} \left[\frac{(2\pi mkT)^{3/2} V}{h^3} \right]^N \left[\sum_n g_n \exp\left(\frac{-\epsilon_n}{kT} \right) \right]^N \left[\sum_{el} g_{el} \exp\left(\frac{-\epsilon_{el}}{kT} \right) \right]^N \tag{1.27}$$

Most compilations of energy levels for electronic and nuclear spectra are listed relative to the ground state. Usually absolute values of the energy levels are not given for series spectra. Consequently the electronic and nuclear energy in the ground state are taken as zero. The nuclear energy of the first excited state of most atoms is of the order of 10^6 electron volts or about 10^{10} degrees Kelvin. It is clear, therefore, from Eq. (1.19), that at ordinary temperatures the atom will be in the nuclear ground state. Since ϵ_n is taken as zero in the nuclear ground state, Eq. (1.27) can be written as

$$\ln Q = N \ln \left[\frac{(2\pi mkT)^{3/2} V}{h^3} \right] - \ln N! + N \ln g_n$$

$$+ N \ln \left[\sum_{el} g_{el} \exp\left(\frac{-\epsilon_{el}}{kT} \right) \right] \tag{1.28}$$

For an ideal gas

$$V = \frac{kNT}{P} \tag{1.29}$$

where P is the pressure of the gas expressed in units of dynes/cm^2 and from Sterling's formula for the factorial of large numbers

$$N! = \left(\frac{N}{e} \right)^N \tag{1.30}$$

where the constant e is 2.7182818. Thus Eq. (1.28) can be written

$$\ln Q = N \ln \left[\frac{\left(2\pi \frac{M}{N} kT \right)^{3/2}}{h^3} \left(\frac{kT}{P} \right) e \right] + N \ln g_n$$

$$+ N \ln \left[\sum_{el} g_{el} \exp\left(\frac{-\epsilon_{el}}{kT} \right) \right] \tag{1.31}$$

Table 1.1. TABLE OF ATOMIC WEIGHTS*

At. no.	Name	Symbol	At. wt	At. no.	Name	Symbol	At. wt
1	Hydrogen	H	1.0080	52	Tellurium	Te	127.61
2	Helium	He	4.003	53	Iodine	I	126.91
				54	Xenon	Xe	131.30
3	Lithium	Li	6.940				
4	Beryllium	Be	9.013	55	Cesium	Cs	132.91
5	Boron	B	10.82	56	Barium	Ba	137.36
6	Carbon	C	12.011	57	Lanthanum	La	138.92
7	Nitrogen	N	14.008				
8	Oxygen	O	16	58	Cerium	Ce	140.13
9	Fluorine	F	19.0	59	Praseodymium	Pr	140.92
10	Neon	Ne	20.183	60	Neodymium	Nd	144.27
				61	Promethium	Pm	..
11	Sodium	Na	22.991	62	Samarium	Sm	150.35
12	Magnesium	Mg	24.32	63	Europium	Eu	152.0
13	Aluminum	Al	26.98	64	Gadolinium	Gd	157.26
14	Silicon	Si	28.09	65	Terbium	Tb	158.93
15	Phosphorus	P	30.975	66	Dysprosium	Dy	162.51
16	Sulfur	S	32.066†	67	Holmium	Ho	164.94
17	Chlorine	Cl	35.457	68	Erbium	Er	167.27
18	Argon	Ar	39.944	69	Thulium	Tm	168.94
				70	Ytterbium	Yb	173.04
19	Potassium	K	39.100	71	Lutetium	Lu	174.99
20	Calcium	Ca	40.08	72	Hafnium	Hf	178.50
21	Scandium	Sc	44.96	73	Tantalum	Ta	180.95
22	Titanium	Ti	47.90	74	Tungsten	W	183.86
23	Vanadium	V	50.95	75	Rhenium	Re	186.22
24	Chromium	Cr	52.01	76	Osmium	Os	190.2
25	Manganese	Mn	54.94	77	Iridium	Ir	192.2
26	Iron	Fe	55.85	78	Platinum	Pt	195.09
27	Cobalt	Co	58.94	79	Gold	Au	197.0
28	Nickel	Ni	58.71	80	Mercury	Hg	200.61
29	Copper	Cu	63.54	81	Thallium	Tl	204.39
30	Zinc	Zn	65.38	82	Lead	Pb	207.21
31	Gallium	Ga	69.72	83	Bismuth	Bi	209.00
32	Germanium	Ge	72.60	84	Polonium	Po	..
33	Arsenic	As	74.91	85	Astatine	At	..
34	Selenium	Se	78.96	86	Radon	Rn	..
35	Bromine	Br	79.916				
36	Krypton	Kr	83.80	87	Francium	Fr	..
				88	Radium	Ra	..
37	Rubidium	Rb	85.48	89	Actinium	Ac	..
38	Strontium	Sr	87.63	90	Thorium	Th	232.05
39	Yttrium	Y	88.92	91	Protactinium	Pa	..
40	Zirconium	Zr	91.22	92	Uranium	U	238.07
41	Niobium	Nb	92.91	93	Neptunium	Np	..
42	Molybdenum	Mo	95.95	94	Plutonium	Pu	..
43	Technetium	Tc	..	95	Americium	Am	..
44	Ruthenium	Ru	101.1	96	Curium	Cm	..
45	Rhodium	Rh	102.91	97	Berkelium	Bk	..
46	Palladium	Pd	106.4	98	Californium	Cf	..
47	Silver	Ag	107.880	99	Einsteinium	Es	..
48	Cadmium	Cd	112.41	100	Fermium	Fm	..
49	Indium	In	114.82	101	Mendelevium	Md	..
50	Tin	Sn	118.70	102	Nobelium	No	..
51	Antimony	Sb	121.76				

* From E. Wickers, *J. Am. Chem. Soc.*, **80**:16 (1958), 4121.

† Because of natural variations in the relative abundance of the isotopes of sulfur, the atomic weight of this element has a range of ± 0.003.

where M is the molecular weight of the gas. A listing of the atomic weights of the elements is given in Table 1.1. We can evaluate the thermodynamic functions of a monatomic gas from Eq. (1.31). The function $(F_T^0 - H_0^0)$ becomes [see Eq. (1.23)]

$$(F_T^0 - H_0^0) = -kT \ln Q \tag{1.32}$$

$$(F_T^0 - H_0^0) = -kNT \left\{ \ln \left[\frac{\left(2\pi \frac{M}{N} kT\right)^{3/2}}{h^3} (kT) \frac{e}{P} \right] \right.$$

$$\left. + \ln g_n + \ln \left[\sum_{el} g_{el} \exp \left(\frac{-\epsilon_{el}}{kT}\right) \right] \right\} \tag{1.33}$$

and the free energy function can be written as

$$\frac{-(F_T^0 - H_0^0)}{RT} = \ln \left[\frac{\left(2\pi \frac{M}{N} kT\right)^{3/2}}{h^3} (kT) \frac{e}{P} \right]$$

$$+ \ln g_n + \ln \left[\sum_{el} g_{el} \exp \left(\frac{-\epsilon_{el}}{kT}\right) \right] \tag{1.34}$$

The heat content function is [see Eq. (1.22)]

$$\frac{(H_T^0 - H_0^0)}{RT} = \frac{1}{N} \left(\frac{d \ln Q}{d \ln T}\right)$$

$$\frac{(H_T^0 - H_0^0)}{RT} = \frac{5}{2} + \ln \left[\frac{\sum_{el} g_{el} \left(\frac{\epsilon_{el}}{kT}\right) \exp \left(\frac{-\epsilon_{el}}{kT}\right)}{\sum_{el} g_{el} \exp \left(\frac{-\epsilon_{el}}{kT}\right)} \right] \tag{1.35}$$

The entropy function is obtained by addition of Eqs. (1.34) and (1.35)

$$\frac{S_T^0}{R} = \frac{-(F_T^0 - H_0^0)}{RT} + \frac{(H_T^0 - H_0^0)}{RT}$$

$$= \ln \left[\frac{\left(2\pi \frac{M}{N} kT\right)^{3/2} kT}{h^3} \frac{e}{P} \right] + \ln g_n + \ln \left[\sum_{el} g_{el} \exp \left(\frac{-\epsilon_{el}}{kT}\right) \right]$$

$$+ \frac{5}{2} + \ln \left[\frac{\sum_{el} g_{el} \left(\frac{\epsilon_{el}}{kT}\right) \exp \left(\frac{-\epsilon_{el}}{kT}\right)}{\sum_{el} g_{el} \exp \left(\frac{-\epsilon_{el}}{kT}\right)} \right] \tag{1.36}$$

The heat capacity at constant pressure [see Eq. (1.21)] for the atom is

$$\frac{C_P^0}{R} = \frac{1}{N}\frac{d}{dT}T\left(\frac{d\ln Q}{d\ln T}\right)$$

$$\frac{C_P^0}{R} = \frac{5}{2} + \left[\frac{\sum_{el} g_{el}\left(\frac{\epsilon_{el}}{kT}\right)^2 \exp\left(-\frac{\epsilon_{el}}{kT}\right)}{\sum_{el} g_{el}\exp\left(-\frac{\epsilon_{el}}{kT}\right)} - \left(\frac{\sum_{el} g_{el}\left(\frac{\epsilon_{el}}{kT}\right)\exp\left(\frac{-\epsilon_{el}}{kT}\right)}{\sum_{el} g_{el}\exp\left(\frac{-\epsilon_{el}}{kT}\right)}\right)^2\right]$$

$$(1.37)$$

In most molecules, rather high temperatures (but not as extreme as for nuclear energy levels) are required for the activation of the higher electronic states. Therefore, the internal partition function for atoms without electronic or nuclear contributions is simply the product of the degeneracies for the electronic and nuclear ground states. This degeneracy in monatomic as well as diatomic and polyatomic molecules is obtained from the spectroscopist's "term value." We present a brief summary of some of the conventions used by spectroscopists in classifying their experimental data.

1.2.2. Electronic structure of an atom [11]

The electronic structure of an atom is determined by four quantum numbers: n, l, m_l, and m_s. *The total energy of a given electron in an atom is determined by the principal quantum number n and the azimuthal quantum number l.* The principal quantum number is integral, $1, 2, 3, \ldots$. Electrons with the principal quantum number equal to $1, 2, 3, \ldots$, are called K, L, M, $\ldots$, electrons, respectively. Consequently, K electrons are electrons with principal quantum number of unity, L electrons are those with n equal to two, and so on. The letters are used to represent a group of electrons in an atom having the same principal quantum number. *The azimuthal quantum number, l, designates the orbital angular momentum of the electron.* For a given value of the principal quantum number, n, the azimuthal quantum number, l, may have any one of the values $0, 1, 2, \ldots, n-1$. Electrons with the azimuthal quantum number equal to $0, 1, 2, 3, \ldots$, are called $s, p, d, f, \ldots$, electrons, respectively. *Each electron has a magnetic quantum number, m_l, that determines the energy of the electron in a magnetic field.* The magnetic quantum number, m_l, may have any one of the values $l, l-1, \ldots, 0, -1, -2, \ldots, -l$ for a given n. Consequently, *the total number of energy states for an electron with azimuthal quantum number, l, resulting from application of a magnetic field is $2l+1$. Each electron has a spin with quantum number m_s. The spin quantum number, m_s, may have either one of the values $+\frac{1}{2}$ or $-\frac{1}{2}$.*

The *Pauli exclusion principle states that no two electrons attached to the*

[11] G. Herzberg, *Atomic Spectra and Atomic Structure* (New York: Dover Publications, Inc., 1944); H. E. White, *Introduction to Atomic Spectra* (New York: McGraw-Hill Book Co., Inc., 1934).

Table 1.2. ELECTRONIC CONFIGURATIONS AND TERM TYPES FOR THE GROUND STATES OF THE ELEMENTS

Element	K	L		M			N				O				
	1s	2s	2p	3s	3p	3d	4s	4p	4d	4f	5s	5p	5d	5f	5g
1. H	1														
2. He	2														
3. Li	2	1													
4. Be	2	2													
5. B	2	2	1												
6. C	2	2	2												
7. N	2	2	3												
8. O	2	2	4												
9. F	2	2	5												
10. Ne	2	2	6												
11. Na	2	2	6	1											
12. Mg	2	2	6	2											
13. Al	2	2	6	2	1										
14. Si	2	2	6	2	2										
15. P	2	2	6	2	3										
16. S	2	2	6	2	4										
17. Cl	2	2	6	2	5										
18. Ar	2	2	6	2	6										
19. K	2	2	6	2	6		1								
20. Ca	2	2	6	2	6		2								
21. Sc	2	2	6	2	6	1	2								
22. Ti	2	2	6	2	6	2	2								
23. V	2	2	6	2	6	3	2								
24. Cr	2	2	6	2	6	5	1								
25. Mn	2	2	6	2	6	5	2								
26. Fe	2	2	6	2	6	6	2								
27. Co	2	2	6	2	6	7	2								
28. Ni	2	2	6	2	6	8	2								
29. Cu	2	2	6	2	6	10	1								
30. Zn	2	2	6	2	6	10	2								
31. Ga	2	2	6	2	6	10	2	1							
32. Ge	2	2	6	2	6	10	2	2							
33. As	2	2	6	2	6	10	2	3							
34. Se	2	2	6	2	6	10	2	4							
35. Br	2	2	6	2	6	10	2	5							
36. Kr	2	2	6	2	6	10	2	6							
37. Rb	2	2	6	2	6	10	2	6			1				
38. Sr	2	2	6	2	6	10	2	6			2				
39. Y	2	2	6	2	6	10	2	6	1		2				
40. Zr	2	2	6	2	6	10	2	6	2		2				
41. Cb	2	2	6	2	6	10	2	6	4		1				
42. Mo	2	2	6	2	6	10	2	6	5		1				
43. To	2	2	6	2	6	10	2	6	6		1				
44. Ru	2	2	6	2	6	10	2	6	7		1				
45. Rh	2	2	6	2	6	10	2	6	8		1				
46. Pd	2	2	6	2	6	10	2	6	10						
47. Ag	2	2	6	2	6	10	2	6	10		1				
48. Cd	2	2	6	2	6	10	2	6	10		2				
49. In	2	2	6	2	6	10	2	6	10		2	1			
50. Sn	2	2	6	2	6	10	2	6	10		2	2			
51. Sb	2	2	6	2	6	10	2	6	10		2	3			
52. Te	2	2	6	2	6	10	2	6	10		2	4			
53. I	2	2	6	2	6	10	2	6	10		2	5			
54. Xe	2	2	6	2	6	10	2	6	10		2	6			

Table 1.2 (cont'd)*

Element	K	L	M	N 4s	4p	4d	4f	O 5s	5p	5d	5f	5g	P 6s	6p	6d	6f	6g	6h	Q 7s...
55. Cs	2	8	18	2	6	10		2	6				1						
56. Ba	2	8	18	2	6	10		2	6				2						
57. La	2	8	18	2	6	10		2	6	1			2						
58. Ce	2	8	18	2	6	10	2	2	6				2						
59. Pr	2	8	18	2	6	10	3	2	6				2						
60. Nd	2	8	18	2	6	10	4	2	6				2						
61. Pm	2	8	18	2	6	10	5	2	6				2						
62. Sm	2	8	18	2	6	10	6	2	6				2						
63. Eu	2	8	18	2	6	10	7	2	6				2						
64. Gd	2	8	18	2	6	10	7	2	6	1			2						
65. Tb	2	8	18	2	6	10	9	2	6				2						
66. Dy	2	8	18	2	6	10	10	2	6				2						
67. Ho	2	8	18	2	6	10	11	2	6				2						
68. Er	2	8	18	2	6	10	12	2	6				2						
69. Tm	2	8	18	2	6	10	13	2	6				2						
70. Yb	2	8	18	2	6	10	14	2	6				2						
71. Lu	2	8	18	2	6	10	14	2	6	1			2						
72. Hf	2	8	18	2	6	10	14	2	6	2			2						
73. Ta	2	8	18	2	6	10	14	2	6	3			2						
74. W	2	8	18	2	6	10	14	2	6	4			2						
75. Re	2	8	18	2	6	10	14	2	6	5			2						
76. Os	2	8	18	2	6	10	14	2	6	6			2						
77. Ir	2	8	18	2	6	10	14	2	6	7			2						
78. Pt	2	8	18	2	6	10	14	2	6	9			1						
79. Au	2	8	18	2	6	10	14	2	6	10			1						
80. Hg	2	8	18	2	6	10	14	2	6	10			2						
81. Tl	2	8	18	2	6	10	14	2	6	10			2	1					
82. Pb	2	8	18	2	6	10	14	2	6	10			2	2					
83. Bi	2	8	18	2	6	10	14	2	6	10			2	3					
84. Po	2	8	18	2	6	10	14	2	6	10			2	4					
85. At	2	8	18	2	6	10	14	2	6	10			2	5					
86. Rn	2	8	18	2	6	10	14	2	6	10			2	6					
87. Fr	2	8	18	2	6	10	14	2	6	10			2	6					1
88. Ra	2	8	18	2	6	10	14	2	6	10			2	6					2
89. Ac	2	8	18	2	6	10	14	2	6	10			2	6	1				2
90. Th	2	8	18	2	6	10	14	2	6	10			2	6	2				2
91. Pa	2	8	18	2	6	10	14	2	6	10	2		2	6	1				2
92. U	2	8	18	2	6	10	14	2	6	10	3		2	6	1				2
93. Np	2	8	18	2	6	10	14	2	6	10	4		2	6	1				2
94. Pu	2	8	18	2	6	10	14	2	6	10	5		2	6	1				2
95. Am	2	8	18	2	6	10	14	2	6	10	6		2	6	1				2
96. Cm	2	8	18	2	6	10	14	2	6	10	7		2	6	1				2
97. Bk	2	8	18	2	6	10	14	2	6	10	8		2	6	1				2
98. Cf	2	8	18	2	6	10	14	2	6	10	9		2	6	1				2
99. Es	2	8	18	2	6	10	14	2	6	10	11		2	6					2
100. Fm	2	8	18	2	6	10	14	2	6	10	12		2	6					2
101. Md	2	8	18	2	6	10	14	2	6	10	13		2	6					2
102. No	2	8	18	2	6	10	14	2	6	10	14		2	6					2

* By permission, from *Handbook of Chemistry and Physics*, 43rd ed., Chemical Rubber Publishing Co., Cleveland, Ohio, 1961–62.

same atom can have the same four quantum numbers. If $n = 1$, l and m_l are zero; consequently, there can be only two electrons with $m_s = +\frac{1}{2}$ and $m_s = -\frac{1}{2}$ having a principal quantum number of unity. Thus, two electrons complete the K shell. If $n = 2$, it can be shown that there will be two electrons with $l = 0$ and six with $l = 1$, making a total of eight electrons required to complete the L shell. The L shell may be divided into subshells, L_1, containing two 2s-electrons, written $2s^2$, and L_2 containing six 2p-electrons, written $2p^6$. For $n = 3$, the M shell contains 18 electrons, two 3s-electrons in M_1, six 3p-electrons in M_2, and ten 3d-electrons in M_3. For $n = 4$, the N shell contains 32 electrons, two 4s-electrons in N_1, six 4p-electrons in N_2, ten 4d-electrons in N_3, and fourteen 4f-electrons in N_4.

To form a neutral atom in its lowest energy state (ground state), the electrons go into the shell of lowest energy. The energy increases with principal quantum number, n, and azimuthal quantum number, l. The value of n is usually the most important in determining the orbit of lowest energy. The energy of an electron increases for small n according to $1s < 2s < 2p < 3s < 3p$. In other words, electrons in the 1s-orbital have lower energy than those in the 2s-orbital. Electrons in the 2p-orbital have lower energy than electrons in the 3s- or 3p-orbitals, and so on. However, for outer orbitals, the azimuthal quantum number, l, becomes important. Thus, a 4s-electron has lower energy than an electron in a 3d-orbital. It is now possible to build up the electronic configuration (Table 1.2) for any atom. For example, the electronic configuration for sulfur is $1s^2 2s^2 2p^6 3s^2 3p^4$. The K, L, M_1, shells are closed, and there are four outer electrons in the 3p-orbital. In order to compute the degeneracy of the electronic state, reference must be made to a description of electrons in filled and unfilled electronic shells.

1.2.3. Russell-Saunders coupling

In *Russell-Saunders or (L, S)-coupling*, the azimuthal quantum numbers, $l_1, l_2, \ldots$, corresponding to the number of electrons, $1, 2, \ldots$, in unfilled shells, combine vectorially to give a resultant orbital angular momentum for the whole atom L. Closed shells and closed subshells give a resultant orbital angular momentum of zero. Similarly, the spin quantum numbers, m_{s_1}, $m_{s_2}, \ldots$, corresponding to the number of electrons, $1, 2, \ldots$, in unfilled shells, combine vectorially to give a resultant spin quantum number, S. Closed shells and closed subshells give a resultant spin quantum number of zero. S can be integral or half-integral, according to whether the number of electrons in the atom is even or odd. For most atoms, the L and S are combined vectorally to give a resultant total angular momentum, J, of all the electrons in the atom. For $L \geq S$, J takes the values $L + S, L + S - 1, \ldots, L - S$. For $S > L$, J takes the values $S + L, S + L - 1, \ldots, S - L$. Each energy state for a given L is split into $2S + 1$ sublevels if $L > S$ or $2L + 1$

sublevels if $S > L$. Since the resultant energy of the state depends on S as well as L, states for a given L have different energies for different values of S, although there is no resolution into sublevels. Atomic energy states with $L = 0, 1, 2, 3, \ldots$, are called $S, P, D, F, \ldots$, states, respectively. *The number of sublevels is known as the multiplicity of the state*, and is denoted by a superscript to the left of the symbol representing the state. For example, the ground state of lithium atom is a ^2S state. The total angular momentum is written as a subscript to the right of the symbol representing the state. For example, the ground state of the lithium atom is usually written as $^2S_{1/2}$. The superscript $2S + 1$ to the left of the term symbol represents the multiplicity of the state for $L > S$.[12] If $L < S$, the multiplicity has no direct meaning. It is found by means of quantum mechanics that only certain atomic states are permitted for electrons in unfilled energy levels. Atoms consisting of closed shells only are always in a $^1S_0$ state. For example, the ground state of atoms with closed shells only, such as s^2, p^6, d^{10}, and f^{14}, is $^1S_0$. A partial listing of permitted terms for electrons in unfilled energy levels is given in Table 1.3.

Table 1.3. PERMITTED ATOMIC
STATES FOR EQUIVALENT ELECTRONS

Electron(s)	Permitted state(s)		
s	^2S		
p		^2P	
p^2	^1S	^3P	^1D
p^3	^4S	^2P	^2D
p^4	^1S	^3P	^1D
p^5		^2P	
d			^2D

As an example, determine the permitted states for an atom with the electronic configuration $1s^2 2s^2 2p^3$ (ground state of nitrogen). There are three electrons in the unfilled L_2 shell of nitrogen. We have $l_1 = 1$, $l_2 = 1$, $l_3 = 1$, $m_{s_1} = \mp\frac{1}{2}$, $m_{s_2} = \mp\frac{1}{2}$, and $m_{s_3} = \mp\frac{1}{2}$. Therefore, S for the atom may be $\frac{3}{2}$ or $\frac{1}{2}$, corresponding to the multiplicities of 4 and 2, respectively. L for the atom may be 3, 2, 1, or 0. The theoretical terms for the atom under consideration are ^4F, ^4D, ^4P, ^4S, ^2F, ^2D, ^2P, and ^2S. Reference to Table 1.3 shows that only the ^4S, ^2P, and ^2D states actually exist. *The ground state usually is the one with the highest multiplicity and the largest L value, respectively.* Consequently, a set of atomic energy levels for nitrogen should list the ^4S term as

[12] The S in the multiplicity formula $2S + 1$ should not be confused with the term symbol S representing a state with $L = 0$.

the ground term. The order of energies for the observed electronic states of nitrogen should be as follows: $^4S < {}^2D$ and ^2P.

1.2.4. The ground state

The complete term symbol for a neutral atom in the ground state also can be determined by application of the *inversion rule* and *Hund's rule*.

The *inversion rule* states that *in subshells less than half full, the lowest J value, $|L - S|$, corresponds to the ground state. For subshells more than half full, the maximum J value, $L + S$, corresponds to the ground state.*

We will consider the arrangement of electrons in subshells of atoms in the ground state. In Fig. 1.1 the various subshells are indicated as groups of

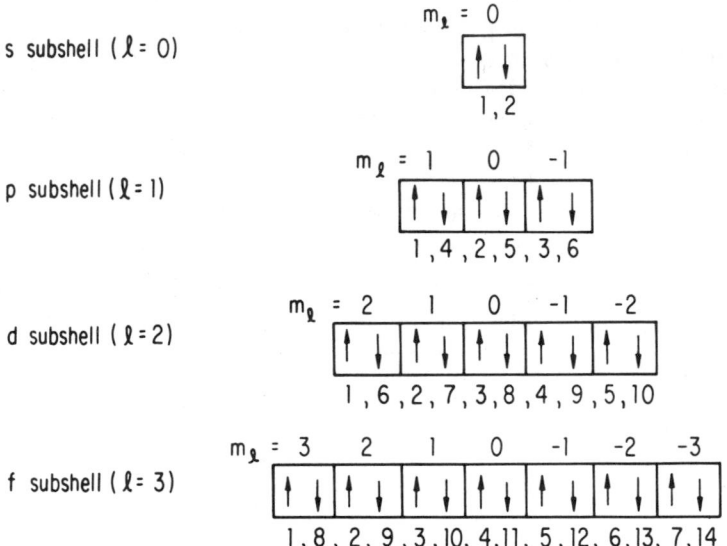

Fig. 1.1 Diagram of electrons in *s*, *p*, *d*, and *f* orbitals

squares. The numbers of squares for the *s*, *p*, *d*, and *f* subshells are 1, 3, 5, and 7, corresponding to the number of possible m_l-orbitals. *In each orbital there is room for two electrons of opposite spins.*

The order in which electrons enter a given subshell (shown just below the square in Fig. 1.1) can be accounted for by *Hund's rule*, which states that *the most stable configuration of an unfilled shell is obtained when the electrons remain unpaired insofar as the Pauli exclusion principle permits.*

Consider three electrons in the *p* subshell. According to Hund's rule, the configuration shown in Fig. 1.2 is obtained. The resultant spin is $\frac{3}{2}$, and is obtained by adding the m_s values, thus the multiplicity $2S + 1$ is 4. The resulting *L* is obtained by adding the m_l values, which are components of *l* in a given direction. For this example, $L = 0$, corresponding to an *S* state.

Since the subshell is half filled, application of the inversion rule indicates that the ground state corresponds to $J = |L - S| = \frac{3}{2}$. Accordingly, the term symbol for an atom having this configuration, with no other partially filled subshells, is $^4S_{3/2}$. If there are other partially filled shells, the total L and S values are obtained by adding contributions to L and S obtained for both partially filled subshells. For example, niobium has four $4d$-electrons and a $5s$-electron. For the four $4d$-electrons, the resultants L and S are 2 and 2. For the single $5s$-electron, $L = 0$ and $S = \frac{1}{2}$. Consequently, the total $L = 2 + 0 = 2$, $S = 2 + \frac{1}{2} = \frac{5}{2}$, $J = |L - S| = \frac{1}{2}$, and the term symbol for the ground state is $^6D_{1/2}$.

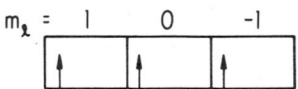

Fig. 1.2 The ground state arrangement of three electrons in the three p orbitals

1.2.5. Alternate notations for atomic term values

The spectroscopist does not always write the value of J as the right-hand subscript. For even states,[13] the spectroscopist does not always write the right-hand superscripts. The spectroscopist sometimes writes the right superscript 0 for odd states. In other words, often no symbol is used when the L is even or zero, and the symbol 0 is used when L is odd.

1.2.6. Total statistical weight of an atomic state

We return now to our discussion of the total degeneracy of an atomic state. In the presence of a magnetic field, there are $2J + 1$ different possible total angular momenta for every value of J. In the absence of a magnetic field, there are $2J + 1$ nearly identical electronic energy levels. In other words, the statistical weight, g_J, of the state associated with the total angular momentum is

$$g_J = 2J + 1 \tag{1.38}$$

In some atoms, the atomic nucleus has a spin quantum number, i. For these atoms there is an additional degeneracy;

$$g_i = 2i + 1 \tag{1.39}$$

The total statistical weight, g_{el}, for the electronic state of an atom is

$$g_{el} = g_J g_i = (2J + 1)(2i + 1) \tag{1.40}$$

Since *the spin quantum number is an intrinsic property of the nucleus, and does not change during chemical reactions*, it is neglected in most calculations of thermodynamic functions. One notable exception arises in connection with the computation of the thermodynamic functions of homopolar diatomic molecules at very low temperatures. This will be discussed in a subsequent section on the influence of nuclei and of the nuclear spin.

---

[13] Even states correspond to $L = 0, 2, 4, \ldots$.

1.2.7. Example: nitrogen atom

The ground state of the nitrogen atom has the electronic configuration $1s^2 2s^2 2p^3$. From Table 1.3 it follows that the ^2P, ^2D, and ^4S are the lowest energy states for nitrogen. *The ground state is that state with the highest multiplicity and maximum orbital angular-momentum quantum number, respectively.* The ground state for nitrogen is the ^4S state. The other states in sequence are the ^2D and ^2P. In accordance with these considerations we find the following energy states listed for the nitrogen atom.[14]

Configuration	Designation	J	ϵ_i (cm^{-1})
$2s^2\,2p^3$	$2p^3\ ^4S$	$\frac{3}{2}$	0
$2s^2\,2p^3$	$2p^3\ ^2D$	$\frac{5}{2}$	19223.9
		$\frac{3}{2}$	19233.1
$2s^2\,2p^3$	$2p^3\ ^2P^0$	$\left\{\begin{matrix}\frac{3}{2}\\\frac{1}{2}\end{matrix}\right\}$	28840

Reference to the list shows that the components of the $^2P^0$ state are not resolved. In this case, the total statistical weight is the sum of the statistical weights for the components. Neglecting the contribution of nuclear spin to the total statistical weight, we find the following statistical weights:

Term	Statistical weight
$^4S^0$	$2J + 1 = (2 \times \frac{3}{2} + 1) = 4$
$^2D_{5/2}$	$(2 \times \frac{5}{2} + 1) = 6$
$^2D_{3/2}$	$(2 \times \frac{3}{2} + 1) = 4$
$^2P^0$	$[2 \times \frac{3}{2} + 1] + [2 \times \frac{1}{2} + 1] = 6$

The next excited state of nitrogen is a $2p^3 3s$ corresponding to the ^4P terms. The energies are:

Configuration	Designation	J	ϵ_i (cm^{-1})
$2s^2\,2p^2(^3P)\,3s$	$3s\ ^4P$	$\frac{1}{2}$	83,285.5
		$\frac{3}{2}$	83,319.3
		$\frac{5}{2}$	83,366.0

In computing thermodynamic functions for the nitrogen atom, it would not be necessary to include energy levels corresponding to the ^4P terms at temperatures below 8328°K because the term $\exp(-\epsilon_i/kT)$ is negligible when $\epsilon_i/kT = 15$.

[14] C. E. Moore, *Atomic Energy Levels* I (Washington, D.C.: U.S. Government Printing Office, 1949).

Table 1.4. SOME ATOMIC ENERGY TERMS

Element	Term symbol	g_i	ϵ_i (cm^{-1})	Element	Term symbol	g_i	ϵ_i (cm^{-1})
Ar	$^1S_0$	1	0	Li	$^2P^0_{1/2,3/2}$	6	30925.38
Al	$^2P^0_{1/2}$	2	0		$^2D_{3/2,5/2}$	10	31283.10
	$^2P_{3/2}$	4	112.04		$^2S_{1/2}$	2	35012.06
	$^2S_{1/2}$	2	25347.69		$^2P^0_{1/2,3/2}$	6	36469.55
	$^4P_{1/2}$	2	29020.32		$^2D_{3/2,5/2}$	10	36623.39
	$^4P_{3/2}$	4	29066.90		$^2F^0_{5/2,7/2}$	14	36630.2
	$^4P_{5/2}$	6	29142.68		$^2S_{1/2}$	2	38299.5
	$^2D_{3/2}$	4	32435.45		$^2P^0_{1/2,3/2}$	6	39015.56
	$^2D_{5/2}$	6	32436.79		$^2D_{3/2,5/2}$	10	39094.93
	$^2P^0_{1/2}$	2	32949.84		$^2F^0_{5/2,7/2}$	14	39104.5
	$^2P^0_{3/2}$	4	32965.67		$^2S_{1/2}$	2	39987.64
	$^2S_{1/2}$	2	37689.32		$^2P^0_{1/2,3/2}$	6	40390.84
	$^2D_{3/2}$	4	38929.42	Mg	$^1S_0$	1	0
	$^2D_{5/2}$	6	38933.96		$^3P^0_0$	1	21850.368
	$^2P^0_{1/2}$	2	40271.98		$^3P^0_1$	3	21870.426
B	$^2P^0_{1/2}$	2	0		$^3P^0_2$	5	21911.140
	$^2P^0_{3/2}$	4	16		$^1P^0_1$	3	35051.36
	$^4P_{1/2,3/2,5/2}$	12	28811		$^3S_1$	3	41197.37
	$^2S_{1/2}$	2	40040	N	$^4S^0_{3/2}$	4	0
Be	$^1S_0$	1	0		$^2D^0_{5/2}$	6	19223
	$^3P^0_0$	1	21979.43		$^2D^0_{3/2}$	4	19231
	$^3P^0_1$	3	21980.11		$^2P^0_{3/2,1/2}$	6	28840
	$^3P^0_2$	5	21982.46	O	$^3P_2$	5	0
	$^1P^0_1$	3	42565.30		$^3P_1$	3	158.5
Br	$^2P^0_{3/2}$	4	0		$^3P_0$	1	226.5
	$^2P^0_{1/2}$	2	3685		$^1D_2$	5	15867.7
C	$^3P_0$	1	0		$^1S_0$	1	33792.4
	$^3P_1$	3	16.4	P	$^4S^0_{3/2}$	4	0
	$^3P_2$	5	43.5		$^2D^0_{3/2}$	4	11361.7
	$^1D_2$	5	10193.7		$^2D^0_{5/2}$	6	11376.5
	$^1S_0$	1	21648.4		$^2P^0_{1/2}$	2	18722.4
	$^5S^0_2$	5	33735.2		$^2P^0_{3/2}$	4	18748.1
Cl	$^2P^0_{3/2}$	4	0	S	$^3P_2$	5	0
	$^2P^0_{1/2}$	2	881		$^3P_1$	3	396.8
F	$^2P^0_{3/2}$	4	0		$^3P_0$	1	573.6
	$^2P^0_{1/2}$	2	404		$^1D_2$	5	9239
H	$^2S_{1/2}$	2	0		$^1S_0$	1	22181.4
He	$^1S_0$	1	0	Si	$^3P_0$	1	0
Li	$^2S_{1/2}$	2	0		$^3P_1$	3	77.15
	$^2P^0_{1/2}$	2	14903.66		$^3P_2$	5	223.31
	$^2P^0_{3/2}$	2	14904		$^1D_2$	5	6298.81
	$^2S_{1/2}$	2	27206.12		$^1S_0$	1	15394.24
					$^3P_0$	1	39683.10
					$^3P_1$	3	39760.20
					$^3P_2$	5	39955.12
					$^1P_1$	3	40991.74

1.2.8. Atomic energy levels and thermodynamic functions

The energy terms required to compute thermodynamic functions to 5000°K are listed in Table 1.4. These term values are for the most important elements in rocket-propellant applications. The values of the energy terms, ϵ_i, are given in cm^{-1}, and are measured from the state of lowest energy.

The elements Ca, K, Na, Pb, Ti, and Zr are of some importance in rocket-propellant applications. However, a large number of energy terms must be considered to calculate the thermodynamic functions to 5000°K for any of these elements. Thus, to conserve space, the energy levels of these elements are not presented; for these data, and for more complete data and references, consult *Atomic Energy Levels* by C. E. Moore.[15] Thermodynamic functions are listed in Appendix 2 for the most important elements in rocket-propellant applications. The revisions to the values of the atomic energy levels of some of these elements have been included in these calculations as suggested in Moore, *Atomic Energy Levels* III.

1.3. THERMODYNAMIC FUNCTIONS FOR IDEAL DIATOMIC MOLECULES

1.3.1. Introduction

In this section we discuss more accurate methods of computing thermodynamic functions at elevated temperatures.

Thermodynamic functions of diatomic and polyatomic molecules are computed usually by assuming that the rotational and vibrational motions are independent. The potential energy function (Sec. 3.2) for the nuclear motion of a diatomic molecule is not a simple function. It is difficult, therefore, to solve the wave equation for the energy levels for the coupled rotational and vibrational motions. As a consequence, usually two approximations are made. (1) The potential function for the nuclear motion of the diatomic molecule is replaced by a parabola which fits the complex potential function in the neighborhood of its minimum. (2) The vibrational and rotational motions are separated from each other by assuming that as far as the rotational motion is concerned the molecule has a fixed equilibrium internuclear distance. The *equilibrium internuclear distance* is the value of the interatomic distance r which corresponds to the minimum of the potential energy function as shown in Fig. 3.1. The rotational motion is thus approximated as a rigid, linear, free rotator, and the vibrational motion as that of a simple harmonic oscillator.

Classically, the principle of equipartition of energy predicts an average rotational energy of $\frac{1}{2}RT$ for each rotational degree of freedom. The rigid-rotator assumption introduces large errors below the temperature at which the

---

[15] C. E. Moore, *Atomic Energy Levels* I (Washington, D.C.: U.S. Government Printing Office, 1949); II (1952); III (1952).

equipartition value of the rotational contribution is reached, but compara-
tively little error above that temperature. Since rotational equipartition is
ordinarily reached well below room temperature, and almost is completed—
even for hydrogen—by room temperature, the rigid-rotator assumption
introduces little error at room temperature and above. The harmonic-
oscillator assumption causes more serious errors. For temperatures below
that for which the ratio (hcv/kT) equals 2.0, this assumption contributes
errors of no more than a few hundredths of a calorie per mole (in the heat
capacity) for each degree of vibrational freedom. For (hcv/kT) less than 0.2
the harmonic oscillator assumption introduces errors of several tenths
calorie per degree of vibrational freedom. The model of a diatomic molecule
as a rigid-rotator harmonic oscillator fails to apply, even approximately, at
elevated temperatures. Consequently, the effects of vibrational anharmonicity,
rotational coupling, and rotation-vibration interaction between levels must
be included in statistical thermodynamic calculations. The complete spectroscopic description of diatomic molecules requires consideration of electronic,
vibrational, and rotational levels. We now discuss these states successively.

1.3.2. Electronic states

The components of the electronic orbital angular momentum vector of all
of the electrons in a molecule along the internuclear axis are identified by the
quantum number Λ.

*In an electric field, the energy of the system is not changed by reversing the
directions of motion of all the electrons, but M_L is changed into $- M_L$.* Consequently, in diatomic molecules, states differing only in the sign of M_L have
the same energy (degenerate). States with different $|M_L|$ have energies quite
different because the electric field that causes splittings is very strong. If L
measures the orbital angular momentum, and is defined for the molecule,
then there are $L + 1$ distinct energy states of the molecule corresponding to:

$$\Lambda = |M_L| = 0, 1, 2, \ldots, L \tag{1.41}$$

The electronic states of diatomic molecules are classified according to the
value of Λ. If $\Lambda = 0, 1, 2, 3, \ldots$, the corresponding molecular state is
designated as Σ, Π, Δ, $\Phi, \ldots$, state, respectively. Σ states are *nondegenerate*
since M_L can have only the value 0, and $\Pi, \Delta, \Phi, \ldots$, states are *doubly degenerate* since M_L can have two values: $+\Lambda$ and $-\Lambda$.

The spins of the individual electrons in the molecules form a resultant S.
S is integral or half-integral according to whether the number of electrons in
the molecule is even or odd. For $\Lambda \neq 0$ ($\Pi, \Delta, \Phi, \ldots$ states), there is an
internal magnetic field in the direction of the internuclear axis resulting from
the orbital motion of the electrons. This magnetic field causes a precession of
S about the field direction with a constant component, M_S $(h/2\pi)$. *For
molecules, M_S is denoted by Σ. Σ is restricted to the $2S + 1$ values, $S, S - 1$,*

$S - 2, \ldots, -S$, and can be positive and negative. It is not defined for states with $\Lambda = 0$; i.e., Σ states.

The quantum number, $\Omega = |\Lambda + \Sigma|$, measures the total electronic angular momentum along the internuclear axis for a molecule. There are $2S + 1$ different values of $\Lambda + \Sigma$ for a given value of Λ ($\Lambda \geq S$), provided that $\Lambda \neq 0$. The different values of Ω correspond to different energies for the molecule because of the interaction of S with the magnetic field produced by Λ. As with atoms, the quantity $2S + 1$ is called the multiplicity even for Σ states ($\Lambda = 0$). *The multiplicity represents the number of close-lying energy levels for other than Σ states.* The Σ states are single as long as the molecule does not rotate. The molecular term value corresponds to the components of orbital electronic angular momentum along the internuclear axis and shows whether or not Λ doubling occurs. If $\Lambda = 0$, Λ doubling does not occur. If $\Lambda \neq 0$, Λ doubling does occur. The subscript value, $\Lambda + \Sigma$, is added to the term value to classify the multiplet components.

The electronic energy of a multiplet term is given to a first approximation by

$$T_e = T_0 + A\Lambda\Sigma \qquad (1.42)$$

where T_0 is the term value when the spin is neglected, and A is a constant for a given multiplet term. Therefore, the components of a molecular multiplet term with $\Lambda \neq 0$ are equidistant. The number of multiplet components is equal to the number of Σ values.

For complete electronic shells, $L = 0$ and $\Lambda = 0$. For this reason, the ground state of many diatomic molecules is a Σ state. *For odd electron molecules, $\Lambda \neq 0$ and states other than the Σ state occur as the ground state.*

Frequently the term values are decorated with additional information relating to the symmetry properties of the electronic eigenfunctions in order to classify molecular electronic states.

If the electronic eigenfunction of a nondegenerate state (Z) remains unchanged, or changes sign when reflected at a plane through the nuclei, the state is called a Σ^+ state or Σ^- state, respectively. Σ^+ and Σ^- states have different energies. Π^+ and Π^-, Δ^+ and Δ^-, etc., states have identical energies.

For nuclei with identical charges (for example, $^{16}O^{16}O$, $^{16}O^{18}O$), reflection of electrons at the center of symmetry leaves the electronic wave function unchanged [a right subscript, g (which stands for *gerade*, even), may be added] or changes the sign of the wave function [add u (for *ungerade*, odd) as right subscript].

The subscript $\Delta + \Sigma$ is deleted whenever a subscript u or g or a superscript $+$ or $-$ is added to the term designation.

For separate multiplets, the electronic degeneracy is 1 for Σ states, and 2 for states in which $\Lambda \neq 0$ (Π, Δ, Φ, etc., states). For a close-lying multiplet, in which only a single electronic term value is given, the electronic degeneracy must be multiplied by the multiplicity.

1.3.3. Vibrational-rotational energy levels

The energy levels for a diatomic molecule can be written in terms of the vibrational quantum number, v, and the rotational quantum number, j, as

$$\frac{\epsilon_i}{hc} = \omega_e \left(v + \frac{1}{2}\right) - \omega_e x_e \left(v + \frac{1}{2}\right)^2 + \omega_e y_e \left(v + \frac{1}{2}\right)^3$$

$$+ B_e j(j+1) - \alpha_e \left(v + \frac{1}{2}\right) j(j+1) - D_e j^2(j+1)^2$$

$$- \beta_e \left(v + \frac{1}{2}\right) j^2 (j+1)^2 \tag{1.43}$$

where ω_e, $\omega_e x_e$, and $\omega_e y_e$ are vibrational constants, and B_e, α_e, D_e are rotational constants. The values of ω_e, $\omega_e x_e$, $\omega_e y_e$, B_e, and α_e are listed in standard reference books on spectroscopy for each electronic state.[16,17] The quantities D_e and α_e are computed from the formula

$$D_e = \frac{4B_e^3}{\omega_e^2} \tag{1.44}$$

$$\beta_e = D_e \left(\frac{8\omega_e x_e}{\omega_e} - \frac{5\alpha_e}{B_e} - \frac{\alpha_e^2 \omega_e}{24B_e^3}\right) \tag{1.45}$$

Typical data are listed below for $^{16}OH^1$ (in cm^{-1}).

Electronic State	T_e	ω_e	$\omega_e x_e$	$\omega_e y_e$	B_e	α_e
$X^2\Pi_i$	0	3727.96	78.15	−1.000	18.862	0.693
$A^2\Sigma^+$	32402.1	3176.74	92.80	−0.967	17.375	0.839

1.3.4. Contribution to total statistical weight

The degeneracy of each vibrational level, g_v, is unity. The degeneracy of a rotational level, g_r, at moderate and high temperatures is given by the relation

$$g_r = (2J + 1) \frac{1}{\sigma} \tag{1.46}$$

The symmetry number, σ, is defined as the number of indistinguishable positions into which the molecule can be turned by simple rigid rotations.[18] For heteronuclear diatomic molecules, σ equals unity; for homonuclear diatomic molecules, σ equals two. The degeneracy of diatomic molecules associated with nuclear spin is

$$g_{spin} = (2I_1 + 1)(2I_2 + 1) \tag{1.47}$$

[16] G. Herzberg, *Spectra of Diatomic Molecules*, vol. 1 (Princeton, N.J.: D. Van Nostrand Co., Inc., 1950).

[17] B. Rosen, *Données Spectroscopiques Concernant Les Molécules Diatomiques* (Paris: Hermann et Cie., Dépositaires 6, rue de la Sorbonne, 1951).

[18] E. B. Wilson, *J. Chem. Phys.*, **27** (1940), 17.

where I_1 and I_2 are the spin quantum numbers for the two atoms of which the molecule is composed. The interaction of electronic and rotational energies, and the influence of nuclear spin, must be considered before the total degeneracy can be computed for an electronic molecular state.

1.3.5. Coupling of electronic and rotational energies

For $^1\Sigma$ states, both Λ and Σ are zero, and the angular momentum of nuclear rotation is identical with the total angular momentum, J. For other states, we must distinguish different modes of coupling of the angular momenta. There are five cases of coupling between electronic and rotational energies [Hund's cases (a) to (e)].[16] Hund's cases (a) and (b) correspond to limiting behavior and are observed most frequently.

Case (a). Weak interaction of rotation and electronic motion. The quantum number, $\Omega = |\Lambda + \Sigma|$, is well-defined. Ω and the angular momentum, j, form the resultant J. Ω is even or half-integral, depending upon whether the number of electrons is even or odd. J is integral when Ω is integral, and half-integral when Ω is half-integral; J cannot be smaller than Ω. For a given Ω, $J = \Omega, \Omega + 1, \Omega + 2$, etc. Levels with $J < \Omega$ do not occur.

As an example of a diatomic molecule with coupling according to case (a), consider NO. The ground electronic states of NO are $^2\Pi_{1/2}$ and $^2\Pi_{3/2}$. For the $^2\Pi_{1/2}$ state, $J = \frac{1}{2}, \frac{3}{2}, \frac{5}{2}$, etc. For the $^2\Pi_{3/2}$ state, $J = \frac{3}{2}, \frac{5}{2}, \frac{7}{2}$, etc. The missing rotational levels do not affect any of the observable thermodynamic properties of NO when a large number of rotational levels are excited.

Case (b). When $\Lambda = 0$ and $S \neq 0$, the spin vector, S, is not coupled to the internuclear axis. Consequently, Ω is not well defined. There are instances where $\Lambda \neq 0$ and $S \neq 0$ and S may be very weakly coupled to the internuclear axis. Weak or zero coupling of S to the internuclear axis is the characteristic of Hund's case (b). For this case, Λ combines with j to form a resultant K. K can have the integral values

$$K = \Lambda, \Lambda + 1, \Lambda + 2, \ldots \tag{1.48}$$

K is the total angular momentum apart from spin. K and S form a resultant J, the total angular momentum including spin. The possible values of J for a given K are

$$J = K + S, K + S - 1, \ldots, |K - S| \tag{1.49}$$

When $K \geq S$, there are $2S + 1$ components for each level with a given K. In other words, each rotational level has a multiplicity of $2S + 1$. These multiplets have slightly different energies because of the (K, S) coupling. As an example, consider the molecule $^{16}O^1H$ in the $^2\Sigma^+$ state. For Σ states, $\Lambda = 0$ and, therefore, $K = 0, 1, 2, 3, \ldots$. For the doublet state, $S = \frac{1}{2}$; therefore, $J = K + \frac{1}{2}$ and $|K - \frac{1}{2}|$. The $K = 0$ level is a singlet because the smallest value of $J = |K - \frac{1}{2}| = \frac{1}{2}$. For all other K values, there are two J values.

Hund[19] and Van Vleck[20] have shown that for a $^2\Sigma$ state the rotational term values are given by

$$F_1(K) = B_v K(K + 1) + \tfrac{1}{2}\gamma K \tag{1.50}$$

$$F_2(K) = B_v K(K + 1) - \tfrac{1}{2}\gamma(K + 1) \tag{1.51}$$

where $F_1(K)$ refers to the components with $J = K + \tfrac{1}{2}$, $F_2(K)$ to components with $J = K - \tfrac{1}{2}$, and γ is the splitting constant. γ is quite small compared to B_v. γ is usually, although not necessarily, positive. For $^2\Sigma$ states, each level is split into two components.

The rotational levels of a $^3\Sigma$ state include spin-spin interaction in addition to magnetic interaction of K and S. Including both effects, the rotational levels of a $^3\Sigma$ state are given by

$$F_1(K) = B_v K(K + 1) + (2K + 3)B_v - \lambda$$
$$\qquad - \sqrt{(2K + 3)^2 B_v^2 + \lambda^2 - 2\lambda B_v} + \gamma(K + 1) \tag{1.52}$$

$$F_2(K) = B_v K(K + 1) \tag{1.53}$$

$$F_3(K) = B_v K(K + 1) - (2K - 1)B_v - \lambda$$
$$\qquad + \sqrt{(2K - 1)^2 B_v^2 + \lambda^2 - 2\lambda B_v} - \gamma K \tag{1.54}$$

where $F_1(K)$, $F_2(K)$, and $F_3(K)$ refer to the levels with $J = K + 1$, K, and $K - 1$, respectively, and λ and γ are constants. For example, the splitting constants of the $^3\Sigma_g^-$ ground state of O_2 are $\lambda = 1.984$, $\gamma = -0.0084$ cm^{-1}.[21]

1.3.6. Influence of nuclear spin

The spin vector, I, of the two nuclei of a diatomic molecule form a resultant T, the total nuclear spin of the molecule. For two identical nuclei, the total nuclear spin

$$T = 2I, 2I - 1, \ldots, 0 \tag{1.55}$$

A state with a given T has a statistical weight $2T + 1$. In a magnetic field, a splitting into $2T + 1$ levels of slightly different energies occurs, which are distinguished by different values of M_T, the quantum number of the component of T in the field direction. We write

$$M_T = T, T - 1, T - 2, \ldots, -T \tag{1.56}$$

When $I = \tfrac{1}{2}$, $T = 1$, and 0. $T = 1$ *corresponds to parallel nuclear spins whereas* $T = 0$ *corresponds to antiparallel spins.* $T = 1$ *is associated with antisymmetric levels and* $T = 0$ *is associated with symmetric levels.* The statistical weights are 3 and 1, respectively. Therefore, for $I = \tfrac{1}{2}$, there are three times as many antisymmetric rotational levels as symmetric levels.

[19] F. Hund, *Z. Physik*, **42** (1927), 93.
[20] J. H. van Vleck, *Phys. Rev.*, **33** (1939), 467.
[21] H. D. Babcock and L. Herzberg, *Astrophysics J.*, **108** (1948), 167.

The total statistical weights are $3(2J + 1)$ and $(2J + 1)$, respectively. The electronic eigenfunction of the ground state of H_2 is symmetric. In other words, for hydrogen the even-numbered rotational levels are symmetric and the odd levels are antisymmetric.

For $I = 1$, $T = 2$, 1, and 0. The corresponding statistical weights are 5, 3, and 1, respectively. Since the symmetric rotational levels occur with even-T values, and the antisymmetric levels occur with odd-T values, the statistical weight of even levels is $(5 + 1) = 6$, and the statistical weight is $6(2J + 1)$ and $3(2J + 1)$, respectively. This is actually observed for N_2 and D_2, where the intensity alternation in the bands is in the ratio of $2:1$.

In the general case, for $I > 1$, the statistical weights of the symmetric and antisymmetric rotational levels are obtained by separately adding quantities $2T + 1$ for even and odd T. For integral I, the total statistical weight for even rotational levels is

$$(2I + 1)(I + 1)(2J + 1) \tag{1.57}$$

and for odd rotational levels

$$(2I + 1)I(2J + 1) \tag{1.58}$$

For half-integral I, the total statistical weight for even rotational levels is

$$(2I + 1)I(2J + 1) \tag{1.59}$$

and for odd rotational levels

$$(2I + 1)(I + 1)(2J + 1) \tag{1.60}$$

When $I = 0$, every second line is missing, as for O_2 and certain other homonuclear molecules.

1.3.7. Examples of computation of total statistical weights

The N_2 molecule has a $^1\Sigma_g^+$ ground state and four excited states: $A\ ^3\Sigma_u^+$, $B\ ^3\Pi_g$, $a\ ^1\Pi_g$, and $C\ ^3\Pi_u$. The nuclear spin I for N is 1. The total statistical weight for the $^1\Sigma_g^+$ state for N_2 is

$$
g_{N_2}\ (^1\Sigma_g^+ \text{ state}) = \overset{g_{spin}}{(2I + 1)(I + 1)} \times \overset{g_{el}}{1} \times \overset{g_v}{1} \times \overset{g_r}{(2J + 1)} \qquad \text{for even } J
$$

$$
= 6(2J + 1) \qquad \text{for } J = 0, 2, 4, \ldots
$$

$$
= (2I + 1)(I)(2J + 1) = 3(2J + 1) \qquad \text{for } J = 1, 3, 5, \text{ etc.}
$$

The total statistical weight for the $A\ ^3\Sigma_u^+$ state of N_2 is

$$
g_{N_2}\ (^3\Sigma_u^+ \text{ state}) = (2I + 1)(I + 1) \times \overset{g_{el}}{3} \times 1 \times (2J + 1) \qquad \text{for even } J
$$

$$
= 18(2J + 1) \qquad \text{for } J = 0, 2, 4, \ldots
$$

$$
= 9(2J + 1) \qquad \text{for } J = 1, 3, 5, \text{ etc.}
$$

The total statistical weights for the $B\,^3\Pi_g$, $a\,^1\Pi_g$, and $C\,^3\Pi_u$ states are
g_{N_2} ($B\,^3\Pi_g$ state) $= g_{el}$ (Λ doubling for Π states)

$$\underset{g_v}{6 \times 1} \times \underset{g_{spin}}{(2I + 1)(2I + 1)} \times \underset{g_r}{(2J + 1)} \times \left(\frac{1}{\sigma}\right)$$

$$\text{symmetry number } \sigma = 2$$

$$= 27(2J + 1) \qquad \text{if the energy difference between the quantum states with } J = K + 1, K, K - 1 \text{ is ignored}$$

g_{N_2} ($a\,^1\Pi_g$ state) $= 2 \times 1 \times 9 \times (2J + 1)\tfrac{1}{2} = 9(2J + 1)$

where $J = K$ with $K = 1, 2, 3, 4, \ldots$ (there are no $K = 0$ states),

g_{N_2} ($C\,^3\Pi_u$ state) $= 27(2J + 1)$ 　　if the energy difference between the
quantum states with $J = K + 1$, K,
$K - 1$ is neglected

1.3.8. General diatomic molecules

The energy levels for a diatomic molecule can be written in terms of the vibrational quantum number, v, and rotational quantum number, j, as

$$\epsilon_i = (v + \tfrac{1}{2})h\nu_e - x_e(v + \tfrac{1}{2})^2 h\nu_e + j(j + 1)B_e hc - D_e hc j^2(j + 1)^2 \\ - \alpha_e hc(v + \tfrac{1}{2})j(j + 1) \qquad (1.61)$$

or, in terms of the wave numbers,

$$\frac{\epsilon_i}{hc} = \left(v + \frac{1}{2}\right)\omega_e - \left(v + \frac{1}{2}\right)^2 x_e\omega_e + j(j + 1)B_e - j^2(j + 1)^2 D_e$$

$$- \left(v + \frac{1}{2}\right)j(j + 1)\alpha_e \qquad (1.62)$$

The terms proportional to $(v + \tfrac{1}{2})^2$, $j^2(j + 1)^2$, and $(v + \tfrac{1}{2})j(j + 1)$ are first-order corrections to the rigid-rotator harmonic oscillator approximation. The anharmonicity constant, x_e, is due to deviations of the true potential energy of the molecule from the Hooke's law equation. The theoretical relations for D_e and α_e are determined from B_e, ω_e, and x_e. The relationships for D_e and α_e are

$$D_e = 4\frac{B_e^3}{\omega_e^2} \qquad (1.63)$$

$$\alpha_e = 6\frac{B_e^2}{\omega_e}\left[\left(\frac{\omega_e x_e}{B_e}\right)^{1/2} - 1\right] \qquad (1.64)$$

Equations (1.63) and (1.64) usually are used when D_e and α_e have not been determined spectroscopically. The reader cannot expect the values obtained from these equations for D_e and α_e always to compare exactly with tabulated values for D_e and α_e in the literature. The reason for such discrepancies is that the empirical values for D_e and α_e always contain a certain average correction due to still higher-order corrections to Eq. (1.62). We prefer the empirical values of D_e and α_e because they give a better approximation to the actual levels by considering the averaged higher-order corrections.

The energy of the lowest level (zero-point energy) is obtained from Eq. (1.62) by setting $v = 0$ and $j = 0$. The zero-point energy for a diatomic molecule is

$$\frac{\epsilon_0}{hc} = \frac{1}{2}\,\omega_e - \frac{1}{4}\,\omega_e x_e \tag{1.65}$$

Subtraction of Eq. (1.65) from Eq. (1.62) yields

$$\frac{\epsilon_i - \epsilon_0}{hc} = v\omega_e - v(v - 1)x_e\omega_e + j(j + 1)B_e - j^2(j + 1)^2 D_e$$

$$- \left(v + \frac{1}{2}\right)j(j + 1)\alpha_e \tag{1.66}$$

The subtraction of the two lowest vibration levels gives the contribution of vibration to the thermodynamic functions most accurately, and the correction terms that subsequently will be developed are smaller at any given temperature.

With the use of Eq. (1.66) to represent the energy levels, we write the total internal partition function as

$$Q = Q_0^0 Q_t Q_{el} Q_v Q_r(v) \tag{1.67}$$

where

$$Q_0^0 = \exp\left(\frac{-hc\epsilon_0}{kT}\right) \tag{1.68}$$

$$Q_t = \frac{V}{h^3}\,(2\pi mkT)^{3/2} \tag{1.69}$$

$$Q_v = \sum_{v=0}^{\infty} \exp\left[-vu + v(v - 1)xu\right] \tag{1.70}$$

$$Q_r = \frac{1}{\sigma}\sum_{j=0}^{\infty}(2j + 1)\exp - j(j + 1)[1 - 4\gamma^2 j(j + 1) - v\delta]\beta_0 \tag{1.71}$$

In these expressions

$$u = \frac{hcv}{kT} = \frac{hc(\omega_e - 2x_e\omega_e)}{kT} \tag{1.72}$$

$$x = \frac{\omega_e x_e}{v} \tag{1.73}$$

$$4\gamma^2 = \frac{D_e}{B_e} \tag{1.74}$$

$$\delta = \frac{\alpha_e}{B_e} \tag{1.75}$$

$$\beta_0 = B_0 \frac{hc}{kT} = hc \frac{\left(B_e - \frac{\alpha_e}{2}\right)}{kT} \tag{1.76}$$

We now show that the vibrational partition function, Q_v, and the rotational partition function, $Q_r(v)$, can be reduced to a series of sums involving only the vibrational quantum numbers. The summation of $Q_r(v)$ analytically involves the expansion of the small exponentials in D_e and α_e and use of the asymptotic Euler-MacLaurin expansion. The Euler-MacLaurin summation formula gives

$$\sum_{J=0}^{\infty} F(J) = \int_0^{\infty} f(y)\, dy + \frac{1}{2} f(0) - \frac{1}{12} \left[\frac{df(y)}{dy}\right]_{y=0} + \frac{1}{720} \left[\frac{d^3 f(y)}{dy^3}\right]_{y=0}$$
$$- \frac{1}{30{,}240} \left(\frac{d^5 f(y)}{dy^5}\right)_{y=0} + \cdots \tag{1.77}$$

Applying this sum to $Q_r(v)$, first we write

$$f(y) = \frac{(2y+1)}{\sigma} \exp\left[-\beta_0 y(y+1) + 4\gamma^2 \beta_0 y^2 (y+1)^2 + v\delta\beta_0 y(y+1)\right] \tag{1.78}$$

In order to integrate $f(y)$ we expand the small exponentials in $4\gamma^2\beta_0$ and $\delta\beta_0$. We obtain

$$f(y) \cong \frac{(2y+1)}{\sigma} \left[\exp - \beta_0 (1 - v\delta) y(y+1)\right]\left[1 + 4\gamma^2 \beta_0 y^2 (y+1)^2\right] \tag{1.79}$$

On integrating by parts

$$\int_0^{\infty} f(y)\, dy \cong \frac{1}{\sigma} \int_0^{\infty} [1 + 4\gamma^2 \beta_0 y^2 (y+1)^2]$$
$$\times [\exp - \beta_0 (1 - \delta v) y(y+1)](2y+1)\, dy \tag{1.80}$$

$$\cong \frac{1}{\beta_0 \sigma} (1 - \delta v)^{-1} \left(1 + \frac{8\gamma^2}{\beta_0}\right) \tag{1.81}$$

$$\cong \frac{1}{\beta_0 \sigma} (1 + \delta v) \left(1 + \frac{8\gamma^2}{\beta_0}\right) \tag{1.82}$$

$$\cong \frac{1}{\beta_0 \sigma} \left(1 + \frac{8\gamma^2}{\beta_0} + \delta v\right) \tag{1.83}$$

Note that $(1 - \delta v)^{-1}$ is expanded in an Euler-MacLaurin series, and that terms of higher than first order are neglected. In addition, the product of δv by $8\gamma^2/\beta_0$ is dropped. Inserting Eq. (1.83) into Eq. (1.77) one obtains

$$\frac{1}{\sigma} \sum_{J=0}^{\infty} (2j+1)[\exp - \beta_0 j(j+1)[1 - 4\gamma^2 j(j+1) - \delta v]]$$

$$= \frac{1}{\beta_0 \sigma} \left(1 + \frac{8\gamma^2}{\beta_0} + \delta v\right) + \frac{1}{2\sigma} - \frac{1}{6\sigma} \tag{1.84}$$

$$= \frac{1}{\beta_0 \sigma} \left(1 + \frac{8\gamma^2}{\beta_0} + \delta v\right) + \frac{1}{3\sigma} \tag{1.85}$$

Observe that both the integral and the original sum for $Q_r(v)$ would be infinite, if integrated or summed correctly. The reason $Q_r(v)$ becomes infinite, if summed correctly, is that the positive part of the exponential, proportional to $j^2(j + 1)^2$, becomes predominant at large values of j. This error is due to the use of the approximate Eq. (1.66), which is not valid to infinite j's. In addition, one should observe that the original sum for Q_v would be infinite, if summed correctly. The reason is that the positive part of the exponential, proportional to v^2, becomes predominant at large values of v's. In other words, Eq. (1.66) is not valid for either infinite v's or j's. $Q_r(v)$ will be satisfactory except for very low temperatures or an extremely large value of B_0 (i.e., large values of β_0).

The summation of Q_v analytically involves the expansion of the small exponential in x. Use is made of the relations

$$\sum_v \exp{(-uv)} = e^u(e^u - 1)^{-1} \tag{1.86}$$

$$\sum_v v \exp{(-uv)} = e^u(e^u - 1)^{-2} \tag{1.87}$$

$$\sum_v v^2 \exp{(-uv)} = e^u(e^u - 1)^{-3}(e^u + 1) \tag{1.88}$$

By expansion of $\exp{v(v - 1)xu}$ in a MacLaurin series, and substitution of Eq. (1.85) into Eq. (1.67), one obtains

$$Q = \frac{Q_0^0 Q_t Q_{el}}{\sigma} \sum_{v=0}^{\infty} [\exp{(-vu + v(v - 1)xu)}] \frac{1}{\beta_0} \left[1 + \frac{8\gamma^2}{\beta_0} + \delta v + \frac{\beta_0}{3} \right] \tag{1.89}$$

$$Q = \frac{Q_0^0 Q_t Q_{el}}{\sigma} \left[\sum_{[v]} [\exp{(-vu)}][1 + uxv(v - 1) + \cdots] \right.$$
$$\left. \times \left[\frac{1}{\beta_0} \left(1 + \frac{8\gamma^2}{\beta_0} + \delta v + \frac{\beta_0}{3} \right) \right] \right] \tag{1.90}$$

$$Q = \frac{Q_0^0 Q_t Q_{el}}{\sigma \beta_0} \left\{ \sum_{[v]} \left(1 + \frac{\beta_0}{3} + \frac{8\gamma^2}{\beta_0} + (\delta - xu)v + xuv^2 \right) [\exp{(-uv)}] \right\} \tag{1.91}$$

We note that the terms $(8\gamma^2/\beta_0)x$ proportional to v^2, δx proportional to v^3, $(\beta_0/3)x$ proportional to v^2, $(8\gamma^2/\beta_0)x$ proportional to v, δx proportional to v^2, and $(\beta_0/3)x$ proportional to v were neglected in the Mayer and Mayer approximation.[22]

The substitution of Eqs. (1.86), (1.87), and (1.88) into Eq. (1.91) yields

$$Q = \frac{Q_0^0 Q_t Q_{el}}{\beta_0 \sigma (1 - e^{-u})} \left[1 + \frac{\beta_0}{3} + \frac{8\gamma^2}{\beta_0} + \frac{\delta}{e^u - 1} + \frac{2xu}{(e^u - 1)^2} \right] \tag{1.92}$$

[22] J. E. Mayer and M. G. Mayer, *Statistical Mechanics* (New York: John Wiley & Sons, Inc., 1940).

Upon developing $\ln (1 + z) = z - \cdots$, the equation for $\ln Q$ is seen to be

$$\ln Q = \ln Q_0^0 + \ln Q_t + \ln Q_{el} - \ln (1 - e^{-u}) - \ln \beta_0 - \ln \sigma + \frac{\beta_0}{3}$$
$$+ \frac{8\gamma^2}{\beta_0} + \frac{\delta}{e^u - 1} + \frac{2xu}{(e^u - 1)^2} \qquad (1.93)$$

The first seven terms of Eq. (1.93) represent the terms developed in the rigid-rotator harmonic oscillator approximation for $\ln Q$. The last three are new correction terms which vanish at low temperatures.

The correction term, $\ln Q_c$, for vibrational anharmonicity and vibration-rotation interaction is

$$\ln Q_c = \frac{8\gamma^2}{\beta_0} + \frac{\delta}{e^u - 1} + \frac{2xu}{(e^u - 1)^2} \qquad (1.94)$$

The contributions to the thermodynamic functions are

$$\frac{-F_c}{RT} = \ln Q_c = \frac{8\gamma^2}{\beta_0} + \frac{\delta}{e^u - 1} + \frac{2xu}{(e^u - 1)^2} \qquad (1.95)$$

$$\frac{H_c}{RT} = \frac{d \ln Q_c}{d \ln T} = \frac{8\gamma^2}{\beta_0} + \frac{\delta u e^u}{(e^u - 1)^2} + \frac{4xu^2 e^u}{(e^u - 1)^3} - \frac{2xu}{(e^u - 1)^2} \qquad (1.96)$$

$$\frac{(C_p)_c}{R} = \frac{d}{dT} T \left(\frac{d \ln Q_c}{d \ln T} \right) = \frac{16\gamma^2}{\beta_0} - \frac{\delta u^2 e^u}{(e^u - 1)^2} + \frac{2u^2 e^{2u} \delta}{(e^u - 1)^3} - \frac{8xu^2 e^u}{(e^u - 1)^3}$$
$$- \frac{4xu^3 e^u}{(e^u - 1)^3} + \frac{12xu^3 e^{2u}}{(e^u - 1)^4} \qquad (1.97)$$

The correction equations derived in this section for the rigid-rotator harmonic oscillator approximation are, in general, applicable to all diatomic molecules. The only exception is that these equations are not valid either at extremely low temperatures or at extremely large values of B_0. The reader should recall that the expansion for $Q_r(v)$ assumes that β_0 is less than unity. Consequently, $Q_r(v)$ should be summed, term by term [Eq. (1.71)], for most molecules at temperatures between 0 and 90°K. Mayer and Mayer[22] give series expansions for the correction [Eq. (1.95), (1.96), (1.97)]. These expansions were proposed only for use at very small values of u. To use these series expansions developed in the Mayer and Mayer treatment, one should be certain that u is less than unity. If a high-speed computer is available, it is not necessary to use such expansions.

1.3.9. Isotopic effect

Diatomic molecules that differ only by the mass of one or both nuclei, but not by their atomic number, are called *isotopic*. For example, the three isotopic molecules of B_2 are $B^{10}B^{10}$, $B^{11}B^{11}$, and $B^{10}B^{11}$. The vibrational frequencies of these three molecules are different.

If one assumes harmonic vibrations, the classical vibrational frequency is

$$\nu = \frac{1}{2\pi} \left(\frac{k}{\mu} \right)^{1/2} \tag{1.98}$$

where k, the force constant, is the same for different isotopic molecules of a given diatomic. Consequently, the frequency, ν^i, of the isotopic molecule is related to the frequency ν of an "ordinary" molecule by the relation

$$\frac{\nu^i}{\nu} = \left(\frac{\mu}{\mu^i} \right)^{1/2} = \rho \tag{1.99}$$

When the effect of anharmonicity is taken into account,[23] it is found that

$$\omega_e^i = \rho \omega_e, \qquad \omega_e^i x_e^i = \rho^2 \omega_e x_e, \qquad \omega_e^i y_e^i = \rho^3 \omega_e y_e \tag{1.100}$$

Since the reduced mass, μ, and the rotational constant, $B = h/8\pi^2 c\mu r^2$, are different, the rotational terms of two isotopic molecules will be different. The rotational constant, B^i, of the isotopic molecule is related to the rotational constant B, of an ordinary molecule by the relation

$$B^i = \rho^2 B \tag{1.101}$$

The relation in Eq. (1.101) holds only for B_e because the equilibrium internuclear distances are the same in the two isotopic molecules, but not for the effective internuclear distance that depends upon the vibrational quantum number v.

For more precise thermodynamic calculations, interaction of vibration and rotation should be considered. Dunham[23] gives for the rotational constants of the isotopic molecules

$$\alpha_e^i = \rho^3 \alpha_e, \qquad D_e^i = \rho^4 D_e \tag{1.102}$$

The thermodynamic functions for an isotopic substance are calculated as if the substance were nonisotopic. The spectroscopic constants used in the computation of thermodynamic functions of the isotopic substance are averages, the result of properly weighing the molecular constants for each of the isotopic varieties.

EXAMPLE

Compute the molecular constants ω_e, $\omega_e x_e$, B_e, and α_e for an isotopic mixture of BBr.

The atomic masses and abundances of B^{10}, B^{11}, Br^{79}, and Br^{81} are as follows.[24]

[23] J. L. Dunham, *Phys. Rev.*, **4** (1932), 721.
[24] D. E. Gray, ed., *American Institute of Physics Handbook* (New York: McGraw-Hill Book Co., Inc., 1957), chap. 7, p. 137.

	Atomic mass	Abundance (mole fraction)
B^{10}	10.016110	0.18715
B^{11}	11.012811	0.81285
Br^{79}	78.943649	0.5052
Br^{81}	80.942320	0.4948

The molecular constants of $B^{11}Br^{79}$ are tabulated in Table 1.5 as

$$\omega_e = 684.31 \text{ cm}^{-1}, \qquad \omega_e x_e = 3.52 \text{ cm}^{-1},$$
$$B_e = 0.49 \text{ cm}^{-1}, \qquad \alpha_e = 3.5 \times 10^{-3} \text{ cm}^{-1}$$

The reduced mass of $B^{11}Br^{79}$ is 9.66.

The molecular constants of $B^{11}Br^{81}$, $B^{10}Br^{79}$, $B^{10}Br^{81}$ are computed from Eqs. (1.100) through (1.102) using $B^{11}Br^{79}$ as the "ordinary" molecule. A table of the results is as follows.

Substance	μ	ρ	ω_e (cm^{-1})	$\omega_e x_e$ (cm^{-1})	B_e (cm^{-1})	$\alpha_e \times 10^3$ (cm^{-1})
$B^{11}Br^{79}$	9.66	1.000	684.31	3.520	0.490	3.500
$B^{11}Br^{81}$	9.69	0.998	683.27	3.509	0.489	3.484
$B^{10}Br^{79}$	8.89	1.043	713.56	3.827	0.533	3.968
$B^{10}Br^{81}$	8.91	1.041	712.57	3.817	0.531	3.952

The fraction x_k of each isotopic molecule in the mixture is obtained by the relation

$$x_k = \frac{a_i a_j}{\sum a_i a_j} \tag{1.103}$$

where a_i and a_j represent the fraction abundance for species i and j, respectively, and the sum is over all molecular species in the mixture. Using Eq. (1.103) we obtain for the fraction of each molecular species in the mixture:

Substance	x_k
$B^{11}Br^{79}$	0.4107
$B^{11}Br^{81}$	0.4022
$B^{10}Br^{79}$	0.0945
$B^{10}Br^{81}$	0.0926

The molecular constants for the isotopic mixture are obtained by the relations

$$\omega_e = \sum_k (\omega_e)_k x_k = 689.28 \text{ cm}^{-1}$$
$$\omega_e x_e = \sum_k (\omega_e x_e)_k x_k = 3.572 \text{ cm}^{-1}$$
$$\alpha_e = \sum_k (\alpha_e)_k x_k = 3.58 \times 10^{-3} \text{ cm}^{-1}$$
$$B_e = \sum_k (B_e)_k x_k = 0.497 \text{ cm}^{-1}$$

Table 1.5. MOLECULAR CONSTANTS FOR SOME DIATOMIC MOLECULES

Compound	Ground state	B_e cm^{-1}	α_e cm^{-1}	ω_e cm^{-1}	$\omega_e x_e$ cm^{-1}	σ	g_e	M g/mole	Ref.
Al$_2$	($^3\Sigma$)			400		2	3	53.96	a
AlBr	$^1\Sigma^+$	0.1591	0.000853	378	1.28	1	1	106.896	b
AlC	($^2\Pi$)			350.01	2.022	1	2	38.991	c
AlCl	$^1\Sigma^+$	0.242	0.002	481.3	1.95	1	1	62.437	b
AlF	$^1\Sigma^+$	0.5523	0.00483	801.95	4.70	1	1	45.98	d
AlH	$^1\Sigma^+$	6.39066	0.18581	1682.563	29.09	1	1	27.988	e
AlH$^+$	$^2\Sigma^+$	6.763	0.398	1610		1	2	27.988	b
AlN	$^3\Pi$	0.6247	0.0072	859	7.1	1	6	40.988	f
AlO	$^2\Sigma^+$	0.64148	0.00575	979.23	7.12	1	2	42.98	b
AlS	$^2\Sigma$	0.280	0.0019	648	3.2	1	2	59.046	f
B$_2$	$^3\Sigma$	1.212	0.014	1051.3	9.4	2	3	21.64	g
BBr	$^1\Sigma^+$	0.490	0.0035	684.31	3.52	1	1	90.736	b
BCl	$^1\Sigma$	0.6838	0.00646	839.12	5.11	1	1	46.277	b
BF	$^1\Sigma^+$	1.5107	0.0165	1402.13	11.84	1	1	29.82	b
BH	$^1\Sigma^+$	12.018	0.412	2366	49	1	1	11.828	g
BH$^+$	$^2\Sigma^+$	[12.374]		[2435]		1	2	11.828	b
BN	$^3\Pi$	1.666	0.025	1514.6	12.3	1	6	24.828	h
BO	$^2\Sigma$	1.7803	0.01648	1885.44	11.769	1	2	26.82	g
BS	$^2\Sigma$	0.7949	0.0061	1173.61	6.38	1	2	42.886	i
BeCl	$^2\Sigma^+$	(0.766)	(0.007)	846.58	5.11	1	2	44.47	i
BeF	$^2\Sigma$	1.4877	0.0168	1265.6	9.12	1	2	28.013	i
BeH	$^2\Sigma^+$	10.308	0.300	2058.6	35.5	1	2	10.021	b
BeH$^+$	$^1\Sigma^+$	10.7996	0.2935	2221.7	39.79	1	1	10.021	b
BeO	$^1\Sigma^+$	1.6510	0.0190	1487.19	11.731	1	1	25.013	i
Br$_2$	$^1\Sigma^+$	0.08091	0.000275	323.2	1.07	2	1	159.832	b
BrCl	$^1\Sigma^+$	0.1508	0.0007597	443	1.8	1	1	115.373	j
BrF	$^1\Sigma^+$	0.357165	0.005214	671	3	1	1	98.916	b
BrO	($^1\Sigma$)			713	7	1	1	95.916	i
C$_2$	$^3\Pi$	1.6326	0.01683	1641.35	11.67	2	6	24.022	b
CCl	$^2\Pi$	0.616	0.001	846	1	1	4	47.468	k
CF	$^2\Pi$	1.419	0.019	1308.4	10.86	1	4	31.011	i
CH	$^2\Pi$	14.457	0.534	2861.6	64.3	1	4	13.019	b
CH$^+$	$^1\Sigma^+$	14.1767	0.4898			1	1	13.019	b
CN	$^2\Sigma^+$	1.8996	0.01735	2068.705	13.144	1	2	26.029	b
CO	$^1\Sigma^+$	1.9314	0.01748	2170.21	13.416	1	1	28.011	b
CO$^+$	$^1\Sigma^+$	1.9772	0.01896	2214.24	15.164	1	1	28.011	b
CP	$^2\Sigma^+$	0.7986	0.00597	1239.67	6.86	1	2	42.986	b
CS	$^1\Sigma$	0.8205	0.00624	1285.1	6.5	1	1	44.077	b
CaBr	$^2\Sigma^+$			285.3	0.86	1	2	119.996	b
CaCl	$^2\Sigma^+$	[0.1491]	[0.00074]	369.8	1.31	1	2	75.537	b
CaF	$^2\Sigma^+$	[0.322]	0.0021	587.1	2.74	1	2	59.08	b
CaH	$^2\Sigma$	4.2778	0.0963	1299	19.5	1	2	41.088	b
CaH$^+$	$^1\Sigma$	5.71				1	1	41.088	b
CaO	$^1\Sigma$	0.445	0.00335	732.1	4.81	1	1	56.008	b
Cl$_2$	$^1\Sigma^+$	0.2438	0.0017	564.9	4	2	1	70.914	b

Table 1.5 (cont'd)

Compound	Ground state	B_e cm^{-1}	α_e cm^{-1}	ω_e cm^{-1}	$\omega_e x_e$ cm^{-1}	σ	g_e	M g/mole	Ref.
Cl$_2{}^+$	$^2\Pi$?	0.2697	0.0018	645.3	2.90	2	4	70.914	b
ClF	$^1\Sigma$	0.516509	0.004359	793.2	9.9	1	1	54.457	b
ClO	$^2\Pi$	0.646	0.007	868	7.5	1	4	51.457	m
F$_2$	$^1\Sigma^+$	0.8901	0.0146	919	13.6	2	1	38	n
H$_2$	$^1\Sigma^+$	68.809	2.993	4395.24	117.995	2	1	2.016	b
He$_2$	$^1\Sigma^+$	7.664	0.131	1811.2	39.2	2	1	8.006	b
HBr	$^1\Sigma^+$	8.473	0.226	2649.67	45.21	1	1	80.924	b
HCl	$^1\Sigma^+$	10.5909	0.3019	2989.74	52.05	1	1	36.465	b
HCl$^+$	$^2\Pi$	9.9463	0.3183	2675.4	53.5	1	4	36.465	b
HF	$^1\Sigma^+$	20.931	0.7699	4138.54	90.054	1	1	20.008	b
HS	$^2\Pi$	(9.47)				1	4	33.074	b
K$_2$	$^1\Sigma^+$	0.05622	0.000219	92.64	0.354	2	1	78.2	i
KBr	$^1\Sigma$	0.08117	0.0004	213	0.8	1	1	119.016	p
KCl	$^1\Sigma$	0.1275	0.000789	281	1.3	1	1	74.557	o
KF	$^1\Sigma$	0.2908	0.00188	400	1.85	1	1	58.1	o
KH	$^1\Sigma$	3.407	0.0673	985	14.65	1	1	40.108	o
Li$_2$	$^1\Sigma^+$	0.6776	0.007118	352.68	2.611	2	1	13.88	b
LiBr	$^1\Sigma$	0.5586	0.005633	576	4.28	1	1	86.856	p
LiCl	$^1\Sigma$	0.625	0.00368	662	2.6	1	1	42.397	p
LiF	$^1\Sigma^+$	1.3780	0.01971	906.2	7.9	1	1	25.94	q
LiH	$^1\Sigma^+$	7.5249	0.2137	1406.75	23.236	1	1	7.948	b
LiO	$^2\Pi$			800	5.5	1	4	22.94	r,s,t
MgBr	$^2\Sigma$	[0.1688]	[0.00085]	373.8	1.34	1	2	104.236	b
MgCl	$^2\Sigma^+$	[0.2516]	[0.00155]	465.4	2.05	1	2	59.777	b
MgF	$^2\Sigma$	[0.5151]	[0.00383]	715.57	3.818	1	2	43.32	b
MgH	$^2\Sigma^+$	5.815	0.1667	1495.3	31.48	1	2	25.328	b
MgH$^+$	$^1\Sigma^+$	6.411	0.206	1695.3	30.2	1	1	25.328	b
MgO	$^3\Sigma$	0.6232	0.00496	902	13	1	3	40.32	u
MgS				525.2	2.93	1		56.386	i
N$_2$	$^1\Sigma_g^+$	2.010	0.0187	2359.61	14.456	2	1	28.016	b
N$_2{}^+$	$^2\Sigma_g^+$	1.932	0.020	2207.19	16.136	2	2	28.016	b
NBr				693	5	1		93.924	b
NF	$^3\Sigma$	1.441	0.019	875	8.4	1	3	33.008	b
NH	$^3\Sigma^-$	16.65	0.64	[3300]		1	3	15.016	b
NO	$^2\Pi$	1.7046	0.0178	1904.03	13.97	1	4	30.008	b
NO$^+$	$^1\Sigma$	1.890	0.018	2371.7	15.8	1	1	30.008	v
NS	$^2\Pi$	0.7736	0.00612	1220	7.75	1	4	46.074	b
Na$_2$	$^1\Sigma_g^+$	0.15471	0.00079	159.23	0.726	2	1	45.994	i
NaBr	$^1\Sigma^+$	0.1495	0.0009394	302	1.50	1	1	102.907	w
NaCl	$^1\Sigma^+$	0.21807	0.00161	366	2.05	1	1	58.454	w
NaF	$^1\Sigma$	0.4786	0.00203	578	2.6	1	1	41.997	x
NaH	$^1\Sigma$	4.886	0.1353	1172.2	19.72	1	1	24.005	i
NaO	$^2\Pi$	0.4898	0.00495	665	4.8	1	4	38.997	f
O$_2$	$^3\Sigma_g^-$	1.44567	0.015791	1580.361	12.073	2	3	32	b
O$_2{}^+$	$^2\Pi_g$	1.6722	0.01984	1876.4	16.53	2	4	32	b

Table 1.5 (cont'd)

Compound	Ground state	B_e cm^{-1}	α_e cm^{-1}	ω_e cm^{-1}	$\omega_e x_e$ cm^{-1}	σ	g_e	M g/mole	Ref.
OH	$^2\Pi$	18.871	0.714	3735.21	82.81	1	4	17.008	b
OH$^+$	$^3\Sigma^-$	16.793	0.732	[2955]		1	3	17.008	b
P$_2$	$^1\Sigma_g^+$	0.30327	0.00142	780.43	2.804	2	1	61.950	b
PH	$^3\Sigma^-$	[8.412]		[2380]		1	3	31.983	b
PF	$^3\Sigma$	0.557	0.0044	940	5.3	1	3	49.975	f
PN	$^1\Sigma$	0.78621	0.00557	1337.24	6.983	1	1	44.983	i
PO	$^2\Pi$	0.7613	0.0055	1230.64	6.52	1	4	46.975	i
Pb$_2$	$^3\Sigma$	0.1715	0.0000835	256.5	2.96	2	3	414.42	i
PbBr	$^2\Pi$	0.0443	0.0001337	207.5	0.50	1	4	287.13	i
PbCl	$^2\Pi$	0.0942	0.0003812	303.9	0.88	1	4	242.67	i
PbF	$^2\Pi$	0.2374	0.0002068	507.2	2.30	1	4	226.21	i
PbH	$^2\Pi$	4.9710	0.144	1564.1	29.75	1	4	208.218	i
PbO	$^1\Sigma^+$	0.3073	0.19	721.8	3.70	1	1	223.21	i
PbS	$^1\Sigma^+$	0.1061	0.000873	428.14	1.201	1	1	239.276	i
S$_2$	$^3\Sigma_g^-$	0.2956	0.0016	725.68	2.852	2	3	64.132	b
SO	$^3\Sigma^-$	0.70894	0.005622	1123.73	6.116	1	3	48.066	b
Si$_2$	$^3\Pi$	0.2596	0.00155	547.94	2.43	2	6	56.18	y
SiBr	$^2\Pi$	0.16622	0.00078	425.4	1.51	1	4	108.006	o
SiCl	$^2\Pi$	0.25595	0.00142	535.4	2.2	1	4	63.547	o
SiF	$^2\Pi$	0.57963	0.00434	856.7	4.7	1	4	47.09	o
SiH	$^2\Pi$	7.498	0.214	2042.47	35.67	1	4	29.098	z
SiN	$^2\Sigma^+$	0.7310	0.00567	1151.68	6.56	1	2	42.098	o
SiO	$^1\Sigma$	0.7263	0.00494	1242.03	6.047	1	1	44.09	o
SiO$^+$	$^2\Sigma$	0.7320	0.0133	851	14.958	1	2	44.09	o
SiS	$^1\Sigma^+$	0.30363	0.00149	749.69	2.58	1	1	60.156	o
TiCl	$^2\Pi$	0.1436	0.001525	456.4	6.3	1	4	83.357	i
TiO	$^3\Pi$	0.5356	0.0031	1008.12	4.519	1	6	63.90	i
ZrCl	$^2\Pi$	0.1226	0.000355	367.5	0.837	1	4	126.677	aa
ZrO	$^3\Pi$	0.6149	0.06	936.5	3.47	1	6	107.22	i

[a] W. Chupka and J. Berkowitz, *J. Phys. Chem.*, **62** (1958), 611.

[b] D. E. Gray, ed., *American Institute of Physics Handbook* (New York: McGraw-Hill Book Co., Inc., 1957), chap. 7, p. 136.

[c] P. B. Zeeman, *Can. J. Phys.*, **32** (1954), 9.

[d] S. M. Naudé and T. J. Hugo, *Can. J. Phys.*, **35** (1957), 64.

[e] P. Zeeman and G. J. Ritter, *Can. J. Phys.*, **32** (1954), 555.

[f] Estimated from data on related molecules.

[g] R. L. Wilkins and R. L. Altman, *J. Chem. Phys.*, **31** (1959), 331.

[h] A. E. Douglas and G. Herzberg, *Can. J. Research*, **18A** (1940), 179.

[i] B. Rosen, *Données Spectroscopiques Concernant Les Molécules Diatomiques* (Paris: Hermann et Cie., Dépositaires, 1951).

[j] W. H. Evans, T. H. Munsen, and D. D. Wagman, *J. Research Natl. Bur. Standards*, **55** (1955), 147.

[k] J. S. Gordon, *J. Chem. Phys.*, **29** (1958), 889.

[l] E. B. Andrews and R. F. Barrow, *Proc. Phys. Soc.*, **A64** (1951), 481.

The fundamental frequency ν for an isotopic mixture of BBr is obtained from Eq. (1.72)

$$\nu = \omega_e - 2\omega_e x_e = 689.28 - 2(3.572) = 682.13 \text{ cm}^{-1}$$

and the moment of inertia from Eq. (1.106)

$$I_0 = \frac{h}{8\pi^2 c B_0} = \frac{27.988898 \times 10^{-40}}{(B_e - \alpha_e/2)} = \frac{27.988898 \times 10^{-40}}{(0.497 - (3.58 \times 10^{-3})/2)}$$

$$= 56.49 \times 10^{-40} \text{ g-cm}^2$$

1.3.10. Molecular constants and thermodynamic functions for some diatomic molecules

The molecular constants for some diatomic molecules of the elements that are of major interest in current propellant development programs are summarized in Table 1.5. The numbers enclosed in brackets have been estimated by techniques discussed in this section. Thermodynamic functions are presented in Appendix 3 for the diatomic molecules tabulated in Table 1.5. All functions were computed with the molecular constants given in Table 1.5 using the method described in Sec. 1.38.

1.4. THERMODYNAMIC FUNCTIONS FOR POLYATOMIC MOLECULES

1.4.1. Introduction

The energy levels of a polyatomic molecule to a first approximation can be written as a sum of the vibrational and rotational energy. The rotational

[m] R. A. Durie and D. A. Ramsay, *Can. J. Phys.*, **36** (1958), 35.

[n] D. Andrychuk, *Can. J. Phys.*, **29** (1951), 151.

[o] G. Herzberg, *Spectra of Diatomic Molecules* (Princeton, N.J.: D. Van Nostrand Co., Inc., 1950).

[p] W. Klemperer and S. H. Rice, *J. Chem. Phys.*, **26** (1957), 618.

[q] G. L. Vidale, "The Infrared Spectrum of the Gaseous LiF Molecule," Aerophysics Research Memo No. 32, Tech. Info. Series No. R59SD359, General Electric Co., Philadelphia, May 14, 1959.

[r] J. Berkowitz, W. A. Chupka, G. D. Blue, and J. L. Margrave, *J. Phys. Chem.*, **63** (1959), 644.

[s] P. A. Akishen and N. B. Rambidi, *Doklady Akad. Nauk S.S.S.R.*, **118** (1958), 973.

[t] H. Smith and T. M. Sugden, *Proc. Royal Soc.*, **A219** (1953), 204.

[u] L. Brewer and R. F. Porter, *J. Chem. Phys.*, **22** (1954), 1867.

[v] C. W. Beckett and L. Haar, *Proceedings*, Conference on Thermodynamic and Transport Properties of Fluids, London, July 10–12, 1957 (London: Inst. of Mech. Engineers, 1958), pp. 27–38.

[w] R. L. Wilkins, *Chemical Engineering Data*, **5** (1960), 337.

[x] A. Hornig, M. Mandel, M. L. Smith, and C. H. Townes, *Phys. Rev.*, **96** (1954), 629.

[y] A. E. Douglas, *Can. J. Phys.*, **33** (1955), 801.

[z] A. E. Douglas, *Can. J. Phys.*, **35** (1957), 71.

[aa] K. S. Krasnov and A. I. Maksimov, *Optics and Spectroscopy*, **8** (1960), 208.

energy has a different representation depending upon the structure of the molecule. Polyatomic molecules are classified according to the type of rigid body that best represents the rotational behavior of the real molecule. For calculations of thermodynamic functions of polyatomic molecules, we now discuss representations of rotational and vibrational levels.

1.4.2. Rotational partition function

The *moment of inertia* of a rigid body about a principal axis is defined as

$$I = \sum_i m_i X_i^2 \tag{1.104}$$

where X_i is the perpendicular distance of the mass, m_i, from the principal axis. There are three principal axes; these are mutually perpendicular going through the center of mass about which the moment of inertia is a maximum or minimum. *The moments of inertia corresponding to the three principal axes are called the principal moments of inertia.* A plot of $1/\sqrt{I}$ along the principal axes corresponds to an ellipsoid. The axes of this ellipsoid are the principal axes. The reader might verify that, if a molecule has symmetry, the direction of one or more of the principal axes through the center of mass can easily be found, since every axis of symmetry is a principal axis, and since the plane of symmetry is always perpendicular to a principal axis. In general, three moments of inertia are required to specify the properties of a rigid body. *Molecules with three different principal moments of inertia are called asymmetric top molecules. Molecules with two equal principal moments of inertia are called symmetric top molecules.* The momental ellipsoid for the latter case is called a *rotational ellipsoid. If the third principal moment of inertia of a symmetric top is zero or near zero, the momental ellipsoid is a circular cylinder.* An example of this case is the linear polyatomic molecules. *Molecules with three equal principal moments of inertia are called spherical top molecules.* In the following sections we consider the four cases mentioned.

(a) *Linear Molecules*

For linear polyatomic molecules (HCN, COS, HC≡CCl, CO_2, C_2H_2, N_2O, etc.) the energy levels are given by an expression similar to that for diatomic molecules. For linear molecules, the rotational energy

$$F_{[v]}(J) = B_{[v]}[J(J + 1) - l^2] - D_{[v]}J^2(J + 1)^2 \tag{1.105}$$

where

$$B_{[v]} = B_0\left(1 - \sum_i b_i^B v_i\right) \tag{1.106}$$

$$B_0 = \frac{h}{8\pi^2 I_B c} \tag{1.107}$$

$$b_i = \frac{\alpha_i}{B_0} \tag{1.108}$$

and $D_{[v]}$ represents the influence of the centrifugal force, l is the vibrational angular momentum about the internuclear axis.

The rotational partition function for linear polyatomic molecules

$$Q_r = \frac{1}{\sigma} \sum_{J=l}^{\infty} (2J + 1) \exp \{-B_{[v]}[J(J + 1) - l^2] + D_v J^2 (J + 1)^2\} \qquad (1.109)$$

For diatomic molecules $l = 0$ and, if $D_v = 0$, the asymptotic expansion first given by Mulholland[25] is

$$Q_r = \frac{kT}{hcB_v} \frac{1}{\sigma} \left[1 + \frac{1}{3}\left(\frac{hcB_v}{kT}\right) + \frac{1}{15}\left(\frac{hcB_v}{kT}\right)^2 + \frac{1}{315}\left(\frac{hcB_v}{kT}\right)^3 + \cdots \right] \qquad (1.110)$$

For small B and large T, Eq. (1.110) reduces to the classical result

$$Q_r = \frac{kT}{hcB_v} \frac{1}{\sigma} \qquad (1.111)$$

The degeneracy for linear molecules is $(2J + 1)/\sigma$, where σ is the symmetry number.

(b) *Spherical Top Molecules*

For spherical top molecules (CCl_4, CH_4, etc.) the energy levels are given by

$$F_{[v]}(J) = B_{[v]}J(J + 1) \qquad (1.112)$$

The degeneracy of a spherical top molecule is

$$g_J = \frac{(2J + 1)^2}{\sigma} \qquad (1.113)$$

The rotational partition function for a spherical top molecule is

$$Q_r = \frac{1}{\sigma} \sum_{J=0}^{\infty} (2J + 1)^2 \exp[-B_{[v]}J(J + 1)] \qquad (1.114)$$

This sum can be evaluated by using the Euler-MacLaurin summation formula (see Viney[26] and Kassel[27,28]). If only the first term of this expansion is retained, it is found that

$$Q_r = \frac{1}{\sigma} \frac{\sqrt{\pi}}{B_{[v]}^{3/2}} \qquad (1.115)$$

(c) *Symmetric Top Molecules*

The rotational energy levels of a symmetric top molecule (C_2H_6, CCl_3, NO_2, etc.) are given by the relation

$$F_{[v]}(J) = B_{[v]}J(J + 1) + [A_{[v]} - B_{[v]}]K^2 \qquad (1.116)$$

[25] H. P. Mulholland, *Proc. Cambridge Phil. Soc.*, 24 (1928), 280.
[26] I. E. Viney, *Proc. Cambridge Phil. Soc.*, 29 (1933), 142, 407.
[27] L. S. Kassel, *J. Chem. Phys.*, 1 (1933), 576.
[28] L. S. Kassel, *Chem. Rev.*, 18 (1936), 277.

where

$$A_{[v]} = A_0 \left(1 - \sum_i \alpha_i v_i\right) \tag{1.117}$$

$$A_0 = \frac{h}{8\pi^2 I_A c} \tag{1.118}$$

Here $J = 0, 1, 2, \ldots$, and $|K| = 0, 1, 2, \ldots$. The degeneracy is

$$g_J = \frac{1}{\sigma}(2J + 1) \qquad \text{for } K = 0 \tag{1.119}$$

$$g_J = \frac{2}{\sigma}(2J + 1) \qquad \text{for } K \neq 0 \tag{1.120}$$

The rotational partition function for symmetric top molecules is

$$Q_r = \frac{1}{\sigma} \sum_{J=0}^{\infty} (2J + 1) \exp\left[-B_{[v]} J(J + 1)\right]$$

$$+ \frac{2}{\sigma} \sum_{J=0, K=1}^{\infty} (2J + 1)$$

$$\times \exp\left\{-[B_{[v]} J(J + 1) + (A_{[v]} - B_{[v]})K^2]\right\} \tag{1.121}$$

Evaluation of the sum in Eq. (1.121) yields

$$Q_r = \frac{1}{\sigma} \frac{\sqrt{\pi}}{A_{[v]}\sqrt{B_{[v]}}} \tag{1.122}$$

(d) Asymmetric Top Molecules

The rotational energy levels of asymmetric top molecules [H_2O, AlF_2, $(LiF)_2$, etc.] are given by the relation

$$F_{[v]}(J) = \tfrac{1}{2}(B_{[v]} - C_{[v]})J(J + 1) + [A_{[v]} - \tfrac{1}{2}(B_{[v]} + C_{[v]})]W_\tau \tag{1.123}$$

where

$$C_{[v]} = C_0 \left(1 - \sum_i C_i v_i\right) \tag{1.124}$$

$$C_0 = \frac{h}{8\pi^2 I_C c} \tag{1.125}$$

and W_τ depends, in a complicated fashion, on $A_{[v]}$, $B_{[v]}$, $C_{[v]}$, and J, and for a given value of J there are $(2J + 1)$ values of W_τ. The $(2J + 1)$ values of W_τ for a given J are the roots of a secular determinant[29] of degree $(2J + 1)$. Although the relation for the rotational energy levels of an asymmetric top is complex, an approximation for the rotational partition function is

$$Q_r = \frac{1}{\sigma} \frac{\sqrt{\pi}}{\sqrt{A_{[v]} B_{[v]} C_{[v]}}} \tag{1.126}$$

[29] G. Herzberg, *Molecular Spectra and Molecular Structure*, vol. 2 (Princeton, N.J.: D. Van Nostrand Co., Inc., 1950).

1.4.3. Moments of inertia of some simple molecules

The moments of inertia, I_A, I_B, I_C, are required to compute A_0, B_0, and C_0, respectively. These values are calculated from bond distances, bond angles, and masses of the atoms. In this subsection we present formulas for computing moments of inertia of some simple molecules.

(a) *Diatomic Molecules*

The moment of inertia of the rigid rotator corresponding to the diatomic molecule is

$$I = \mu r_0^2 \tag{1.127}$$

where

$$\mu = \frac{m_1 m_2}{m_1 + m_2} \tag{1.128}$$

represent the reduced mass where m_1 and m_2 are the masses of the atoms of which the molecule is composed, and r_0 denotes the distance between atomic centers.

(b) *Nonlinear* XY_2 *Molecules*

The moments of inertia of a nonlinear XY_2 molecule are

$$I_A = 2m_y r_{xy}^2 \cos^2 \theta \left[1 - 2\frac{m_y}{m}\right] \tag{1.129}$$

$$I_B = 2m_y r_{xy}^2 \sin^2 \theta \tag{1.130}$$

$$I_C = I_A + I_B \tag{1.131}$$

where r_{xy} denotes the X—Y distance, m_y is the mass of atom Y, and θ is the bond angle YXY, m is the total mass of XY_2.

(c) *Linear XYZ Molecules*

The moment of inertia of a linear XYZ molecule is

$$I = m_x r_{xy}^2 + m_z r_{yz}^2 - \frac{(-m_x r_{xy} + m_z r_{yz})^2}{m_x + m_y + m_z} \tag{1.132}$$

where m_x, m_y, and m_z are the masses of atoms X, Y, and Z, respectively, and r_{xy}, r_{yz} are the X—Y and Y—Z distances, respectively.

(d) *Linear Symmetrical* XY_2 *Molecules*

The moment of inertia is

$$I = 2m_x r_{xy}^2 \tag{1.133}$$

(e) *Plane* XY_3 *Molecules*

For a plane and symmetrical molecule XY_3, the X—Y distance $r(X—Y)$ is sufficient to determine the geometrical structure. For the plane XY_3 molecule, the moments of inertia are

$$I_A = I_B = \frac{3}{2} m_y r_{xy}^2 \tag{1.134}$$

$$I_C = I_A + I_B \tag{1.135}$$

(f) *Plane* XY_2Z *Molecules*

The moments of inertia are

$$I_A = \frac{3}{2} m_y r_{xy}^2 \tag{1.136}$$

$$I_B = \frac{1}{2} m_y r_{xy}^2 + m_z r_{xz}^2 - \frac{(-m_y r_{xy} + m_z r_{xz})^2}{m_x + 2m_y + m_z} \tag{1.137}$$

$$I_C = I_A + I_B \tag{1.138}$$

(g) *Nonplanar* XY_3 *Molecules*

For nonplanar XY_3 molecules, there are two quantities that determine the geometrical structure. They are the X—Y distance r_{xy} and the angle β of X—Y with the threefold axis. The moments of inertia for nonplanar XY_3 molecules are

$$I_A = 3m_y r_{xy}^2 \sin^2 \beta \tag{1.139}$$

$$I_B = I_C = \frac{3m_y r_{xy}^2}{2\left(1 + \frac{3m_y}{m_x}\right)} \left[2 - \left(1 - 3\frac{m_y}{m_x}\right) \sin^2 \beta\right] \tag{1.140}$$

In these equations,

$$\sin^2 \beta = \frac{4}{3} \sin^2 \theta \tag{1.141}$$

where θ is the YXY angle. The height of the pyramid is $h_0 = r_{xy} \cos \beta$.

(h) *Nonplanar* ZXY_3 *Molecules*

The moments of inertia are

$$I_A = 3m_y r_{xy}^2 \sin^2 \beta \tag{1.142}$$

$$I_B = I_C = m_z r_{xz}^2 + 3m_y r_{xy}^2 \cos^2 \beta - \frac{(m_z r_{xz} - 3m_y r_{xy} \cos \beta)^2}{m_x + m_z + 3m_y} \tag{1.143}$$

(i) *Tetrahedral Molecules* XY_4

The structure is determined by one $r(X—Y)$ distance. The moments of inertia are

$$I_A = I_B = I_C = \frac{8}{3} m_y r_{xy}^2 \tag{1.144}$$

(j) *Tetrahedral* XY_3Z *Molecules*

The moments of inertia are

$$I_A = I_B = I_C = \left[\frac{5}{3} m_y + m_z - \frac{(m_z - m_y{}^2)}{m_x + 3m_y + m_z}\right] r_{xy}^2 \tag{1.145}$$

For the simple molecules discussed above it is quite easy to compute the principal moments of inertia. However, the computation of the principal moments of inertia becomes more complex for larger molecules. When the position of the principal axes is not obvious, the computation of the product of the three principal moments of inertia involves the evaluation of the determinant

$$I_A I_B I_C = \begin{vmatrix} I_{xx} & -I_{xy} & -I_{xz} \\ -I_{xy} & I_{yy} & -I_{yz} \\ -I_{xz} & -I_{yz} & I_{zz} \end{vmatrix} \qquad (1.146)$$

where

$$I_{xx} = \sum_i m_i(y_i^2 + z_i^2) - \frac{1}{m}\left(\sum_i m_i y_i\right)^2 - \frac{1}{m}\left(\sum_i m_i z_i\right)^2 \qquad (1.147)$$

$$I_{xy} = \sum_i m_i x_i y_i - \frac{1}{m}\left(\sum_i m_i x_i\right)\left(\sum_i m_i y_i\right) \qquad (1.148)$$

and

$$m = \sum_i m_i \qquad (1.149)$$

where m_i is the mass of atom i with coordinates (x_i, y_i, z_i).

EXAMPLE

Compute the product $I_A I_B I_C$ of the three principal moments of inertia of the molecule HOAl.

The geometric parameters of HOAl, taken from Table 1.9, are

$$r(H\text{—}O) = 0.94 \times 10^{-8} \text{ cm}$$
$$r(O\text{—}Al) = 1.87 \times 10^{-8} \text{ cm}$$
$$\sphericalangle HOAl = 105°$$

The coordinates of the three atoms are therefore

O   (0, 0, 0)
Al $(1.87 \times 10^{-8}, 0, 0)$
H $(-0.94 \times 10^{-8} \sin 15°, 0.94 \times 10^{-8} \cos 15°, 0)$

If the origin is shifted to the center of mass, one obtains the following new coordinates for each atom:

O $(-1.15 \times 10^{-8}, -0.021 \times 10^{-8}, 0)$
Al $(0.72 \times 10^{-8}, -0.021 \times 10^{-8}, 0)$
H $(-1.35 \times 10^{-8}, +0.89 \times 10^{-8}, 0)$

From Eqs. (1.147)-(1.149) the terms for the determinant are

$$\begin{array}{ll} I_{xx} = 1.35 \times 10^{-40} \text{ g-cm}^2 & I_{xz} = 0 \\ I_{yy} = 61.61 \times 10^{-40} \text{ g-cm}^2 & I_{yz} = 0 \\ I_{zz} = 62.96 \times 10^{-40} \text{ g-cm}^2 & I_{xy} = 0 \end{array}$$

Substituting these values into Eq. (1.146) the value of product $I_A I_B I_C$ of the principal moments of inertia is

$$I_A I_B I_C = 5236.65 \times 10^{-120} \text{ g}^3\text{-cm}^6$$

1.4.4. Symmetry number

The *symmetry number*, σ, is defined as the number of *indistinguishable positions into which the molecule can be turned by simple rigid rotations.*[30] Thus, the symmetry number for homopolar diatomic molecules is two. The symmetry number for heteropolar diatomic molecules is unity. The symmetry numbers of some polyatomic molecules are:

$$B(OH)_3 \ (3); \ AlF_3 \ (6); \ AlF_2 \ (2); \ Al_2O \ (2); \ C_6H_6 \ (12); \ NH_3 \ (3);$$

$$CH_4 \ (12); \ H_2O \ (2); \ (LiF)_2 \ (4).$$

The reader may verify the symmetry numbers stated for the above examples.

In standard texts on spectroscopy, the symmetry of a molecule is the symmetry of the nuclear frame. The position and type of nuclei determine the symmetry. Some of the symmetry elements that a molecule might have are a plane, a center, and an axis of symmetry. A symmetry operation corresponds to each symmetry element. A symmetry operation represents a coordinate transformation that may be a reflection or rotation that will produce a configuration of the nuclei *indistinguishable* from the original one. Excellent examples of various symmetry elements are given in standard texts on spectra.[29] *A possible combination of symmetry operations that leaves at least one point unchanged is a point group.*[29] The symmetry number can be found by using a table of symmetry numbers for various point groups. A partial compilation is given in Table 1.6.

Table 1.6.[29] Symmetry Numbers (σ) for Various Point Groups

Point group	σ	Point group	σ	Point group	σ
$C_1, \ C_i, \ C_s$	1	$D_2, \ D_{2d}, \ D_{2h} \equiv V_h$	4	$C_{\infty v}$	1
$C_2, \ C_{2v}, \ C_{2h}$	2	$D_3, \ D_{3d}, \ D_{3h}$	6	$D_{\infty h}$	2
$C_3, \ C_{3v}, \ C_{3h}$	3	$D_4, \ D_{4d}, \ D_{4h}$	8	$T, \ T_d$	12
$C_4, \ C_{4v}, \ C_{4h}$	4	$D_6, \ D_{6d}, \ D_{6h}$	12	O_h	24
$C_6, \ C_{6v}, \ C_{6h}$	6	S_6	3		

1.4.5. Vibrational partition function

The vibrational energy of a molecule can be written as

$$G(v) = \sum_{i=1} v_i v_i + \sum_{i=1} x_{ii} v_i (v_i - 1) + \sum_{i<j} x_{ij} v_i v_j + \sum_{i=1} g_{ii}(l_i^2 - v_i) \quad (1.150)$$

with

$$v_i = \omega_i + x_{ii}(1 + d_i) + \tfrac{1}{2} \sum_{i \neq j} x_{ij} d_j + g_{ii} \quad (1.151)$$

where v is the fundamental frequency, d is the degeneracy, ω is the wave number, x_{ii}, x_{ij}, and g_{ii} are anharmonic constants, and l is the vibrational

[30] E. B. Wilson, *J. Chem. Phys.*, **27** (1940), 17.

angular momentum. These summations are over the vibrational degrees of freedom. For example, Herzberg lists the anharmonic constants of HCN in cm^{-1} as

$$\omega_1 = 2000.6 \quad x_{11} = +52 \quad x_{12} = -4.2 \quad g_{22} = +3.25$$
$$\omega_2 = 729.3 \quad x_{22} = -2.85 \quad x_{13} = -14.4 \quad y_{333} = +0.768$$
$$\omega_3 = 3451.5 \quad x_{33} = -55.48 \quad x_{23} = -19.53$$

The degeneracies $d_1 = 1$, $d_2 = 2$, and $d_3 = 1$. When these values are substituted into Eq. (1.151), the following values in cm^{-1} are obtained for the fundamental frequencies.

$$\nu_1 = 2096.4 \quad \nu_2 = 712.1 \quad \nu_3 = 3313.8$$

For linear molecules there are $3N - 5$ vibrational degrees of freedom and for nonlinear molecules there are $3N - 6$ vibrational degrees of freedom. If one neglects the anharmonic constants, Eq. (1.150) reduces to the equation for the harmonic oscillator

$$G(v) = \sum_{i=1} v_i \nu_i \tag{1.152}$$

The vibrational partition for a linear harmonic oscillator is

$$Q_v = \sum_{v_i=0}^{\infty} \exp\left(-\sum_{i=1} v_i u_i\right) = \prod_{i=1} (1 - e^{-u_i})^{-1} \tag{1.153}$$

where

$$u_i = \frac{hc\nu_i}{kT} \tag{1.154}$$

There are three methods of determining the normal vibration frequencies, ν_i. The first method involves using tabulated spectroscopic data such as Herzberg.[29, 31] The second method depends upon estimating the frequencies using structural data and transferring force constants from similar molecules.[32] The third method, which is quite complex, computes vibrational frequencies by a careful normal coordinate analysis.[33]

In Sec. 1.4.6 we use Eq. (1.150) with the proper equation for the rotation energy for the molecule under consideration, to compute the effect of vibrational anharmonicity and rotation-vibration interaction on the thermodynamic functions.

In using spectroscopic tabulations for ν_i, the following rules apply:

1. *Linear molecules.* Wave numbers identified by Σ are used once; those identified by Π, Δ, etc., are used twice.

[31] G. Herzberg, *Spectra of Diatomic Molecules*, vol. 1 (Princeton, N.J.: D. Van Nostrand Co., Inc., 1950).

[32] J. Overend and J. R. Schener, *J. Chem. Phys.*, **32** (1960), 1289.

[33] E. B. Wilson, J. D. Decius, and P. C. Cross, *Molecular Vibrations* (New York: McGraw-Hill Book Co., Inc., 1955).

2. *Nonlinear molecules.* Frequencies or wave numbers identified a, A, b, B are used once; those denoted with e or E are used twice; frequencies designated as f or F are used three times.[33]

1.4.6. General polyatomic molecules

(a) Linear Molecules

The energy levels of a linear molecule can be written as

$$T - G_0 = \sum_i v_i \nu_i + \sum_i x_{ii}v_i(v_i - 1) + \sum_{i<j} x_{ij}v_iv_j + \sum_i g_{ii}(l_i^2 - v_i) + F_v(J) \tag{1.155}$$

where

$$F_v(J) = B_{[v]}[J(J + 1) - l^2] - D_v J^2(J + 1)^2 \tag{1.156}$$

and

$$B_v = B_0 \left(1 - \sum_i b_i v_i\right) \tag{1.157}$$

with

$$b_i = \frac{\alpha_i^B}{B_0} \tag{1.158}$$

$$B_0 = B_e - \frac{\alpha_e}{2} \tag{1.159}$$

and

$$\alpha_i^B = \alpha_i^{\text{harmonic}} + \alpha_i^{\text{anharmonic}} + \alpha_i^{\text{Coriolis}} \tag{1.160}$$

$$\nu_i = \omega_i + x_{ii}(1 + d_i) + \frac{1}{2}\sum_{i \neq j} x_{ij}d_j + g_{ii} \tag{1.161}$$

For the case of linear, as well as nonlinear, molecules, formulas for α_i^B have been given by Nielsen[34] (see also Sayvetz[35]). We give only the formulas for the linear XY_2 molecule.

$$\alpha_1^{(\text{harm})} = -\frac{6B_e^2}{\omega_i}, \qquad \alpha_2^{(\text{harm})} = +\frac{B_e^2}{\omega_2}, \qquad \alpha_3^{(\text{harm})} = \frac{2B_e^2}{\omega_3} \tag{1.162}$$

$$\alpha_1^{(\text{anharm})} = -\frac{24B_e^3 I_e^{3/2}\alpha_{111}}{\omega_1^3 hc}, \qquad \alpha_2^{(\text{anharm})} = \frac{8B_e^3 I_e^{3/2}\alpha_{122}}{\omega_1^2\omega_2 hc} \tag{1.163}$$

$$\alpha_3^{(\text{anharm})} = -\frac{8B_e^3 I_e^{3/2}\alpha_{133}}{\omega_1^2\omega_3 hc} \tag{1.164}$$

$$\alpha_1^{(\text{Cor})} = 0, \qquad \alpha_2^{(\text{Cor})} = \frac{4B_e^2\omega_2}{\omega_3^2 - \omega_2^2}, \qquad \alpha_3^{(\text{Cor})} = -\frac{8B_e^2\omega_3}{\omega_3^2 - \omega_2^2} \tag{1.165}$$

The α_{111}, α_{122}, α_{133} are the anharmonic potential constants[36] in the potential

[34] H. H. Nielsen, *Phys. Rev.*, **60** (1941), 794.
[35] H. Sayvetz, *J. Chem. Phys.*, **7** (1939), 383.
[36] G. Herzberg, *Molecular Spectra and Molecular Structure*, vol. 2, (Princeton, N.J.: D. Van Nostrand Co., Inc., 1950), p. 204.

energy equation. The reader should note that D_v, a centrifugal distortion term, has been included for the case of linear molecules.

With the use of Eq. (1.155) to represent the energy levels, we write a "generalized" internal partition function as

$$Q = Q_0^0 Q_v' Q_l Q_r(v, l) \tag{1.166}$$

$$Q_0^0 = \exp\left(-hc\frac{G_0}{kT}\right) \tag{1.167}$$

$$Q_v' = \sum_{[v]} \exp\left[-\sum_i u_i v_i + \sum_i x_{ii}' u_i v_i(v_i - 1) + \sum_{i<j} x_{ij}'(u_i u_j)^{1/2} v_i v_j\right] \tag{1.168}$$

$$Q_l = \sum_l \exp\left[-\sum_i g_{ii}' u_i(l_i^2 - v_i)\right] \tag{1.169}$$

$$Q_r(v, l) = \exp(\beta_v l^2) \sum_{J=l}^{\infty} (2J + 1) \exp\left[-\beta_v J(J + 1) + \beta_v \delta_v J^2(J + 1)^2\right] \tag{1.170}$$

$$u_i = \frac{hcv_i}{kT}, \quad x_{ij}' = -\frac{x_{ij}}{(v_i v_j)^{1/2}}, \quad x_{ii}' = -\frac{x_{ii}}{v_i} \tag{1.171}$$

$$g_{ii}' = -\frac{g_{ii}}{v_i}, \quad \beta_v = \frac{hcB_v}{kT}, \quad \delta_v = \frac{D_v}{B_v}$$

We now show that the vibrational partition function, Q_v', the rotational partition function, $Q_r(v, l)$, and the vibrational angular-momentum partition functions, Q_l, can be reduced to a series of sums involving only the vibrational quantum numbers. The sum in Eq. (1.170) over the rotational levels for $J \geq |l|$ follows from a summation formula of the Euler-MacLaurin type.

$$\sum_{J=l}^{\infty} f(J) = \int_l^{\infty} f(x)\, dx + \frac{1}{2}f(l) - \frac{1}{12}f^{\mathrm{I}}(l) + \frac{1}{720}f^{\mathrm{III}}(l)$$

$$-\frac{1}{30{,}240}f^{\mathrm{V}}(l) + \cdots \tag{1.172}$$

It follows from Eq. (1.170)

$$f(x) = (2x + 1) \exp\left[-\beta_v x(x + 1) + \delta_v \beta_v x^2(x + 1)^2\right] \tag{1.173}$$

In order to integrate $f(x)$ we expand the small exponentials using a Mac-Laurin expansion. We obtain

$$f(x) \cong (2x + 1)[\exp\{-\beta_v x(x + 1)\}][1 + \delta_v \beta_v x^2(x + 1)^2] \tag{1.174}$$

On integrating by parts,

$$\int_l^{\infty} f(x)\, dx = \left[\frac{2\delta_v}{\beta_v^2} + \frac{2\delta_v l(l + 1)}{\beta_v} + \frac{1 + \delta_v \beta_v l^2(l + 1)^2}{\beta_v}\right]$$

$$\times \exp\{-\beta_v l(l + 1)\} \tag{1.175}$$

Neglecting second-order terms in v and l we have

$$\int_l^\infty f(x)\,dx = \frac{1}{\beta_v}\left(1 + \frac{2\delta_v}{\beta_v}\right) \tag{1.176}$$

When we take the derivatives of $f(x)$, evaluate $f(x)$ at l, and neglect second-order terms in l, we obtain

$$f(l) = 1 \tag{1.177}$$

$$f'(l) = 2 - \beta_v \tag{1.178}$$

$$f^{\mathrm{III}}(l) = 12\beta_v^3 - 6\delta_v\beta_v^2 - 12\beta_v + 24\delta_v\beta_v - \beta_v^3 \tag{1.179}$$

$$f^{\mathrm{V}}(l) = -180\beta_v^3 + 360\delta_v\beta_v^3 + 120\beta_v^2 - 1080\delta_v\beta_v^2 - 20\delta_v\beta_v^4$$

$$\qquad\qquad - 240\delta_v\beta_v - \beta_v^5 \tag{1.180}$$

Equation (1.172) is evaluated by using Eqs. (1.176) through (1.180), and neglecting second-order terms in v. We obtain

$$Q_r(v, l) = \left(1 - \sum_i b_i v_i\right)^{-1}\left(1 + \frac{2\delta_v}{\beta_0}\right) Q_r^0 \tag{1.181}$$

where

$$Q_r^0 = \frac{1}{\sigma}\frac{1}{\beta_0}\left(1 + \frac{\beta_0}{3} + \frac{\beta_0^2}{15} + \frac{4}{315}\beta_0^3 + \cdots\right), \qquad \beta_0 < 1 \tag{1.182}$$

The coefficient of the term following the term $\frac{4}{315}\beta_0^3$ in Eq. (1.182) is $\frac{1}{315}$, obtainable by evaluating derivatives of order higher than $f^{\mathrm{V}}(l)$. This procedure is an involved one; an easier procedure is to use an asymptotic expansion developed by Mulholland.[37] The reader should note that the expansion in Eq. (1.182) is satisfactory except for large values of β_0. The term $(1 - \sum b_i v_i)^{-1}$ can be expanded in a MacLaurin series. We obtain

$$\left(1 - \sum_i b_i v_i\right)^{-1} \cong 1 + \sum_i (b_i + b_i^2)v_i + \sum_i b_i^2 v_i(v_i - 1) + 2 \sum_{i<j} b_i b_j v_i v_j \tag{1.183}$$

If purely second-order terms are neglected, we have

$$\left(1 - \sum_i b_i v_i\right)^{-1} \cong 1 + \sum_i (b_i + b_i^2)v_i = 1 + \sum_i r_i v_i \tag{1.184}$$

The quantum numbers, l_i, of the degenerate vibrations take on the values $v_i, v_i - 2, v_i - 4, \ldots, 1$, or 0. The summation over the l_i represented by Q_l may be accomplished in the following manner. For a particular l_i, and by using a MacLaurin expansion, we obtain

$$\sum_{l_i} \exp\left[-g'_{ii}u_i(l_i^2 - v_i)\right] \cong \sum_{l_i} [1 - g'_{ii}u_i(l_i^2 - v_i) + \cdots] \tag{1.185}$$

[37] H. P. Mulholland, *Proc. Cambridge Phil. Soc.*, **24** (1928), 280.

$$\sum_{l_i} 1 = v_i + 1 \tag{1.186}$$

$$\sum_{l_i} (l_i^2 - v_i) = \frac{v_i(v_i + 1)(v_i - 1)}{3} \tag{1.187}$$

It follows that

$$\sum_{l_i} \exp\left[-g'_{ii}u_i(l_i^2 - v_i)\right] \cong (v_i + 1)\left[1 - \frac{g'_{ii}u_iv_i(v_i - 1)}{3}\right] \tag{1.188}$$

With this result, Q_l may be put in the convenient form for substitution into the partition function

$$Q_l = \prod_i \binom{v_i + d_i - 1}{v_i} \exp\left[\frac{-g'_{ii}u_iv_i(v_i - 1)}{3}\right] \tag{1.189}$$

where

$$\binom{v_i + d_i - 1}{v_i} = \frac{(v_i + d_i - 1)!}{v_i!(d_i - 1)!} = p_i \tag{1.190}$$

and d_i is the degeneracy associated with the ith fundamental frequency and p_i is the statistical weight for a given vibrational level, specified by vibrational quantum numbers, v_i. If a function, $f_i(z)$, is defined as

$$f_i(z) = \frac{v_i!}{(v_i - z)!} \tag{1.191}$$

it is easy to show that

$$\sum_{v_i = 0}^{\infty} p_i e^{-u_iv_i} = (1 - e^{-u_i})^{-d_i} \tag{1.192}$$

and that

$$\sum_{v_i = 0}^{\infty} f_i(z)p_i e^{-u_iv_i} = \frac{(d_i + z - 1)!}{(d_i - 1)!}\left[\frac{e^{-zu_i}}{(1 - e^{-u_i})^{(d_i + z)}}\right] \tag{1.193}$$

Application of the results for $Q_r(v, l)$ and Q_l reduces the partition function to a series of sums over the vibrational quantum numbers only. The form is

$$Q = Q_s^0 Q_r^0 \left(1 + \frac{2\delta}{\beta_0}\right) Q_v \tag{1.194}$$

$$Q_v = \sum_v \left[\prod_i p_i\right]\left[1 + \sum_i r_iv_i\right]$$

$$\exp\left[-\sum_i u_iv_i + \sum_i x''_{ii}u_iv_i(v_i - 1) + \sum_{i<j} x'_{ij}(u_iu_j)^{1/2}v_iv_j\right] \tag{1.195}$$

where

$$x''_{ii} = x'_{ii} - \frac{g'_{ii}}{3} = -\frac{x_{ii} + \frac{g_{ii}}{3}}{v_i} \tag{1.196}$$

The summation of Q_v analytically involves a MacLaurin expansion of the small exponentials in x_{ii} and x_{ij}. We have

$$Q_v = \sum_v \exp\left[-\sum_i u_i v_i + \sum_i x''_{ii} u_i v_i(v_i - 1) + \sum_{i<j} x'_{ij}(u_i u_j)^{1/2} v_i v_j\right]$$

$$= \sum_v \left[\exp\left(-\sum_i u_i v_i\right)\right]\left[1 + \sum_i x''_{ii} u_i v_i(v_i - 1) + \cdots\right]$$

$$\times \left[1 + \sum_{i<j} x'_{ij}(u_i u_j)^{1/2} v_i v_j + \cdots\right]$$

$$= \sum_v \exp\left(-\sum_i u_i v_i\right) + \sum_i x''_{ii} u_i v_i^2 \exp\left(-\sum_i u_i v_i\right)$$

$$- \sum_i x''_{ii} u_i v_i \exp\left(-\sum_i u_i v_i\right)$$

$$+ \sum_{i<j} x'_{ij}(u_i u_j)^{1/2} v_i v_j \exp\left(-u_i v_i\right) + \cdots \tag{1.197}$$

If second-order terms are neglected, Eq. (1.195) can be written as

$$Q_v = \sum_i p_i \exp\left(-\sum_i u_i v_i\right) + \sum_i x''_{ii} u_i p_i v_i^2 \exp\left(-\sum_i u_i v_i\right)$$

$$- \sum_i x''_{ii} u_i p_i v_i \exp\left(-\sum_i u_i v_i\right) + \sum_{i<j} x'_{ij}(u_i u_j)^{1/2} v_i v_j p_i p_j$$

$$\times \exp\left(-\sum_i u_i v_i\right) + \sum_i r_i p_i v_i \exp\left(-\sum_i u_i v_i\right) \tag{1.198}$$

By use of Eqs. (1.192) and (1.193) we can write

$$Q_v = \prod_i (1 - e^{-u_i})^{-d_i}\left[1 + \sum_i x''_{ii} u_i[f_i(2) + f_i(1)] - \sum_i x''_{ii} u_i f_i(1)\right.$$

$$\left. + \sum_{i<j} x'_{ij}(u_i u_j)^{1/2} f_i(1) f_j(1) + \sum_i r_i f_i(1)\right] \tag{1.199}$$

In Eq. (1.199), functions of v in terms of $f(s) = v!/(v - s)!$ are expressed as

$$v = f(1) \quad \text{and} \quad v^2 = f(2) + f(1) \tag{1.200}$$

From Eq. (1.193)

$$f_i(1) = d_i e^{-u_i}(1 - e^{-u_i})^{-(d_i + 1)} = \frac{d_i e^{-u_i}(1 - e^{-u_i})^{-d_i}}{(1 - e^{-u_i})} \tag{1.201}$$

$$f_i(2) = \frac{d_i(d_i + 1)e^{-2u_i}(1 - e^{-u_i})^{-d_i}}{(1 - e^{-u_i})^2} \tag{1.202}$$

If the Pennington and Kobe[38] nomenclature is used

$$f_i(1) = d_i(1 - e^{-u_i})^{-d_i}\, {}^1\phi_i \tag{1.203}$$

$$f_i(2) = \frac{d_i(d_i + 1)(1 - e^{-u_i})^{-d_i}\, {}^4\phi_i}{2u_i} \tag{1.204}$$

$${}^1\phi_i = (e^{u_i} - 1)^{-1} \tag{1.205}$$

$${}^4\phi_i = 2u_i(e^{u_i} - 1)^{-2} \tag{1.206}$$

Substitution of Eqs. (1.203) and (1.204) into Eq. (1.199) yields

$$Q_v = \prod_i (1 - e^{-u_i})^{-d_i} \left[1 + \frac{1}{2}\sum_i d_i(d_i + 1)\, {}^4\phi_i + \sum_{i<j} d_i d_j x_{ij}'\, {}^7\phi_i\, {}^7\phi_j \right.$$

$$\left. + \sum_i r_i d_i^1\, {}^1\phi_i \right] \tag{1.207}$$

where

$${}^7\phi = u^{1/2}(e^u - 1)^{-1} \tag{1.208}$$

Upon developing $\ln(1 + z) \cong z - \cdots$, the equation for $\ln Q$ is seen to be

$$\ln Q = \ln Q_0^0 + \ln Q_r^0 - \sum_i d_i \ln(1 - e^{-u_i}) + \ln\left(1 + \frac{2\delta}{\beta_0}\right) + \sum_i r_i d_i^1\, {}^1\phi_i$$

$$+ \frac{1}{2}\sum_i d_i(d_i + 1)x_{ii}''\, {}^4\phi_i + \sum_{i<j} d_i d_j x_{ij}'\, {}^7\phi_i\, {}^7\phi_j \tag{1.209}$$

In the Pennington-Kobe method [38]

$$\ln\left(1 + \frac{2\delta}{\beta_0}\right) = \frac{2\delta}{\beta_0} \tag{1.210}$$

The first three terms of Eq. (1.209) are harmonic-oscillator results. The last four are new correction terms which vanish at low temperatures. The correction term, $\ln Q_c$, for vibration anharmonicity, centrifugal stretching, and vibration-rotation interaction is

$$\ln Q_c = \frac{2\delta}{\beta_0} + \sum_i d_i r_i^1\, {}^1\phi_i + \frac{1}{2}\sum_i d_i(d_i + 1)x_{ii}''\, {}^4\phi_i + \sum_{i<j} d_i d_j x_{ij}'\, {}^7\phi_i\, {}^7\phi_j \tag{1.211}$$

where

$$r_i = b_i + b_i^2 \tag{1.212}$$

The small corrections to the rigid harmonic-oscillator approximation are expressed in terms of ${}^n\phi_i$ and constants characteristic of the molecule. Additional information will be given about these constants characteristic of the molecule in subsequent sections (b), (c), and (d).

[38] R. E. Pennington and K. A. Kobe, *J. Chem. Phys.*, **22** (1954), 1442.

The contributions to the thermodynamic functions are

$$-\frac{F_c}{RT} = \frac{2\delta}{\beta_0} + \sum_i d_i r_i{}^1\phi_i + \frac{1}{2}\sum_i d_i(d_i + 1)x_{ii}''{}^4\phi_i + \sum_{i<j} d_i d_j x_{ij}'{}^7\phi_i{}^7\phi_j \qquad (1.213)$$

$$\frac{H_c}{RT} = \frac{2\delta}{\beta_0} + \sum_i d_i r_i{}^2\phi_i + \frac{1}{2}\sum_i d_i(d_i + 1)x_{ii}''{}^5\phi_i$$

$$\qquad + \sum_{i<j} d_i d_j x_{ij}'{}^7\phi_i{}^7\phi_j({}^8\phi_i + {}^8\phi_j) \qquad (1.214)$$

$$\frac{C_c}{R} = \frac{2\delta}{\beta_0} + \sum_i d_i r_i{}^3\phi_i + \frac{1}{2}\sum_i d_i(d_i + 1)x_{ii}''{}^6\phi_i$$

$$\qquad + \sum_{i<j} d_i d_j x_{ij}'{}^7\phi_i{}^7\phi_j[({}^8\phi_i + {}^8\phi_j)^2 + {}^9\phi_i + {}^9\phi_j - 1] \qquad (1.215)$$

For these relations the ${}^n\phi$ and vibrational constants are defined as follows:

$$ {}^1\phi = (e^u - 1)^{-1} \qquad (1.216)$$

$$ {}^2\phi = ue^u(e^u - 1)^{-2} \qquad (1.217)$$

$$ {}^3\phi = u^2 e^u(e^u + 1)(e^u - 1)^{-3} \qquad (1.218)$$

$$ {}^4\phi = 2u(e^u - 1)^{-2} \qquad (1.219)$$

$$ {}^5\phi = 2u(2ue^u - e^u + 1)(e^u - 1)^{-3} \qquad (1.220)$$

$$ {}^6\phi = 4u^2 e^u(2ue^u - 2e^u + u + 2)(e^u - 1)^{-4} \qquad (1.221)$$

$$ {}^7\phi = u^{1/2}(e^u - 1)^{-1} \qquad (1.222)$$

$$ {}^8\phi = \frac{1}{2}(2ue^u - e^u + 1)(e^u - 1)^{-1} \qquad (1.223)$$

$$ {}^9\phi = u^2 e^u(e^u - 1)^{-2} = \left(\frac{(C_p)_{vib}}{R}\right)_{HO} \qquad (1.224)$$

$$ {}^{10}\phi = u(e^u - 1)^{-1} = \left(\frac{H_{vib}}{RT}\right)_{HO} \qquad (1.225)$$

$$ {}^{11}\phi = -\ln(1 - e^{-u}) = \left(\frac{-F_{vib}}{RT}\right)_{HO} \qquad (1.226)$$

$$ u_i = hc\frac{\nu_i}{kT} \qquad (1.227)$$

$$ x_{ii}'' = \frac{(-x_{ii} - g_{ii}/3)}{\nu_i} \qquad (1.228)$$

$$ x_{ij}' = -\frac{x_{ij}}{(\nu_i\nu_j)^{1/2}} \qquad (1.229)$$

In order to facilitate the calculation of the correction terms, Pennington and Kobe[38] presented a compilation of the ${}^n\phi_i$ over a wide range of the argument u. We have used a high-speed computer to evaluate the ${}^n\phi_i$ over a smaller interval of the argument u than given by these authors. The new compilation is given in Appendix 1. The Mayer and Mayer and Pennington-Kobe approximations for $\ln Q_c$ are identical for diatomic molecules. The contributions to the thermodynamic functions given in Eqs. (1.213)–(1.215) are applicable to all molecules when r_i, which depends upon the structure of the molecule, is defined properly. For the three classes of molecules which will be discussed now, δ in Eqs. (1.213)–(1.215) is zero.

(b) *Spherical Top Molecules*

For a spherical top molecule

$$Q_r = \frac{1}{\sigma} \frac{\sqrt{\pi}}{B_v^{3/2}} = \frac{\sqrt{\pi}}{\sigma} \frac{1}{B_0^{3/2}} \left(1 - \sum_i b_i v_i\right)^{3/2} \tag{1.230}$$

Using a MacLaurin expansion in v_i we obtain, neglecting second-order terms in v_i,

$$Q_r = (Q_r)_{HO} \left(1 - \sum_i b_i v_i\right)^{-3/2} \tag{1.231}$$

$$Q_r = (Q_r)_{HO} \left[1 + \sum_i \left(\frac{3}{2} b_i + \frac{15}{8} b_i^2\right) v_i + \cdots\right] \tag{1.232}$$

where $(Q_r)_{HO}$ is the rotation partition function for the rigid harmonic oscillator approximation. It follows that for spherical top molecules

$$r_i = \frac{3}{2} b_i + \frac{15}{8} b_i^2 \tag{1.233}$$

(c) *Symmetric Top Molecules*

For a symmetric top molecule

$$Q_r = \frac{1}{\sigma} \frac{\sqrt{\pi}}{B_v \sqrt{A_v}} = \frac{1}{\sigma} \frac{\sqrt{\pi}}{B_0 \sqrt{A_0}} \frac{1}{(1 - \sum_i b_i v_i)} \frac{1}{(1 - \sum_i a_i v_i)^{1/2}} \tag{1.234}$$

Using a MacLaurin expansion in v_i we obtain, neglecting second-order terms in v_i,

$$Q_r = (Q_r)_{HO} \left[1 + \sum_i \left(b_i + \frac{a_i}{2} + b_i^2 + \frac{a_i b_i}{2} + \frac{3a_i^2}{8}\right) v_i + \cdots\right] \tag{1.235}$$

It follows that for symmetric top molecules

$$r_i = b_i + \frac{a_i}{2} + b_i^2 + \frac{a_i b_i}{2} + \frac{3a_i^2}{8} \tag{1.236}$$

(d) *Asymmetric Top Molecules*

The rotational partition function for an asymmetric top molecule in a first approximation is

$$Q_r = \frac{1}{\sigma} \frac{\sqrt{\pi}}{\sqrt{A_v B_v C_v}} = \frac{\sqrt{\pi}}{\sigma} \frac{1}{\sqrt{A_0 B_0 C_0}} \frac{1}{\sqrt{(1 - \sum_i a_i v_i)(1 - \sum_i b_i v_i)(1 - \sum_i c_i v_i)}} \tag{1.237}$$

Using a MacLaurin expansion in v_i, we obtain, neglecting second-order terms in v_i,

$$Q_r = (Q_r)_{HO} \left\{ 1 + \sum_i \left[\frac{a_i + b_i + c_i}{2} + \frac{a_i^2 + b_i^2 + c_i^2}{4} \right. \right.$$
$$\left. \left. + \frac{(a_i + b_i + c_i)^2}{8} \right] v_i + \cdots \right\} \qquad (1.238)$$

It follows that for asymmetric top molecules

$$r_i = \frac{a_i + b_i + c_i}{2} + \frac{a_i^2 + b_i^2 + c_i^2}{4} + \frac{(a_i + b_i + c_i)^2}{8} \qquad (1.239)$$

1.4.7. Direct summation method

In the direct summation method of computing thermodynamic functions for a diatomic or polyatomic molecule, the vibrational partition function is summed term by term over a set of vibrational quantum numbers, and the rotational partition function for each vibration quantum number is summed term by term over a set of rotational quantum numbers. The maximum number of vibrational states v_{max} required for the summation over vibrational levels is determined by the conditions that

$$G_0(v_{max}) = D_0^0 \quad \text{and} \quad \left[\frac{dG_0(v_{max})}{dv} \right]_{v = v_{max}} = 0 \qquad (1.240)$$

The maximum number of rotational levels used for each vibrational level is estimated as follows. An effective potential function $V_{eff}(r)$ is defined as the sum of the potential function (see Sec. 3.2) for a nonrotating molecule and the equation for the rotational energy levels $F_v(J)$ [see Eq. (1.156)], i.e.,

$$V_{eff}(r) = V(r) + F_v(J) \qquad (1.241)$$

where

$$F_v(J) = \frac{r^2 B_e J(J + 1)}{r_e^2} - \frac{r^6 D_e J^2(J + 1)^2}{r_e^6} \qquad (1.242)$$

For values of $J \neq 0$, Eq. (1.241) gives potential energy curves lying above the potential energy curve for a nonrotating molecule. Each effective potential energy curve has a minimum, and a maximum which lies above the dissociation limit. The spacing between this minimum and maximum is called the *potential barrier* and represents the stability of a molecule in a given vibrational state. As J increases, the potential barrier decreases, and consequently at some value of $J = J_n$, the value of the minimum and maximum energies become identical and the molecule becomes unstable. Since a molecule has a zero-point energy $G(0)$, we have $J_{max} < J_n$ for $v = 0$. Consequently, each vibrational quantum number v should have a J_{max} at which the potential barrier is at least $G(v)$. The potential barrier is calculated from Eq. (1.241) by solving $dV_{eff}(r)/dr = 0$ for the critical points of $V_{eff}(r)$ and evaluating V_{eff}

at these two extremal points. The potential barrier $\Delta V_{\text{eff}}(r)$ is defined by the relation

$$\Delta V_{\text{eff}}(r) = V_{\text{eff}}(r_{\max}) - V_{\text{eff}}(r_{\min}) \tag{1.243}$$

The value of $J_{\max}$ for each vibrational quantum number v is determined by a graph of $\Delta V_{\text{eff}}(r)$ versus J. $J_{\max}$ is that value of J at which

$$\Delta V_{\text{eff}}(r) = G(v) \tag{1.244}$$

For diatomic molecules with large dissociation energies, a rule-of-thumb approximation is usually made for the higher vibrational levels; for each vibrational state, rotational levels are taken up to the point where the total energy (vibrational plus rotational) is as much above the dissociation energy D_0^0 as the vibrational energy alone is below it. The latter statement may be written mathematically as

$$2[D_0^0 - G(v)] = F_v(K) \tag{1.245}$$

When Eq. (1.245) is used to determine the rotational cutoff for a given vibrational level, v, only slight divergence in the thermodynamic functions may result at the higher temperatures. We now illustrate the direct summation method of computing thermodynamic functions for diatomic gases.

The vibrational energy can be written as

$$G(v) = \sum_{i=1}^{i=\bar{N}} A_i v^i \tag{1.246}$$

where $\bar{N}$ and A_i are determined by the expansion of the best representation possible of the vibrational energy of the molecule in terms of the anharmonic constants.

The rotational energy can be written as

$$F_v^0(K) = B_v K(K + 1) - D_v K^2 (K + 1)^2 + H_v \cdot K^3 (K + 1)^3 \tag{1.247}$$

$$B_v = \sum_{j=0} b_j v^j \tag{1.248}$$

$$D_v = \sum_{j=0} d_j v^j \tag{1.249}$$

$$H_v = \sum_{j=0} h_j v^j \tag{1.250}$$

The computation of the total statistical weight for diatomic molecules was discussed in Sec. 1.3.4.

(a) *Vibrational Contributions*

The vibrational partition function is given by the expression

$$Q_v = \sum_{[v]=0}^{\infty} \exp\left[-hc\,\frac{G(v)}{kT}\right] \tag{1.251}$$

The vibrational contributions to the thermodynamic functions are

$$\left(-\frac{F}{RT}\right)_v = \ln \sum_{[v]=0}^{\infty} \exp\left[-hc\,\frac{G(v)}{kT}\right] \tag{1.252}$$

$$\left(\frac{H}{RT}\right)_v = \frac{d\ln Q_v}{d\ln T} = \frac{\displaystyle\sum_{[v]=0}^{\infty}\frac{hc}{kT}G(v)\exp\left[-hc\,\frac{G(v)}{kT}\right]}{\displaystyle\sum_{[v]=0}^{\infty}\exp\left[-hc\,\frac{G(v)}{kT}\right]} \tag{1.253}$$

$$\left(\frac{C_p}{R}\right)_v = \frac{d}{dT}T\frac{d\ln Q_v}{d\ln T} = \frac{\displaystyle\sum_{[v]=0}^{\infty}\left[\frac{hc}{kT}G(v)\right]^2\exp\left[-hc\,\frac{G(v)}{kT}\right]}{\displaystyle\sum_{[v]=0}^{\infty}\exp\left[-hc\,\frac{G(v)}{kT}\right]}$$

$$-\frac{\left[\displaystyle\sum_{[v]=0}^{\infty}\frac{hc}{kT}G(v)\exp\left(-hc\,\frac{G(v)}{kT}\right)\right]^2}{\left[\displaystyle\sum_{[v]=0}^{\infty}\exp\left(-hc\,\frac{G(v)}{kT}\right)\right]^2} \tag{1.254}$$

(b) *Rotational Contributions*
The rotational partition function is given by the relation

$$Q_r = \sum_J (2J+1)\exp\left[-\frac{hcF(J)}{kT}\right]\ . \tag{1.255}$$

The rotational contributions to the thermodynamic functions are

$$\left(-\frac{F}{RT}\right)_r = \ln \sum_J (2J+1)\exp\left[-\frac{hcF(J)}{kT}\right] \tag{1.256}$$

$$\left(\frac{H}{RT}\right)_r = \frac{\displaystyle\sum_J (2J+1)\left[\frac{hcF(J)}{kT}\right]\exp\left[-\frac{hcF(J)}{kT}\right]}{\displaystyle\sum_J (2J+1)\exp\left[-\frac{hcF(J)}{kT}\right]} \tag{1.257}$$

$$\left(\frac{C_p}{R}\right)_r = \frac{\displaystyle\sum_J (2J+1)\left[\frac{hcF(J)}{kT}\right]^2\exp\left[-\frac{hcF(J)}{kT}\right]}{\displaystyle\sum_J (2J+1)\exp\left[-\frac{hcF(J)}{kT}\right]}$$

$$-\left[\frac{\displaystyle\sum_J (2J+1)\left[\frac{hcF(J)}{kT}\right]\exp\left[-\frac{hcF(J)}{kT}\right]}{\displaystyle\sum_J (2J+1)\exp\left[-\frac{hcF(J)}{kT}\right]}\right]^2 \tag{1.258}$$

With the proper definitions of $G(v)$ and $F(J)$ for any molecule, it is possible to develop the correct contributions of vibrational and rotational energies to thermodynamic functions. For example, the simple approximation for including the effect of the multiplicity by an electronic factor to the partition function is not valid for the multiplet electronic states of some of the lighter diatomic molecules. Hill and Van Vleck[39] give the following equations for calculating the rotational levels of diatomic molecules in a $^2\Pi$ state.

$$H_1(J) = B_v \left\{ \left(J + \frac{1}{2} \right)^2 - 1 - \left[\left(J + \frac{1}{2} \right)^2 + \left(\frac{A}{2B_v} \right)^2 - \frac{A}{B_v} \right]^{1/2} \right\} - D_v J^4$$
(1.259)

$$H_2(J) = B_v \left\{ \left(J + \frac{1}{2} \right)^2 - 1 + \left[\left(J + \frac{1}{2} \right)^2 + \left(\frac{A}{2B_v} \right)^2 - \frac{A}{B_v} \right]^{1/2} \right\}$$
$$- D_v(J + 1)^4 \quad (1.260)$$

B_v is the rotational function and A is the separation of the minima of the potential energy curve. The rotational quantum number, J, can assume only half-integral values. To refer the potential functions to the lowest molecular energy level as the zero of energy, the lowest molecular energy, β, must be subtracted from $H_1(J)$ and $H_2(J)$. For molecules in a $^2\Pi$ ground state $\beta = H_1(\frac{3}{2})$.

Let

$$X = \beta_v^2 \left[J(J + 1) + \left(\frac{A}{2B_v} \right)^2 - \frac{A}{B_v} + \frac{1}{4} \right]$$
(1.261)

$$\gamma = \frac{A}{2B_v} - \frac{1}{4}$$
(1.262)

$$Y = -\beta_v J(J + 1) + X^{1/2} + \frac{hc}{kT} D_v J^2 (J + 1)^2$$
(1.263)

$$Z = -\beta_v J(J + 1) - X^{1/2} + \frac{hc}{kT} D_v J^2 (J + 1)^2$$
(1.264)

then Q_r can be written as

$$Q_r = 2 \left[\exp \left(\frac{hc}{kT} \beta + \frac{3}{4} \beta_v \right) \right] \left\{ \sum_{J = 1/2, 3/2, \dots} (2J + 1) \exp Y \right.$$
$$\left. + \sum_{J = 1/2, 3/2, \dots} (2J + 1) \exp Z - 2 \exp (-\gamma \beta_v) \right\} \quad (1.265)$$

The term $\exp(-\gamma \beta_v)$ must be included to account for the fact that only one level with $J = \frac{1}{2}$ exists. The entire expression contains the factor 2 to account for the electronic degeneracy. The contributions to the thermodynamic functions are

$$\left(-\frac{F}{RT} \right)_r = \ln 2 \left[\exp \left(\frac{hc}{kT} \beta + \frac{3}{4} \beta_v \right) \right]$$
$$\left[\sum_J (2J + 1) \exp Y + \sum_J (2J + 1) \exp Z - 2 \exp (-\gamma \beta_v) \right]$$
(1.266)

[39] E. L. Hill and J. H. Van Vleck, *Phys. Rev.*, **32** (1923), 250.

$$\left(\frac{H}{RT}\right)_r = -2\left[\frac{hc\beta}{kT} + \frac{3}{4}\beta_v\right] + \frac{2\left[\exp\left(\frac{hc\beta}{kT} + \frac{3}{4}\beta_v\right)\right]}{Q_r}$$

$$\left[\sum_J (2J + 1)(-Y)\exp Y + \sum_J (2J + 1)(-Z)\exp Z - 2\gamma\beta_v\right.$$

$$\left.\exp\left(-\gamma\beta_v\right)\right] \qquad (1.267)$$

$$\left(\frac{C_p}{R}\right)_r = \frac{2}{Q_r}\exp\left(\frac{hc\beta}{kT} + \frac{3}{4}\beta_v\right)$$

$$\left[\sum_J (2J + 1)\exp Y + \sum_J (2J + 1)Y^2\exp Y + \sum_J (2J + 1)Z\exp Z\right.$$

$$\left. + \sum_J (2J + 1)Z^2\exp Z - 2\gamma\beta_v(\gamma\beta_v - 1)\exp\left(-\gamma\beta_v\right)\right]$$

$$+ 2\left\{\sum_J (2J + 1)(-Y)\exp Y + \sum_J (2J + 1)(-Z)\exp Z\right.$$

$$\left. - 2\gamma\beta_v\exp\left(-\gamma\beta_v\right)\right\}\cdot\frac{1}{Q_r^2}$$

$$\left[\exp\left(\frac{hc\beta}{kT} + \frac{3}{4}\beta_v\right)\right]\left[-\left(\frac{hc\beta}{kT} + \frac{3}{4}\beta_v\right) - Q_r'\right] \qquad (1.268)$$

Haar and Friedman[40] have developed an approximation similar to the procedure described in developing the Mayer and Mayer and Pennington-Kobe methods.

1.4.8. Darling-Dennison and Fermi resonance

When two vibrational levels belonging to different vibrations (or combinations of vibrations) of the same electronic state have nearly the same energy, the interactions between the different vibrations are sufficient to produce a perturbation. Such a vibrational perturbation which causes the appearance of two spectral lines instead of one is called *Fermi resonance*. It is shown[36] that Fermi resonance[41] can occur only between levels of the same species. Fermi first observed the resonance effect in CO_2.

When two vibrational levels of the same electronic state have nearly the same energy but belong to different species, they cannot perturb each other. However, any state v_1, v_2, v_3 with $v_1 > 1$ is perturbed by a state $v_1 - 2$, v_2, $v_3 + 2$. The latter vibrational perturbation was observed in H_2O by Darling and Dennison,[42] and consequently is called *Darling-Dennison resonance*.

The effects on thermodynamic functions due to resonance of the Darling-Dennison type and of the Fermi type have been calculated by Woolley.[43]

[40] L. Haar and A. S. Friedman, *J. Chem. Phys.*, **23** (1955), 869.
[41] E. Fermi, *Z. Physik*, **71** (1931), 250.
[42] B. T. Darling and D. M. Dennison, *Phys. Rev.*, **57** (1940), 128.
[43] H. W. Woolley, *J. Research Natl. Bur. Standards*, **54** (1955), RR2592.

Woolley evaluated these effects by working directly with the elements of the secular determinants that define the energy levels.

The correction equations derived by Woolley[43] for the effect on thermodynamic functions of Darling-Dennison resonance are

$$-\left(\frac{F_T^0}{RT}\right)_c = \frac{\gamma^2 u^2 e^{-2u}}{\omega^2 (1 - e^{-u})^4} \tag{1.269}$$

$$\left(\frac{H_T^0}{RT}\right)_c = \frac{\gamma^2}{\omega^2} u^2 \frac{2e^{-2u}}{(1 - e^{-u})^4} \left\{\frac{u(1 + e^{-u})}{(1 - e^{-u})} - 1\right\} \tag{1.270}$$

$$\left(\frac{C_p^0}{R}\right)_c = \frac{\gamma^2}{\omega^2} \frac{u^2 e^{-2u}}{(1 - e^{-u})^4} \cdot 2 \left\{1 - 4u\frac{(1 + e^{-u})}{(1 - e^{-u})} + 2u^2 \frac{(1 + 3e^{-u} + e^{-2u})}{(1 - e^{-u})^2}\right\} \tag{1.271}$$

ω is the average value of the two levels that have nearly the same energy, u is the $hc\omega/kT$, and γ depends only on the potential constants of a given molecule.

The correction equations derived by Woolley[43] for the effect on thermodynamic functions of Fermi resonance are

$$-\left(\frac{F_T^0}{RT}\right)_c = \frac{1}{2} \frac{W_0^2}{\omega_2^2} \frac{u^2 e^{-2u}}{(1 - e^{-2u})(1 - e^{-u})^2} \tag{1.272}$$

$$\left(\frac{H_T^0}{RT}\right)_c = -\left(\frac{F_T^0}{RT}\right)_c \cdot 2 \left[u\left(1 + \frac{e^{-u}}{1 - e^{-u}} + \frac{e^{-2u}}{1 - e^{-2u}}\right) - 1\right] \tag{1.273}$$

$$\left(\frac{C_p^0}{R}\right)_c = -\left(\frac{F_T^0}{RT}\right)_c \cdot 2 \left\{2\left[u\left(1 + \frac{e^{-u}}{1 - e^{-u}} + \frac{e^{-2u}}{1 - e^{-2u}}\right) - 1\right]^2\right.$$
$$\left. - u^2\left[\frac{e^{-u}}{(1 - e^{-u})^2} + \frac{2e^{-2u}}{(1 - e^{-2u})^2}\right] - 1\right\} \tag{1.274}$$

In Eqs. (1.272)–(1.274), u is $hc\omega_2/kT$, W_0 is the value of a matrix element of the perturbation function W, and the distinction between ω_1 and $2\omega_2$ is disregarded.

The effects of Darling-Dennison resonance on thermodynamic functions for H_2O are summarized in Table 1.7.

Table 1.7. EFFECT OF DARLING-DENNISON RESONANCE ON THE THERMODYNAMIC FUNCTIONS FOR H_2O[43]

Temp., °K	$(-F_T^0/RT)_c$	$(H_T^0/RT)_c$	$(C_p^0/R)_c$
1000	2.6 × 10⁻⁷	24 × 10⁻⁷	206 × 10⁻⁷
2000	1.88 × 10⁻⁵	7.81 × 10⁻⁵	33.1 × 10⁻⁵
3000	0.784 × 10⁻⁴	2.37 × 10⁻⁴	8.01 × 10⁻⁴
4000	1.75 × 10⁻⁴	4.52 × 10⁻⁴	14.2 × 10⁻⁴
5000	3.03 × 10⁻⁴	7.23 × 10⁻⁴	22.1 × 10⁻⁴

The values obtained in Table 1.7 were calculated from Eqs. (1.269)–(1.271) using $\gamma = 77.52$ cm^{-1} and $\omega = 3,650$ cm^{-1}. The effects of Fermi resonance on the thermodynamic functions for H_2O are summarized in Table 1.8.

Table 1.8. EFFECT OF FERMI RESONANCE ON
THERMODYNAMIC FUNCTIONS FOR H_2O [43]

Temp., °K	$(-F_T^0/RT)_c$	$(H_T^0/RT)_c$	$(C_p^0/R)_c$
1000	3×10^{-6}	8×10^{-6}	2×10^{-5}
2000	1×10^{-5}	2×10^{-5}	4×10^{-5}
3000	2×10^{-5}	3×10^{-5}	5×10^{-5}
4000	3×10^{-5}	4×10^{-5}	7×10^{-5}
5000	4×10^{-5}	4×10^{-5}	9×10^{-5}

The values obtained in Table 1.8 were calculated from Eqs. (1.272)–(1.274) using $W_0^2 = 200$ cm^{-2} and $\omega_2 = 1,600$ cm^{-1}. The effect of Fermi resonance on the thermodynamic functions for H_2O is smaller than Darling-Dennison resonance at higher temperatures, although it is larger at $1,000°K$ and below.

1.4.9. Molecules with internal rotation

For the most simple molecules it is reasonable to assume the molecule to be semirigid. A molecule is said to be *semirigid* if the *amplitudes of the oscillations are small compared to the internuclear distances,* and if *any centrifugal stretching is small.* Molecules that are not semirigid can have *free internal rotation* or *slow torsional oscillations.* In order to account for this effect in computing thermodynamic functions, one assumes a reasonable shape of the potential function opposing the rotation, based on the internal geometry of the molecule. Since the calculated thermodynamic functions depend on the height and shape of the potential barrier, one repeats the calculations for several heights until the calculated values agree with the experimental values. When these calculated and observed thermodynamic quantities are compared, it is found that the internal rotation is in general not free but more or less hindered. Herzberg[36] has given a detailed discussion of the partition function for molecules with internal rotation. Some of these equations are rather complicated and will not be given here.

1.5. SUMMARY OF THERMODYNAMIC FUNCTIONS

The presentation in the foregoing sections forms the basis for the equations given below for the ideal gas state.

1.5.1. Ideal monatomic gas

(a) Translation

$$C_p^0 = 4.968125 \text{ cal deg}^{-1} \text{ mole}^{-1} \tag{1.275}$$

$$\frac{H_T^0 - H_0^0}{T} = 4.968125 \text{ cal deg}^{-1} \text{ mole}^{-1} \tag{1.276}$$

$$\frac{-(F_T^0 - H_0^0)}{T} = 4.968125 \ln T + 2.980875 \ln M$$
$$- 7.28348232 \text{ cal deg}^{-1} \text{ mole}^{-1} \tag{1.277}$$

$$S_T^0 = 4.968125 \ln T + 2.980875 \ln M$$
$$- 2.31535732 \text{ cal deg}^{-1} \text{ mole}^{-1} \tag{1.278}$$

(b) Electronic

$$C_p^0 = 1.98725 \left[\frac{Q_{el}''}{Q_{el}} - \left(\frac{Q_{el}'}{Q_{el}} \right)^2 \right] \text{ cal deg}^{-1} \text{ mole}^{-1} \tag{1.279}$$

$$\frac{H_T^0 - H_0^0}{T} = 1.98725 \left(\frac{Q_{el}'}{Q_{el}} \right) \text{ cal deg}^{-1} \text{ mole}^{-1} \tag{1.280}$$

$$\frac{-(F_T^0 - H_0^0)}{T} = 1.98725 \ln Q_{el} \text{ cal deg}^{-1} \text{ mole}^{-1} \tag{1.281}$$

$$S_T^0 = 1.98725 \ln Q_{el} + 1.98725 \left(\frac{Q_{el}'}{Q_{el}} \right) \text{ cal deg}^{-1} \text{ mole}^{-1} \tag{1.282}$$

where

$$Q_{el} = \sum_i g_i \exp - \frac{1.4388018\nu_i}{T} \tag{1.283}$$

$$Q_{el}' = \sum_i g_i \left(\frac{1.4388018\nu_i}{T} \right) \exp - \frac{1.4388018\nu_i}{T} \tag{1.284}$$

$$Q_{el}'' = \sum_i g_i \left(\frac{1.4388018\nu_i}{T} \right)^2 \exp - \frac{1.4388018\nu_i}{T} \tag{1.285}$$

1.5.2. Diatomic molecules

(a) Translation and Rotation

$$C_p^0 = 6.955375 \text{ cal deg}^{-1} \text{ mole}^{-1} \tag{1.286}$$

$$\frac{H_T^0 - H_0^0}{T} = 6.955375 \text{ cal deg}^{-1} \text{ mole}^{-1} \tag{1.287}$$

$$\frac{-(F_T^0 - H_0^0)}{T} = 6.955375 \ln T + 2.980875 \ln M + 1.98725 \ln (I_0 \times 10^{40})$$
$$- 1.98725 \ln \sigma - 14.6275965 \text{ cal deg}^{-1} \text{ mole}^{-1} \tag{1.288}$$

$$S_T^0 = 6.955375 \ln T + 2.980875 \ln M + 1.98725 \ln (I_0 \times 10^{40})$$
$$- 1.98725 \ln \sigma - 7.67222465 \text{ cal deg}^{-1} \text{ mole}^{-1} \tag{1.289}$$

(b) *Vibration*

$$C_p^0 = 1.98725 \sum_i g_i u_i^2 e^{-u_i}(1 - e^{-u_i})^{-2} \text{ cal deg}^{-1} \text{ mole}^{-1} \quad (1.290)$$

$$\frac{H_T^0 - H_0^0}{T} = 1.98725 \sum_i g_i u_i e^{-u_i}(1 - e^{-u_i})^{-1} \text{ cal deg}^{-1} \text{ mole}^{-1} \quad (1.291)$$

$$\frac{-(F_T^0 - H_0^0)}{T} = -1.98725 \sum_i g_i \ln(1 - e^{-u_i}) \text{ cal deg}^{-1} \text{ mole}^{-1} \quad (1.292)$$

$$S_T^0 = -1.98725 \left\{ \sum_i g_i[\ln(1 - e^{-u_i}) - u_i e^{-u_i}(1 - e^{-u_i})^{-1}] \right\}$$
$$\text{cal deg}^{-1} \text{ mole}^{-1} \quad (1.293)$$

where

$$u_i = \left(\frac{1.4388018}{T} \right) \nu_i \quad (1.294)$$

(c) *Electronic*

Same as Sec. 1.51(b).

(d) *Anharmonic Corrections*

$$C_p^0 = 1.98725 \left[\frac{16\gamma^2}{\beta_0} - \frac{\delta u^2 e^u}{(e^u - 1)^2} + \frac{2u^2 e^{2u}\delta}{(e^u - 1)^3} - \frac{8xu^2 e^u}{(e^u - 1)^3} \right.$$
$$\left. - \frac{4xu^3 e^u}{(e^u - 1)^3} + \frac{12xu^3 e^{2u}}{(e^u - 1)^4} \right] \text{ cal deg}^{-1} \text{ mole}^{-1}$$
$$(1.295)$$

$$\frac{H_T - H_0}{T} = 1.98725 \left[\frac{8\gamma^2}{\beta_0} + \frac{\delta u e^u}{(e^u - 1)^2} + \frac{4xu^2 e^u}{(e^u - 1)^3} - \frac{2xu}{(e^u - 1)^2} \right]$$
$$\text{cal deg}^{-1} \text{ mole}^{-1} \quad (1.296)$$

$$\frac{-(F_T^0 - H_0^0)}{T} = 1.98725 \left[\frac{8\gamma^2}{\beta_0} + \frac{\delta}{e^u - 1} + \frac{2xu}{(e^u - 1)^2} \right] \text{ cal deg}^{-1} \text{ mole}^{-1}$$
$$(1.297)$$

$$S_T^0 = 1.98725 \left[\frac{16\gamma^2}{\beta_0} + \frac{\delta}{e^u - 1} + \frac{\delta e^u u}{(e^u - 1)^2} + \frac{4xu^2 e^u}{(e^u - 1)^3} \right]$$
$$\text{cal deg}^{-1} \text{ mole}^{-1} \quad (1.298)$$

where

$$u = \frac{1.4388018\nu}{T} \quad (1.299)$$

$$\beta_0 = \left(\frac{1.4388018}{T} \right)\left(B_e - \frac{\alpha_e}{2} \right) \quad (1.300)$$

$$\delta = \frac{\alpha_e}{B_e} \quad (1.301)$$

$$\gamma^2 = \frac{1}{4}\left(\frac{D_e}{B_e} \right) \quad (1.302)$$

$$x = \frac{\omega_e x_e}{\nu} \tag{1.303}$$

1.5.3. Linear polyatomic molecules

(a) *Translation and Rotation*
Same as for 1.5.2(a).
(b) *Vibration*
Same as 1.5.2.(b) for each degree of freedom.
(c) *Electronic*
Same as 1.5.1(b) where levels and multiplicities are known.
(d) *Anharmonic Corrections*
See Sec. 1.4.6 for a discussion and equations for anharmonic corrections.

1.5.4. Nonlinear molecules

(a) *Translation and Rotation*

$$C_p^0 = 7.949 \ \text{cal deg}^{-1} \ \text{mole}^{-1} \tag{1.304}$$

$$\frac{H_T^0 - H_0^0}{T} = 7.949 \ \text{cal deg}^{-1} \ \text{mole}^{-1} \tag{1.305}$$

$$-\frac{(F_T^0 - H_0^0)}{T} = 7.949 \ln T + 2.980875 \ln M - 1.98724 \ln \sigma$$
$$+ \ 0.993625 \ln (I_A I_B I_C \times 10^{120}) - 17.16222601$$
$$\text{cal deg}^{-1} \ \text{mole}^{-1} \tag{1.306}$$

$$S_T^0 = 7.949 \ln T + 2.980875 \ln M - 1.98725 \ln \sigma$$
$$+ \ 0.993625 \ln (I_A I_B I_C \times 10^{120}) - 9.21322601$$
$$\text{cal deg}^{-1} \ \text{mole}^{-1} \tag{1.307}$$

(b) *Vibration*
Same as 1.5.2(b) for each degree of freedom.
(c) *Electronic*
Same as 1.5.1(b) where levels and multiplicities are known.
(d) *Anharmonic Corrections*
See Sec. 1.4.6.

1.5.5. Molecular constants and thermodynamic functions for some polyatomic molecules

Molecular constants are listed in Table 1.9 for some polyatomic molecules of interest in rocket-propellant applications. Anharmonic constants are available for some of these molecules and are listed in Table 1.10. Thermodynamic functions are presented in Appendix 4 for these polyatomic molecules. All thermodynamic functions were calculated using the Pennington-Kobe method with the available anharmonic constants tabulated in Table 1.10. If anharmonic constants are not available the procedure reduces to the rigid rotation-harmonic oscillator approximation.

Table 1.9. Molecular Constants for Some Polyatomic Molecules

Cpd.	Sym.	M	ω_e cm^{-1}	r_e Å	$I \times 10^{40}$ g-cm^2	σ	g_e	Ref.*
AlClF$_2$	C_{2v}	100.437	850 350 750 250 550 200	r(Al—F) = 1.70 r(Al—Cl) = 2.10 ∢FAlF = 120° ∢FAlCl = 120°	136.7 276.0 412.7	2	1	a
AlClO	$C_{\infty v}$	78.437	900 450 350(2)	r(O=Al) = 1.62 r(Al—Cl) = 2.14	286.5	1	1	a
AlCl$_2$	C_{2v}	97.894	600 350 150	r(Al—Cl) = 2.10 ∢ClAlCl = 120°	35.77 389.41 425.18	2	2	a
AlCl$_2$F	C_{2v}	116.894	750 300 650 200 450 150	r(Al—F) = 1.70 r(Al—Cl) = 2.10 ∢FAlCl = 120° ∢ClAlCl = 120°	195.7 389.4 585.1	2	1	a
AlCl$_3$	D_{3h}	133.351	350 610(2) 250 150(2)	r(Al—Cl) = 2.10 ∢ClAlCl = 120°	389.41 389.41 778.82	6	1	a
AlFO	$C_{\infty v}$	61.98	900 750 500(2)	r(O=Al) = 1.62 r(Al—F) = 1.65	154.8	1	1	a
AlF$_2$	C_{2v}	64.98	900 700 300	r(Al—F) = 1.70 ∢FAlF = 120°	18.93 136.74 155.67	2	2	a
AlF$_3$	D_{3h}	83.98	700 900(2) 400 300(2)	r(Al—F) = 1.70 ∢FAlF = 120°	136.75 136.75 273.50	6	1	a

* See pages 71 and 72 for reference data.

Table 1.9. (cont'd)

Cpd.	Sym.	M	ω_e cm^{-1}	r_e Å	$I \times 10^{40}$ g-cm^2	σ	g_e	Ref.*
O=AlH	$C_{\infty v}$	43.988	1600, 1000(2), 900	$r(\text{O}{=}\text{Al}) = 1.62$; $r(\text{Al}{-}\text{H}) = 1.64$	53.1	1	1	a
AlOH	C_s	43.988	3400, 1200, 800	$r(\text{Al}{-}\text{O}) = 1.87$; $r(\text{O}{-}\text{H}) = 0.94$; ∢AlOH $= 105°$	1.35; 61.61; 62.96	1	1	a
O=AlOH	C_s	59.988	3400, 1200, 1100; 700, 500, 400	$r(\text{O}{=}\text{Al}) = 1.62$; $r(\text{Al}{-}\text{O}) = 1.87$; $r(\text{O}{-}\text{H}) = 0.94$; ∢OAlO $= 180°$	1.3; 169; 170.3	1	1	a
Al$_2$O	C_{2v}	69.96	500, 977, 1580	$r(\text{Al}{-}\text{Al}) = 2$; $r(\text{Al}{-}\text{O}) = 1.618$; ∢Al$-O-$Al $= 110°$	51; 90; 141	2	1	b
Al$_2$C$_2$	$C_{\infty v}$	77.982	1872, 489, 1010; 315(2), 108(2)		471	2	1	c
BBrCl$_2$	C_{2v}	161.65	885, 408, 209; 958, 408, 209	$r(\text{B}{-}\text{Cl}) = 1.73$; $r(\text{B}{-}\text{Br}) = 1.87$; ∢BrBCl $= 120°$; ∢ClBCl $= 120°$	264.28; 472.34; 736.62	2	1	d
BBr$_2$Cl	C_{2v}	206.109	925, 347, 172; 834, 192, 408	$r(\text{B}{-}\text{Cl}) = 1.73$; $r(\text{B}{-}\text{Br}) = 1.87$; ∢BrBCl $= 120°$	695.95; 345.64; 1041.59	2	1	d
BBr$_3$	D_{3h}	250.568	279, 371, 819; 819, 151, 151	$r(\text{B}{-}\text{Br}) = 1.87$; ∢BrBBr $= 120°$	695.95; 695.95; 1391.90	6	1	d

63

* See pages 71 and 72 for reference data.

Table 1.9. (cont'd)

Cpd.	Sym.	M	ω_e cm^{-1}		r_e Å	$I \times 10^{40}$ g-cm^2	σ	g_e	Ref.*
BBrF$_2$	C_{2v}	128.736	1215 633 330	1427 346 573	r(B—F) = 1.29 r(B—Br) = 1.87 $\angle$FBBr = 120° $\angle$FBF = 120°	78.74 288.92 367.66	2	1	d
BBr$_2$F	C_{2v}	189.652	1310 418 183	888 283 496	r(B—F) = 1.29 r(B—Br) = 1.87 $\angle$BrBF = 120° $\angle$BrBBr = 120°	695.95 147.84 843.79	2	1	d
BClF	$C_{\infty v}$	65.277	537 720(2) 1450		r(B—F) = 1.29 r(B—Cl) = 1.73	193.01	1	2	e
BClF$_2$	C_{2v}	84.277	1250 697 427	1430 366 609	r(B—F) = 1.28 r(B—Cl) = 1.73 $\angle$ClBF = 120° $\angle$FBF = 120°	77.52 175.03 252.55	2	1	d
BClO	$C_{\infty v}$	62.277	666 410(2) 1900		r(B—O) = 1.208 r(B—Cl) = 1.74	169.14	1	1	e
BCl$_2$	C_{2v}	81.734	405 480 1110		r(B—Cl) = 1.73 $\angle$ClBCl = 110°	5.45 311.15 316.60	2	2	e
BCl$_2$F	C_{2v}	100.734	1320 555 266	1000 339 528	r(B—F) = 1.29 r(B—Cl) = 1.73 $\angle$ClBF = 120° $\angle$FBF = 120°	117.18 264.28 381.46	2	1	d
BCl$_3$	D_{3h}	117.191	471	986	r(B—Cl) = 1.73	264.28	6	1	d

* See pages 71 and 72 for reference data.

64

Table 1.9. (cont'd)

Cpd.	Sym.	M	ω_e cm^{-1}	r_e Å	$I \times 10^{40}$ g-cm^2	σ	g_e	Ref.*
BFO	$C_{\infty v}$	45.82	471 243	∢ClBCl = 120°	264.28	1	1	e
			986 243	r(B—O) = 1.208	528.56			
			910	r(B—F) = 1.291	90.36			
			400(2)					
			2000					
BF$_2$	$D_{\infty h}$	48.82	785	r(B—F) = 1.28	103.37	2	2	e
			905(2)					
			1665					
BF$_3$	D_{3h}	67.82	888 1495	r(B—F) = 1.28	78.74	6	1	d
			714 481	∢FBF = 120°	78.74			
			1495 481		157.48			
BHO$_2$	C_s	43.828	3680 1250	r(B═O) = 1.208	1.0567	1	1	f
			2030 700	r(B—O) = 1.34	85.6992			
			1420 600	r(O—H) = 1.00	86.7559			
				∢OBO = 180°				
				∢HOB = 120°				
BH$_3$	D_{3h}	13.844	2265 1557	r(B—H) = 1.25	3.92	6	1	g
			1210 2245	∢HBH = 120°	3.92			
			1557 2245		7.84			
B(OH)$_3$	C_{3h}	61.844	880 1430(2)	r(B—O) = 1.31	166.16	3	1	h
			3250 3180(2)	r(O—H) = 1.11	166.16			
			1060 544(2)	∢OBO = 120°	332.32			
			639 1140(2)	∢BOH = 120°				
			800 209(2)					
B$_2$O$_2$	$C_{\infty v}$	53.64	2000 600(2)	r(B—B) = 1.589	235.062	2	1	f
			750 300(2)	r(B═O) = 1.2049				

* See pages 71 and 72 for reference data.

Table 1.9. (cont'd)

Cpd.	Sym.	M	ω_e cm^{-1}	r_e Å	$I \times 10^{40}$ g-cm^2	σ	g_e	Ref.*
B_2O_3	C_{2v}	69.64	1890 2035(2) 1411 1300 873	r(B=O) = 1.20 r(B—O) = 1.34 ∡B—O—B = 1.20° ∡O=B—O = 180°	33.64 343.95 377.59	2	1	f
BeFCl	$C_{\infty v}$	63.47	1200 800	∡ClBeF = 180° r(Be—F) = 1.40 r(Be—Cl) = 1.75	209.1	1	1	a
BeFBr	$C_{\infty v}$	107.929	650(2) 1250 425 325(2)	∡BrBeF = 180° r(Be—F) = 1.40 r(Be—Br) = 1.91	301.5	1	1	e
BeClBr	$C_{\infty v}$	124.386	975 400 250(2)	∡BrBeCl = 180° r(Be—Br) = 1.91 r(Be—Cl) = 1.75	554.8	1	1	e
BeF_2	$D_{\infty h}$	47.013	1520 825(2) 675	r(Be—F) = 1.40 ∡FBeF = 180°	123.6	2	1	i
$BeCl_2$	$D_{\infty h}$	79.927	1113 482(2) 375	r(Be—Cl) = 1.75 ∡ClBeCl = 180°	360.6	2	1	i
$BeBr_2$	$D_{\infty h}$	168.845	1550 400(2) 675	r(Be—Br) = 1.91 ∡BrBeBr = 180°	968.1	2	1	e
BeC_2	$D_{\infty h}$	33.035	1025 450(2) 1975	r(Be—Cl) = 1.33 ∡CBeC = 180°	70.6	2	1	e

66

* See pages 71 and 72 for reference data.

Table 1.9. (cont'd)

Cpd.	Sym.	M	ω_e cm^{-1}	r_e Å	$I \times 10^{40}$ g-cm^2	σ	g_e	Ref.*
CCl_4	T_d	153.839	450, 214(2), 762(3), 305(3)	$r(\text{C—Cl}) = 1.767$ $\angle\text{ClCCl} = 109°\ 28'$	486.0 486.0 486.0	12	1	j
CF_2	C_{2v}	50.011	1162, 667, 1350	$r(\text{C—F}) = 1.30$ $\angle\text{FCF} = 120°$	6.4 80 86.4	2	1	k
CF_2O	C_{2v}	66.011	1942, 965, 626, 1249, 584, 774		71.3093 71.3093 143.8131	2	1	l
CF_3	D_{3h}	69.011	890, 667, 480(2), 1400(2)	$r(\text{C—F}) = 1.33$ $\angle\text{FCF} = 120°$	83.706 83.706 167.412	6	2	k
CF_4	T_d	88.011	904, 435(2), 1283(3), 632(3)	$r(\text{C—F}) = 1.36$ $\angle\text{FCF} = 109°\ 28'$	155.634 155.634 155.634	12	1	l
CHF_3	C_{3v}	70.019	3035, 1140, 700, 1378, 1378, 508, 508, 1152, 1152	$r(\text{C—H}) = 1.098$ $\angle\text{FCF} = 108°\ 48'$ $r(\text{C—F}) = 1.332$	90.48 110.14 200.62	3	1	l
CH_2	$D_{\infty h}$	14.027	2990, 1444, 3106	$r(\text{C—H}) = 1.03$	0.35 3.59 3.94	2	3	m
CH_3	D_{3h}	15.035	2923, 1450	$r(\text{C—H}) = 1.09$ $\angle\text{HCH} = 120°$	2.9985 2.9985	6	2	m

* See pages 71 and 72 for reference data.

Table 1.9. (cont'd)

Cpd.	Sym.	M	ω_e cm^{-1}	r_e Å	$I \times 10^{40}$ g-cm^2	σ	g_e	Ref.*
CH_4	T_d	16.043	3025(2) 1602(2) 2916.5 1533.6(2) 3018.7(3) 1306.2(3)	$r(C-H) = 1.091$ $\angle HCH = 109°\ 28'$	5.9970 5.33 5.33 5.33	12	1	1
CO_2	$D_{\infty h}$	44.011	1342.86 667.30(2) 2349.15	$r(C-O) = 1.926$	71.87	2	1	n
CS_2	$D_{\infty h}$	76.143	659.23 396.55(2) 1537.63	$r(C-S) = 1.553$ $\angle SCS = 180°$	256.4	2	1	o
C_2F_2	$D_{\infty h}$	62.022	2100 750 1180 380(2) 210(2)	$r(C-F) = 1.3$ $r(C=C) = 1.2$	242	2	1	k
C_2H_2	$D_{\infty h}$	26.038	3374 1974 3287 612(2) 729(2)	$B_0 = 1.17684$ cm^{-1}	23.786	2	1	p
C_2H_4	V_n	28.054	3019.3 1623.3 1342.4 1027 3108 2989.5 1236 949.2 943 3105.5 810.3 1443.5		5.7972 27.955 33.795	4	1	q
C_3H_8		42.081	3081 1043 3012 919 2979 417		18.2781 90.1710	2	1	r

* See pages 71 and 72 for reference data.

Table 1.9. (cont'd)

Cpd.	Sym.	M	ω_e cm^{-1}			r_e Å	$I \times 10^{40}$ g-cm^2	σ	g_e	Ref.*
			2916	2960	2852		103.2254			
			1472	1647	1166					
			1448	996	1416					
			936	1399	578					
			1287	177	1224					
C_2N_2	$D_{\infty h}$	52.038	2328.5		850.6	$B_0 = 0.15752$ cm^{-1}	177.68	2	1	s
			2157.6		507.2(2)					
			235(2)							
C_3	$D_{\infty h}$	36.033				r(C≡C) = 1.30	67.40	2	5	t
ClH_3Si	C_{3v}	66.571	1076	1957	598(2)	∡HSiCl = 110° 34'	10.16	3	1	u
			2196	1098	551	∡HSiH = 109° 28'	126.28			
			2147(2)		951(2)	r(Si—H) = 1.49	126.28			
			666(2)			r(Si—Cl) = 2.048				
Cl_2H_2Si	C_{2v}	101.02	188	710	531	∡ClSiCl = 110° 34'	54.75	2	1	v
			877	592	953	∡HSiH = 111° 20'	339.23			
				610	2200(2)	r(Si—Cl) = 2.05	393.98			
						r(Si—H) = 1.49				
Cl_2Mg	$D_{\infty h}$	95.234	597	300	295(2)	r(Mg—Cl) = 2.18	55.96	2	1	i
$ClFMg$		78.777	650	450	400(2)		338.6	1	1	e
Cl_2Li_2		84.794	650	318	344		395.4	4	1	e
			659	344	344		33.14			
							428.5			
Cl_2Si	C_{2v}	99.004	560	500	200	∡ClSiCl = 110° 34'	43.34	2	1	e
						r(Si—Cl) = 2.0	318.19			
							361.53			
Cl_3HSi	C_{3v}	135.469	2256		802(2)	r(Si—H) = 1.49	362.6	3	1	w

* See pages 71 and 72 for reference data.

Table 1.9. (cont'd)

Cpd.	Sym.	M	ω_e cm⁻¹		r_e Å	$I \times 10^{40}$ g-cm²	σ	g_e	Ref.*
			486, 253	583(2), 181(2)	$r(\text{Si—Cl}) = 2.05$; ∢ClSiCl = 113° 30'; ∢HSiCl = 110° 34'	362.6, 692.1			
Cl₄Ti	T_d	189.728	386, 495(3)	120(2), 141(3)	$r(\text{Ti—Cl}) = 2.4$; ∢ClTiCl = 109° 28'	746, 746, 746	12	1	x
Cl₃Zr	C_{3v}	197.591	375, 175, 150(2)	350(2)	$r(\text{Zr—Cl}) = 2.32$; ∢ClZrCl = 120°	475.27, 475.27, 950.54	3	2	e
Cl₄Zr	T_d	233.048	335, 93(2), 98(3)	440(3)	$r(\text{Zr—Cl}) = 2.32$; ∢ClZrCl = 109° 28'	844.93, 844.93, 844.93	12	1	x
Cl₂Pb	C_{2v}	278.124	299, 75	310	$r(\text{Pb—Cl}) = 2.43$; ∢ClPbCl = 110°	60.59, 613.89, 674.48	2	1	e
ClPbBr	$C_{\infty v}$	322.583	309, 72	199(2)	$r(\text{Pb—Cl}) = 2.43$; $r(\text{Pb—Br}) = 2.57$	115.1	1	1	e
ClFPb	$C_{\infty v}$	261.667	509, 95	301(2)	$r(\text{Pb—F}) = 2.64$; $r(\text{Pb—Cl}) = 1.65$	33.1	1	1	e
ClPbO	$C_{\infty v}$	258.667	723, 101	302(2)	$r(\text{Pb—Cl}) = 2.43$; $r(\text{Pb—O}) = 1.922$	24.9	1	2	e
Cl₄Pb	T_d	349.038	326, 246(3)	83(2), 99(3)	$r(\text{Pb—Cl}) = 2.43$; ∢ClPbCl = 109° 28'	926.95, 926.95, 926.95	12	1	e
Cl₄Si	T_d	169.918	424, 608(3)	150(2), 221(3)	∢ClSiCl = 109° 28'; $r(\text{Si—Cl}) = 2.05$	659.7, 659.7	12	1	x

* See pages 71 and 72 for reference data.

Table 1.9. (cont'd)

Cpd.	Sym.	M	ω_e cm^{-1}	r_e Å	$I \times 10^{40}$ g-cm^2	σ	g_e	Ref.
ClF$_3$	C_{2v}	92.457	247 318 426 508 710 750	r(Cl—F) = 1.698 r(Cl—F) = 1.598 $\angle$F'ClF = 87° 27'	659.7 61.127 181.803 243.148	2	1	y
ClO$_2$	C_{2v}	67.457	450.1 958.0 1128.2	A_0 = 1.6006 cm^{-1} B_0 = 0.33283 cm^{-1} C_0 = 0.27553 cm^{-1}	84.11 17.48 101.60	2	2	y
Cl$_2$O	C_{2v}	86.914	320 684 971	r(Cl—O) = 1.701 $\angle$ClOCl = 110.8°	20.23 230.82 251.05	2	1	y

[a] National Bureau of Standards Report 6297, Jan. 1, 1959.
[b] M. A. Cook and A. S. Filler, *J. Phys. Chem.*, **61** (1957), 189.
[c] W. A. Chupka, J. Berkowitz, C. F. Giese, and M. G. Inghram, *J. Phys. Chem.*, **62** (1958), 611.
[d] L. P. Linderman and M. K. Wilson, *J. Chem. Phys.*, **24** (1956), 242.
[e] Estimated from data on related molecules.
[f] D. White, P. N. Walsh, D. E. Mann, and A. Sommer, *Proceedings*, The Propellant Thermodynamic and Handling Conference, Ohio State University, Columbus, Ohio, 1959, pp. 1–18, Special Report 12.
[g] A. R. Emery and R. C. Taylor, *J. Chem. Phys.*, **28** (1958), 1029.
[h] R. Servoss and H. M. Clark, *J. Chem. Phys.*, **26** (1957), 1175.
[i] A. Büchler and W. Klemperer, *J. Chem. Phys.*, **29** (1958), 121.
[j] J. S. Gordon, *J. Chem. Phys.*, **29** (1958), 889.
[k] R. M. Potocki and D. E. Mann, National Bureau of Standards Report 1439, U.S. Department of Commerce, 1952.
[l] D. E. Gray, ed., *American Institute of Physics Handbook* (New York: McGraw-Hill Book Co., Inc., 1957), chap. 7, p. 148.
[m] A. M. Gurvich and A. V. Frost, *Uchenye Zapiski Moskov. Gosudarst. Univ. im. M. V. Lomonosova*, **164** (1953), 129.

[n] H. W. Woolley, *J. Research Natl. Bur. Standards*, **52** (1954), 289.

[o] B. P. Stoicheff, *Can. J. Phys.*, **36** (1958), 218.

[p] H. C. Allen, Jr., E. D. Tidwell, and E. K. Plyler, *J. Research Natl. Bur. Standards*, **57** (1956), 213.

[q] J. M. Dowling and B. P. Stoicheff, *Can. J. Phys.*, **37** (1959), 703.

[r] D. R. Lide and D. E. Mann, *J. Chem. Phys.*, **27** (1957), 868.

[s] T. Miyazawa, *J. Chem. Phys.*, **29** (1958), 421.

[t] W. E. Shuler and W. H. Fletcher, *J. Molecular Spectra*, **1** (1957), 95; B. P. Stoicheff, *Can. J. Phys.*, **35** (1957), 837.

[u] A. Monfils, *Compt. rend.*, **236** (1953), 795.

[v] J. A. Hawkins, S. R. Polo, and M. K. Wilson, *J. Chem. Phys.*, **21** (1953), 1122.

[w] T. G. Gibian and D. S. McKinney, *J. Am. Chem. Soc.*, **73** (1951), 1431.

[x] G. Herzberg, *Molecular Spectra and Molecular Structure* (Princeton, N.J.: D. Van Nostrand Co., Inc., 1945).

[y] W. H. Evans, T. H. Munson, and D. D. Wagman, *J. Research Natl. Bur. Standards*, **55** (1955), 147.

Table 1.10. Molecular Constants for Some Polyatomic Molecules with Anharmonic Constants*

	CO_2	COS	CS_2	ClCN	HCN	H_2O	H_2S	N_2O	NO_2	SO_2
ν_1	1341.54	859	667.04	733.4	2096.61	3656.65	2614.56	1276.90	1320.6	1151.74
ν_2	667.40(2)	524(2)	395.93(2)	379.9(2)	711.90(2)	1594.78	1182.68	588.78(2)	749.6	517.69
ν_3	2349.16	2064	1535.58	2219	3311.40	3755.79	2627.48	2223.75	1617.0	1361.76
x_{11}	−3.75	−4.0	−0.98	−5[a]	−10.45	−45.18	−25.09	−5.21	−9.0	−3.99
x_{12}	3.62	−6.8	7.56	−4[a]	−2.90	−15.14	−19.69	0.52	−9.7	−2.05
x_{13}	−19.37	−4.5	−8.04	−2.0	−14.43	−165.48	−94.68	−27.26	−28.7	−13.71
x_{22}	−0.63	−0.4	−1.56	2.1	−2.50	−17.04	−5.72	−0.17	−0.5	−3.00
x_{23}	−12.53	−11.5	−6.45	−11.0	−19.19	−19.99	−21.09	−14.22	−2.7	−3.90
x_{33}	−12.63	−7.0	−6.66	−17[a]	−52.50	−44.62	−24.00	−15.10	−16.4	−5.17
g_{22}	0.775	3.2	−2.16	−0.1	3.63			0.52		
A						27.379	10.351[b]		8.003[c]	2.027359[c]
B	0.391625	0.203724	0.109277	0.199165[d]	1.4849	14.5844	9.023[b]	0.421181	0.434[c]	0.3441741[c]
C						9.5256	4.825[b]		0.412[c]	0.2935345[c]
$\alpha_1^A \times 10^3$						750	125[b]			
$\alpha_2^A \times 10^3$						−2941	−346[b]			
$\alpha_3^A \times 10^3$						1253	173[b]			
$\alpha_1^B \times 10^3$	1.26	0.6044	0.156		9.50	238	159[b]	1.99		
$\alpha_2^B \times 10^3$	−0.76	−0.3532	−0.256		−3.5	−160	−219[b]	−0.56		
$\alpha_3^B \times 10^3$	3.0875	1.838	0.711		10.79	78	124[b]	3.45		
$\alpha_1^C \times 10^3$						201.8	69[b]			
$\alpha_2^C \times 10^3$						139.2	62[b]			
$\alpha_3^C \times 10^3$						144.5	55[b]			
$D_{000} \times 10^8$	13.5	4.24	1.05	5.547	285			18		
Statistical weight	1	1	1	1	1	1	1	1	2	1
σ	2	1	2	1	1	2	2	1	2	1
References*	e	f,g,h	i,j	k,l	m,n	o,p	q	r,s,t	u	v,w

73

* See page 74 for footnote and references.

* The units of the molecular constants in this table are in cm^{-1}. The molecular constants required for the method described in Sec. 1.4.6. were taken from a paper by B. J. McBride and S. Gordon, *J. Chem. Phys.*, **35** (1961), 2198, and are tabulated here with references.

[a] Estimated by B. J. McBride and S. Gordon, *J. Chem. Phys.*, **35** (1961), 2198.

[b] Derived from the moments of inertia given by H. C. Allen, Jr., and E. K. Plyler, *J. Chem. Phys.*, **25** (1956), 1132. Values were taken from Ref. (a).

[c] A_{000}, B_{000}, C_{000}.

[d] B_{000}.

[e] C. P. Courtoy, *Can. J. Phys.*, **35** (1957), 608.

[f] C. H. Townes, A. N. Holden, and F. R. Meritt, *Phys. Rev.*, **74** (1948), 1113.

[g] T. Wentink, Jr., *J. Chem. Phys.*, **30** (1959), 105.

[h] W. Gordy, W. V. Smith, and R. F. Trambarulo, *Microwave Spectroscopy* (New York: John Wiley & Sons, Inc., 1953).

[i] Private communication of Ref. (a) with B. P. Stoicheff.

[j] A. H. Guenther, T. A. Wiggins, and D. H. Rank, *J. Chem. Phys.*, **28** (1958), 682.

[k] W. O. Freitag and E. R. Nixon, *J. Chem. Phys.*, **24** (1956), 109.

[l] C. A. Burrus and W. Gordy, *Phys. Rev.*, **101** (1956), 599.

[m] H. C. Allen, Jr., E. D. Tidwell, and E. K. Plyler, *J. Chem. Phys.*, **25** (1956), 302.

[n] A. E. Douglas and D. Sharma, *J. Chem. Phys.*, **21** (1953), 448.

[o] G. A. Khachkuruzov, *Optics and Spectroscopy*, **6** (1959), 294.

[p] W. S. Benedict, N. Gailar, and E. K. Plyler, *J. Chem. Phys.*, **24** (1956), 1139.

[q] H. C. Allen, Jr., and E. K. Plyler, *J. Chem. Phys.*, **25** (1956), 1132.

[r] M. L. Grenier-Besson, *Cahiers phys.*, **10** (1956), 44.

[s] K. N. Roo and H. H. Nielsen, *Can. J. Phys.*, **34** (1956), 1147.

[t] E. T. Arakawa and A. H. Nielsen, *J. Mol. Spectroscopy*, **2** (1958), 413.

[u] A. E. Douglas and C. K. Moller, *J. Chem. Phys.*, **22** (1954), 275.

[v] R. D. Shelton, A. H. Nielsen, and W. H. Fletcher, *J. Chem. Phys.*, **21** (1953), 2178. *Erratum*: *ibid.*, **22** (1954), 1791.

[w] D. Kivelson, *J. Chem. Phys.*, **22** (1954), 904.

2

CALCULATION OF THERMO-DYNAMIC FUNCTIONS OF SOLIDS AND LIQUIDS

2.1. INTRODUCTION

It is possible to calculate thermodynamic functions of solids from spectroscopic data. Although many investigations have been made on the vibrational spectra of crystals, most studies have not produced complete assignment of the fundamental frequencies necessary to calculate the thermodynamic functions of crystalline, amorphous, or vitreous solids. This chapter presents a brief outline of a method for computing the thermodynamic functions of a solid from spectroscopic data and several methods of estimating the frequency spectrum distribution of a crystal from experimental thermodynamic data. Thermodynamic functions are obtained by evaluation of an integral equation involving the frequency spectrum distribution function and the associated thermodynamic function of a single harmonic oscillator. A brief description is given of a method of estimating the thermodynamic properties of normal liquids.

2.2. CALCULATION OF HEAT CAPACITY AT CONSTANT PRESSURE

The heat capacity of a solid at constant volume is the temperature derivative of its internal energy. The heat capacity of a solid is measured generally at constant pressure, while theory permits direct calculation of the heat capacity of a solid at constant volume. The heat capacity at constant volume C_V can be converted to the heat capacity at constant pressure C_P by means of the general thermodynamic relation

$$C_P - C_V = \frac{a^2}{b} VT \tag{2.1}$$

where

$$a = \frac{1}{V}\left(\frac{dV}{dT}\right)_P \tag{2.2}$$

$$b = -\frac{1}{V}\left(\frac{dV}{dP}\right) \tag{2.3}$$

a is the coefficient of expansion, V is the specific volume, and b is the isothermal compressibility. In the absence of sufficient data for calculating a and b, the differences between C_P and C_V are estimated often by the Nernst-Lindemann[1] empirical relation

$$C_P - C_V = 0.0214 C_P^2 \left(\frac{T}{T_m}\right) \tag{2.4}$$

where T_m is the melting temperature expressed in absolute degrees Kelvin. The quadratic solution of Eq. (2.4) for C_P yields

$$C_P = \frac{1 + \sqrt{1 - \frac{T}{T_m}(0.0856)C_V}}{\left(\frac{T}{T_m}\right)(0.0428)} \tag{2.5}$$

It is obvious that Eq. (2.5) is valid only when

$$\frac{T}{T_m}(0.0856)C_V \le 1 \tag{2.6}$$

Equation (2.1) is preferred to Eq. (2.5) since the former is an exact relation.

2.3. CALCULATION OF HEAT CAPACITY OF SOLIDS FROM SPECTROSCOPIC DATA

There is no simple, adequate theory for computing the heat capacity of solids. Classically, the equipartition principle predicts an average kinetic energy of $\frac{1}{2}RT$ for each of the three translational degrees of freedom plus an equal amount of potential energy due to displacement of the atoms from their equilibrium positions in the solid. According to the classical theory the heat capacity of a monatomic solid at constant volume is $3R$. This is true at high temperatures for most monatomic crystals. It is customary to estimate the heat capacity of a solid compound by assuming each atom in the compound

[1] W. Nernst and F. Lindemann, Z. Elektrochem., **17** (1911), 817.

has its equipartition value. If there are N atoms in a solid compound, its heat capacity will be $3NR$. If one assumes this point of view, there is no problem in dealing with a large number of particles bound together to form a solid. The solid is stable, and its heat energy is the energy of a set of vibrating particles; the average energy is $3NRT$, from which it follows that the heat capacity at constant volume is $3NR$ and is independent of temperature. Thus, the classical theory explains the *law of Dulong and Petit* which states that *the atomic heat capacity at constant pressure is approximately 6 calories per degree per gram atom for a large number of substances*. However, classical theory does not explain the exceptions to the law of Dulong and Petit. For example, many solid substances (such as boron, carbon, silicon) at room temperature have heat capacities much lower than the 6 calories per degree per gram atom predicted by Dulong and Petit but obey the law of Dulong and Petit at high temperatures. In particular, at sufficiently low temperatures the heat capacities of solid substances decrease rapidly with decreasing temperature.

Einstein[2] resolved this difficulty by applying Planck's quantum theory to the motion of the particles of a solid. The classical mean energy for a linear harmonic oscillator is

$$\bar{E} = k \tag{2.7}$$

Einstein replaced k by $h\nu/[\exp(h\nu/kT) - 1]$. Equation (2.7) becomes

$$\bar{E} = \frac{h\nu}{\exp\left(\dfrac{h\nu}{kT}\right) - 1} \tag{2.8}$$

where ν is the frequency of the oscillation. *Every particle in the solid is assumed to vibrate with a single frequency.* The heat capacity for a solid with N particles, therefore, assumes the form

$$C_V = \left(\frac{dE}{dT}\right)_V = 3Nk\left(\frac{h\nu}{kT}\right)^2 \frac{e^{h\nu/kT}}{[e^{h\nu/kT} - 1]^2} \tag{2.9}$$

The characteristic temperature θ is defined in terms of the characteristic vibration frequency ν as

$$\theta = \frac{h\nu}{k} \tag{2.10}$$

Substituting Eq. (2.10) into Eq. (2.9) we obtain

$$C_V = \frac{3Nk\left(\dfrac{\theta}{T}\right)^2 e^{\theta/T}}{(e^{\theta/T} - 1)^2} \tag{2.11}$$

When T is sufficiently large, C_V reduces to the classical value. The more stable the crystal configuration, the higher the frequency of oscillation of the

[2] A. Einstein, *Ann. Physik*, **22** (1907), 180, 800.

atoms in the crystal. The higher the frequency, the higher the temperature one must obtain to realize the classical behavior. As the temperature goes to absolute zero, C_V decreases monotonically and approaches zero.

The characteristic frequency or characteristic temperature is obtained from an empirical fit of experimental data to the Einstein equation. The Einstein equation gives a reasonable fit to the experimental heat-capacity data at all but extremely low temperatures. At extremely low temperatures the Einstein equation does not agree with the experimental observed law, for three-dimensional crystals, that C_V is directly proportional to T^3. If one defines

$$E\left(\frac{h\nu}{kT}\right) = \frac{k\left(\frac{h\nu}{kT}\right)^2 e^{h\nu/kT}}{[e^{h\nu/kT} - 1]^2} \tag{2.12}$$

then Eq. (2.9) becomes

$$C_V = 3NE\left(\frac{h\nu}{kT}\right) \tag{2.13}$$

Einstein's theory resolved the fundamental difficulties of the theory of heat capacities of solids but did not resolve the details of the motion of the particles. Consequently, one cannot expect accurate agreement of this theory with experiment.

If accurate heat capacities are to be calculated theoretically, one must know more about the frequencies of vibrations of the solid. One can, in principle, use the theory of normal vibrations to determine these frequencies. Once they are known, the total heat capacity is the sum of the contributions due to the individual vibrations; that is

$$C_V = \sum_\nu E\left(\frac{h\nu}{kT}\right) \tag{2.14}$$

The summation Eq. (2.14) can be turned into an integral if one introduces a function $\rho(\nu)\,d\nu$ which gives the number of frequencies between ν and $\nu + d\nu$. $\rho(\nu)$ represents the vibrational spectrum. In terms of $\rho(\nu)$, the heat capacity

$$C_V = \int_0^{\nu_m} \rho(\nu)E\left(\frac{h\nu}{kT}\right) d\nu \tag{2.15}$$

where ν_m is the maximum frequency with which the solid can vibrate. ν_m depends on the binding forces in the solid and on the masses of the particles taking part in the vibration. The lower limit of the frequency spectrum is sufficiently low to be put to zero for the purpose of calculating the heat capacity. Since $E(h\nu/kT)$ is a monotonically increasing function of temperature, it follows that the heat capacity also must have this property of being a monotonically increasing function of temperature. An accurate description of the heat capacity of a solid depends on a knowledge of its spectrum. For a review of the various theoretical approximations to the spectrum implicit in the different theories of heat capacity, see, for example, the excellent review article by Blackman.[3] For the purpose of this discussion, we will omit these theories and consider how the Debye, and the Born-von Karman approximations can be used as tools for estimating heat capacities.

The Debye theory[4] of specific heats assumes atomic solids are continuous elastic bodies possessing $3N$ modes of vibration, corresponding to the $3N$ degrees of freedom of a system containing N atoms. Debye showed that $\rho(\nu)$ was directly proportional to ν^2. The heat capacity of the solid is obtained by evaluation of Eq. (2.15) and by choosing the cutoff frequency ν_D so as to give the correct number of vibrations. Subscript D stands for "Debye." Debye obtained

$$C_V = 3Nk \left\{ 12 \frac{T^3}{\theta_D^3} \int_0^{\theta_D/T} \frac{Z^3 \, dZ}{(e^Z - 1)} - \frac{3(\theta_D/T)}{(e^{\theta_D/T} - 1)} \right\} \tag{2.16}$$

$$= 3ND\left(\frac{\theta_D}{T}\right) \quad \text{with } \theta_D = \frac{h\nu_D}{k} \tag{2.17}$$

The cutoff frequency ν_D can be calculated from the elastic constants of the elastic continuum. The integral in Eq. (2.16) can be approximated, and Eq. (2.17) becomes

$$C_V = 3Nk \left[\frac{4}{5} \pi^4 \frac{T^3}{\theta_D^3} - \frac{3(\theta_D/T)}{(e^{\theta_D/T} - 1)} \right.$$

$$\left. - 12 \frac{\theta_D}{T} \sum_{n=1}^{\infty} e^{-n\theta_D/T} \left(\frac{T}{n\theta_D} + \frac{3T^2}{n^2\theta_D^2} + \frac{6T^3}{n^3\theta_D^3} + \frac{6T^4}{n^4\theta_D^4} \right) \right] \tag{2.18}$$

We see that the Debye theory of the heat capacity of a solid is determined by one parameter, θ/T. At very low temperatures ($T < \theta/12$) the heat capacity is proportional to T^3, and Eq. (2.18) becomes

$$C_V = \frac{12Nk}{5} \pi^4 \left(\frac{T}{\theta_D}\right)^3 \tag{2.19}$$

One can show by expanding[5]

$$\bar{E} = \frac{1}{2} h\nu + \frac{kT(h\nu/kT)}{[e^{h\nu/kT} - 1]} \tag{2.20}$$

in powers of $h\nu/kT$ that

$$\bar{E} = kT \left[1 - \sum_{n=1}^{\infty} (-1)^n \frac{B_n}{(2n)!} \left(\frac{h\nu}{kT}\right)^{2n} \right] \tag{2.21}$$

---

[3] M. Blackman, *Reports on Progress in Physics*, vol. 8 (London: The Physical Society, 1949), pp. 11–29.

[4] P. Debye, *Ann. Physik*, **39** (1912), 789.

[5] Equation (2.20) differs from Eq. (2.8) by the term $\frac{1}{2}h\nu$ which is called the *zero-point energy*. The $\frac{1}{2}h\nu$ is derived in quantum mechanics in the solution to the wave equation for the harmonic-oscillator model. The term $\frac{1}{2}h\nu$ does not change the values of the thermodynamic functions derived using Eq. (2.8).

where B_n are the Bernoulli numbers. The first four Bernoulli numbers are

$$B_1 = \frac{1}{6}, \quad B_2 = \frac{1}{20}, \quad B_3 = \frac{1}{42}, \quad B_4 = \frac{1}{30} \tag{2.22}$$

The heat capacity of the linear oscillator becomes

$$C_V = k \left[1 + \sum_{n=1}^{\infty} (-1)^n \frac{B_n}{(2n)!} (2n-1) \left(\frac{h\nu}{kT} \right)^{2n} \right] \tag{2.23}$$

The heat capacity for a lattice is obtained from Eq. (2.23) for the $3N$ frequencies of vibration of the lattice. The heat capacity of the crystal becomes

$$C_V = k \left[3N + \sum_{n=1}^{\infty} (-1)^n \frac{B_n(2n-1)}{(2n)!} \left(\frac{h}{kT} \right)^n \sum_{\nu} \nu^{2n} \right] \tag{2.24}$$

Equation (2.24) is convergent for $h\nu/kT < 2\pi$ and contains terms depending only on even powers of the frequencies. At extremely high temperatures the classical value of $3Nk$ is approached in the form

$$C_V = 3Nk \left[1 - \frac{1}{20} \left(\frac{\theta_D}{T} \right)^2 \right] \tag{2.25}$$

The characteristic temperature θ_D can be obtained from an empirical fit of the experimental data to Eq. (2.19) at extremely low temperatures. The values of θ_D obtained from this T^3 fit are not the same as those which give the best fit at higher temperatures, but reasonable agreement is obtained. Once θ_D has been found, Eq. (2.18) can be used to calculate the heat-capacity curve down to absolute zero. The Debye theory of specific heats is applicable only to monatomic crystals. However, it is used as a tool for extrapolating heat capacities of other solid substances measured in a convenient experimental region down to very low, inaccessible temperatures.

Born and von Kármán[6] showed that the vibrations of a crystal could be divided into $3s$ groups, where s is the number of particles in a unit cell of the crystal. Three of the $3s$ groups represent low-frequency vibrations, which in the limit become identical with the vibrations of an elastic continuum. These three vibrations are called *acoustical vibrations*. The remaining $(3s - 3)$ vibrations are called *optical vibrations*. The optical vibrations are usually of the same order as optical frequencies. Therefore, to a close approximation the crystal may be considered as composed of two portions; the three acoustical groups of vibrations are represented by a *Debye spectrum* and the optical vibrations are represented by an *Einstein spectrum*. The heat capacity becomes

$$C_V = \sum_{j=1,2,3} D \left(\frac{\theta_j}{T} \right) + \sum_{j=4}^{3s} E \left(\frac{\theta_j}{T} \right) \tag{2.26}$$

In many instances, the acoustical vibrations are calculated from elastic constants and the values of the optical frequencies are obtained from the

[6] M. Born and Th. von Karman, *Physik. Z.*, **13** (1912), 297; **14** (1913), 15.

absorption bands in the solid. Such absorption bands, in general, are not accurate representations of the positions of the maxima in the spectra.

More recently, Lord and Morrow[7] used spectroscopic data to compute the heat capacity of quartz and vitreous silica. They found that the results for the quartz were in excellent agreement with recent heat-capacity measurements but were less satisfactory for vitreous silica because of incomplete knowledge of the distribution of frequencies below 500 cm^{-1}.

EXAMPLE

The unit cell of a quartz consists of three SiO_2 groups. Each unit cell of a quartz contributes 27 vibrational degrees of freedom to the total for the crystal. Three of these will be translational. Assume that the three translational frequencies have a Debye distribution. Lord and Morrow derived the characteristic temperature $\theta = 254°K$ from experimental heat-capacity data below 10°K using the Debye low-temperature expression Eq. (2.19). The remaining 24 degrees of freedom will be assumed to have an Einstein distribution. Lord and Wilmot[8] give the following values for the 24 fundamental vibration frequencies of quartz. The degeneracies are listed in parentheses.

207	365	128(2)	695(2)
365	520	264(2)	800(2)
466	780	397(2)	1064(2)
1082	1055	452(2)	1160(2)

We now compute the heat capacity at constant pressure for one formula-weight of SiO_2 at 100°K and 300°K using Eq. (2.26). At temperatures of 100°K and 300°K, we find $C_V = 3.743$ and 10.566 cal/mole °K respectively. Lord and Morrow[7] have carefully computed $C_P - C_V$ from data listed by Sosman.[9] They obtained at 100° and 300°K that $C_P - C_V$ for quartz is 0.005 and 0.070 cal/mole °K, respectively. It follows that the heat capacities at constant pressure for these two temperatures are 3.744 and 10.703, corresponding to discrepancies of 0.03 and 0.62 per cent, respectively, in the calculated values. The agreement was quite good in the low-temperature range, suggesting an endorsement for the low-frequency assignment.

2.4. CALCULATION OF VIBRATIONAL SPECTRUM FROM EXPERIMENTAL HEAT-CAPACITY DATA

We have shown in Sec. 2.3 a procedure for computing the heat capacity of a solid from a knowledge of its vibrational spectrum. A more formidable problem might be stated. Given experimental heat-capacity data over a

[7] R. C. Lord and J. C. Morrow, *J. Chem. Phys.*, **26** (1957), 230.
[8] R. C. Lord and G. B. Wilmot, *Anal. Chem.*, **27** (1955), 326.
[9] R. B. Sosman, *The Properties of Silica* (New York: Chemical Catalog Co., 1927).

range of temperatures, is it possible to obtain the vibrational spectrum? A knowledge of the frequency distribution spectrum of a crystal would permit one to evaluate the heat capacity at constant volume over any temperature range of interest. Montroll[10] ar.d Katz[11] demonstrated that with the use of even moments of the frequency spectrum one can determine a substitute spectrum from which the high-temperature part of the experimental heat-capacity curve may be exactly reproduced. Katz was able to obtain only the first several moments because of the low precision of the thermal data. Hwang[12] concluded that if the specific-heat data are given with infinite accuracy, the frequency spectrum is uniquely determined. However, if the data have only the present experimental accuracy, various kinds of equivalent spectra exist, all of them being able to reproduce the same observed heat-capacity data.

We now introduce several methods of obtaining an equivalent spectrum which reproduces the observed heat-capacity curve. The equivalent spectrum is used to approximate the thermodynamic functions of the solid to higher temperatures than those covered in the experimental range.

The contribution of a single harmonic oscillator to C_V is denoted by $E(h\nu/kT)$. As a result of the statistical independence of the oscillators we have

$$C_V(T) = \int_0^\infty g(\nu)E\left(\frac{h\nu}{kT}\right) d\nu \qquad (2.27)$$

We are required to calculate the frequency distribution spectrum $g(\nu)$ from experimental heat-capacity data $C_V(T)$ and from the theoretical form of $E(h\nu/kT)$. Montroll[10] demonstrated the formal solution of Eq. (2.27) as

$$g(\nu) = \frac{1}{2\pi} \int_{-\infty}^\infty \frac{du}{\zeta(2+iu)\Gamma(3+iu)} \int_0^\infty C(\theta)(\nu\theta)^{iu} d\theta \qquad (2.28)$$

where $\theta = h/kT$ and $C(\theta) = (1/k)C_V(T)$.

$\zeta(Z)$ is the Reimann zeta function defined by

$$\zeta(Z) = \sum_{n=1}^\infty n^{-z} \qquad (2.29)$$

The computation of $g(\nu)$ involves gamma and zeta functions of a complex argument. These functions have not been tabulated since their evaluation involves laborious numerical integration.

A formulation by Kroll[13] avoids the use of complex functions. The

[10] E. W. Montroll, *J. Chem. Phys.*, **10** (1942), 218.
[11] E. J. Katz, *J. Chem. Phys.*, **19** (1951), 488.
[12] Jenn-Lin Hwang, *J. Chem. Phys.*, **22** (1954), 154.
[13] W. Kroll, *Progress Theor. Phys.*, **8** (1952), 457.

distribution function is found to be

$$p(Z) = \frac{2}{\pi} \int_0^\infty \gamma(Zt)\, dt \int_0^\infty F(u) \cos{(ut)}\, du \tag{2.30}$$

where

$$Z = \frac{\nu}{\nu_0} \tag{2.31}$$

$$\gamma(Zt) = \sum_{n=1}^{\infty} \frac{\mu(n)}{n^2} \operatorname{Re}\left\{ \frac{J_4[2(iZt/n)^{1/2}]}{i(Zt/n)^2} \right\} \tag{2.32}$$

J_4 is the Bessel function of order 4, and $\mu(n)$ is the Moebius function defined by

$$\frac{1}{\zeta(x)} = \sum_{n=1}^{\infty} \frac{\mu(n)}{n^x} \tag{2.33}$$

where $p(x)$ is the Riemann zeta function, and the function $F(y)$ in Eq. (2.30) is related to the specific heat function $C_V(T)$. If one defines

$$y = \frac{kT}{h\nu_0} \tag{2.34}$$

then

$$ky^3 F(y) = C_V(y) \tag{2.35}$$

where ν_0 is a suitably chosen standard frequency. A practical application of the method of Kroll for computing the vibrational frequency spectrum has not been published.

Grayson-Smith and Stanley[14] tried to calculate the vibrational spectrum from specific-heat data using a less rigorous approach. The spectral distribution function is expanded in terms of a Fourier series. The Fourier series in principle is infinite but in practice is used as a finite series.

The heat capacity of a solid which is due to lattice vibrations is written in the form

$$\tau^2 \gamma(T) = \left(\frac{3R}{p}\right) \sum_{n=1}^{\infty} n \int_0^\infty t^2 g(t) e^{-nt/\tau}\, dt \tag{2.36}$$

where

$$C(T) = \gamma(\tau), \quad \tau = \frac{pkT}{h}, \quad p\nu = t, \quad p(\nu) = g(t)$$

and p is an arbitrary constant. The density function $t^2 g(t)$ in Eq. (2.36) is expanded in a Fourier series

$$t^2 g(t) = \frac{2p}{\pi} \sum_{m=1}^{\infty} \frac{a_m(1 - \cos{mt})}{m} \tag{2.37}$$

[14] H. Grayson-Smith and J. P. Stanley, J. Chem. Phys., 18 (1950), 236.

When Eq. (2.37) is substituted into Eq. (2.36) we obtain

$$\gamma(\tau) = 3R \sum_{m=1}^{\infty} a_m \left(\coth m\pi\tau - \frac{1}{m\pi\tau} \right) \tag{2.38}$$

The coefficients a_m must be chosen such that

$$\gamma(\tau) \longrightarrow 3R \text{ for large } \tau \quad \text{and} \quad \gamma(\tau) \longrightarrow AT^3 \text{ as } \tau \longrightarrow 0.$$

The correct form of $\gamma(\tau)$ can be chosen if the following conditions are met.

$$\sum_m a_m = 1 \tag{2.39}$$

$$\sum_m m a_m = 0 \tag{2.40}$$

$$\sum m^3 a_m = \frac{15A}{R} \left(\frac{h}{\pi p k} \right)^3 \tag{2.41}$$

The arbitrary parameter p is chosen to make the important values of τ lie within an accessible range. Grayson-Smith and Stanley found that only six terms of the series Eq. (2.37) are sufficient to make the function Eq. (2.38) agree quite well with experimental heat-capacity data. This method was applied to the heat-capacity curve of bismuth. It was found that the results for the vibrational spectrum distribution were extremely sensitive to the details of the specific-heat curve in the region where (dC_V/dT) is large. A slight change in the smoothing technique of the experimental heat-capacity data produced a radical change in the resulting spectrum.

These results are not surprising, since it is a well-known fact that the heat-capacity curve is not sensitive to changes in the vibrational spectrum. Consequently one expects all of these inversion methods to demonstrate that the distribution function is very sensitive to the detailed heat-capacity curve where the slope of the heat capacity is large.

Taylor[15] noted that when the heat capacity is plotted on a logarithmic temperature scale, the heat capacity is the resultant of the frequency distribution function $g(\theta)$ and $h(\theta/T)$. The frequency distribution function is found to be

$$\bar{g}(s) = \frac{1}{2\pi} \int_{-\infty}^{\infty} [\bar{k}_1(u) \cos su + \bar{k}_2(u) \sin su] \, du$$

$$+ i \frac{1}{2\pi} \int_{-\infty}^{\infty} [\bar{k}_2(u) \cos su - \bar{k}_1(u) \sin su] \, du \tag{2.42}$$

where

$$\bar{k}_1(u) = \left\{ \frac{\bar{H}_1(u)\bar{F}_1(u) + \bar{H}_2(u)\bar{F}_2(u)}{[\bar{H}_1(u)]^2 + [\bar{H}_2(u)]^2} \right\} \tag{2.43}$$

$$\bar{k}_2(u) = \left\{ \frac{\bar{H}_1(u)\bar{F}_2(u) - \bar{H}_2(u)\bar{F}_1(u)}{[\bar{H}_1(u)]^2 + [\bar{H}_2(u)]^2} \right\} \tag{2.44}$$

[15] W. J. Taylor, J. Chem. Phys., 25 (1956), 721.

$$\bar{H}_1(u) = \left(\frac{1}{2\pi}\right)^{1/2} \int_{-\infty}^{\infty} \bar{h}(t) \cos ut \cdot dt \tag{2.45}$$

$$\bar{H}_2(u) = \left(\frac{1}{2\pi}\right)^{1/2} \int_{-\infty}^{\infty} \bar{h}(t) \sin ut \cdot dt \tag{2.46}$$

$$\bar{F}_1(u) = \left(\frac{1}{2\pi}\right)^{1/2} \int_{-\infty}^{\infty} \bar{f}(t) \cos ut \cdot dt \tag{2.47}$$

$$\bar{F}_2(u) = \left(\frac{1}{2\pi}\right)^{1/2} \int_{-\infty}^{\infty} \bar{f}(t) \sin ut \cdot dt \tag{2.48}$$

$$t = \log T \tag{2.49}$$

$$s = \log \theta \tag{2.50}$$

$$\bar{f}(t) = f(T) = C_V(T) \tag{2.51}$$

$$\bar{h}(t) = h\left(\frac{\theta}{T}\right) = E\left(\frac{\theta}{T}\right) \tag{2.52}$$

$$\bar{g}(s) = \theta g(\theta) \tag{2.53}$$

The frequency distribution Eq. (2.42) must be real and nonnegative if the harmonic-oscillator model is valid. Consequently, the imaginary part of $\bar{g}(s)$ must vanish identically for all s. The latter condition should be quite useful as a check on the applicability of the theoretical model and the accuracy of the computations. This method provides a more practical way of making the calculations of the vibrational frequency distribution than those of Montroll[10] and Kroll.[11]

Blackman[16] suggested that one may have to consider the properties of the "integral spectrum" instead of a detailed vibrational spectrum. The "integral spectrum" is less detailed than the vibrational spectrum. Consider

$$n(v) = \int_0^v \rho(v) \, dv \tag{2.54}$$

$n(v)$ is a monotonic increasing function ranging from zero to $v = 3sN$, where s is the number of particles per cell of the lattice and N is the number of cells. Blackman shows that $dn(v)/dv$ is finite in general and nonnegative.

We now write

$$C_V(T) = \int_0^{\infty} \rho(v) E\left(\frac{hv}{kT}\right) dv$$

$$= \left[E\left(\frac{hv}{kT}\right) n(v)\right]_0^{\infty} - \int_0^{\infty} n(v) \frac{d}{dv} E\left(\frac{hv}{kT}\right) dv \tag{2.55}$$

Since $n(0) = 0$, $n(v) = 3sN$ for $v > v_m$ and $E(hv/kT)$ approaches zero for v sufficiently large for a fixed temperature. Therefore, Eq. (2.55) becomes

$$C_V(T) = -\int_0^{\infty} n(v) \left(\frac{dE}{dv}\right) dv \tag{2.56}$$

[16] M. Blackman, *Handbuch der Physik*, 7 (1955), 325.

The Einstein function $E(h\nu/kT)$ can be calculated exactly. Therefore only a knowledge of $n(\nu)$ is required if one is to calculate the heat capacity.

The contributions to the other thermodynamic functions are obtained from the relations

$$H_T^0 - H_{T_0}^0 = \int_{T_0}^{T} C_p(T)\, dT \tag{2.57}$$

$$S_T^0 - S_{T_0}^0 = \int_{T_0}^{T} \frac{C_p(T)\, dT}{T} \tag{2.58}$$

$$\frac{-(F_T^0 - H_{T_0}^0)}{RT} = \frac{-(H_T^0 - H_{T_0}^0)}{RT} + \frac{S_T^0}{R} \tag{2.59}$$

2.5. ESTIMATION OF THE HEAT CAPACITY OF A SOLID AT ELEVATED TEMPERATURES

(a) *Kopp's law* can be used to estimate the molar C_p^0 of a solid at elevated temperatures. The heat capacity of a solid according to Kopp's law is

$$C_p = 3Rn + \frac{a^2 VTn}{b} \simeq 6.2n \tag{2.60}$$

where n is the number of atoms in the solid molecule. Equation (2.60) assumes that each atom in the solid has its equipartition value of $3R$ and $a^2 VT/b$ is set equal to 0.3 cal/g-atom °K. Equation (2.60) is not sufficient for several light elements at ordinary temperatures. Better values for the C_V part of Eq. (2.60) are 1.8 for C, 2.4 for H, 2.7 for B, 3.8 for Si, 4.0 for O, 5.0 for F, 5.4 for P, and 5.4 for S.

(b) The heat capacity of a solid can be represented in any temperature range by a power series in T, which may have one of two forms.

$$C_P = a + bT + cT^2 + dT^3 \tag{2.61}$$

or

$$C_P = a' + b'T + \frac{c'}{T^2} + \cdots \tag{2.62}$$

The other thermodynamic functions are obtained by numerical or graphical integration of the relations given in Eqs. (2.57) through (2.59). Equation (2.61) or Eq. (2.62) can be used to extrapolate to high temperatures when data are not available. One should be careful, however, when extrapolating since extrapolation by its very nature must lead to very considerable uncertainties if extended far beyond the temperature range of the empirical fit.

(c) The heat content function of a solid or liquid can be represented by the empirical relation

$$H_T^0 - H_{298.15}^0 = AT + BT^2 + CT^{-1} + D \log_{10} T + E \tag{2.63}$$

Values of the constants in Eq. (2.63) are listed in Table 2.1 for several condensed species of interest in rocket-propellant applications. Reliable thermal functions are obtained for each compound at temperatures within the stated temperature range. Thermal functions of these condensed species can be calculated using Eq. (2.63) and the appropriate thermodynamic relation for the function in question. In Table 2.2 are listed the thermal functions for these solids at 298.15°K. Thermal properties were computed from references given in Tables 2.1 and 2.2.

We have calculated the heat-content function for several silicon species in the solid state. A least-square fit was made using experimental heat-content data and assuming the heat-content function to be of the form

$$H_T^0 - H_{298.15}^0 = A + \frac{B}{X} + CX + DX^2 + EX^3 + FX^4 + G \ln X$$

$$(2.64)$$

where

$$X = \frac{T}{1000}$$

The empirical fits to the heat-content data with the standard deviation of each fit from the experimental data are presented in Table 2.3. The heat-content data for the solids were taken from Kelley.[17]

2.6. ESTIMATION OF THERMODYNAMIC FUNCTIONS OF LIQUIDS

The theory of the liquid state has not been developed to the point where it is possible to calculate thermodynamic properties of liquids from partition functions. Kirkwood,[18] Born and Green[19] have made important contributions to the theory of the liquid state, but one cannot use these theories to calculate *rigorously* the thermodynamic properties of liquids.

We can compute some thermodynamic functions for normal liquids by applying the *free volume* theory for liquids. A *normal liquid* is one in which *the internal degrees of freedom of each molecule are not disturbed to any extent by the closeness of other molecules in the liquid*. The *free volume theory* for a liquid requires that *the molecules in the liquid be constrained to move in a small volume rather than the total volume*.[20] This is different from gas molecules, which move in the total volume. In Sec. 2.7 we will describe a procedure

[17] K. K. Kelley, *Contributions to the Data on Theoretical Metallurgy X, High-Temperature Heat Content, Heat Capacity, and Entropy Data for Inorganic Compounds*, U.S. Bureau of Mines Bulletin 476 (1949).

[18] J. G. Kirkwood *et al.*, *J. Chem. Phys.*, **18** (1950), 1040.

[19] M. Born and H. S. Green, *A General Kinetic Theory of Liquids* (New York: Cambridge University Press, 1949).

[20] J. E. Lennard-Jones and A. F. Devonshire, *Proc. Roy. Soc. (London)*, **A163** (1937), and **A165** (1938), 1.

Table 2.1. Heat Content* of Some Condensed Substances†

$$H_T^\circ - H_{298.15}^\circ = AT + BT^2 + CT^{-1} + D \log_{10} T + E$$

Compound	State	Temp. range, °K	A	B	C	D	E	Ref.
Al	c	298–932	4.95	$1.48(10^{-3})$	0	0	−1605	a
Al	$c + l$	932 ± 1	Heat of fusion = 2570 cal/mole					a
Al	l	932–1300	7.00				+330	a
Al_2O_3	$c(\alpha)$	298–400						b
Al_2O_3	$c(\alpha)$	400–1200	35.51	$-4.088(10^{-4})$	$8.47(10^5)$	−11232	+17240	c
Al_2O_3	$c(\alpha)$	1200–1800	27.43	$1.53(10^{-3})$	$2.30(10^5)$	0	−11155	d
AlF_3	$c(\beta)$	298–727	17.27	$5.48(10^{-3})$		0	−6408	e
AlF_3	$c(\beta)$	727–1400	20.93	$1.50(10^{-3})$		0	−6500	e
$AlCl_3$	c	298–465.6	13.25	$14.00(10^{-3})$		0	−5195	g
$AlCl_3$	$c + l$	465.6	Heat of fusion = 8500 cal/mole					g
$AlCl_3$	l	465.6–500	31.2	0		0	−2018	g
Be	c	367–1170						h
Be	c	1556						i
Be	$c + l$	1556	Heat of fusion = 2800 cal/mole					j
BeO	c	298–1200	14.088	$4.878(10^{-5})$	0	−5548.7	9522.88	b
Mg	c	298–923	4.689	$1.718(10^{-3})$	$-2.0776(10^4)$	0	−1481	k, l, m, n
Mg	$c + l$	923	Heat of fusion = 2140 cal/mole					m
Mg	l	923–1100	5.292	$1.30(10^{-3})$	$1.179(10^4)$	0	409.8	m
MgO	c	298–1200	13.7146	$-2.247(10^{-5})$	0	−3267.1	3997.2	b
$Mg(OH)_2$	c	298–600	10.981	$9.3(10^{-3})$	$-1.71(10^5)$	0	−3527	o
MgF_2	c	298–1536	17.125	$1.189(10^{-3})$	$2.7996(10^5)$	0	−6150	p
MgF_2	$c + l$	1536	Heat of fusion = 13,900 cal/mole					p
MgF_2	l	1536–1800	22.57	0	0	0	2450	p
$MgCl_2$	c	298–987	18.90	$0.71(10^{-3})$	$2.06(10^5)$	0	−6390	q
$MgCl_2$	$c + l$	987	Heat of fusion = 10,300 cal/mole					q
$MgCl_2$	l	987–1500	22.10	0	0	0	1650	q
Li	c	298–453.7						r
Li	$c + l$	453.7	Heat of fusion = 717 cal/mole					
Li	l	453.7–1200						
Li_2O	c	298–1050	14.939	$3.04(10^{-3})$	$3.38(10^5)$	0	−5858	s
$LiOH$	c	298–744.3	11.988	$4.12(10^{-3})$	$2.26(10^5)$	0	−4701	s

Table 2.1. (cont'd)

Compound	State	Temp. range, °K	A	B	C	D	E	Ref.
LiOH	c + l	744.3	Heat of fusion = 5010 cal/mole					s
LiOH	l	744.3–900	20.74	0	0	0	–3638	s
LiF	c	298–1121						t, u
LiF	c + l	1121.3	Heat of fusion = 6470 cal/mole					t, u
LiF	l	1121.3–1400	15.31	0	0	0	–180	t, u
LiCl	c	298–880	10.9036	$2.2944(10^{-3})$	0	–484.89	–2255.2	v
LiCl	c + l	880	Heat of transition (727°K) = 150 cal/mole. Heat of fusion = 4715 cal/mole					v
LiCl	l	880–1200	17.0691	$-7.6(10^{-4})$	0	0	–2028.3	v

* $H_T^0 - H_{298.15}^0$ defined cal/g formula weight (T in °K).

† "Preliminary Report on the Thermodynamic Properties of Lithium, Beryllium, Magnesium, Aluminum, and Their Compounds with Oxygen, Hydrogen, Fluorine, and Chlorine," unpublished report (1959) by T. B. Douglas and A. C. Victor, National Bureau of Standards.

a K. K. Kelley, U.S. Bureau of Mines Bulletin 476 (1949).

b National Bureau of Standards Report 6297, Jan 1, 1959.

c G. T. Furukawa, T. B. Douglas, R. E. McCoskey, and D. C. Ginnings, J. Research Natl. Bur. Standards, 57 (1956), 67.

d C. H. Shomate and B. F. Naylor, J. Am. Chem. Soc., 67 (1945), 72.

e C. J. O'Brien and K. K. Kelley, J. Am. Chem. Soc., 79 (1957), 5616.

f Heat of transition (727°K) = 150 cal/mole.

g W. Fischer, Z. anorg. allgem. Chem., 200 (1931), 332.

h D. C. Ginnings, T. B. Douglas, and A. F. Ball, J. Am. Chem. Soc., 73 (1951), 1236.

i O. Kubaschewski, P. Brizgys, O. Huchler, R. Jauch, and K. Reinartz, Z. Elektrochem., 54 (1950), 250.

j D. R. Stull and G. C. Sinke, The Thermodynamic Properties of the Elements in their Standard States (Midland, Mich.: Dow Chemical Co., 1955).

k W. G. Saba, K. F. Sterrett, R. S. Craig, and W. E. Wallace, J. Am. Chem. Soc., 79 (1957), 3637.

l R. S. Craig, C. A. Krier, L. W. Coffer, E. A. Bates, and W. E. Wallace, J. Am. Chem. Soc., 76 (1954), 238.

m R. Stull and R. A. McDonald, J. Am. Chem. Soc., 77 (1955), 5293.

n H. Seekamp, Z. anorg. allgem. Chem., 195 (1931), 345.

o P. N. Lashchenko and D. I. Kompanskii, J. Applied Chem. (U.S.S.R.), 8 (1935), 628.

p B. F. Naylor, J. Am. Chem. Soc., 67 (1945), 150.

q G. E. Moore, J. Am. Chem. Soc., 65 (1943), 1700.

r T. B. Douglas, L. F. Epstein, J. L. Dever, and W. H. Howland, J. Am. Chem. Soc., 77 (1955), 2144.

s C. H. Shomate and A. J. Cohen, J. Am. Chem. Soc., 77 (1955), 285.

t T. B. Douglas and J. L. Dever, J. Am. Chem. Soc., 76 (1954), 4826.

u N. K. Voskresenskaya, V. A. Sokalov, E. I. Banushek, and N. E. Schmidt, Izvest. Sektor. Fiz.-Khim. Anal. Inst. Obschei Neorg. Khim. Akad. Nauk S.S.S.R., 27 (1956), 233.

v T. B. Douglas, J. L. Dever, and A. W. Harman, unpublished data.

Table 2.2. THERMAL FUNCTIONS FOR SOME SOLIDS AT 298.15°K

Compound	C_p^0 cal/mole °K	$H_{298.15}^0 - H_0^0$ kcal/mole	$S_{298.15}^0$ cal/mole °K	Ref.
Al(c)	5.82	1.070	6.77	a
$Al_2O_3(\alpha)$	18.884	2.394	12.175	b
AlF_3(c)	17.950	2.772	15.89	c
B(c)	2.650	0.2904	1.402	d, e
B (amorphous)	2.858	0.3143	1.564	d, e
B_2O_3(c)	15.04	2.2231	12.905	d, g, h
B_2O_3 (glass)	14.6	6.586[f]	19.03	d
BN(c)	4.783	0.641	3.673	i
B_4C(c)	12.621	1.3429	6.482	g
Be(c)	3.95	0.468	2.28	j
BeO(c)	6.07	0.6867	3.37	k
C(s) (graphite)	2.101	0.256	1.352	l
Li(c)	5.892	1.090	6.777	m
Li_2(c)	12.927	1.732	9.056	n
LiOH(c)	11.85	1.771	10.23	o
LiF(c)	10.015	1.551	8.52	p
LiCl(c)	11.57	2.0028	13.9	q
Mg(c)	5.929	1.189	7.780	r
MgO(c)	8.960	1.254	6.670	s
MgF_2(c)	14.630	2.375	13.717	t
$MgCl_2$(c)	17.020	3.323	21.429	u
Mg_3N_2(c)	25.000	4.031	23.630	v
Si(c)	4.733	0.765	4.495	w
SiO_2 (quartz)	10.619	1.646	9.826	w
SiO_2 (cristobalite)	10.560	1.666	10.298	w
SiO_2 (tridymite)	10.660	1.692	10.483	w
SiO_2 (glass)	10.600	1.669	10.379	w
SiC(c)	6.370	0.777	3.940	w

[a] W. F. Giauque and P. F. Meads, *J. Am. Chem. Soc.*, **63** (1941), 1897.
[b] G. T. Furukawa, T. B. Douglas, R. E. McCoskey, and D. C. Ginnings, *J. Research Natl. Bur. Standards*, **57** (1956), 67.
[c] E. G. King, *J. Am. Chem. Soc.*, **79** (1957), 2056.
[d] W. H. Evans, D. D. Wagman, and E. J. Prosen, National Bureau of Standards Report 4943, *Thermodynamic Properties of Some Boron Compounds*, Aug. 21, 1956.
[e] H. L. Johnston, H. N. Hersh, and E. C. Kerr, *J. Am. Chem. Soc.*, **73** (1951), 1112.
[f] Relative to B_2O_3(c) at 0°K.
[g] K. K. Kelley, *J. Am. Chem. Soc.*, **63** (1941), 1137.
[h] E. C. Kerr, H. N. Hersh, and H. L. Johnston, *J. Am. Chem. Soc.*, **72** (1950), 4738.
[i] A. S. Dworkin, D. J. Sasman, and E. R. Van Artsdalen, *J. Chem. Phys.*, **21** (1953), 954.
[j] R. W. Hill and P. L. Smith, *Phil. Mag.*, **44** (1953), 636.
[k] K. K. Kelley, *J. Am. Chem. Soc.*, **61** (1939), 1217.
[l] W. De Sorbo and W. W. Tyler, *J. Chem. Phys.*, **21** (1953), 1660.

[m] T. B. Douglas, L. F. Epstein, J. L. Dever, and W. H. Howland, *J. Am. Chem. Soc.*, **77** (1955), 2144.

[n] H. L. Johnston and T. W. Bauer, *J. Am. Chem. Soc.*, **73** (1951), 1119.

[o] T. W. Bauer, H. L. Johnston, and E. C. Kerr, *J. Am. Chem. Soc.*, **72** (1950), 5174.

[p] T. B. Douglas and J. L. Dever, *J. Am. Chem. Soc.*, **76** (1954), 4826.

[q] K. K. Kelley, *U.S. Bureau of Mines Bulletin 477* (1950), 60.

[r] R. S. Craig, C. A. Krier, L. W. Coffer, E. A. Bates, and W. E. Wallace, *J. Am. Chem. Soc.*, **76** (1954), 238.

[s] G. S. Parks and K. K. Kelley, *J. Phys. Chem.*, **30** (1926), 47.

[t] S. S. Todd, *J. Am. Chem. Soc.*, **71** (1949), 4115.

[u] K. K. Kelley and G. E. Moore, *J. Am. Chem. Soc.*, **65** (1943), 1264.

[v] D. W. Mitchell, *Ind. Eng. Chem.*, **41** (1949), 2027.

[w] K. K. Kelley, *Contributions to the Data on Theoretical Metallurgy X, High-Temperature, Heat Content, Heat Capacity, and Entropy Data for Inorganic Compounds*, U.S. Bureau of Mines Bulletin 476 (1949).

---

which has been used for computing thermodynamic properties of a normal liquid using a partition function.

Experimental results indicate that the heat capacity of the liquid state will be higher than that of the solid state. The heat capacity of a liquid at constant pressure is usually estimated as 8 cal/gram-atom/degree. The molar heat capacity of a liquid is $8n$ where n is the number of atoms in the molecule. $8n$ is too high for several light elements. Better values for C_P per g/atom °K are 2.8 for C, 4.3 for H, 4.7 for B, 5.8 for Si, 6.0 for O, 7.0 for F, 7.4 for P, and 7.4 for S. The thermodynamic functions are obtained by numerical integration of Eqs. (2.57) through (2.59).

2.7. CALCULATION OF THERMODYNAMIC FUNCTIONS OF A MONATOMIC LIQUID[21]

The partition function Q for a monatomic liquid is defined by

$$Q = \left(\frac{2\pi mkT}{h^2}\right)^{3N/2} \frac{Q_\tau}{N!} \tag{2.65}$$

where

$$Q_\tau = \int \cdots \int e^{-W/kT} (d\omega)^N \tag{2.66}$$

W in Eq. (2.66) represents the configuration energy of the whole system, referred to zero for infinite separation of the molecules, and $(d\omega)^N$ is the product of N elements of volume to which the centers of the N molecules belong. Q_τ is called the *configuration integral*. The harmonic-oscillator model or the cell model requires the molecules to be confined to a small volume surrounding the equilibrium position. It is possible, therefore, to define q_τ

[21] F. A. Matsen and G. M. Watson, *J. Chem. Phys.*, **11** (1943), 343.

Table 2.3. Heat Content* of Some Silicon Species

$$H_T^0 - H_{298.15}^0 = A + \frac{B}{X} + CX + DX^2 + EX^3 + FX^4 + G\ln X$$

$$X = T/1000$$

Substance	A	B	C	D	E	F	G	Temp. range of heat-content measurements °K		σ Standard deviation
Si(c)	3.185147	0.935918	−4.222690	6.380596	−2.973126	0.753073	4.552011	400	1200	0.001
SiO₂ (quartz)	9.894928	6.973260	−14.647642	10.702572	−2.224545	0.225023	22.391939	848	2000	0.003
SiO₂ (cristobalite)	8.696053	2.313382	−10.619405	13.977	−4.197473	0.58068	11.903873	523	2000	0.006
SiO₂ (tridymite)	−52.905009	−6.527234	99.895015	−41.20971	13.094612	−1.754907	−39.656342	390	2000	0.007
SiO₂ (glass)	8.377543	2.65151	−12.073273	15.378233	−4.835588	0.764947	12.12475	400	2000	0.017
SiC(c)	12.847179	3.413125	−21.477235	16.67453	−5.555605	1.007902	15.678432	400	1700	0.006
Si₃N₄(c)	−0.263571	−0.719317	−2.641189	43.780929	−24.188283	6.339360	0.0	400	900	0.007

* $H_T^0 - H_{298.15}^0$ defined kcal/mole (T in °K).

92

for each molecule. Let us assume a spherical symmetry in the potential function

$$q_\tau = 4\pi \int_0^\infty \exp\left(\frac{-U}{kT}\right) r^2 \, dr \tag{2.67}$$

Here U is the potential energy per molecule and r is the displacement of the molecule from its equilibrium position. The potential energy U is divided into two parts.

$$U = U_0 + U_r \tag{2.68}$$

U_0 is the potential energy of the molecules in their equilibrium positions and U_r is the potential energy as a function of its displacement from the equilibrium positions. For the harmonic-oscillator model

$$U_r = 2\pi^2 \nu^2 m r^2 \tag{2.69}$$

If Eqs. (2.68) and (2.69) are substituted into Eq. (2.67) we obtain

$$q_\tau = 4\pi \exp\left(\frac{-U_0}{kT}\right) \int_0^\infty \exp\left(\frac{-2\pi^2\nu^2 m r^2}{kT}\right) r^2 \, dr$$

$$= \exp\left(\frac{-U_0}{kT}\right)\left[\frac{kT}{2\pi m \nu^2}\right]^{3/2} \tag{2.70}$$

In a real liquid it is known that the molecules usually migrate from one part of the system to another. This has the effect of increasing the entropy by R. To correct the cell model for this effect this configuration integral per molecule q_τ is related to the configuration integral Q_τ of the whole system by

$$(eq_\tau)^N = \frac{Q_\tau}{N!} \tag{2.71}$$

e^N is called the *communal entropy factor*.[22] Using Eq. (2.71) we can rewrite Eq. (2.70) as

$$\frac{Q_\tau}{N!} = e^N \exp\left(\frac{-NU_0}{kT}\right)\left[\frac{kT}{2\pi m \nu^2}\right]^{3N/2} \tag{2.72}$$

The partition function Eq. (2.65) becomes

$$Q = \left(\frac{2\pi m kT}{h^2}\right)^{3N/2} e^N \left(\frac{kT}{2\pi m \nu^2}\right)^{3N/2} \exp\left(\frac{-NU_0}{kT}\right) \tag{2.73}$$

The contributions to the thermodynamic functions are

$$F = -kT \ln Q = NU_0 - 3NkT \ln\left(\frac{kT}{h\nu}\right) - NkT \tag{2.74}$$

$$H = kT\left(\frac{d \ln Q}{d \ln T}\right) + PV = NU_0 + 3NkT + PV \tag{2.75}$$

$$P = kT\left(\frac{d \ln Q}{dV}\right) = -N\frac{dU_0}{dV} - 3NkT\frac{d \ln \nu}{dV} \tag{2.76}$$

[22] H. Eyring and H. Hirschfelder, *J. Phys. Chem.*, **41** (1937), 249.

where V and P are the volume and pressure of the liquid, respectively. To compute these thermodynamic functions we must express U_0 and ν as functions of the volume.

Matsen and Watson[21] used the technique of Lennard-Jones and Devonshire[23] to approximate U_0 and ν for a Morse potential function (see Sec. 3.2). They obtained

$$U_0 = \frac{CA}{2}\{\exp[-2n(a - R_1)] - 2\exp[-n(a - R_1)]\} \tag{2.77}$$

$$K = \frac{CA}{3a}\{2\exp[-2n(a - R_1)](n^2a - n)$$
$$- \exp[-n(a - R_1)](n^2a - 2n)\} \tag{2.78}$$

$$\nu = \frac{1}{2\pi}\left(\frac{K}{m}\right)^{1/2} \tag{2.79}$$

$$R_0 = \left(\frac{u}{v}\right)^{1/6} \tag{2.80}$$

$$R_1 = \left(\frac{2u}{v}\right)^{1/6} \tag{2.81}$$

$$A = \frac{v^2}{4u} \tag{2.82}$$

$$n = \frac{5.65}{(u/v)^{1/6}} \tag{2.83}$$

where u and v are constants in the Lennard-Jones potential

$$\phi(R) = \frac{u}{R^{12}} - \frac{v}{R^6} \tag{2.84}$$

C is the number of nearest neighbors in a cell (for example, $C = 12$ for a face-centered cubic structure), a is the average distance between the molecules in the liquid, and R is the internuclear separation between pairs of nuclei. If Eqs. (2.77) and (2.78) are substituted into Eq. (2.73) we obtain

$$Q = \left(\frac{2\pi mkT}{h^2}\right)^{3N/2} e^N \exp\left\{\frac{-NCA}{2kT}[\exp\{-2n(a - R_1)\}\right.$$
$$\left. - 2\exp\{-n(a - R_1)\}]\right\}$$

$$\left[\frac{6\pi akT}{CA\{2\exp[-2n(a - R_1)](n^2a - n) - \exp[-n(a - R_1)](n^2a - 2n)\}}\right]^{3N/2}$$
$$\tag{2.85}$$

The potential function Q can be expressed in terms of the *smoothed potential*

[23] J. E. Lennard-Jones and A. F. Devonshire, *Proc. Roy. Soc.* (*London*), **A163** (1937), 53.

model.[24] In this model the molecule is assumed to move in a uniform potential field in a small volume called the free volume, v_f, and

$$Q = \left(\frac{2\pi mkT}{h^2}\right)^{3N/2} \left[\exp\left(\frac{-NU_0}{kT}\right)\right] (v_f)^N e^N \tag{2.86}$$

By comparison of Eq. (2.86) with Eq. (2.85) we have

$$v_f = \left[\frac{6\pi akT}{CA\{2\exp\left[-2n(a-R_1)\right](n^2a-n) - \exp\left[-n(a-R_1)\right](n^2a-2n)\}}\right]^{3/2} \tag{2.87}$$

Table 2.4 lists the constants required in the Morse equation for argon and neon. In Fig. 2.1 the molar free volume, Nv_f, is plotted against the molar

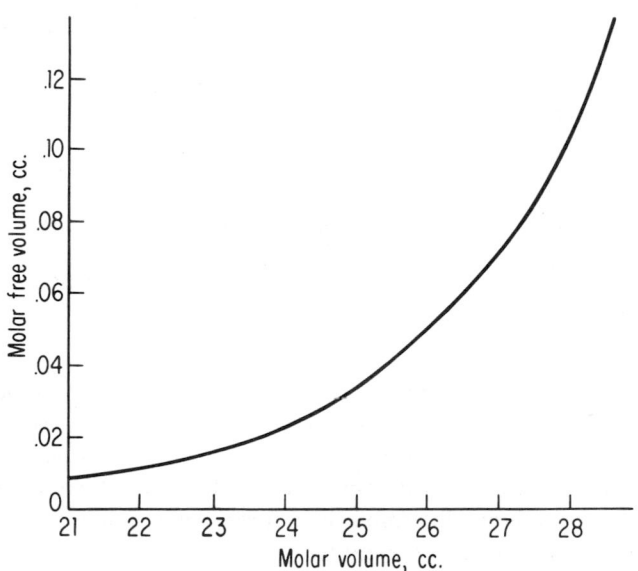

Fig. 2.1 Free volume of argon as a function of the molar volume. [From F. A. Matsen and G. M. Watson, *J. Chem. Physics* **11** (1943), 346.]

volume of argon at 80°K. These values are in good agreement with those estimated by Eyring[22,25] for liquid argon.

[24] R. H. Fowler and E. A. Guggenheim, *Statistical Thermodynamics* (New York: The Macmillan Co., 1939).

[25] J. O. Hirschfelder, O. P. Stevenson, and H. Eyring, *J. Chem. Phys.*, **5** (1937), 896. J. F. Kincaid and H. Eyring, *J. Chem. Phys.*, **6** (1938), 620.

The equation of state P can be obtained by substituting Eq. (2.85) into Eq. (2.76). The heat of vaporization of a monatomic liquid can be obtained by subtraction of the heat content of the liquid, Eq. (2.75), from the heat content of the gas. One obtains for the heat of vaporization

$$\Delta H_{vap} = H_{gas} - H_{liq} = \tfrac{5}{2}NkT - NU_0 - 3NkT$$
$$= -NU_0 - \tfrac{1}{2}NkT \qquad (2.88)$$

In Eq. (2.88) the PV term in H_{liq} is neglected since it is quite small at ordinary pressures. Equation (2.88) has been used by Matsen and Watson[21] to evaluate the heat of vaporization of argon and neon. Their values were in close agreement with the experimental values.

Table 2.4.* CONSTANTS FOR MORSE EQUATION†

	Argon	Neon
u	16.2×10^{-8}	35.5×10^{-10} erg A^6
v	10.3×10^{-11}	83.2×10^{-10} erg A^{12}
$R \times 10^8$ cm	3.83	3.08
A in ergs	16.4×10^{-15}	4.87×10^{-15}
$n \times 10^{-8}$ cm^{-1}	1.66	2.06

* Values of u and v were taken from R. A. Buckingham, *Proc. Roy. Soc. (London)*, **A168** (1938), 264.

† From F. A. Matsen and G. M. Watson, *J. Chem. Physics*, **11** (1943), 346.

In summary, one may say that this theory briefly outlined gives a qualitative description of the thermodynamic functions of a monatomic liquid as long as the axis is not greater than R_1. It is questionable that the cell model has any significance for large values of a. These calculations are very useful for pure liquids far from the critical point. This method for a given model is not very sensitive to different intermolecular force fields. Therefore the major error in the method is due to the model.

3

THEORETICAL METHODS
FOR ESTIMATING
STANDARD HEATS OF
FORMATION

3.1. INTRODUCTION

Besides the thermodynamic functions discussed in Chaps. 1 and 2, theoretical performance calculations require a knowledge of thermochemical heats of formation of reactants and product species. Performance calculations are only as good as the thermodynamic and thermochemical data used to make the calculations. In principle, heats of formation can be calculated theoretically by application of quantum mechanics. In practice, however, because of the large number of electrons involved in diatomic and polyatomic molecules, such calculations have been made only for a few diatomic molecules containing a total of less than twenty electrons. In most instances, with the exception of the binding energy of hydrogen, the results of such calculations do not agree with thermochemical values determined by experimental methods. This discrepancy in the theoretical calculations is due to the difficulty of solving the wave equation for a system of many electrons. Consequently, experimental data must be relied upon to provide accurate heats of formation. The experimental evaluation of the heats of formation of chemical species in many instances necessitates not only many analyses, but also the building of new laboratory apparatus. If one cannot wait for the experimental analyses required to provide accurate values of heats of formation, which are usually quite time-consuming, one must be able to estimate interim values of unknown heats of formation for species required for theoretical engine-performance calculations.

In this chapter, values of heats of formation are presented for compounds of elements in the first three rows of the periodic table, which can be used with some confidence in theoretical performance calculations. The "V" shape method is described for estimating heats of formation for any missing molecule in a family of molecules which form a "V" configuration. Methods are described for estimating bond dissociation energies of diatomic and polyatomic molecules. The group substitution method is presented as a technique for estimating heats of formation of compounds for which thermochemical data are not available.

3.2. SPECTROSCOPIC DETERMINATION OF HEATS OF DISSOCIATION OF DIATOMIC MOLECULES

The *heat of dissociation*, D_0^0, of a diatomic molecule AB is the energy required to break the bond AB (from lowest vibrational level $v = 0$) into two separate atoms A and B, where both atoms are in their ground states. For example, the ground states of HF, H, and F are $^1\Sigma^+$, $^2S_{1/2}$, and $^2P_{3/2}$ respectively. The heat of dissociation D_0^0 of HF is the energy required to break the bond for HF in its lowest vibrational state (with HF in a $^1\Sigma^+$ electronic state) into a hydrogen atom in a $^2S_{1/2}$ state and a fluorine atom in a $^2P_{3/2}$ state.

A *potential energy curve* (Fig. 3.1) is used to represent the potential energy of a set of atoms as a function of their interatomic distances. Potential energy curves are used to determine molecular structure of molecules. The potential energy minima determine bond lengths. The force constant is the second derivative of the potential energy with respect to distance. Force constants are used to compute vibrational and rotational levels of molecules. The anharmonic constants of a molecule are computed from higher-order derivatives of the potential energy curve. The potential energy curve for a diatomic molecule is fitted usually by using the experimental constants, r_e, the internuclear distance at equilibrium; D_e^0, the dissociation energy at equilibrium; k_e, the force constant; a_e, the rotational constant; and $\omega_e x_e$ and $\omega_e y_e$, the anharmonic constants.

The potential functions $V(r)$ are chosen usually such that $V(r)$ approaches a finite constant as r approaches infinity, $V(r)$ has a minimum at $r = r_e$, and $V(r)$ approaches plus infinity as r approaches zero. To make use of the experimental constants available one usually expands $V(r)$ as a power series

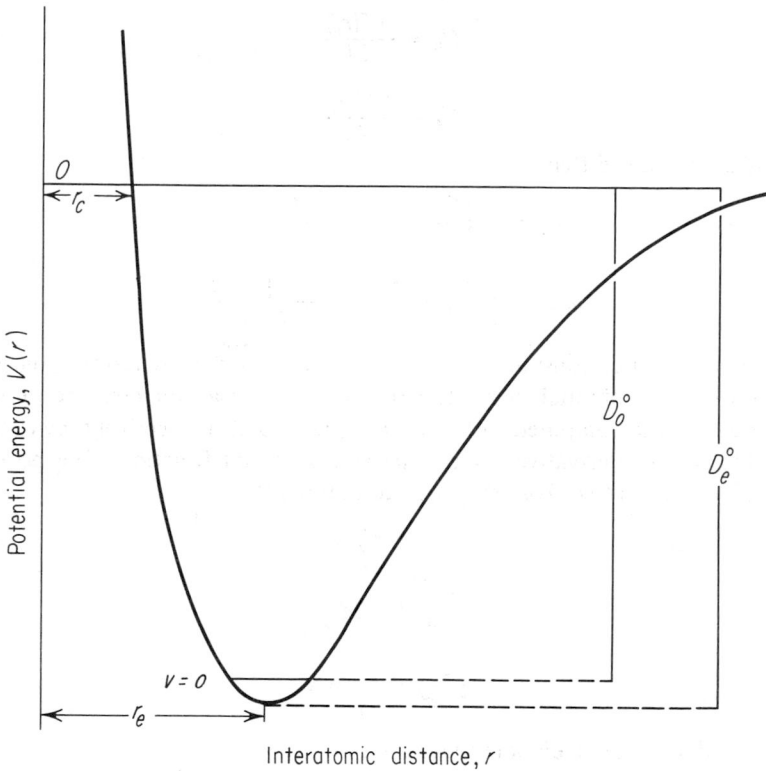

Fig. 3.1. Simple potential energy curve of a diatomic molecule.

in $(r - r_e)$ and compares the resulting coefficients of the terms with the series

$$G(v) = \omega_e(v + \tfrac{1}{2}) - \omega_e x_e(v + \tfrac{1}{2})^2 + \omega_e y_e(v + \tfrac{1}{2})^3 + \cdots \qquad (3.1)$$

for the vibrational energy of an anharmonic oscillator.

If one expresses $V(r)$ by the relation

$$V(r) = C_1(r - r_e) + C_2(r - r_e)^2 + C_3(r - r_e)^3 + \cdots \qquad (3.2)$$

then one can, by the method of successive differentiation, show that

$$V(r) = \frac{1}{2!} V''(r_e)(r - r_e)^2 + \frac{1}{3!} V'''(r_e)(r - r_e)^3 + \frac{1}{4!} V''''(r_e)(r - r_e)^4 + \cdots \qquad (3.3)$$

The *primes* represent the order of differentiation. From Eq. (3.3) it is clear that the constants in Eq. (3.2) are

$$C_2 = \frac{V''(r_e)}{2!} \qquad (3.4)$$

$$C_3 = \frac{V'''(r_e)}{3!} \tag{3.5}$$

$$C_4 = \frac{V''''(r_e)}{4!} \tag{3.6}$$

Dunham[1] showed that

$$a_e = -\left[\frac{C_3}{C_2}r_e + 1\right]\frac{6B_e^2}{\omega_e} \tag{3.7}$$

$$\omega_e x_e = \left[\frac{15}{8}\left(\frac{C_3}{C_2}\right)^2 - \frac{3}{2}\left(\frac{C_4}{C_2}\right)\right]\frac{h}{8\pi^2 c\mu_A} \tag{3.8}$$

The experimental constants k_e, r_e, and D_e^0 are used to determine the three constants in a potential energy function with three parameters. The values of a_e and $\omega_e x_e$ are computed from Eqs. (3.7) and (3.8), respectively, by evaluating the proper derivatives of the derived potential function. The potential energy curve is fitted from the three conditions that

$$V(r_e) - V(\infty) = -D_e^0 \tag{3.9}$$

$$\left(\frac{dV}{dr}\right)_{r=r_e} = 0 \tag{3.10}$$

$$\left(\frac{d^2V}{dr^2}\right)_{r=r_e} = k_e \tag{3.11}$$

Consider the Morse[2] potential function

$$V(r) = D_e^0[1 - e^{-a(r-r_e)}]^2 \tag{3.12}$$

To compute the constant a in Eq. (3.12) we use Eq. (3.11) and obtain

$$a = \left(\frac{k_e}{2D_e^0}\right)^{1/2} \tag{3.13}$$

Substitution of Eq. (3.12) into Eqs. (3.4) through (3.8) gives

$$C_2 = a^2 D_e^0 \tag{3.14}$$

$$C_3 = -a^3 D_e^0 \tag{3.15}$$

$$C_4 = \frac{14}{24}a^4 D_e^0 \tag{3.16}$$

$$\alpha_e = [ar_e - 1]\frac{6B_e^2}{\omega_e} = \left[\left(\frac{k_e}{2D_e^0}\right)^{1/2}r_e - 1\right]\frac{6B_e^2}{\omega_e} \tag{3.17}$$

$$\omega_e x_e = \left(\frac{k_e}{2D_e^0}\right)\frac{h}{8\pi^2 c\mu_A} \tag{3.18}$$

[1] J. L. Dunham, *Phys. Rev.*, **41** (1932), 713, 721.
[2] P. M. Morse, *Phys. Rev.*, **34** (1929), 57.

Since from Eq. (1.98)

$$\omega_e = \frac{1}{2\pi c} \sqrt{\frac{k_e}{u_A}}$$

we can simplify Eq. (3.18) to

$$D_e^0 = \frac{\omega_e^2}{4\omega_e x_e} \tag{3.19}$$

where D_e^0 is expressed in cm^{-1}.

Equation (3.19) can be used to compute the equilibrium dissociation energy of a diatomic molecule when the wave number ω_e and the anharmonicity constant $\omega_e x_e$ are available. The relation in Eq. (3.19) corresponds to the Birge-Sponer extrapolation.[3] Gaydon[4] shows that Eq. (3.19) usually gives rather high values for the dissociation energy. This example illustrates how a choice of a potential function leads quite naturally to a relation between dissociation energy and other experimental parameters.

Lippincott[5] investigated the potential function

$$V(r) = D_e^0 \left\{ 1 - \exp\left[\frac{-n(r - r_e)^2}{2r} \right] \right\} [1 + af(r)] \tag{3.20}$$

where a and n are constants, and $f(r)$ is a function of the interatomic distance chosen such that $f(r)$ approaches zero as r approaches infinity and $f(r)$ approaches infinity as r approaches zero. To a first approximation one neglects $f(r)$. $V(r)$ in Eq. (3.20) gives

$$V(r) = D_e^0 \left[1 - \exp\left(\frac{-n(r - r_e)^2}{2r} \right) \right] \tag{3.21}$$

Substitution of Eq. (3.21) into Eq. (3.11) yields

$$n = \frac{k_e r_e}{D_e^0} \tag{3.22}$$

By using Eq. (3.22) we can compute the equilibrium dissociation energy from the bond length r_e, the force constant k_e, and the constant n. Lippincott and Schroeder[6] evaluated n empirically by

$$n = n_0 \left(\frac{I}{I_0} \right)_A^{1/2} \left(\frac{I}{I_0} \right)_B^{1/2} \tag{3.23}$$

where $(I/I_0)_A$ and $(I/I_0)_B$ are the ionization potentials of atoms A and B respectively, relative to those of the same atoms in the same row and the first column of the periodic table. In Eq. (3.23) $n_0 = 4.21 \times 10^8$ for diatomic

[3] R. T. Birge and H. Sponer, *Phys. Rev.*, **28** (1926), 259.
[4] A. G. Gaydon, *Dissociation Energies and Spectra of Diatomic Molecules* (London: Chapman and Hall, 1953).
[5] E. R. Lippincott, *J. Chem. Phys.*, **21** (1953), 2070; **23** (1955), 603.
[6] E. R. Lippincott and R. Schroeder, *J. Chem. Phys.*, **23** (1955), 1099.

alkali metals and alkali hydrides and $n_0 = 6.32 \times 10^8$ for most other diatomic molecules. For the H atom, the value $I/I_0 = 0.88$ is assigned instead of 1. Table 3.1 lists the first ionization potential of atoms in the first three rows of the periodic chart.

EXAMPLE

Estimate the frequency ω_e of CP assuming $n_0 = 6.32 \times 10^8$.

The dissociation energy D_e^0 equals 6.9 electron volts and the internuclear distance $r(C—P)$ equals 1.5621×10^{-8} cm. Table 3.1 lists the ionization potentials as follows.

$$
\begin{array}{ll}
C \quad 11.264 & P \quad 11.0 \\
Li \quad 5.390 & Na \quad 5.138
\end{array}
$$

Using these values in Eq. (3.23), we find that

$$n = n_0 \left(\frac{I}{I_0}\right)_C^{1/2} \left(\frac{I}{I_0}\right)_P^{1/2} = 6.32 \times 10^8 \left(\frac{11.264}{5.390}\right)^{1/2} \left(\frac{11.0}{5.138}\right)^{1/2} = 13.37 \times 10^8$$

The force constant k_e is computed using Eq. (3.22)

$$k_e = \frac{nD_e^0}{r_e} = \frac{(13.37 \times 10^8)(6.9)(1.6 \times 10^{-12})}{1.5621 \times 10^{-8}} = 9.46 \times 10^5 \frac{dynes}{cm}$$

The frequency ω_e is computed from Eq. (1.98) and is found to be

$$\omega_e = \frac{I}{2\pi c}\sqrt{\frac{k_e}{\mu}} = 1337 \text{ cm}^{-1}$$

The value of ω_e in Table 1.5 derived from spectroscopic data is 1239.67 cm^{-1}.

Table 3.1.* FIRST IONIZATION POTENTIAL OF ATOMS IN FIRST THREE ROWS OF PERIODIC CHART[†]

H 13.595							He 24.580
Li 5.390	Be 9.320	B 8.296	C 11.264	N 14.54	O 13.614	F 17.42	Ne 21.559
Na 5.138	Mg 7.644	Al 5.984	Si 8.149	P 11.0	S 10.357	Cl 13.01	Ar 15.755

* The unit of the ionization potential in this table is the electron volt.

† The ionization potentials are tabulated from C. E. Moore, *Atomic Energy Levels* I (Washington, D.C.: U.S. Government Printing Office, 1949).

Lippincott and Schroeder[7] used Eq. (3.20) with

$$af(r) = -a\left(\frac{r_e}{r}\right)^6 \left[1 - \exp\left(\frac{-b^2 n r^{11}}{2r_e^{12}}\right)\right]^{1/2}$$
$$+ a\left(\frac{r_e}{r}\right)^{12} \left[1 - \exp\left(\frac{-b^2 n r^{11}}{2r_e^{12}}\right)\right] \quad (3.24)$$

[7] E. R. Lippincott and R. Schroeder, *J. Chem. Phys.*, **23** (1955), 1131.

Substitution of Eq. (3.20) into Eq. (3.11) gives

$$n = \frac{\omega_e^2}{2D_e^0 r_e B_e} \tag{3.25}$$

$$\alpha_e = ab \left(\frac{nr_e}{2}\right)^{1/2} \frac{6B_e^2}{\omega_e} \tag{3.26}$$

$$\omega_e x_e = \frac{3}{2} B_e \left[\frac{1}{4}(1 + nr_e) + ab \left(\frac{nr_e}{2}\right)^{1/2} + \frac{(5a^2b^2 - ab^2)}{2} nr_e\right] \tag{3.27}$$

The constants a and b were found invariant for most molecules. Varshni[8] found the best values of a_e and ω_e are obtained from

$$\alpha_e = [0.11\Delta + 0.36] \frac{6B_e^2}{\omega_e} \tag{3.28}$$

$$\omega_e x_e = (5\Delta + 9) \frac{h}{64\pi^2 cr_e^2 \mu_A} \tag{3.29}$$

$$\Delta = \frac{k_e r_e^2}{2D_e^0} \tag{3.30}$$

When Eq. (3.29) is solved for D_e^0 one obtains

$$D_e^0 = \frac{5Wk_e r_e^2}{2\omega_e x_e r_e^2 \mu_A - 9W} \tag{3.31}$$

where

$$W = \frac{h}{64\pi^2 cN\mu_A} \tag{3.32}$$

Varshni[8] recommends that one estimate the dissociation energy of diatomic molecules from Eq. (3.31) instead of the Birge-Sponer extrapolation or the Morse relation for D_e^0 [Eq. (3.19)]. Somayajulu[9] estimated the dissociation energy of eighteen sequences of similar molecules by noting that the relation

$$\frac{k_e r_e}{D_e^0} = \text{constant} \tag{3.33}$$

There are other potential functions which can be used to derive relations for the experimental spectroscopic constants, but, instead of their being discussed here, the reader is referred to the review article by Varshni[8] on potential energy functions for diatomic molecules. In most of the relations discussed

[8] Y. P. Varshni, *Revs. Modern Phys.*, **29** (1957), 664.
[9] G. R. Somayajulu, *J. Chem. Phys.*, **33** (1960), 1541.

D_e^0 is given instead of D_0^0. D_0^0 is related to D_e^0 by

$$D_0^0 = D_e^0 - \frac{1}{2} hc\omega_e \tag{3.34}$$

The force constant can be estimated by application of "Badger's rule." Badger[10] proposed the empirical relation between the force constant k_e of the chemical bond and the interatomic distance r_e,

$$r_e = \left(\frac{c_{ij}}{k_e}\right)^{1/3} + d_{ij} \tag{3.35}$$

c_{ij} and d_{ij} are constants which vary with the row in the periodic table to which the bonded atoms belong. If both atoms are in the first row of the periodic system d_{ij} equals 0.68 Å, and if both are in the second row d_{ij} equals 1.18 Å. If element i is in row one and element j in row two, d_{ij} equals 0.90 Å. c_{ij} is the same for all molecules and equals 1.86×10^5 if k_e is expressed in dynes/cm and the internuclear distance r_e and d_{ij} units are Å.

Several methods have been described for estimating vibrational frequencies of molecules. These methods relate the frequency of the molecule with an interatomic distance r_e, anharmonicity constant $\omega_e x_e$, dissociation energy D_e^0, and a force constant, k_e. The interatomic distances are not known for all diatomic molecules. Consequently a formula which relates the frequency of a diatomic molecule with a parameter such as the reduced mass (μ) (which is known) would prove quite useful. Krasnov and Maksimov[11] were able to show the dependence of ω_e on μ for a group of similar diatomic molecules XY, where X belongs to one group of the periodic table and Y to another group. ω_e can be related to μ with sufficient accuracy by the equation

$$\omega_e = \frac{A}{\mu} + B \tag{3.36}$$

Table 3.2 lists the coefficients of Eq. (3.36) and the values of the average relative errors ϵ for various groups of molecules.

Table 3.3 gives values of ω_e calculated by Krasnov and Maksimov for several molecules for which experimental data is not available. The numbers which appear in boldface in Table 3.3 were determined from infrared spectra. The numbers which appear in square brackets were extrapolated by Rice and Klemperer[12] and those numbers which appear in parentheses were computed by Gordy.[13] All other numbers appearing in Table 3.3 were calculated according to Eq. (3.36). The alkali halides are used as examples in Table 3.3.

[10] R. M. Badger, *J. Chem. Phys.*, **2** (1934), 128.

[11] K. S. Krasnov and A. I. Maksimov, *Optics and Spectroscopy*, **8** (1960), 208.

[12] S. A. Rice and W. Klemperer, *J. Chem. Phys.*, **27** (1957), 573.

[13] W. Gordy, *J. Chem. Phys.*, **14** (1946), 305; W. Gordy and W. J. Orville-Thomas, *J. Chem. Phys.*, **24** (1956), 439.

Table 3.2. Constants for Calculating ω_e from Eq. (3.36)*

Types of compound	Group of the periodic table	Compounds	Coefficients of Eq. (3.36)		Average error (%)
			A	B	ϵ
Halides	VII	Interhalogen compounds	8,775	$+85$	2.8
		Mn	8,118	$+28$	2.7
	V	..	7,793	$+74$	4.9
	IV	Fluorides	10,320	-58	2.8
		Chlorides and bromides	6,678	$+106$	3.0
	III	B	16,260	$-1,038$	5.4
		Al	7,657	-17	2.8
		Ga, In, Tl	7,089	$+63$	2.3
	II	Fluorides of the main subgroup	7,784	-12	2.7
		Chlorides of the main subgroup	5,685	$+70$	1.4
		Bromides of the main subgroup	5,559	$+77$	1.9
		Iodides of the main subgroup	4,765	$+80$	1.8
		Halides of the secondary subgroup	8,071	$+37$	4.2
	I	Na subgroup	4,402	$+47$	2.3
		Secondary subgroup	7,621	$+88$	4.5
Hydrides	V	..	24,125	$-22,345$	0.4
	IV	..	12,136	$-10,383$	5.2
	III	..	11,318	$-9,922$	1.7
	II	Main subgroup	8,621	$-7,443$	1
		Secondary subgroup	2,380	-909	4.8
	I	Na subgroup	6,270	$-5,380$	2
Others		CO, CS, CSe	23,275	$-1,266$	5.8
		SiO, SiS, SiSe, SiTe	13,567	-108	3.8
		GeO, GeS, GeSe, GeTe	11,857	$+71$	3.1
		SnO, SnS, SnSe, SnTe	10,027	$+106$	2.6
		PbO, PbS, PbSe, PbTe	9,147	$+104$	2.6

* From K. S. Krasnov and A. I. Maksimov, *Optics and Spectroscopy*, **8** (1960), 208.

Table 3.3. Vibrational Frequencies of Several Molecules*

	H	F	Cl	Br	I	At
Na	..	465 ± 20	366 ± 6 363 (398)	302 ± 6 293 (330)	258 ± 4 273 (206)	260 ± 10
K	..	386 ± 20	281 ± 4 284 (309)	213 ± 4 215 (248)	189 [173]	181 ± 6
Rb	..	325 ± 15	228 ± 4 223 (260)	149 [166]	128 [128]	120 ± 5
Cs	..	307 ± 15	209 ± 4 205 (237)	130 [139]	111 [101]	101 ± 4
Fr	868 ± 20	299 ± 10	191 ± 6	122 ± 4	103 ± 4	88 ± 4
Ca	..	592 ± 20	..	..	..	..
Ba	..	..	..	..	152 ± 5	..
Ra	1148 ± 60	430 ± 15	255 ± 5	171 ± 5	137 ± 5	..
Ga	1468 ± 25	..	..	..	..	..
In	1405 ± 25	..	..	..	..	..
Ge	1823 ± 100	625 ± 20	..	..	..	..
Sn	1758 ± 100	..	..	..	..	..
As	1910 ± 10	..	..	..	..	..
Sb	1785 ± 10	..	..	..	..	..

* From K. S. Krasnov and A. I. Maksimov, *Optics and Spectroscopy*, **8** (1960), 208.

3.3. SPECTROSCOPIC DETERMINATION OF BINDING FORCES IN POLYATOMIC MOLECULES

A complete analysis of the molecular vibrational spectrum of most polyatomic molecules is, in general, impossible. It is difficult to determine the anharmonic constants since the overtones are usually very weak in relation to the fundamentals. Although the anharmonic constants are required to determine the fundamental vibrational constants of the molecule, one can use the observed frequencies to calculate thermodynamic functions and force constants of chemical bonds. These inexact force constants help advance our knowledge of the binding forces in molecules.

The theory of small vibrations[14] is used along with the observed frequencies to evaluate the force constants of bond stretching and valency angle deformation. Such information reveals the relative strength of chemical bonds and therefore is of great interest to the chemist. Table 3.4 lists stretching force constants for several bonds. These constants were generally computed using the method of small vibrations assuming a valence force field.[15] It is found

Table 3.4. APPROXIMATE BOND STRETCHING FORCE
CONSTANTS*

Bond	Molecule	k, md/A	Bond	Molecule	k, md/A
H—F	HF	9.67	F—B	BF_3	8.8
H—Cl	HCl	5.15	Cl—B	BCl_3	4.6
H—Br	HBr	4.11	Br—B	BBr_3	3.7
H—I	HI	3.16	P—P	P_4	2.1
H—O	H_2O	7.8	Si—Si	Si_2H_6	1.7
H—S	H_2S	4.3	S—S	S_2H_2	2.5
H—Se	H_2Se	3.3	B—N	$B_3N_3H_6$	6.3
H—N	NH_3	6.5	C⋯C	C_6H_6	7.62
H—P	PH_3	3.1	N⋯O	N_2O	11.5
H—As	AsH_3	2.6	C—C		4.5–5.6
H—C	CH_3X	4.7–5.0	C=C		9.5–9.9
H—C	C_2H_4	5.1	C≡C		15.6–17.0
H—C	C_6H_6	5.1	N—N		3.5–5.5
H—C	C_2H_2	5.9	N=N		13.0–13.5
H—Si	SiH_4	2.9	N≡N		22.9
F—O	F_2O	5.6	O—O		3.5–5.0
Cl—O	Cl_2O	4.9	C—N		4.9–5.6
F—C	CH_3F	5.6	C=N		10–11
Cl—C	CH_3Cl	3.4	C≡N		16.2–18.2
Br—C	CH_3Br	2.8	C—O		5.0–5.8
I—C	CH_3I	2.3	C=O		11.8–13.4

* From E. B. Wilson *et al.*, *Molecular Vibrations*, by permission.

that the bending force constants have values of the order of one-tenth those of the stretching constants. Some numerical values for bending constants are collected in Table 3.5. Some of the constants listed in Tables 3.4 and 3.5 were computed using potential functions which included interaction terms.

[14] E. B. Wilson, J. D. Decius, and P. C. Cross, *Molecular Vibrations* (New York: McGraw-Hill Book Co., Inc., 1955).

[15] The potential energy of a system depends on the relative positions of the nuclei. It is assumed usually in computing the potential energy of a system that the force fields causing the displacement of nuclei are either *valency forces* or *central forces*. The *valency forces* are assumed to act along chemical bonds and they oppose the binding of directed bonds. The *central forces* act between any pair of atoms and are independent of the chemical structure of the molecule.

Table 3.5. APPROXIMATE BOND
BENDING FORCE CONSTANTS*

Angle	Molecule	$F_a/r_1^0 r_2^0$, md/A
HOH	H_2O	0.69
HSH	H_2S	0.43
HNH	NH_3	0.4–0.6
HPH	PH_3	0.33
HCH	CH_4	0.46
HCH	C_2H_4	0.30
FOF	F_2O	0.69
ClOCl	Cl_2O	0.41
FCF	CF_4	0.71
ClCCl	CCl_4	0.33
BrCBr	CBr_4	0.24
FBF	BF_3	0.37
ClBCl	BCl_3	0.16
BrBBr	BBr_3	0.13
HCF	CH_3F	0.57
HCCl	CH_3Cl	0.36
HCBr	CH_3Br	0.30
HCI	CH_3I	0.23
NNO	N_2O	0.49
OCO	CO_2	0.57
SCS	CS_2	0.23
HCC	C_2H_2	0.12
HCN	HCN	0.20

* From E. B. Wilson *et al.*, *Molecular
Vibrations*, by permission.

It is clear that to obtain the zero-order frequencies a great deal of information on the spectrum is required. One should consider the observed frequencies of most polyatomic molecules as a first approximation, to be corrected when exact measurements of bands become available. One interesting observation made on bond force constants is that a given bond may have the same force constant in many compounds of the same family. It is therefore possible to use force constants obtained from bonds in simple molecules as estimates for similar bonds in complex molecules. The invariance of force constants of a given bond in a family can be used to compute the characteristic frequencies of various groups. Table 3.6 summarizes the characteristic frequencies for a number of groups; for example, the bond stretching vibration of a $\equiv$C—H group is approximately 3,300 cm^{-1} and the bond bending vibration is about 700 cm^{-1}.

It is not always possible to make the transfer from a simple structure to a

Table 3.6. CHARACTERISTIC FREQUENCIES OF VARIOUS GROUPS*

Group	Bond stretching vibration (cm⁻¹)	Group	Bond stretching vibration (cm⁻¹)	Group	Bond bending vibration (cm⁻¹)
≡C—H	3300	—C≡C—	2050	≡C—H	700
=C—H	3020	C=C	1650	=C (H, H)	1100
—C—H	2960	—C—C—	900	—C—H (H, H)	1000
—O—H	3680	—C—F	1100	C (H, H)	1450
—S—H	2570	—C—Cl	650	C—H (H, H)	1450
—N—H	3350	—C—Br	560	C—C≡C	300
C=O	1700	—C—I	500		
—C≡N	2100				

* From G. Herzberg, *Infrared and Raman Polyatomic Molecules* (Princeton, N.J.: D. Van Nostrand Co., Inc., 1951).

complex structure, since such assignment of force constants may not accurately describe the interaction of bonds. However, in most instances when force constants are carried over from simple to complex molecules we find excellent agreement between calculated and observed frequencies.

When a force constant for a given bond differs considerably from its normal value in a family of compounds, it is assumed usually that *resonance* exists between several possible configurations of the molecule.

In general, double and triple bonds have individual specific values of force constants. The influence of neighboring atoms must be considered when one is transferring force constants from one type of structure to another.

3.4. THE V-SHAPED METHOD FOR ESTIMATING HEATS OF FORMATION

The *heat of formation* of a substance is *the energy required to form one mole of the substance from its elements in their standard states*. The *standard state*

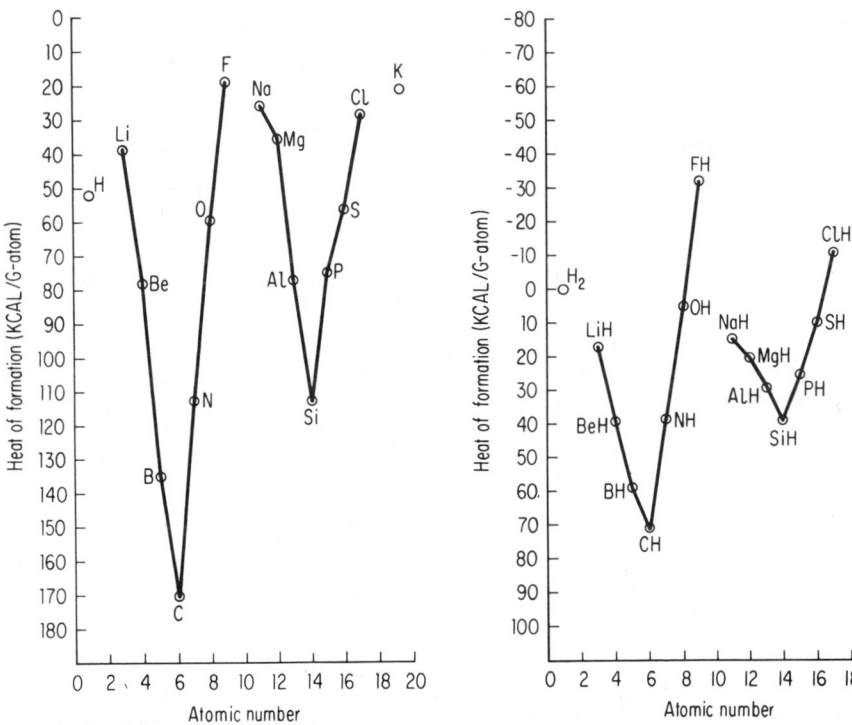

Fig. 3.2 Estimation of heats of formation of gaseous elements. [From C. J. O'Brien and J. R. Perrin and J. Perrine "Estimation of the Heats of Formation and Gaseous Combustion Product Molecules," in *Kinetics, Equilibria Performance of High Temperature Systems*, ed. Bahn and Zukoski (Washington, Butterworth Inc., 1960), p. 5.]

Fig. 3.3 Estimation of heats of formation of diatomic hydrides. [From C. J. O'Brien and J. R. Perrin and J. Perrine "Estimation of the Heats of Formation and Gaseous Combustion Product Molecules," in *Kinetics, Equilibria Performance of High Temperature Systems*, ed. Bahn and Zukoski (Washington, Butterworth Inc., 1960), p. 5.]

for an element is *that form of the element which is most stable at room temperature (25°C) and one atmosphere pressure*. Thermochemical properties of chemical species of compounds of some elements in the first three rows of the periodic table[16] are tabulated in Tables 3.7 and 3.8. Standard heats of formation are written with a superscript zero, i.e., ΔH_f^0, and expressed in kcal/mole. Estimated values in Tables 3.7 and 3.8 are shown in parentheses.

In Fig. 3.2 are plotted the heats of formation versus atomic numbers of the gaseous elements tabulated in Table 3.7. A V shape is obtained. In Figs. 3.3

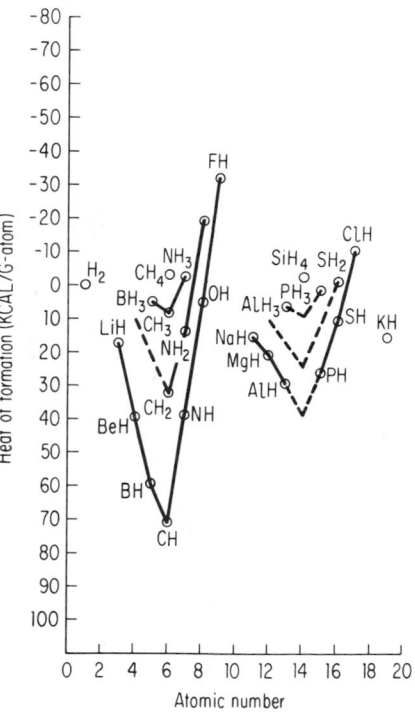

Fig. 3.4 Estimation of heats of formation of gaseous hydrides. [From C. J. O'Brien and J. R. Perrin and J. Perrine "Estimation of the Heats of Formation and Gaseous Combustion Product Molecules," in *Kinetics, Equilibria Performance of High Temperature Systems*, ed. Bahn and Zukoski (Washington, Butterworth Inc., 1960), p. 5.]

through 3.5 are plotted the heats of formation versus atomic numbers of the elements in diatomic hydrides and polyatomic hydrides using data in Tables 3.7 and 3.8. In each case a V shape is obtained. It becomes evident that a plot of the heats of formation versus atomic numbers for a family of molecules can be used to estimate the heat of formation for any missing molecule in a family. O'Brien and Perrin[17] have used this method to estimate heats of

[16] R. L. Wilkins, R. M. Lodwig, and S. A. Greene, The Chemical Composition of Metallized Flame, *Eighth Symposium (International) on Combustion*, pp. 375–388 (Baltimore: Williams and Wilkins Company, 1962).

[17] C. J. O'Brien, J. R. Perrin, and J. Perrine, "Estimation of the Heats of Formation of Gaseous Combustion Product Molecules," in *Kinetics, Equilibria, and Performance of High Temperature Systems*, ed. Bahn and Zukoski (Washington: Butterworth Inc., 1960), p. 5.

formation of gaseous combustion product molecules. In their paper, heats of formation are presented for gaseous chlorides, hydrides, fluorides, nitrides, oxides, phosphides, and sulfides of elements with atomic numbers less than twenty.

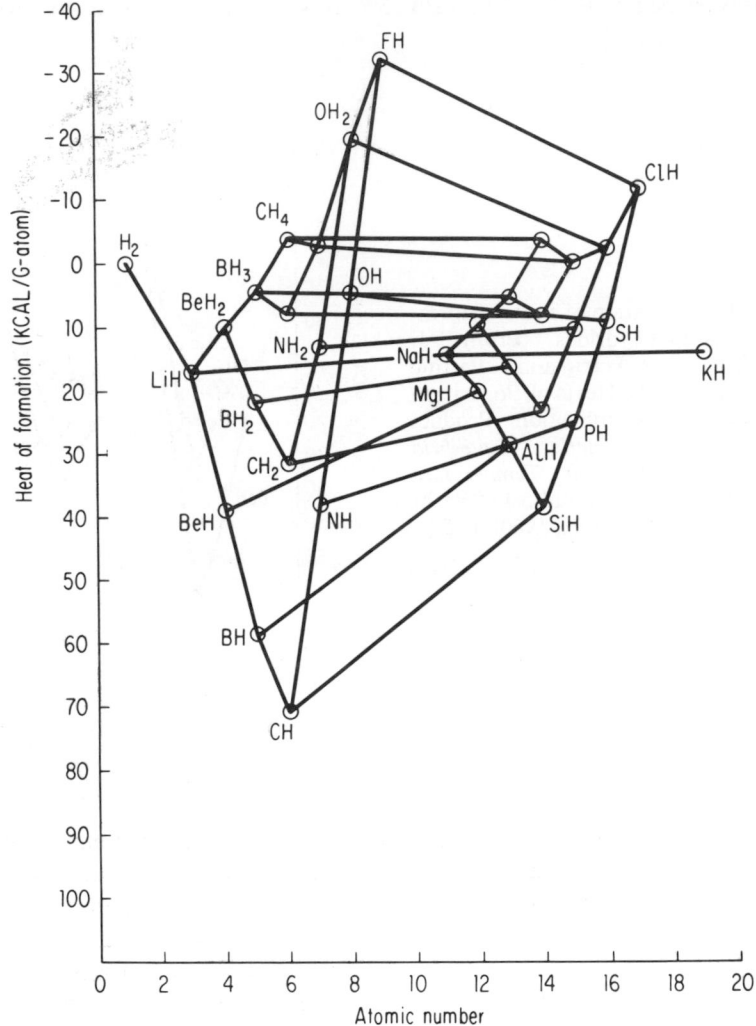

Fig. 3.5 Estimation of heats of formation of gaseous hydrides. [From C. J. O'Brien and J. R. Perrin and J. Perrine "Estimation of the Heats of Formation and Gaseous Combustion Product Molecules," in *Kinetics, Equilibria Performance of High Temperature Systems*, ed. Bahn and Zukoski (Washington, Butterworth Inc., 1960), p. 5.]

Table 3.7. STANDARD HEATS OF FORMATION OF THE ELEMENTS

Substance	State	$(\Delta H_f)_0^0$ kcal/mole	$(\Delta H_f)_{298.15}^0$ kcal/mole	$H_{298.15}^0 - H_0^0$ kcal/mole
H	g	51.621	52.090[a]	1.4812
H_2	g	0	0	2.0239
Li	c	0	0	1.0901
Li	g	38.05	38.439[a]	1.4812
Be	c	0	0	0.2904
Be	g	76.887	77.9[a]	1.4812
B	c	0	0	0.2880
B	g	134.0[b]	135.22	1.5110
C	c, graphite	0	0	0.2512
C	g	169.988[a]	171.299	1.5623
N	g	112.52[a]	112.96	1.4812
N_2	g	0	0	2.0724
O	g	58.980	59.550[a]	1.6075
O_2	g	0	0	2.0747
F	g	18.357	18.860[c]	1.5580
F_2	g	0	0	2.1105
Na	c	0	0	1.5444
Na	g	25.92[d]	25.857	1.4812
Mg	c	0	0	1.189
Mg	g	35.313[a]	35.6	1.4812
Al	c	0	0	1.070
Al	g	76.940	77.5[a]	1.6536
Si	c	0	0	0.765
Si	g	112	113[e]	1.8047
P	c, white	0	0	1.275
P	g	74.97	75.18[f]	1.4812
S	c, rhombic	0	0	1.053
S	g	56.4	56.9[a]	1.591
Cl	g	28.540	28.942[a]	1.4991
Cl_2	g	0	0	2.1935
Br	g	28.19	26.74[f]	1.4812
Br_2	l	0	0	5.8636

[a] R. D. Stull and C. G. Sinke, *The Thermodynamic Properties of the Elements* (Washington, D.C.: American Chemical Society, 1956).

[b] W. H. Evans, D. D. Wagman, and E. J. Prosen, National Bureau of Standards Report 6252, Washington, D.C., 1958.

[c] J. G. Stamper and R. F. Barrow, *Trans. Faraday Soc.*, **54** (1958), 1592.

[d] W. H. Evans, R. Jacobson, T. R. Munson, and D. D. Wagman, *J. Research Natl. Bur. Standards*, **55**, Research Report 2608, 1955.

[e] L. Brewer, *Heat of Sublimation of the Elements*, Atomic Energy Commission/University of California Radiation Laboratory Report UCRL-2854 (Jan. 6, 1958).

[f] F. D. Rossini et al., *Selected Values of Chemical Thermodynamic Properties*, National Bureau of Standards Circular 500 (Feb. 1, 1952).

Table 3.8.[*] STANDARD HEAT OF FORMATION AND DISSOCIATION ENERGY
TO GASEOUS ATOMS AT $0°$K AND $298.15°$K

Substance	State	Heat of formation (kcal/mole)		Dissociation energy (kcal/mole)	
		$0°$K	$298.15°$K	$0°$K	$298.15°$K
HYDROGEN COMPOUNDS					
H	g	51.621	52.090[a]	0	0
H_2	g	0	0	103.242	104.180[a]
OH	g	10.0	10.06[b]	100.601	101.58
H_2O	g	−57.101	−57.7979[b]	219.323	221.528
LITHIUM COMPOUNDS					
Li	g	38.05	38.439[a]	0	0
Li	c	0	0	38.05	38.439[a]
Li_2	g	50.35	50.47[c]	25.75	26.41
LiO	g	14.03	14.028	83[d]	83.961
Li_2O	g	−38.81	−37.11	169.89[e]	173.538
Li_2O	c	−140.91	−142.4[b]	275.99	278.83
LiH	g	33.67	33.66	56[f]	56.859
LiOH	g	−66.53[g]	−68.55	215.181	218.627
LiOH	c	−115.03	−116.4[h]	263.68	266.48
LiF	g	−79.26	−79.3	80.6717	82.777
LiF	c	−145.70	−146.3[i]	202.107	203.599
$(LiF)_2$	g	(−221)	(−223)	(334)	(337)
BERYLLIUM COMPOUNDS					
Be	g	76.889	77.9[a]	0	0
Be	c	0	0	76.889	77.9[a]
Be_2	g	137.8	137.8	16[j]	16
BeO	c		−143.1[k]		280.55
BeO	g	29.87	30.44	106[l]	107
BeH	g	77.51	78.1	51[m]	51.9
$Be(OH)_2$	c		−216.8		517.98[b]
$Be(OH)_2$	g		−162.4		463.58[b]
BeF	g	3.24	3.80	92[n]	92.96
BeF_2	c		−227[n]		342.62
BeF_2	g	−177.8	−178[o]	291.4	293.62
BeCl	g	36.43	36.98	69[m]	69.86
$BeCl_2$	c		−109.2[p]		224.98
$BeCl_2$	g	−84.0	−84[b]	217.8	219.78

[*] References are listed on pages 117 and 118.

Table 3.8. (cont'd)

Substance	State	Heat of formation (kcal/mole)		Dissociation energy (kcal/mole)	
		0°K	298.15°K	0°K	298.15°K
BORON COMPOUNDS					
B	g	134.0[q]	135.22	0	0
B	c	0	0	134.0[q]	135.22
B	c, amorph.	0.376[q]	0.4[q]	133.624	134.82
B_2	g	203.0[q]	204.51[q]	65	65.93
BO	g	5[q]	5.75[q]	187.980	189.020
B_2O_2	g	−105[q]	−104.75	490.960	494.290
B_2O_3	g	−207[q]	−207.62[q]	651.94	656.71
B_2O_3	c	−303.87[q]	−305.34[q]	748.81	754.43
BH	g	117[q]	117.76[q]	68.621	69.55
BH_3	g	18.91[q]	18.0[q]	269.953	273.49
HBO_2	g	−135.0[r]	−135.74	438.581	442.15
$B(OH)_3$	g	−263.13[q]	−238.6[q]	701.933	708.84
BF	g	−46.3[q]	−42.87[q]	195.957	196.95
BF_2	g	(−156)	(−157)	(327)	(330)
BF_3	g	−269.33[q]	−270.0[q]	458.401	461.80
BN	g	154	154.75[q]	92.52	93.43
BN	c	−59.61[q]	−60.3[q]	306.13	308.48
OBF	g	(−159)	(−159)	(370)	(372)
CARBON COMPOUNDS					
C	g	169.988[a]	171.299	0	0
C	c, graphite	0	0	169.988[a]	171.299
C_2	g	196.3	197.87[s]	143.676	144.728
C_3	g	182.6	184.4[s]	327.364	329.497
CH	g	142	142.8[b]	79.61	80.59
CH_2	g	69[t]	69.1	204.23	205.38
CH_3	g	33.4[b]	32.51	291.45	295.06
CH_4	g	−15.987	−17.889[b]	392.459	397.569
CCl	g	120.7	121.6	77.83	78.64
CCl_4	g	−25.023	−25.5[b]	309.17	312.57
CF	g	73.636	74.5[u]	114.71	115.66
CF_2	g	−30.106	−30[v]	236.81	238.02
CF_3	g	−119.878	−120.5[w]	344.94	346.88
CF_4	g	−216.574	−218[x, y]	459.99	462.74
C_2F_2	g	−50[z]		326.69	

Table 3.8. (cont'd)

Substance	State	Heat of formation (kcal/mole)		Dissociation energy (kcal/mole)	
		0°K	298.15°K	0°K	298.15°K
C_2H_2	g	54.329	54.194[b]	388.89	392.58
C_2H_4	g	14.522	12.496[b]	531.94	538.46
C_2H_6	g		−16.517[b]		671.66
CN	g	95.51[aa]	96.29	187.00	187.97
C_2N_2	g	73.13	73.60[b]	491.89	494.92
CO	g	−27.202	−26.416[b]	256.17	257.27
CO_2	g	−93.969	−94.052[b]	381.92	384.45
NITROGEN COMPOUNDS					
N	g	112.52[bb]	112.96	0	0
N_2	g	0	0	225.04[bb]	225.92
NO	g	21.477[b]	21.6[b]	150.023	150.910
NH_3	g	−9.368[b]	−11.04	276.751	280.27
OXYGEN COMPOUNDS					
O	g	58.980	59.550[a]	0	0
O_2	g	0	0	117.96	119.1[a]
O_3	g	34.638	34.0[b]	142.302	144.65
FLUORINE COMPOUNDS					
F	g	18.357	18.860[cc]	0	0
F_2	g	0	0	36.714	36.72[cc]
HF	g	−64.17	−64.2[b]	134.148	134.59
MAGNESIUM COMPOUNDS					
Mg	g	35.313[a]	35.6	0	0
Mg	c	0	0	35.313[a]	35.6
Mg_2	g	63.43		7.2[dd]	
MgO	c	−142.7	−143.7[ee]	236.99	238.5
MgO	g	4.29	4.19	90[ff]	91
MgH	g	40.93	40.83	46[aa]	46.89
MgO_2	c		−148.9[gg]		303.6
MgF	g	−20.33	−20.44	74[aa]	74.9
MgF_2	c	−262.5	−263.5[b]	234.53	336.82
MgCl	g	1.85	1.80	62[aa]	62.74
$MgCl_2$	c	−153.3	−153.4[b]	245.69	246.88

Table 3.8. (cont'd)

Substance	State	Heat of formation (kcal/mole)		Dissociation energy (kcal/mole)	
		0°K	298.15°K	0°K	298.15°K
Mg_3N_2	c	−108.6	−110.24[b]	439.58	442.96
MgS	g			66.9[hh]	
ALUMINUM COMPOUNDS					
Al	g	76.94	77.5[a]	0	0
Al	c	0	0	76.94	77.5[a]
Al_2	g	(104)	(104)	(50)	(51)
Al_2O	g	−38.76	−39.4[ii]	251.62	253.95
AlO	g	16.92	16.89	119[ii]	120.16
Al_2O_2	g	104.16[jj]	−105.28	376	379.38
Al_2O_3	c	−397.5	−400.4[kk]	728.32	734.05
AlH	g	57.56	57.56	71.0[m]	72.03
AlH_3	g		(18)		215.77
$Al(OH)_3$	c		−304.0[b]		716.42
AlF	g	−59.98	−60	155.27[ii]	156.36
AlF	c		(−102)[n]		(198.36)
AlF_2	g	(−144)	(−144)	(257.654)	(259.22)
AlF_2	c		(−184)[mm]		(299.22)
AlF_3	g	−283.77	−284.8[nn]	415.78	418.88
AlN	c		−76.5[oo]		266.96
AlOH	g	(−48)	(−49)	(235)	(238)
OAlH	g	(−2)	(−3)	(190)	(193)
OAlF	g	(−120)	(−120)	(274)	(276)
CHLORINE COMPOUNDS					
Cl	g	28.540	28.942[a]	0	0
Cl_2	g	0	0	57.08	57.884[a]
HCl	g	−22.02	−22.06[b]	102.18	103.084

[a] R. D. Stull and C. G. Sinke, *The Thermodynamic Properties of the Elements* (Washington, D.C.: American Chemical Society, 1956).

[b] F. D. Rossini et al., *Selected Values of Chemical Thermodynamic Properties*, National Bureau of Standards Circular 500 (Feb. 1, 1952).

[c] W. H. Evans, R. Jacobson, T. R. Munson, and D. D. Wagman, *J. Research Natl. Bur. Standards*, Research Report 2608, **55** (1956), 83.

[d] G. D. Blue, J. Berkowitz, and W. A. Chupka, Paper presented at American Chemical Society Meeting, Chicago, Ill., Sept. 7–12, 1958.

[e] J. Berkowitz, W. A. Chupka, G. D. Blue, and J. L. Margrave, *J. Phys. Chem.*, **63** (1959), 644.

[f] R. Velasco, *Can. J. Phys.*, **35** (1957), 1204.

[g] W. A. Chupka, Paper presented at Joint Army-Navy-Air Force Ad Hoc Panel on Performance Calculation Methods and Thermodynamic Data Meeting, Silver Spring, Maryland, April 27–29, 1959.

[h] N. W. Gregory and R. H. Mahr, *J. Am. Chem. Soc.*, **77** (1955), 2142.

[i] J. H. Payne, *J. Am. Chem. Soc.*, **59** (1937), 947.

[j] J. Drowart and R. E. Honig, *J. Phys. Chem.*, **61** (1957), 980.

[k] L. A. Cosgrove and P. E. Synder, *J. Am. Chem. Soc.*, **75** (1953), 3102.

[l] W. A. Chupka, J. Berkowitz, and C. F. Giese, Paper presented at American Chemical Society Meeting, Chicago, Ill., Sept. 7–12, 1958.

[m] G. Herzberg, *Molecular Spectra and Molecular Structure Spectra of Diatomic Molecules* (Princeton, N.J.: D. Van Nostrand Co., Inc., 1950).

[n] L. Brewer, L. A. Bromley, and P. W. Gilles, "Thermodynamics," chap. 6 in *The Chemistry of Metallurgy of Miscellaneous Materials*, ed. L. L. Quill (New York: McGraw-Hill Book Co., Inc., 1950).

[o] K. A. Sense, M. J. Snyder, and J. W. Clegg, *J. Phys. Chem.*, **58** (1954), 223.

[p] H. Siemonsen, *Z. Elektrochem.*, **55** (1951), 327.

[q] W. H. Evans, D. D. Wagman, and E. J. Prosen, National Bureau of Standards Report 6252, Washington, D.C., 1958.

[r] J. L. Margrave, Paper presented at American Rocket Society Meeting, Columbus, Ohio, July 21–22, 1959.

[s] R. Thorn and G. Winslow, *J. Chem. Phys.*, **26** (1957), 186.

[t] G. Duffey, *J. Chem. Phys.*, **17** (1949), 840.

[u] E. B. Andrews and R. Barrow, *Proc. Phys. Soc.*, **64A** (1951), 481.

[v] P. Venkateswarlu, *Phys. Rev.*, **77** (1950), 676.

[w] B. S. Rabinowitch and J. F. Reed, *J. Chem. Phys.*, **22** (1954), 2092.

[x] F. Kirkbride and F. Davidson, *Nature*, **174** (1954), 79.

[y] C. Neugebauer and J. L. Margrave, *J. Phys. Chem.*, **60** (1956), 1318.

[z] R. M. Potocki and D. E. Mann, *Thermal Properties of Fluorine Compound*, National Bureau of Standards Report 1439, Feb. 1952.

[aa] A. G. Gaydon, *Dissociation Energies and Spectra of Diatomic Molecules* (2nd ed.; London: Chapman and Hall, Ltd., 1953).

[bb] L. Brewer and A. W. Searcy, *Ann. Rev. Phys. Chem.*, **7** (1956), 271.

[cc] J. G. Stamper and F. R. Barrow, *Trans. Faraday Soc.*, **54** (1958), 1592.

[dd] J. R. Soulen, P. Sthapitanonda, and J. L. Margrave, *J. Phys. Chem.*, **59** (1955), 132.

[ee] C. E. Holley, Jr., and E. J. Huber, Jr., *J. Am. Chem. Soc.*, **73** (1951), 5577.

[ff] R. F. Porter, W. A. Chupka, and M. G. Inghram, *J. Chem. Phys.*, **23** (1955), 1347.

[gg] M. Blumenthal, *Roczniki Chem.*, **13** (1933), 4.

[hh] G. Herzberg, *Spectra of Diatomic Molecules* (Princeton, N.J.: D. Van Nostrand Co., Inc., 1950).

[ii] L. Brewer, U.S. Atomic Energy Comm. Report UCRL 8356, 1958.

[jj] G. DeMaria, J. Drowart, and M. G. Inghram, *J. Chem. Phys.*, **30** (1959), 318.

[kk] A. D. Mah, *J. Phys. Chem.*, **61** (1957), 1572.

[ll] R. F. Barrow, J. W. C. Jahns, and F. J. Smith, *Trans. Faraday Soc.*, **52** (1956), 913.

[mm] F. Irmann, *Helv. Chim. Acta.*, **33** (1950), 1449.

[nn] W. Olbrich, *Gmelin's Handbuch der anorganischen Chemie* (Berlin: Verlag Chemie, 1934), System No. 35, p. 160.

[oo] C. A. Neugebauer and J. L. Margrave, *Z. anorg. allgem. Chem.*, **290** (1957), 82.

Table 3.9. ENERGIES OF SINGLE AND DOUBLE BONDS[*][a]

Bond	Bond energy, kcal/mole	Bond	Bond energy kcal/mole
C—C	85.5	N—N	60.0
C—H	98.2	N—H	88.0
C=C	143.0	N≡N	225.5
C≡C	194.3	Si—Si	44.0
C—Cl	78.3	Ge—Ge	39.2
C—Br	66.8	As—As	34.5
C—I	64.2	P—P	47.9
C—F	101.7	S—S	50.3
C—N	81.0	O—O	33.1
C—O	85.8	O—H	110.6
C—S	63.7	Si—H	77.8
C=O	167 (formaldehyde)	Si—F	132.7
	172 (higher aldehydes)	Si—Cl	87.4
	183 (ketones)	Si—O	102.9
C≡N	210.6	Si—Br	70.4
F—F	36.4	Si—S	57.3
Br—Br	46.4	H—P	76.4
Cl—Cl	58.0	H—As	58.6
I—I	36.5	H—S	81.1
H—H	104.2	N—F	64.9
H—F	134.5	P—Cl	78.5
Br—F	50.7 or 60.8[b]	P—Br	63.9
I—F	46.5 or 67.0[c]	As—F	111.2
I—Br	42.5	As—Cl	73.2
Cl—F	59.9 or 61.2[d]	As—Br	58.4
Br—Cl	52.2	S—Cl	60.0
I—Cl	50.3	S—Br	53.4
H—Cl	103.2	F—O	45.0
H—Br	87.6	Cl—O	49.5
H—I	71.6	N—Cl	38.4

[*] From S. S. Penner, *Chemistry Problems in Jet Propulsion* (New York: Pergamon Press, Inc., 1957).

[a] Based on Pauling's original table but including modifications to allow for recent changes in the preferred values of some of the thermodynamic functions. See W. F. Oftermatt, AE Thesis, California Institute of Technology, Pasadena, 1953.

[b] The first value listed applies if an excited Br atom and a normal F atom are formed; the second value refers to the production of excited F and normal Br atoms.

[c] The first value refers to excited I and normal F atoms; for the second value, normal I and excited F atoms are formed.

[d] The first value refers to normal Cl and excited F atoms; for the second value, normal F and excited Cl atoms are produced.

Table 3.10. EMPIRICAL RESONANCE-ENERGY VALUES[*a]

Substance	Resonance energy, kcal/mole	Reference structure
Benzene, C_6H_6	48.9	
Naphthalene, $C_{10}H_8$	88.0	
Aniline, $C_6H_5NH_2$	69.6	
Dialkylcarbonates, R_2CO_3	32.7	
Furfural, C_4H_3OCHO	30.1	
Phenyl acetylene, C_6H_5CCH	55.5	

Substance	Resonance energy, kcal/mole	Reference structure
Phenylcyanide, C_6H_5CN	57.0	
Acetophenone, $C_6H_5COCH_3$	49.0	

* From S. S. Penner, *Chemistry of Problems in Jet Propulsion* (New York: Pergamon Press, Inc., 1957).

ᵃ Based on Pauling's original table but including modifications to allow for changes in the preferred values of some of the thermodynamic functions. See W. F. Oftermatt, AE Thesis, California Institute of Technology, Pasadena, 1953.

3.5. CALCULATION OF ENTHALPY CHANGES ACCOMPANYING PHYSICAL CHANGES OF STATE

The *heat of reaction* is the change in enthalpy when products are formed from reactants at standard conditions (constant reference temperature and pressure). If this enthalpy change is *positive* the reaction is *endothermic*, which means heat is *absorbed* in the process. If this enthalpy change is *negative* the reaction is *exothermic*, which means heat is *evolved* in the process.

Consider the chemical reaction

$$aA + bB \rightleftharpoons cC + dD \tag{3.37}$$

where capital letters represent chemical substances and lower-case letters indicate the number of moles of each associated substance. The heat of reaction for Eq. (3.37) can be defined in terms of the heats of formation

$$\Delta H_r^0 = c(\Delta H_f^0)_C + d(\Delta H_f^0)_D - a(\Delta H_f^0)_A - b(\Delta H_f^0)_B \tag{3.38}$$

where ΔH_r^0 is the heat of reaction and $(\Delta_f^0 H)$ is the heat of formation. A more general relation for the heat of reaction is

$$\Delta H_r^0 = \sum_i n_i (\Delta H_f^0)_i - \sum_j n_j (\Delta H_f^0)_j \qquad (3.39)$$

where subscript i is over product species, subscript j is over reaction species, and n is the number of moles. Relation (3.39) can be used to calculate the heat of formation of one species if the heats of formation of all the other species involved in the specified chemical reaction, and the heat of reaction of the specified chemical reaction, are known. For example, if ΔH_r, $(\Delta H_f)_C$, $(\Delta H_f)_A$, and $(\Delta H_f)_B$ are known in Eq. (3.38), one can solve Eq. (3.38) for

$$(\Delta H_f^0)_D = \frac{1}{d} [\Delta H_r - c(\Delta H_f^0)_C + a(\Delta H_f^0)_A + b(\Delta H_f^0)_B] \qquad (3.40)$$

Equation (3.39) can be used to compute the heat of formation of a substance from a measured *heat of combustion*. The *heat of combustion* corresponds to the heat evolved when a stable substance at standard conditions is burned in a gas to form known product species. For example, the heat of combustion ΔH_r^0 of graphite burned in fluorine assuming only CF_4 gas is formed can be expressed by the equation

$$C(s) + 2F_2(g) \longrightarrow CF_4(g) \qquad \Delta H_r^0 = -230 \text{ kcal/mole} \qquad (3.41)$$

where the letters in parentheses represent the phase of the chemical species (s for solid, g for gas). Large errors can be made in heat of combustion measurements owing to uncertainties about which product species are formed and composition of reaction species before combustion. Side reactions do indeed complicate many calorimetric studies; consequently it is almost impossible to evaluate an accurate heat of formation since one cannot be certain which products were formed. The heat of dissociation of $CF_4(g)$ can be computed from the ΔH_r in Eq. (3.41) and the *heat of sublimation* of carbon and the heat of dissociation of fluorine given in Table 3.7. The *heat of sublimation* is defined as the heat absorbed per mole when a solid substance changes phase from a solid state to the gaseous state. We will not discuss further the calculation of heats of formation from direct measurements of heats of combustion and heats of reaction, since these topics have been treated adequately in standard texts on physical chemistry and thermochemistry.

It should be clear at this point that the calculation of the heat content of a system in a given state requires, in addition to heat-capacity data on product species, information on the heat effects accompanying a physical change of state experienced by the system in reaching the specified state of equilibrium. We will discuss briefly some of these heat effects. The *heat of vaporization* is defined usually as *the heat absorbed per mole when the vapor pressure of the liquid is one atmosphere*. The *melting point of a substance* is *that tempera-*

ture at which the solid phase of a substance is in equilibrium with the liquid phase at one atmosphere of pressure. The heat required to melt one mole of a substance at its melting point is the *heat of fusion*. Theoretical calculations of the composition of a chemical system require information on the vapor pressure of liquids and solid substances. If the vapor is a perfect gas and the volume of the liquid is negligible compared to the volume of the vapor, the change in enthalpy at any other temperature can be calculated from the approximate relation

$$\frac{d(\Delta H)}{dT} = \Delta C_p = (C_p^0)_g - (C_p^0)_l \tag{3.42}$$

if the heat of vaporization at the normal boiling point is known. ΔC_p is the change in heat capacity at constant pressure of one mole of liquid into one mole of vapor. ΔC_p is negative since C_p in the liquid state is higher than in the gaseous state. Therefore, the heat of vaporization at constant pressure decreases with increasing temperature. The temperature coefficient of the heat of fusion can be approximated[18] by the relation

$$\frac{d(\Delta H)_f}{dT} = \Delta C_p + \frac{\Delta H_f}{T} = (C_p^0)_l - (C_p^0)_s + \frac{\Delta H_f}{T} \tag{3.43}$$

There are rules for estimating heats of vaporization and heats of fusion of chemical substances.[18] There are many exceptions to these rules, and consequently such rules should be used only as a last resort when experimental data are not available.

A heated substance can absorb heat at a constant temperature without melting or vaporizing. The heat absorption is due to (1) a change in the crystal arrangement of the lattices in the molecule or (2) the onset of rotation in the crystal. The *molar heat of transition* of a substance is the heat absorbed per mole. Some substances, such as silicon and sulfur, exhibit a series of such transitions. The form stable at the lowest temperature is designated α, the next highest temperature β, and so forth. Evidence of the existence of heats of transition is obtained only through experimental observations. Consequently empirical methods cannot be presented for estimating heats of transition.

3.6. ESTIMATION OF BOND ENERGIES OF POLYATOMIC MOLECULES

In Sec. 3.3 we inferred that the energy of a given bond between two atoms is constant regardless of the relation that these two atoms have to other atoms

[18] See, for example, R. Wenner, *Thermochemical Calculations* (New York: McGraw-Hill Book Co., Inc., 1941), pp. 20–26; G. J. Janz, *Estimation of Thermodynamic Properties of Organic Compounds* (New York: Academic Press, Inc., 1958), pp. 103–108. S. W. Benson and J. H. Buss, *J. Chem. Phys.*, **29** (1958), 546–572.

in the same configuration. We also indirectly inferred the *transferability* of these bond energies from simple molecules to complex molecules. These assumptions are made usually in most approximate methods for estimating heats of formation. The heat of formation can be estimated from

$$\Delta H_f^0 = - \sum_i n_i q_i + \sum_j (\Delta H_A^0)_j \tag{3.44}$$

where n_i and q_i are the number and bond energies, respectively, of the ith bond in the molecular structure, and $(\Delta H_A)_j$ is the heat of formation of the jth gaseous atom produced by complete decomposition of the compound. For example, estimate the heat of formation of normal propane using the bond energy data in Table 3.9. The heat of formation at $0°K$ is estimated by assuming that the eight C—H bonds and the two C—C bonds are equivalent. From Eq. (3.44) and Table 3.9 we have

$$\Delta H_f^0 = -8(98.2) - 2(78.3) + 3(170) + 8(51.6)$$
$$= -19.4 \text{ kcal/mole at } 0°K$$

The experimental heat of formation[19] of normal propane is -19.482 kcal/mole.

In some instances there is a large discrepancy between the calculated heat of formation and the experimental heat of formation. The energy in excess of the experimental heat of formation is called the *resonance energy*. Such resonance energies are used to calculate standard heats of formations for chemical compounds that exhibit resonance. For example, the benzene molecule C_6H_6 can resonate between five structures. Consequently, the first term in Eq. (3.44) is much larger in absolute magnitude than the sum of three C=C, three C—C, and six C—H bond energies. When Eq. (3.44) is used along with the bond energies given in Table 3.9 we obtain $\Delta H_f^0 = 68.7$ kcal/mole. Heat-of-combustion measurements yield a value of $\Delta H_f^0 = 19.8$ kcal/mole. To adjust for the discrepancy between these two values a resonance energy of 48.9 kcal/mole is assigned to benzene. This has the effect of increasing the first term in Eq. (3.44) by 48.9 and reducing $\Delta H_f^0 = 68.7$ by 48.9 so as to obtain the experimental value for the heat of formation of benzene of 19.8. A list of resonance energies to be added to the bond energies in calculating heats of formation of several chemical compounds is given in Table 3.10.

3.7. GROUP SUBSTITUTION METHOD FOR ESTIMATING HEATS OF FORMATION

The *group substitution* method can be used to estimate heats of formation of chemical species whose thermochemical values have not been measured.

[19] F. D. Rossine *et al.*, *Selected Values of Properties of Hydrocarbons*, National Bureau of Standards C461 (Washington, D.C.: U.S. Government Printing Office, 1947).

The technique is based on *group substitution* instead of *group contribution*. The latter has been discussed in many textbooks on thermodynamics. The group substitution method can perhaps be best understood by an example. Suppose that as a result of thermochemical measurements the heats of formation of XY_3 and XZY_2 are a kcal/mole and b kcal/mole respectively. The replacement of Y by Z on X, therefore, requires the addition of $(b - a)$ kcal/mole to the heat of formation of XY_3. Table 3.11 summarizes values

Table 3.11. CONTRIBUTIONS TO HEATS OF FORMATION USING GROUP SUBSTITUTION METHOD

To replace	on	by	Add kcal/mole
=O	C	=NOH	+30
H	C	—OH	−40
C=O—NH$_2$	C	C—H=NOH	+58
H	N	CH$_3$	0
H	C	NH$_2$	−7
H	N	HNNH$_2$	+30
H	C	Cl	+13
H	O	F	+30
H	N	OH	−6
H	N	F	−12
=O	N	HH	+12

which may be used to estimate heats of formation of some chemical species using the group substitution method. This method is an approximation which will be in error in a large number of cases but can be used to estimate heats of formation of new high-energy propellant ingredients. The use of the group substitution method and of bond energies to compute heats of formation can be dangerous. One must take great care to see that *consistent* thermochemical bond energy values and other parameters are used. A great deal of information on heats of formation in the literature is in a confused state. Consequently one finds an inconsistent mass of meaningless numbers. In the absence of sufficient thermochemical data one may have to use some such technique as the bond energy method or the group substitution method to estimate heats of formation.

4

CALCULATION OF
CHEMICAL EQUILIBRIUM
IN COMPLEX SYSTEMS

4.1. INTRODUCTION

We have shown in Chaps. 1 and 2 how to calculate thermodynamic properties of ideal gases from spectroscopic data, and how to compute thermodynamic properties of solids and liquids using statistical thermodynamics. In Chap. 3 we discussed several methods for estimating heats of formation of chemical species. In this chapter we will show how the results of these previous chapters are used to calculate equilibrium constants for individual chemical species. Equilibrium constants are used to calculate chemical equilibria occurring in chemical systems. The methods described in this chapter for computing chemical equilibria are quite general and involve no restrictions on the chemical nature of the system, and can be applied to systems consisting of a gas phase which may—though it need not—be in equilibrium with one or more condensed phases.

We will show how the evaluations of equilibrium composition and thermodynamic properties of mixtures are formulated when one of the *state variables*[1] is pressure and the other is temperature.

---

[1] Thermodynamic properties of the system that are independent of the path taken in going from an initial state to a final state are called *state variables*.

4.2. CHEMICAL REACTIONS

It is shown in standard texts on statistical thermodynamics[2] that by application of the second law of thermodynamics and by proper thermodynamic arguments, the change in *chemical potential*[3] $\Delta\mu$ of a reaction in equilibrium is zero. The starting point for the proof of this statement is usually that the second law can be considered in the form that the entropy S is a *maximum* for an *isolated system*[4] or that the free energy F is a *minimum* for a system in equilibrium at constant pressure and temperature. Let us use the fact that F is a minimum for a system in chemical equilibrium to show that $\Delta\mu = 0$ for a chemical reaction. Consider a *closed system*[5] in chemical equilibrium at temperature T, pressure P, and containing s chemical species. An arbitrary chemical reaction involving the s chemical species may be written

$$\sum_{i=1}^{s} \nu_i y^{(i)} \rightleftharpoons \sum_{i=1}^{s} \nu_i' y^{(i)} \tag{4.1}$$

where the *molecular formula* $y^{(i)}$ for the ith molecular constituent[6] is

$$y^{(i)} = (X_{a_{i1}}^{(1)} X_{a_{i2}}^{(2)} \cdots X_{a_{ik}}^{(k)} \cdots X_{a_{im}}^{(m)}) \tag{4.2}$$

and $X^{(k)}$ is the symbol of the kth element, m is the total number of elements in the system, and a_{ik}, $k = 1, 2, \ldots, m$, the coefficient of the subscript to the kth element of $y^{(i)}$; ν_i and ν_i' are the number of moles of the ith reactant and product, respectively. For example, in the chemical reaction

$$H_2 + \tfrac{1}{2} O_2 \rightleftharpoons H_2O$$

there are two different elements in the system: hydrogen and oxygen. The three constituents in the reaction are H_2, O_2, and H_2O. The molecular formulas for these three constituents are[6]

$$y^{(1)} = H_2 = (H_2, O_0), \quad y^{(2)} = O_2 = (H_0, O_2), \quad y^{(3)} = H_2O = (H_2, O_1)$$

and from Eqs. (4.2) and (4.1)

$$a_{11} = 2, \quad a_{12} = 0, \quad a_{21} = 0, \quad a_{22} = 2, \quad a_{31} = 2, \quad a_{32} = 1$$
$$\nu_1 = 1, \quad \nu_2 = \tfrac{1}{2}, \quad \nu_3 = 0, \quad \nu_1' = 0, \quad \nu_2' = 0, \quad \nu_3' = 1$$

In other words, both the left and right sides of Eq. (4.1) are written as a linear combination of the s chemical species in the system. In a representation

[2] See, for example, T. Hill, *Introduction to Statistical Thermodynamics* (Reading, Mass.: Addison-Wesley Publishing Co., Inc., 1961).

[3] The *chemical potential*, μ_i of species i is the partial molal free energy and is an intensive property. $\Delta\mu$ as used here refers to the change in chemical potential for a specified reaction.

[4] An *isolated system* is one that has no interactions with the surroundings.

[5] A *closed system* is one in which there is no exchange of mass between system and surroundings.

[6] The array of subscripts used to represent each $y^{(i)}$ defines a vector called the *formula vector* of species i.

[Eq. (4.1)] in which each reaction is written as a linear combination of s chemical species, those species which are present in the system but do not take part in the particular chemical reaction have zero coefficients.

The Gibbs free energy of the system

$$F = \sum_{i=1}^{s} N_i \mu_i \tag{4.3}$$

where N_i represents the number of molecules of the ith species. Consider an infinitesimal process for Eq. (4.1) and write

not right

$$\sum_{n=1}^{s} \nu_i \, d\xi = \sum_{n=1}^{s} \nu_i' \, d\xi \tag{4.4}$$

where $d\xi = dN_i/\nu_i$ is arbitrary, and represents the *degree of development of the reaction*.[7] The chemical potential μ is an *intensive property*[8] and as such will not change a great deal for an infinitesimal process. The chemical potentials μ_i are taken, therefore, as constants for the process. The change in free energy for the system is

not necessary

$$dF = \sum_{i=1}^{s} \mu_i \, dN_i = \sum_{i=1}^{s} (-\mu_i \nu_i + \nu_i' \mu_i) \, d\xi \equiv \Delta\mu \, d\xi \tag{4.5}$$

According to the second law of thermodynamics, for a closed system in equilibrium at constant pressure and temperature $dF = 0$, and one concludes that $\Delta\mu = 0$ in Eq. (4.5) since $d\xi$ is arbitrary. It follows for a chemical reaction in equilibrium that

$$\sum_{i=1}^{s} \nu_i \mu_i = \sum_{i=1}^{s} \nu_i' \mu_i \tag{4.6}$$

where $\mu_i = \mu_i(T)$ is the equilibrium value of the chemical potential of the ith species. Relation (4.6) is quite general and applies to any chemical reaction.

The free energy [Eq. (1.23)] of the ith species can be expressed in terms of its partition function

$$\frac{(F_T^0)_i}{RT} = -\ln (Q)_i \tag{4.7}$$

where the molar partition function

$$(Q)_i = \frac{(Q_t Q_{el} Q_r Q_{el,r} Q_v \cdots)^{N_i}}{(N_i)!} = \frac{(Q_T)_i^{N_i}}{(N_i)!} \tag{4.8}$$

[7] When $\xi < 0$ the reaction in Eq. (4.1) goes from left to right and when $\xi > 0$ it goes from right to left. The term "degree of development of the reaction" was introduced by Th. de Donder, *Leçons de thermodynamique et de chimie physique* (Paris, 1920), p. 117.

[8] Thermodynamic properties of the system which are independent of the mass of the system are called *intensive properties*.

We use the Stirling formula for large N

$$\ln N! = N \ln N - N$$

and write for Eq. (4.7)

$$\frac{(F_T^0)_i}{kT} = -\ln \left[\frac{(Q_T)_i^{N_i}}{(N_i)!} \right] = -N_i \ln (Q_T)_i + N_i \ln N_i - N_i \qquad (4.9)$$

From the definition of the chemical potential of the ith chemical species we write

$$\mu_i = \left(\frac{\partial (F_T^0)_i}{\partial N_i} \right)_{T,P,N_j} = -kT \left(\frac{\partial \ln Q_i}{\partial N_i} \right)_{T,P,N_j} \qquad (4.10)$$

or

$$\left(\frac{\partial \ln Q_i}{\partial N_i} \right)_{T,P,N_j} = \frac{-\mu_i(T)}{kT} \qquad (4.11)$$

Substitution of Eq. (4.8) into Eq. (4.11) yields

$$\mu_i(T) = -kT \left(\frac{\partial \ln Q_i}{\partial N_i} \right)_{T,P,N_j} = -kT \ln \left[\frac{(Q_T)_i}{N_i} \right] \qquad (4.12)$$

We know that Q_T for each species is a function of volume V and temperature T. This is clear since the translational partition function Q_t in Eq. (4.8) is shown in Eq. (1.7) to contain the volume V. Consequently we can write

$$Q_T = Q_T(V, T) \qquad (4.13)$$

We now substitute Eq. (4.12) into Eq. (4.6) to obtain

$$\prod_{i=1}^{s} (N_i)^{\nu_i' - \nu_i} = \prod_{i=1}^{s} (Q_T)^{\nu_i' - \nu_i} \qquad (4.14)$$

where the N_i's represent the number of molecules of the ith species present when chemical equilibrium has been established. Since each Q_T is a function of temperature multiplied by a volume V [see, for example, Eq. (4.8)], division of Q_T/V is a function of temperature only. We write therefore

$$q(T) = \frac{Q_T}{V} \qquad (4.15)$$

and Eq. (4.14) becomes

$$\prod_{i=1}^{s} (\rho_i)^{\nu_i' - \nu_i} = \prod_{i=1}^{s} [q_i(T)]^{\nu_i' - \nu_i} = K(T) \qquad (4.16)$$

where $\rho_i = N_i/V$ and $K(T)$ is a function of temperature only and is called the *equilibrium constant*. For an ideal gas the partial pressure p_i of the ith species is

$$p_i = \rho_i kT \qquad (4.17)$$

and substitution of Eq. (4.17) into Eq. (4.16) gives

$$\prod_{i=1}^{s} (p_i)^{\nu_i' - \nu_i}(kT)^{\nu_i' - \nu_i} = K(T) = \prod_{i=1}^{s} [q_i(T)]^{\nu_i' - \nu_i}$$

or

$$\prod_{i=1}^{s} (p_i)^{\nu_i' - \nu_i} = \prod_{i=1}^{s} (kT)^{\nu_i' - \nu_i} K(T) = K_p(T) \qquad (4.18)$$

$K_p(T)$ is the equilibrium constant used in computing composition of chemical species in chemical equilibrium. The chemical potential of the ith species in thermodynamics is written

$$\mu_i(T) = \mu_i^0(T) + kT \ln p_i \qquad (4.19)$$

where $\mu_i^0(T)$ is the chemical potential of the ith species in the standard state. If one substitutes Eq. (4.19) into Eq. (4.18) one obtains

$$\prod_{i=1}^{s} (p_i)^{\nu_i' - \nu_i} = e^{-\Delta F_T^0/kT} = K_p(T) \qquad (4.20)$$

where

$$\Delta F_T^0 = \sum_{i=1}^{s} (\nu_i' - \nu_i)\mu_i \qquad (4.21)$$

ΔF_T^0 is called the *standard free energy change* for the chemical reaction. The zero-point energy chosen for the various chemical species in the system must be self-consistent if the change in chemical potential for each reaction is to be zero. The zero of energy H_0^0 is chosen usually as zero for the separated atoms at rest for each atom in the molecule. This choice is excellent, since the same atoms occur on both sides of the chemical equation (4.1) and this choice leads to the same zero for reactants and products.

4.3. EXAMPLES OF CHEMICAL EQUILIBRIA

In this section we will give two examples of the use of free energy functions and partition functions to evaluate the equilibrium constants $K_p(T)$ for the dissociation of H_2 and the ionization of H. The dissociation of H_2 is given by

$$H_2 \rightleftharpoons 2H \qquad (4.22)$$

Equilibrium constants $K_p(T)$ can be evaluated by using the free energy functions $-(F_T^0 - H_0^0)/RT$ for each chemical species involved in the reaction. We write, from Eq. (4.21) for the reaction in Eq. (4.22)

$$\ln K_p(T) = \frac{-\Delta F_T^0}{RT} = \frac{(F_T^0 - H_0^0)_{H_2}}{RT} - \frac{2(F_T^0 - H_0^0)_H}{RT} + \frac{(H_0^0)_{H_2} - 2(H_0^0)_H}{RT}$$

$$(4.23)$$

If we use the values of the free energy functions for atomic hydrogen [Appendix 2] and molecular hydrogen [Appendix 3], we find at 2000°K

$$\frac{(F_T^0 - H_0^0)_H}{T} = -31.880 \frac{cal}{mole} \quad and \quad \frac{(F_T^0 - H_0^0)_{H_2}}{T} = -37.669 \frac{cal}{mole}$$

The standard state for hydrogen is gaseous molecular hydrogen, and for convenience H_0^0 for gaseous atomic hydrogen is assigned a value of zero. The dissociation energy D_0^0 for molecular hydrogen at 0°K is given in Table 3.7 as 103.242 kcal/mole. To evaluate $(H_0^0)_{H_2}$ one has from Eq. (4.22) that

$$2(H_0^0)_H - (H_0^0)_{H_2} = (D_0^0)_{H_2} = 103.242 \; kcal/mole$$

or, solving for $(H_0^0)_{H_2}$ with $(H_0^0)_H$ assigned a value of zero, we have $(H_0^0)_{H_2} = -103.242$ kcal/mole. It follows on this basis that the ground state of H_2 $[(H_0^0)_{H_2} - 2(H_0^0)_H]$ in Eq. (4.23) is -103.242 kcal/mole. The natural logarithm of the equilibrium constant Eq. (4.23) for H_2 at 2000°K is -12.847.

If the free energy functions were not available, one could calculate $K_p(T)$ from partition functions. At 2000°K the rotation in hydrogen is classical. The ground state of H_2 is a $^1\Sigma$ which corresponds to an electronic degeneracy of unity. Molecular constants of H_2 are given in Table 1.5 and those of H in Table 1.4. The free energy function for atomic hydrogen is obtained by addition of Eqs. (1.277) and (1.281), and for molecular hydrogen by addition of Eqs. (1.288), (1.292), and (1.213). Equation (1.107) is used to evaluate the moment of inertia of H_2. The frequency ν is obtained from Eq. (1.161). Equation (1.228) is used to evaluate the anharmonic constant x_{11}''. For a given u [Eq. (1.227)], corresponding values of the functions $^1\phi$, $^4\phi$, and $^{11}\phi$ are obtained from Appendix 1.

The two methods used in this section to compute $K_p(T)$ for molecular hydrogen can be used to compute $K_p(T)$ for any chemical reactions involving ideal gas species. The calculations for the free energy functions for polyatomic molecules become more tedious if anharmonic constants are available. Of course, the effect of vibrational anharmonicity on thermodynamic properties is large and should be included in all calculations if the necessary anharmonic constants are available.

We can use the value of $K_p(T)$ for H_2 at 2000°K to find the amount of H_2 which dissociates at a total pressure P. If α represents the moles of H_2 dissociated at total pressure P and temperature T, then 2α represents the moles of H formed and $1 - \alpha$ the moles of H_2 remaining after dissociation. The total number of moles in the system at equilibrium is $1 - \alpha + 2\alpha = 1 + \alpha$. The partial pressures for the chemical species become

$$p_H = \frac{2\alpha}{1 + \alpha} P \tag{4.24}$$

$$p_{H_2} = \frac{1 - \alpha}{1 + \alpha} P \tag{4.25}$$

Substituting Eq. (4.24) and Eq. (4.25) into Eq. (4.20) one obtains

$$\frac{p_H^2}{p_{H_2}} = \frac{4\alpha^2}{1 - \alpha^2} P = K_p(T) \tag{4.26}$$

from which the fraction of molecular hydrogen dissociated becomes

$$\alpha = \sqrt{\frac{K_p}{K_p + 4P}} \tag{4.27}$$

The fraction of hydrogen dissociated at 2000°K and a pressure of one atmosphere is 2.6×10^{-3}. The fraction of hydrogen dissociated [Eq. (4.27)] at a specified temperature is greater, the lower the total pressure.

At extremely high temperatures collisions between gas particles lead to a type of ionization called *thermal ionization*. The reason for the name is that the gas particles which are in different stages of ionization are in thermal equilibrium. We now consider thermal ionization of a monatomic gas. This case is of a great deal of interest in *plasma*[9] research since at the high temperatures studied, chemical bonds are usually completely dissociated. Ionization equilibrium is a special type of chemical equilibrium. In the case of a system consisting of only hydrogen there is only one ionization reaction

$$H \rightleftarrows H^+ + e^- \tag{4.28}$$

The equilibrium constant $K_p(T)$ for this reaction is written

$$K_p(T) = \frac{Q_{H^+} \cdot g_{e^-}}{Q_H} e^{\epsilon_{el}/kT} = \left[2\pi \frac{(m_H)(m_{e^-})}{m_H h^2} kT\right]^{3/2} \frac{V}{N} \frac{g_{H^+} \cdot g_{e^-}}{g_H} e^{+\epsilon_{el}/kT} \tag{4.29}$$

The degeneracy of electron gas g_{e^-} is two. The electron spin of H is $\frac{1}{2}$. Consequently $g_H = 2S + 1 = 2$. The proton spin degeneracy is neglected since it appears in both H and H^+ and cancels out in $K_p(T)$. The zero of energy is taken as a proton and electron at rest. The ground state of an hydrogen atom, therefore, on this basis has an energy $\epsilon_{el} = -13.595$ ev (Table 3.1). Substituting these data into Eq. (4.29) we have from Eq. (4.16)

$$K_p(T) = \frac{p_{H^+} \cdot p_{e^-}}{p_H} = \left[2\pi \frac{(m_{H^+})(m_{e^-})}{m_H h^2} kT\right]^{3/2} \left(\frac{kT}{P}\right) e^{+\epsilon_{el}/kT} \tag{4.30}$$

Electrical neutrality requires that $P_{H^+} = P_{e^-}$ for the reaction in Eq. (4.28). If α represents the moles of H which ionize, then $1 - \alpha$ represents H remaining after ionization, α the moles of H^+ and e^- formed. The total number of moles in the system, therefore, is $1 - \alpha + \alpha + \alpha = 1 + \alpha$. The concentration of H^+, e^-, and H is

$$p_{H^+} = p_{e^-} = \frac{\alpha}{1 + \alpha} P \tag{4.31}$$

$$p_H = \frac{1 - \alpha}{1 + \alpha} P \tag{4.32}$$

[9] An ionized gas is called a *plasma*.

where P is the total pressure of the mixture. The degree of ionization for the system is found by substituting Eqs. (4.31) and (4.32) into Eq. (4.30). We have

$$\alpha = \sqrt{\frac{K_p}{K_p + P}} \tag{4.33}$$

Let us compute the amount of ionization of H at a temperature of $10,000°K$ and a pressure of one atmosphere. K_p is computed from Eq. (4.29) and is 4.98×10^{-4} at $10,000°K$. Finally α is computed from Eq. (4.33) and is 2.1×10^{-2}. The degree of ionization α at $2000°K$ and a total pressure of one atmosphere is calculated in a similar manner and is found to be 6.8×10^{-17}, which indicates that the extent of ionization at this temperature and pressure is negligible. We were, therefore, justified in neglecting H ionization in our first calculation on hydrogen dissociation.

In these examples it was quite easy to calculate the composition of the system with a single reaction with one dependent constituent. When many chemical species with several dependent constituents are present in the chemical system the composition cannot be found so easily, since the equilibria equations form a system of nonlinear relations. We will describe in Sec. 4.4 and 4.5 two general methods which we have used to evaluate chemical composition and thermodynamic properties of complex systems at constant pressure and temperature.

Let us now consider several ionization reactions taking place simultaneously. For example,

$$\begin{aligned} \text{Ar} &= \text{Ar}^+ + \text{e}^- \\ \text{Ar}^+ &= \text{Ar}^{++} + \text{e}^- \\ \text{Ar}^{++} &= \text{Ar}^{+++} + \text{e}^- \\ &\cdots \end{aligned} \tag{4.34}$$

wrong symbol for argon.

Ar is neutral, Ar^+ is singly ionized, Ar^{++} is doubly ionized, etc., and e^- is electron gas. In addition to the ionization equilibrium equations in (4.34) we must write an equation for electrical neutrality.

$$\text{e}^- = (\text{Ar}^+) + 2\,(\text{Ar}^{++}) + 3\,(\text{Ar}^{+++}) + \cdots \tag{4.35}$$

The system of equations in (4.34) and (4.35) determines the concentration of the different ions at ionization equilibrium for the monatomic gas argon. The removal of one electron from a neutral atom forming a single ionized gas is called *first-order ionization*. The order of ionization is n if n electrons are removed from a neutral atom. Complete ionization of a given order occurs as the temperature increases and the equilibrium constant K_p for Eq. (4.34) decreases to unity. *Complete ionization does not occur at the temperature at which the thermal energy kT equals the ionization energy I_n where n is the order of ionization but occurs at much lower temperatures.* This statement can be verified by considering the coefficient of $e^{-I_n/kT}$ for $K_p(T)$ in Eq. (4.34). We have

$$K_p^{(n)}(T) = \left[2\pi \frac{(m_{Ar^{n+}})(m_{e^-})}{m_{Ar^{(n-1)+}}}\right]^{3/2} (kT)^{3/2} \frac{g_{Ar^{n+}} g_{e^-}}{g_{Ar^{(n-1)+}}} \cdot \frac{(kT)}{P} e^{-I_n/kT} \qquad (4.36)$$

When I_n is of the order kT the coefficient of $e^{-I_n/kT}$ is of the order $V/N = kT/P$ of the gas. We refer to Eq. (4.33) and note that complete ionization of order n occurs when $P/K_p^{(n)}$ approaches zero. We conclude that when kT is of the order of the ionization energy, the gas is almost completely ionized. The gas will consist of electrons and bare nuclei at temperatures corresponding to the ionization energy required to remove the last electron in the atom.

4.4. CALCULATION OF EQUILIBRIUM COMPOSITION USING THE EQUILIBRIUM-CONSTANT APPROACH

The composition and thermodynamic properties of a system in equilibrium are independent of the path by which the equilibrium is attained. One can, therefore, to calculate conditions for equilibrium, make any assumptions as to the way the reaction took place. We have shown in Sec. 4.3 that the required equation for chemical equilibrium [Eq. (4.6)] is one in which the change in chemical potential of each reaction in the system is zero. We note that in Eq. (4.6) the chemical potential μ_i replaced the symbol $Y^{(i)}$ in Eq. (4.1). Equation (4.6) is written for each possible reaction in the system. The criterion that $\Delta\mu = 0$ for a chemical reaction in equilibrium is quite general and applies to systems in which the reacting substances are in two different phases. The fact that $\Delta\mu = 0$ for any chemical reaction in equilibrium follows, since at equilibrium if the reacting species are in two different phases the chemical potential of each species is the same in the two different phases because of the *phase equilibrium conditions*.[10] In Sec. 4.3 we also derived the *law of mass action* by showing in Eq. (4.18) that the product $p_i^{\nu_i' - \nu_i}$ is constant for a specified temperature and pressure. This law of mass action is quite general and is shown in thermodynamic texts to apply to dilute solutions as well as species in pure condensed phases. When solids and gases take part in the chemical reaction, one assumes since the gas pressure is small that the chemical potential of the solid is independent of pressure. The relation [Eq. (4.20)] between equilibrium constant and pressure remains the same but the product $p^{\nu_i' - \nu_i}$ is over gaseous species only.

Consider a closed system containing s chemical species in equilibrium at

---

[10] Two species in different states which exist simultaneously in equilibrium with each other are said to be, while in contact with each other, different phases of the same species. The condition for equilibrium of the two phases is that the temperature, pressure, and chemical potentials of the two phases be equal.

constant temperature and pressure. From Eq. (4.2) we write the formula vector of species i

$$y_i = (a_{i1}, a_{i2}, a_{i3}, \ldots, a_{ik}, \ldots, a_{im}) \tag{4.37}$$

where m is the total number of elements in the system. If the rank of the matrix of the vector elements of the s species is c, then from a well-known theorem of algebra we have that there are c linearly independent vectors and, if $c \le s$, there are $s - c$ linear dependent vectors which can be expressed as a linear combination of c independent vectors. The c species sufficient to describe the composition are called the *components* of the system. Brinkley[11] has published an analytic criterion for the choice of components. For example, consider a system having as product species H_2, O_2, H_2O, H, O, and OH. The matrix of the vector elements for the system is

$$\begin{array}{c@{}c} & \begin{array}{cc} H & O \end{array} \\ \begin{array}{c} H_2 \\ O_2 \\ H_2O \\ H \\ O \\ OH \end{array} & \left[\begin{array}{cc} 2 & 0 \\ 0 & 2 \\ 2 & 1 \\ 1 & 0 \\ 0 & 1 \\ 1 & 1 \end{array}\right] \end{array} \tag{4.38}$$

and can be shown by elementary row operations to have rank two. We can, therefore, choose any two species of the six whose vector elements are linearly independent. For example the combinations (H_2, H), (O_2, O) are not allowed since the matrices of the vector elements of (H_2, H) and (O_2, O) have a rank of unity and either choice leads to two species whose formula

$$\begin{array}{c@{}c} & \begin{array}{cc} H & O \end{array} \\ \begin{array}{c} H_2 \\ H \end{array} & \left[\begin{array}{cc} 2 & 0 \\ 1 & 0 \end{array}\right] \end{array}, \qquad \begin{array}{c@{}c} & \begin{array}{cc} H & O \end{array} \\ \begin{array}{c} O_2 \\ O \end{array} & \left[\begin{array}{cc} 0 & 2 \\ 0 & 1 \end{array}\right] \end{array} \tag{4.39}$$

vectors are linearly dependent. We conclude that our choice of components must contain no two species whose vector elements are linearly dependent. For this system we could choose as components any one of the following thirteen combinations.

$$\begin{array}{llll} (H_2, O_2) & (H_2, H_2O) & (H_2, O) & (H_2, OH) \\ (O_2, H_2O) & (O_2, H) & (O_2, OH) & (H_2O, H) \\ (H_2O, O) & (H_2O, OH) & (H, O) & (H, OH) \\ (O, OH) \end{array} \tag{4.40}$$

[11] S. R. Brinkley, Jr., *J. Chem. Phys.*, **14** (1946), 563–564; 686.

Usually one chooses as components species which appear in large concentrations. Such species are called *major components*. Components in smaller concentrations than the major components are called *minor components*.

We write the formula vectors of the $s - c$ dependent species as a linear combination of c independent species

$$y_i = \sum_{j=1}^{c} v_{ij} y_j, \qquad i = c + 1, c + 2, \ldots, s \qquad (4.41)$$

where v_{ij} is the coefficient of the jth independent species for a specific i. For example, if we choose H_2O and OH in Eq. (4.40) as our major components we can express the other species as a linear combination of these two. We have by inspection

i		$j = 1$	$j = 2$
3	$H_2 =$	$2\ H_2O$	$-\ 2\ OH$
4	$O_2 =$	$-2\ H_2O$	$+\ 4\ OH$
5	$H\ =$	$1 \cdot H_2O$	$-\ 1 \cdot OH$
6	$O\ =$	$-1 \cdot H_2O$	$+\ 2\ OH$

(4.42)

or in matrix notation

$$\begin{pmatrix} H_2 \\ O_2 \\ H \\ O \end{pmatrix} = \begin{pmatrix} 2 & -2 \\ -2 & 4 \\ 1 & -1 \\ -1 & 2 \end{pmatrix} \begin{pmatrix} H_2O \\ OH \end{pmatrix} \qquad (4.43)$$

In Eq. (4.43), $v_{31} = 2$, $v_{32} = -2$, $v_{41} = -2$, $v_{42} = 4$, $v_{51} = 1$, $v_{52} = -1$, $v_{61} = -1$, and $v_{62} = 2$. In many instances it is not possible to write by inspection the formula vectors of the $s - c$ dependent species as a linear combination of the c independent species. To find the coefficients v_{ij} of each dependent species in Eq. (4.41) we multiply the formula vector of the ith dependent species by the inverse of the matrix of the formula vectors of the c independent species. For example, the matrix for a system with H_2O and OH as major components is

$$\begin{array}{cc} & \begin{array}{cc} H & O \end{array} \\ \begin{array}{c} H_2O \\ OH \end{array} & \begin{bmatrix} 2 & 1 \\ 1 & 1 \end{bmatrix} \end{array} \qquad (4.44)$$

and has as its inverse

$$\begin{array}{cc} & \begin{array}{cc} H & \quad O \end{array} \\ \begin{array}{c} H_2O \\ OH \end{array} & \begin{bmatrix} 1 & -1 \\ -1 & 2 \end{bmatrix} \end{array} \qquad (4.45)$$

The coefficients v_{ij} in Eq. (4.41) for the dependent species are obtained by multiplying the formula vector for each dependent species by the inverse matrix Eq. (4.45). We have for the system considered in Eq. (4.42) that

$$H_2 = \begin{pmatrix} 1 & -1 \\ -1 & 2 \end{pmatrix}\begin{pmatrix} 2 \\ 0 \end{pmatrix} = (2, -2)\begin{pmatrix} H_2O \\ OH \end{pmatrix} = 2\,H_2O - 2\,(OH)$$

$$O_2 = \begin{pmatrix} 1 & -1 \\ -1 & 2 \end{pmatrix}\begin{pmatrix} 0 \\ 2 \end{pmatrix} = (-2, 4)\begin{pmatrix} H_2O \\ OH \end{pmatrix} = -2\,H_2O + 4\,(OH)$$

$$H = \begin{pmatrix} 1 & -1 \\ -1 & 2 \end{pmatrix}\begin{pmatrix} 1 \\ 0 \end{pmatrix} = (1, -1)\begin{pmatrix} H_2O \\ OH \end{pmatrix} = 1 \cdot H_2O - 1 \cdot (OH)$$

$$O = \begin{pmatrix} 1 & -1 \\ -1 & 2 \end{pmatrix}\begin{pmatrix} 0 \\ 1 \end{pmatrix} = (-1, 2)\begin{pmatrix} H_2O \\ OH \end{pmatrix} = -1 \cdot H_2O + 2\,(OH)$$

$$(4.46)$$

The relations in Eq. (4.46) allow us to write the equilibrium constants [Eq. (4.18)] for hydrogen/oxygen systems

$$(K_p)_{H_2} = \frac{p_{H_2}}{p_{H_2O}^2 p_{OH}^{-2}} \tag{4.47}$$

$$(K_p)_{O_2} = \frac{p_{O_2}}{p_{H_2O}^{-2} p_{OH}^4} \tag{4.48}$$

$$(K_p)_H = \frac{p_H}{p_{H_2O}^1 p_{OH}^{-1}} \tag{4.49}$$

$$(K_p)_O = \frac{p_O}{p_{H_2O}^{-1} p_{OH}^2} \tag{4.50}$$

For a system at constant pressure Dalton's law requires that the total pressure

$$P = \sum_{i=1}^{s} p_i \tag{4.51}$$

The conservation of mass in the system requires

$$\sum_{i=1}^{s} \bar{a}_{ki} n_i = \sigma_k, \qquad k = 1, 2, \ldots, m \tag{4.52}$$

where $\bar{a}_{ki} = a_{ik}$ is the coefficient to the kth element in the formula vector y_i in Eq. (4.2), n_i is the number of moles of the ith species in the system, and σ_k is the total number of moles per gram-atom of the kth element in the system. For example, in the hydrogen/oxygen system Eq. (4.51) is written

$$P = p_{H_2O} + p_{OH} + p_{H_2} + p_{O_2} + p_H + p_O \tag{4.53}$$

and the conservation of mass in this system requires according to Eq. (4.52) that

$$2n_{H_2O} + 1 \cdot n_{OH} + 2n_{H_2} + n_H = \sigma_H \tag{4.54}$$

$$1 \cdot n_{H_2O} + 1 \cdot n_{OH} + 2n_{O_2} + n_O = \sigma_O \tag{4.55}$$

For a system with only a gas phase we assume the ideal gas law holds and write

$$n\frac{p_i}{P} = n_i = \frac{p_i}{A} \tag{4.56}$$

where n is the total number of moles in the system and $A = p/n$. Substituting Eq. (4.56) into Eq. (4.52) one obtains

$$\sum_{i=1}^{s} \bar{a}_{ki} p_i = A\sigma_k, \qquad k = 1, 2, \ldots, m \tag{4.57}$$

We can write Eqs. (4.54) and (4.55) in the form of Eq. (4.57).

$$2p_{H_2O} + 1 \cdot p_{OH} + 2p_{H_2} + p_H = A\sigma_H \tag{4.58}$$

$$1 \cdot p_{H_2O} + 1 \cdot p_{OH} + 2p_{O_2} + p_O = A\sigma_O \tag{4.59}$$

The equilibrium constants in Eq. (4.18) are known functions of temperature. We can determine for a given temperature and pressure the s unknown partial pressures and the one additional variable n which represents the total number of moles in the system by solving a system of $(s - c + m + 1)$ equations [Eqs. (4.18), (4.51), and (4.57)]. This system of equations is nonlinear in the equilibrium constants [Eq. (4.18)] and linear in pressure [Eq. (4.51)] and mass balance [Eq. (4.57)]. A closed-form solution is usually not possible because of the nonlinear algebraic equations. The system of equations can be solved by trial and error or by an iterative method. Descriptions of the *trial and error methods* are available in the literature.[12] We prefer iterative methods and will discuss the method of successive approximation described in a report by Huff *et al.*[13] The nonlinear relations in Eq. (4.18) can be linearized by writing the equilibrium relation for each reaction in Eq. (4.41) in logarithmic form.

$$\ln p_i - \sum_{j=1}^{c} \nu_{ij} \ln p_j = \ln (K_p)_i, \qquad i = c + 1, c + 2, \ldots, s \tag{4.60}$$

The equations (4.60), (4.51), and (4.57) can be expanded in a Taylor's series. The resulting equations are

$$\Delta \ln p_i^{(r)} - \sum_{j=1}^{c} \nu_{ij} \Delta \ln p_j^{(r)} = \left(\frac{d \ln (K_P)}{d \ln T}\right)_i \Delta \ln T^{(r)} = \left(\frac{\Delta H}{RT}\right)_i \Delta \ln T^{(r)}$$

$$i = c + 1, c + 2, \ldots, s \tag{4.61}$$

$$P^{(r)} \ln \frac{P}{P^{(r)}} = \sum_{i=1}^{s} p_i^{(r)} \Delta \ln p_i^{(r)} \tag{4.62}$$

[12] See, for example, G. S. Bahn and E. E. Zukoski, *Kinetic, Equilibria and Performance of High Temperature Systems* (Washington, D.C.: Butterworth Inc., 1960).

[13] V. Huff, S. Gordon, and V. E. Morrell, *General Method and Thermodynamic Tables for Computation of Equilibrium Composition and Temperatures of Chemical Reactions*, National Advisory Committee for Aeronautics Report 1037 (1951).

$$\sum_{i=1}^{s} \bar{a}_{ki} p_i^{(r)} \Delta \ln p_i^{(r)} - (A)^{(r)}(\sigma_k)^{(r)} \Delta \ln (A)^{(r)} = (A)^{(r)} \sigma_k^{(r)} \ln \frac{\sigma_k}{\sigma_k^{(r)}} \qquad (4.63)$$

where

$$(\Delta H)_i = (H_T^0 - H_0^0)_i - \sum_{j=1}^{c} \nu_{ij}(H_T^0 - H_0^0)_j + (H_0^0)_i - \sum_{j=1}^{c} \nu_{ij}(H_0^0)_j \qquad (4.64)$$

and superscript (r) represents the rth approximation. For a fixed pressure P [Eq. (4.62)], the pressure $P^{(r)}$ of the rth approximation must approach P as the solution of the problem is found. In addition $\sigma_k^{(r)}$ in Eq. (4.63) must approach σ_k assigned as the solution of the problem is found. For a system at constant temperature $\Delta \ln T = 0$ and Eq. (4.61) is then written

$$\Delta \ln p_i^{(r)} - \sum_{j=1}^{c} \nu_{ij} \ln p_j^{(r)} = 0, \qquad i = c + 1, c + 2, \ldots, s \qquad (4.65)$$

The values of $\Delta \ln P_i$ and $\Delta \ln (A)$ are computed by means of a matrix constructed in the following manner. The order of the columns in the matrix is written

(1) $\Delta \ln p_i$ of the $(s - c)$ gaseous species
(2) $\Delta \ln p_i$ of the c components chosen as majors
(3) $\Delta \ln (A)$ (4.66)
(4) Constant terms of the equations

The order of the rows in the matrix is written

(1) Equilibrium equations in the same order as the $(s - c)$ gaseous species
(2) Mass-balance equations   (4.67)
(3) Total-pressure equation

For example, in our hydrogen/oxygen systems, Eqs. (4.47) through (4.50) and Eqs. (4.53), (4.58), and (4.59) when expanded in a Taylor's series take the form shown in Eqs. (4.65), (4.62), and (4.63). A matrix can be constructed as described in (4.66) and (4.67).

	$\Delta \ln p_{H_2}$	$\Delta \ln p_{O_2}$	$\Delta \ln p_H$	$\Delta \ln p_O$	$\Delta \ln p_{H_2O}$	$\Delta \ln p_{OH}$	$\Delta \log (A)$	Constant
Eq. (4.65)	1	0	0	0	2	-2	0	0
	0	1	0	0	-2	4	0	0
	0	0	1	0	1	-1	0	0
	0	0	0	1	-1	$+2$	0	0
Eq. (4.63)	$2p_{H_2}^{(r)}$	0	$p_H^{(r)}$	0	$2p_{H_2O}^{(r)}$	$p_{OH}^{(r)}$	$-(A)^{(r)}\sigma_H^{(r)}$	$(A\sigma_H)^{(r)} \ln \frac{\sigma_H}{\sigma_H^{(r)}}$
	0	$2p_{O_2}^{(r)}$	0	$p_O^{(r)}$	$p_{H_2O}^{(r)}$	$p_{OH}^{(r)}$	$-(A^{(r)})\sigma_O^{(r)}$	$(A\sigma_O)^{(r)} \ln \frac{\sigma_O}{\sigma_O^{(r)}}$
Eq. (4.62)	$p_{H_2}^{(r)}$	$p_{O_2}^{(r)}$	$p_H^{(r)}$	$p_O^{(r)}$	$p_{H_2O}^{(r)}$	$p_{OH}^{(r)}$	0	$P^{(r)} \ln \frac{P}{P^{(r)}}$

$$(4.68)$$

The matrix in Eq. (4.68) can be partitioned such that a unit matrix U_m of order $(s - c)$ appears in the upper left corner. We can write the matrix in Eq. (4.68) as

$$\begin{bmatrix} U_m & \vdots & \alpha_1 \\ \cdots & \cdots & \cdots \\ \alpha_2 & \vdots & \alpha_3 \end{bmatrix} \tag{4.69}$$

This system of linear equations can best be solved by the method of Crout.[14] In the Crout method an auxiliary matrix of the same order as the original matrix is constructed from an original matrix by a simple routine. The solution to the set of linear equations is obtained by a back substitution in the auxiliary matrix. When the Crout matrix is applied to the original augmented matrix, the Crout auxiliary matrix can be written

$$\begin{bmatrix} U_m & \vdots & \alpha_1 \\ \cdots & \cdots & \cdots \\ \alpha_2 & \vdots & \alpha_4 \end{bmatrix} \tag{4.70}$$

where

$$[\alpha_4] = [\alpha_3] - [\alpha_2][\alpha_1] = [\alpha_2 \ \vdots \ \alpha_3] \begin{bmatrix} -\alpha_1 \\ \overline{U_K} \end{bmatrix} \tag{4.71}$$

and the $[U_K]$ is a unit matrix of order equal to the number of columns of $[\alpha_3]$. The numerical solution is obtained by evaluating $[\alpha_4]$ in Eq. (4.71). The values $\Delta \ln p_i$, $i = 1, 2, \ldots, c$ and $\Delta \ln (A)$ are obtained by the method of back substitution given by Crout. From Eq. (4.68) we have for the example hydrogen/oxygen system

$$[\alpha_1] = \begin{bmatrix} 2 & -2 & 0 & 0 \\ -2 & 4 & 0 & 0 \\ 1 & -1 & 0 & 0 \\ -1 & 2 & 0 & 0 \end{bmatrix} \tag{4.72}$$

$$[\alpha_2] = \begin{bmatrix} 2p_{H_2}^{(r)} & 0 & p_H^{(r)} & 0 \\ 0 & 2p_{O_2}^{(r)} & 0 & p_O^{(r)} \\ p_{H_2}^{(r)} & p_{O_2}^{(r)} & p_H^{(r)} & p_O^{(r)} \end{bmatrix} \tag{4.73}$$

$$[\alpha_3] = \begin{bmatrix} 2p_{H_2O}^{(r)} & p_{OH}^{(r)} & -(A\sigma_H)^{(r)} & (A\sigma_H)^{(r)} \ln \dfrac{\sigma_H}{\sigma_H^{(r)}} \\[2ex] p_{H_2O}^{(r)} & p_{OH}^{(r)} & -(A\sigma_O)^{(r)} & (A\sigma_O)^{(r)} \ln \dfrac{\sigma_O}{\sigma_O^{(r)}} \\[2ex] p_{H_2O}^{(r)} & p_{OH}^{(r)} & 0 & p^{(r)} \ln \dfrac{P}{P^{(r)}} \end{bmatrix} \tag{4.74}$$

---

[14] P. D. Crout, *AIEE Trans. (Suppl.)*, **60** (1941), 1235.

$[\alpha_2 \vdots \alpha_3] =$

$$
\begin{bmatrix}
2p_{H_2}^{(r)} & 0 & p_H^{(r)} & 0 & 2p_{H_2O}^{(r)} & p_{OH}^{(r)} & -(A\sigma_H)^{(r)} & (A\sigma_H)^{(r)} \ln \dfrac{\sigma_H}{\sigma_H^{(r)}} \\
0 & 2p_{O_2}^{(r)} & 0 & p_O^{(r)} & p_{H_2O}^{(r)} & p_{OH}^{(r)} & -(A\sigma_O)^{(r)} & (A\sigma_O)^{(r)} \ln \dfrac{\sigma_O}{\sigma_O^{(r)}} \\
p_{H_2}^{(r)} & p_{O_2}^{(r)} & p_H^{(r)} & p_O^{(r)} & p_{H_2O}^{(r)} & p_{OH}^{(r)} & 0 & P^{(r)} \ln \dfrac{P}{P^{(r)}}
\end{bmatrix}
$$

$$\text{(4.75)}$$

$$
\begin{bmatrix}
-\alpha_1 \\
\cdots \\
U_K
\end{bmatrix}
=
\begin{bmatrix}
-2 & +2 & 0 & 0 \\
+2 & -4 & 0 & 0 \\
-1 & +1 & 0 & 0 \\
+1 & -2 & 0 & 0 \\
1 & 0 & 0 & 0 \\
0 & 1 & 0 & 0 \\
0 & 0 & 1 & 0 \\
0 & 0 & 0 & 1
\end{bmatrix}
$$

$$\text{(4.76)}$$

From Eq. (4.71) we write the auxiliary matrix of the augmented matrix

$$
[\alpha_4] = [\alpha_2 \vdots \alpha_3]\begin{bmatrix} -\alpha_1 \\ \overline{U_K} \end{bmatrix}
$$

$[\alpha_4] =$

$\Delta \ln p_{H_2O}^{(r)}$	$\Delta \ln p_{OH}^{(r)}$	$\Delta \ln (A)^{(r)}$	Constant
$-4p_{H_2}^{(r)} - p_H^{(r)} + 2p_{H_2O}^{(r)}$	$+4p_{H_2}^{(r)} + p_H^{(r)} + p_{OH}^{(r)}$	$-A^{(r)}\sigma_H^{(r)}$	$A^{(r)}\sigma_H^{(r)} \ln \dfrac{\sigma_H}{\sigma_H^{(r)}}$
$4p_{O_2}^{(r)} + p_O^{(r)} + p_{H_2O}^{(r)}$	$-8p_{O_2}^{(r)} - 2p_O^{(r)} + p_{OH}^{(r)}$	$-A^{(r)}\sigma_O^{(r)}$	$A^{(r)}\sigma_O^{(r)} \ln \dfrac{\sigma_O}{\sigma_O^{(r)}}$
$-2p_{H_2}^{(r)} + 2p_{O_2}^{(r)}$ $- p_H^{(r)} + p_O^{(r)} + p_{H_2O}^{(r)}$	$2p_{H_2}^{(r)} - 4p_{O_2}^{(r)} + p_H^{(r)}$ $- 2p_O^{(r)} + p_{OH}^{(r)}$	0	$P^{(r)} \ln \dfrac{P}{P^{(r)}}$

$$\text{(4.77)}$$

The matrix in Eq. (4.77) is solved for the corrections $\Delta \ln p_{H_2O}^{(r)}$, $\Delta \ln p_{OH}^{(r)}$, and $\Delta \ln (A)^{(r)}$. The new values of the components and (A) are obtained for the $(r + 1)$th approximation from relations for the rth approximation

$$\ln p_{H_2O}^{(r+1)} = \ln p_{H_2O}^{(r)} + \Delta \ln p_{H_2O}^{(r)}$$

$$\ln p_{OH}^{(r+1)} = \ln p_{OH}^{(r)} + \Delta \ln p_{OH}^{(r)} \tag{4.78}$$

$$\ln (A)^{(r+1)} = \ln (A)^{(r)} + \Delta \ln (A)^{(r)}$$

It is required that the equilibrium relations hold at each stage of the iteration. Therefore, Eq. (4.60) is used to compute the composition of the $(s - c)$ dependent constituents from the composition of the c independent species [Eq. (4.78)]. Methods of preventing divergence of this matrix in Eq. (4.77) have been described elsewhere [15] and consequently will not be repeated here.

[15] G. S. Bahn and E. E. Zukoski, *Kinetic, Equilibria and Performance of High Temperature Systems* (Washington, D.C.: Butterworth Inc., 1960).

The method described in this section for computing composition of a gas-phase system in equilibrium at constant temperature and pressure has the advantage that by proper choice of major components based on the stoichiometry of the problem, divergence can be prevented in almost all cases.

If there are solids or liquids in the system the equilibrium constants [Eq. (4.18)] are written for the reactions in Eq. (4.41) with the fugacity of the condensed phases assumed unity. We have

$$-\sum_{j=1}^{c} v_{qj} \ln p_j = \ln (K_p)_q, \qquad q = 1, 2, \ldots, p \qquad (4.79)$$

where p represents the number of condensed phases. The equations (4.60), (4.79), (4.51), and (4.52) are expanded in a Taylor's series. The resulting equations for the rth approximation are

$$\Delta \ln p_i^{(r)} - \sum_{j=1}^{c} v_{ij} \Delta \ln p_j^{(r)} = 0, \qquad i = c + 1, c + 2, \ldots, (s - p) \qquad (4.80)$$

$$-\sum_{j=1}^{c} v_{qj} \Delta \ln p_j^{(r)} = 0, \qquad q = s - p + 1, s - p + 2, \ldots, s \qquad (4.81)$$

$$\sum_{i=1}^{s-p} \bar{a}_{ki} p_i^{(r)} \Delta \ln p_i^{(r)} + (A) \sum_{q=s-p+1}^{s} \bar{a}_{kq} n_q^{(r)} \Delta \ln An_q^{(r)} - (A)^{(r)} \sigma_k^{(r)} \Delta \ln (A)^{(r)}$$
$$= (A)^{(r)} \sigma_k^{(r)} \ln \frac{\sigma_k}{\sigma_k^{(r)}}, \qquad k = 1, 2, \ldots, m \qquad (4.82)$$

$$\sum_{i=1}^{s-p} p_i^{(r)} \Delta \ln p_i^{(r)} = P^{(r)} \ln \frac{P}{P^{(r)}} \qquad (4.83)$$

Equations (4.80) through (4.83) are used to construct the Crout auxiliary matrix. The order of the columns in this matrix is written

    (1) $\Delta \ln p_i$ of the $s - c - p$ gaseous species
    (2) $\Delta \ln p_i$ of the c gaseous components chosen as major
    (3) $\Delta \ln n_i A$ of the condensed species   (4.84)
    (4) $\Delta \ln A$
    (5) Constant terms of the equations

The order of rows in the matrix is

    (1) Equilibrium equations in the same order as the $s - c - p$ gaseous species
    (2) Mass balance equations   (4.85)
    (3) Equilibrium equations for the condensed phases
    (4) Total pressure equation

4.5. CALCULATION OF EQUILIBRIUM COMPOSITION USING MINIMIZATION OF FREE ENERGY APPROACH

The method just discussed is called the *equilibrium-constant approach* and uses the Newton-Raphson method to expand each of the unknown functions in a truncated Taylor series about the estimates of the unknowns. We will now discuss the *minimization of free energy method* described by White, Johnson, and Dantzig[16] for computing chemical equilibrium in complex mixtures.

This approach is different from the equilibrium-constant approach although it leads to the same set of fundamental relationships. The free energy method makes no distinction between major and minor components, as it considers the free energy of each material on the same basis. The solution is obtained by minimization of the total chemical potential subject to mass balance constraint. In the White, Johnson, and Dantzig paper[16] two methods have been employed to obtain a numerical solution. One method uses a steepest-descent technique applied to a quadratic fit; the other makes use of linear programming. The linear programming method is not recommended, as it requires a great deal of machine time to solve large linear systems. The method of steepest descent described should offer little difficulty for gaseous systems but should not prove tractable for condensed phases present in trace amounts. In general, the equilibrium-constant approach works quite well for gaseous systems and gases in the presence of a single condensed phase. With more than one condensed phase, proper introduction of the most probable phase at each stage of the iterative technique should eliminate most divergent problems, if not all.[17] The method presented by White, Johnson, and Dantzig[16] was for gaseous systems. An extension of their method to multiphase systems is developed here using their nomenclature.

4.5.1. Formulation of method

The free energy of a mixture containing n gaseous species, m elements, and p condensed species can be expressed as

$$F(X) = \sum_{i=1}^{n} f_i^q + \sum_{j=1}^{p} f_j^c \qquad (4.86)$$

where

$X = (X_1^q, X_2^q, \ldots, X_n^q, X_1^c, X_2^c, \ldots, X_p^c)$, the set of mole numbers

$$f_i^q = X_i^q \left[C_i^q + \ln\left(\frac{X_i^q}{\bar{X}}\right) \right]$$

$$C_i^q = \left(\frac{F_T^0}{RT}\right)_i^g + \ln P \qquad (4.87)$$

$$f_j^c = X_j^c \left(\frac{F_T^0}{RT}\right)_j^c$$

[16] W. B. White, S. M. Johnson, and G. B. Dantzig, *J. Chem. Phys.*, **28** (1958), 751.

[17] R. L. Wilkins, "Note on the Linearization Method for Computing Chemical Equilibrium in Complex Systems," in *Kinetic, Equilibria and Performance of High Temperature Systems*, eds. G. S. Bahn and E. E. Zukoski (Washington, D.C.: Butterworth Inc., 1960).

P = the total pressure in atmospheres, superscript g and c represent gaseous and condensed constituents, respectively, and

$$\bar{X} = \sum_{i=1}^{n} X_i^g \tag{4.88}$$

The determination of the equilibrium composition is equivalent to finding the nonnegative set of values X_i^g and X_j^c which minimizes

$$F(X) = \sum_{i=1}^{n} f_i^g + \sum_{j=1}^{p} f_j^c \tag{4.89}$$

and satisfies the mass balance constraint

$$\sum_{i=1}^{n} a_{ik}X_i^g + \sum_{j=1}^{p} a_{jk}X_j^c = b_k, \qquad k = 1, 2, \ldots, m \tag{4.90}$$

where there are m different types of atoms, the a_{ik} and a_{jk} are formula numbers indicating the numbers of atoms of element k of species g or c respectively, and b_k is the total number of atomic weights of element k originally present in the mixture. We consider the usual cases involving many constituents in which the rank of the constituent matrix is equal to m.

4.5.2. The method of steepest descent

Let Y represent the set of positive mole values ($Y_1^g, Y_2^g, \ldots, Y_n^g, Y_1^c, Y_2^c, \ldots, Y_p^c$) which satisfy the mass balance equation (4.90). The free energy of the mixture is expressed by

$$F(Y) = \sum_{i=1}^{n} f_i^g(Y) + \sum_{j=1}^{p} f_j^c(Y) \tag{4.91}$$

where

$$\bar{Y} = \sum_{i=1}^{n} Y_i^g \tag{4.92}$$

Let

$$\begin{aligned}
\Delta_j^c &= X_j^c - Y_j^c \\
\Delta_i^g &= X_i^g - Y_i^g \\
\bar{\Delta} &= \bar{X} - \bar{Y}
\end{aligned} \tag{4.93}$$

A Taylor's expansion of $F(X)$ about Y is possible since $Y_i > 0$ and gives $Q(X)$, the quadratic approximation to $F(X)$, as follows:

$$\begin{aligned}
Q(X) = F(Y) &+ \sum_{i=1}^{n} \frac{\partial F}{\partial X_i^g}\bigg|_{X=Y} \Delta_i^g + \sum_{j=1}^{p} \frac{\partial F}{\partial X_j^c}\bigg|_{X=Y} \Delta_j^c \\
&+ \frac{1}{2} \sum_{i=1}^{n} \sum_{l=1}^{n} \frac{\partial^2 F}{\partial X_i^g \partial X_l^g}\bigg|_{X=Y} \Delta_i^g \Delta_l^g \\
&+ \frac{1}{2} \sum_{i=1}^{n} \sum_{j=1}^{p} \frac{\partial^2 F}{\partial X_i^g \partial X_j^c}\bigg|_{X=Y} \Delta_i^g \Delta_j^c \\
&+ \frac{1}{2} \sum_{j=1}^{p} \sum_{\sigma=1}^{p} \frac{\partial^2 F}{\partial X_j^c \partial X_\sigma^c}\bigg|_{X=Y} \Delta_j^c \Delta_\sigma^c
\end{aligned} \tag{4.94}$$

From Eq. (4.86) we have

$$\frac{\partial F}{\partial X_i^q} = C_i^q + \ln\left(\frac{X_i^q}{\overline{X}}\right) \tag{4.95}$$

$$\frac{\partial F}{\partial X_j^c} = \left(\frac{F_T^0}{RT}\right)_j^c \tag{4.96}$$

$$\frac{\partial^2 F}{\partial X_i^q \, \partial X_l^q} = \frac{1}{X_i^q} - \frac{1}{\overline{X}} \qquad \text{if } i = l \tag{4.97}$$

$$\frac{\partial^2 F}{\partial X_i^q \, \partial X_l^q} = -\frac{1}{\overline{X}} \qquad \text{if } i \neq l \tag{4.98}$$

$$\frac{\partial^2 F}{\partial X_i^q \, \partial X_j^c} = \frac{\partial^2 F}{\partial X_j^c \, \partial X_\sigma^c} = 0 \tag{4.99}$$

Substitution of the partial derivatives in Eqs. (4.96) through (4.99) into Eq. (4.94) gives

$$Q(X) = F(Y) + \sum_{i=1}^{n}\left(C_i^q + \ln\frac{Y_i^q}{\overline{Y}}\right)\Delta_i^q + \sum_{j=1}^{p}\left(\frac{F_T^0}{RT}\right)_j^c \Delta_j^c$$
$$+ \frac{1}{2}\sum_{i=1}^{n} y_i^q \left(\frac{\Delta_i^q}{Y_i^q} - \frac{\overline{\Delta}}{\overline{Y}}\right)^2 \tag{4.100}$$

from which it follows that the second partial derivatives of both $F(X)$ and $Q(X)$ are nonnegative and hence both functions are convex. To find the next approximation to the desired solution we minimize $Q(X)$ subject to Eq. (4.90) and restrict X_i^q and X_j^c to positive values. Let

$$G(X) = Q(X) + \sum_{k=1}^{m} \Pi_k\left(-\sum_{i=1}^{n} a_{ik}X_i^q - \sum_{j=1}^{p} a_{jk}X_j^c + b_k\right) \tag{4.101}$$

where Π_k are Lagrange multipliers. To minimize $G(X)$ we set

$$\frac{\partial G(X)}{\partial X_i^q} = 0 \quad \text{and} \quad \frac{\partial G(X)}{\partial X_j^c} = 0$$

From Eq. (4.101) it can be shown that

$$\frac{\partial G}{\partial X_i^q} = \left[C_i^q + \ln\left(\frac{Y_i^q}{\overline{Y}}\right)\right] + \left[\frac{X_i^q}{Y_i^q} - \frac{\overline{X}}{\overline{Y}}\right] - \sum_{k=1}^{m} \Pi_k a_{ik} = 0 \tag{4.102}$$

and

$$\frac{\partial G(X)}{\partial X_j^c} = \left(\frac{F_T^0}{RT}\right)_j^c - \sum_{k=1}^{m} \Pi_k a_{jk} = 0 \tag{4.103}$$

Equations (4.88), (4.90), (4.102), and (4.103) constitute $(n + p + m + 1)$ linear equations in $(n + p)$ unknowns X_i^q and X_j^c, the m unknown multipliers

Π_k, and the total mole number $\bar{X}$. Since $Y_i^g > 0$ we may solve for X_i^g in Eq. (4.102), obtaining

$$X_i^g = Y_i^g \left(\sum_{j=1}^{m} \Pi_j a_{ij} + \frac{\bar{X}}{\bar{Y}} \right) - Y_i^g \left(C_i^g + \ln \frac{Y_i^g}{\bar{Y}} \right) \qquad (4.104)$$

or

$$X_i^g = -F_i^g(Y^g) + Y_i^g \left(\frac{\bar{X}}{\bar{Y}} \right) + \left(\sum_{k=1}^{m} \Pi_k a_{ik} \right) Y_i^g \qquad (4.105)$$

where

$$F_i^g(Y^g) = Y_i^g \left(C_i^g + \ln \frac{Y_i^g}{\bar{Y}} \right) \quad \text{and} \quad Y^g = (Y_1^g, Y_2^g, \ldots, Y_n^g) \qquad (4.106)$$

Summing over i in Eq. (4.104) gives

$$\sum_{i=1}^{n} F_i^g(Y^g) = \sum_{k=1}^{m} \Pi_k \sum_{i=1}^{n} a_{ik} Y_i^g \qquad (4.107)$$

From $\partial G/\partial X_j^c$ in Eq. (4.103) we get an equation for each condensed product which does not involve any terms corresponding to the free energy of mixing or the effect of pressure. If $u + 1 = \bar{X}/\bar{Y}$, Eq. (4.105) becomes

$$X_i^g = -F_i^g(Y^g) + Y_i^g(u + 1) + \left(\sum_{k=1}^{m} \Pi_k a_{ik} \right) Y_i^g \qquad (4.108)$$

There is no similar equation for X_j^c, which must be obtained through the material balance relationships. If we denote the constants

$$r_{il} = r_{lk} = \sum_{i=1}^{n} (a_{ik} a_{il}) Y_i^g \qquad (i, l = 1, \ldots, m) \qquad (4.109)$$

then the substitution of Eq. (4.108) in the material balance equation (4.90) yields

$$\sum_{l=1}^{m} r_{kl} \Pi_k + (u + 1) \sum_{i=1}^{n} a_{ik} Y_i^g + \sum_{j=1}^{p} a_{jk} x_j^c$$

$$= b_k + \sum_{i=1}^{n} a_{ik} F_i^g(Y^g) \qquad (k = 1, 2, \ldots, m) \qquad (4.110)$$

The m equations (4.110) and (4.103) for each condensed product, and Eq. (4.107) are solved simultaneously to give the $\Pi_k(u + 1)$, and the X_j^c. It follows that the number of equations to be solved at each point of the iteration is $(m + 1)$ plus the number of condensed products. The general matrix equation becomes:

$$
\begin{bmatrix}
r_{11} & r_{12} & r_{1m} & \sum\limits_{i=1}^{n} a_{i1} Y_i^g & a_{11} & \cdots \\
r_{21} & r_{22} & r_{2m} & \sum\limits_{i=1}^{n} a_{i2} Y_i^g & a_{12} & \cdots \\
\cdot & \cdot & \cdot & \cdot & \cdot & \cdots \\
\cdot & \cdot & \cdot & \cdot & \cdot & \cdots \\
\cdot & \cdot & \cdot & \cdot & \cdot & \cdots \\
r_{m1} & r_{m2} & r_{mm} & \sum\limits_{i=1}^{n} a_{im} Y_i^g & a_{1m} & \cdots \\
\sum\limits_{i=1}^{n} a_{i1} Y_i^g & \sum\limits_{i=1}^{n} a_{i2} Y_i^g \cdots & \sum\limits_{i=1}^{n} a_{im} Y_i^g & 0 & 0 & \cdots \\
a_{11} & a_{12} & \cdots a_{1m} & 0 & 0 & \cdots \\
\cdot & \cdot & \cdot & \cdot & \cdot \\
\cdot & \cdot & \cdot & \cdot & \cdot \\
\cdot & \cdot & \cdot & \cdot & \cdot \\
a_{p1} & a_{p2} & a_{pm} & 0 & 0
\end{bmatrix}
\begin{bmatrix}
\Pi_1 \\ \cdot \\ \cdot \\ \cdot \\ \cdot \\ \Pi_m \\ u+1 \\ x_1^c \\ \cdot \\ \cdot \\ \cdot \\ X_p^{(c)}
\end{bmatrix}
=
\begin{bmatrix}
b_1 + \sum\limits_{i=1}^{n} a_{i1} F_i^g \\
b_2 + \sum\limits_{i=1}^{n} a_{i2} F_i^g \\
\cdot \\
\cdot \\
\cdot \\
b_m + \sum\limits_{i=1}^{n} a_{im} F_i^g \\
\sum\limits_{i=1}^{n} F_i^g \\
\left(\dfrac{F_T^0}{RT} \right)_1^c \\
\cdot \\
\cdot \\
\cdot \\
\left(\dfrac{F_T^0}{RT} \right)_p^c
\end{bmatrix}
\tag{4.111}
$$

4.5.3. Computation method

Positive values of $(Y_1^g, Y_2^g, \ldots, Y_n^g, Y_1^c, \ldots, Y_p^c)$ are selected such that the mass balance equations (4.90) are satisfied. The function of $F_i^g(Y^g)$ is determined by Eq. (4.106) and r_{kl} by Eq. (4.109). Next solve the system of Eqs. (4.110), (4.107), and (4.103) for $\Pi_1, \ldots, \Pi_m, (u + 1), X_1^c, \ldots, X_p^c$. Note that m represents the number of different types of atoms present in the mixture and p the number of condensed phases. It follows that the number of simultaneous linear equations to be solved is usually a much smaller number than the possible molecular constituents. The improved values for X_i^g follow from Eq. (4.105). These values, if all positive, could be used as a starting point for the next computation cycle. However, a short additional step eliminates the possibility of negative X_i^g's and X_j^c's.

Let $\Delta_i = X_i - Y_i$ be direction numbers indicating the preferred direction of descent. The distance traveled will be limited to fractional amounts $\lambda_i \Delta_i$ using the smallest value of λ_i satisfying the conditions:

Step 1. All mole numbers are positive.

Step 2. The directional derivative $dF/d\lambda$ does not become positive. $F(\lambda)$ is a convex function of λ and the derivative is easily computed, since

$$
\frac{dF(\lambda)}{d\lambda} = \sum_{i}^{n} \Delta_i^g \left[C_i^g + \ln \frac{Y_i^g + \lambda \Delta_i^g}{\overline{Y} + \lambda \overline{\Delta}} \right] + \sum_{j=1}^{p} \left(\frac{F_T^0}{RT} \right)_j^c \Delta_j^c
\tag{4.112}
$$

In general, step 2 is not required, as a value of λ can be obtained as follows. Compute λ_i for all components with negative X_i by the relation

$$
\lambda_i = -\frac{Y_i}{\Delta_i}
\tag{4.113}
$$

and choose the smallest value of

$$\lambda' = \min (\lambda_i) \qquad (i = 1, 2, \ldots, n, \ldots, p) \tag{4.114}$$

and compute

$$Y_i^{(r+1)} = Y_i^{(r)} + [\lambda' \Delta_i]^{(r)} \tag{4.115}$$

where (r) represents the rth approximation. Test the values computed in Eq. (4.115) to find the Y_i that will be exactly zero, and replace the Y_i with the value from gaseous trace component relations given by White, Johnson, and Dantzig.[16] We have

$$Y_i^{(r+1)} = (\bar{Y})^{(r+1)} \exp \left[-C_i^g + \sum_{k=1}^{m} \Pi_k a_{ik} \right] \tag{4.116}$$

where

$$(\bar{Y})^{(r+1)} = (\bar{Y})^{(r)} [\lambda'(u + 1) + 1 - \lambda'] \tag{4.117}$$

Every other gaseous "trace" component should be recomputed at the same time, since the values of the Π_k are converging to the correct value. This method cannot be applied to condensed phases present in trace amounts.

4.6. COMPARISON OF TWO METHODS

In a recent note by Brinkley[18] it was shown that the working equations obtained by White et al.[16] by a variational technique can be derived from ordinary conditions for equilibrium. The important conclusion of this result is that the derivation of the working equations based on a variational technique is identical to those based on equilibrium conditions and, consequently, the former has no inherent superiority because its derivation is based on a variational method. In the equilibrium-constant method the equilibrium equations are derived by minimization of the free energy and the resulting equilibrium relations were linearized. The variational technique derives linear relations by minimization of a quadratic approximation to the free energy. These results are, therefore, of the same degree, since it is well known that the free energy is of degree unity in the mole numbers, and the partial molal free energy or the chemical potential is of degree zero in the mole numbers. It follows that the variational technique is another procedure for linearizing the equilibrium conditions. The two methods differ only in the manner in which terms are collected in linear truncation of the expansion of the equilibrium conditions, and consequently the efficiency of the free energy method must be based on a study of higher-order terms which are neglected in the linear approximation used in the equilibrium-constant approach, and the variables used for the expansion in the free energy method.

[18] S. R. Brinkley, "Discussion," in *Kinetic, Equilibria and Performance of High Temperature Systems*, ed. G. S. Bahn and E. E. Zukoski (Washington, D.C.: Butterworth Inc., 1960), p. 73.

5

PERFORMANCE OF

CHEMICAL PROPELLANTS

FOR ROCKET ENGINES

5.1. INTRODUCTION

The effectiveness of a chemical propellant[1] depends upon the total energy released in burning the reactants of the propellant to combustion products. It is shown in standard texts on rocket propulsion[2] that for high performance of a given propellant it is desirable to have a maximum value of the ratio of the adiabatic flame temperature to the molecular weight of the product mixture.[3] This ratio can be made large by having a high adiabatic flame temperature or a low molecular weight of the product mixture, or both. Consequently, propellants whose reactants have high endothermic heats of formation and whose product species have high exothermic heats of formation are expected to have high adiabatic flame temperatures, and possibly high performance depending upon the molecular weight of the product mixture. If the temperature is high (in excess of 2000°K), a large amount of the total

---

[1] A propellant consists usually of a fuel and an oxidizer or a mixture of both.
[2] See, for example, G. P. Sutton, *Rocket Propulsion Elements* (New York: John Wiley & Sons, Inc., 1956).
[3] The performance depends also on the parameter $\gamma = C_P/C_V$ of the mixture but only to a small extent.

energy released in burning the reactants of the propellant to products is consumed in dissociating molecular species. Dissociation, therefore, reduces the amount of energy available for conversion into kinetic energy during adiabatic[4] isentropic[4] flow through a nozzle and limits the maximum attainable adiabatic flame temperature and exit velocity[5] of product species. The dissociation process, generally, increases the specific volume[6] of the combustion mixture by lowering the molecular weight of product species which are formed. Since the temperature of the gas decreases when the product species are expanded adiabatically and isentropically through a nozzle, some of the species which were dissociated are formed in the nozzle by *recombination* of atomic or molecular species. Recombination causes a lowering of the exhaust temperature.

These considerations led propellant specialists to consider three types of flow processes in rocket nozzles. One type of flow, called *frozen flow*, assumes the reaction to take place so slowly during the expansion process that the product species do not reach a state of thermodynamic equilibrium but remain in the same relative proportions at each exit pressure as in the combustion chamber, where a state of thermodynamic equilibrium is established. The second type of flow is called *equilibrium flow* or *shifting flow* and assumes that the product species are in thermodynamic equilibrium at each exit pressure. The third type of flow, called *nonequilibrium flow*, assumes that the product species are in a nonequilibrium state and requires the application of finite reaction rates to describe chemical reactions which occur in rocket nozzles. So little valid information is available on reaction rates even for simple systems that it seems unlikely that much valid information will be found which will permit a description of nonequilibrium flow process in rocket nozzles. We shall, therefore, restrict our discussion to the first two types of flow processes. The performance values are lower for the *frozen flow* assumption than for the *equilibrium flow* assumption, since the former does not permit chemical reactions to take place during the expansion process.

In this book we have limited our discussion of performance of rocket systems to the first fifteen elements in the periodic table. These elements have a lower energy content per gram as fuels. Both the low molecular weight and the heat content per gram of product species of these lightweight elements make them desirable. From Table 3.7 it can be seen that the oxides of lithium, aluminum, and boron form solid stable oxides which have extremely high energy release. The formation of these solid species presents many problems

---

[4] Any process in which heat is not lost is called *adiabatic*. Any adiabatic and reversible process in which $\Delta S = 0$, where S is the entropy of the system, is an *isentropic process*.

[5] The *exit velocity* is the velocity at which product species are ejected at the nozzle exit of the rocket.

[6] The *specific volume* is the reciprocal of the density of the product mixture.

in design and operation of equipment. For example, alumina and boron trioxide are excellent heat fluxes and both give high heat rejection and lead to erosion of metal walls. The formation of condensed particles in the nozzle can lead to lower performance because such particles may have drag and turbulence effects on the flow. The latter phenomenon is not well understood and will not concern us in this discussion. In our calculations of performance we will assume that the condensates, if present, are such small particles that irreversible effects in the flow process are negligible. When condensation occurs in the chamber or nozzle, the heat of condensation raises the adiabatic flame temperature or the exit temperature, or both, depending on whether condensation occurs in the rocket combustion chamber or in the rocket nozzle, or both. This increase in temperature due to the heat of condensation causes an increase in the gas molecular weight at either chamber or nozzle exit, or both. Consequently, the performance increase may not be as large an amount as one would expect. The heats of formation tabulated in Table 3.8 and the atomic weights listed in Table 1.1 can be used to compute the energy content per gram of product species. Combustion product species with low energy content per gram are most desirable. Most high-energy propellants contain a large amount of hydrogen because of its low molecular weight. We find, therefore, that maximum performance occurs usually at fuel-rich stoichiometries.

In this chapter we will discuss two methods of computing rocket performance. The first method uses exact thermodynamic relations to describe the flow process in a nozzle, whereas the second method uses what some propellant scientists call an *average gamma*. The latter is an approximate technique, and when used to compute performance it can lead to large discrepancies, especially when the *equilibrium flow* assumption is invoked. The discrepancy between the two methods can be in excess of 2 per cent of specific impulse values for some propellant systems even when the *frozen flow* assumption is used.

In Sec. 5.17 we give a review of performance of propellant systems containing hydrogen, oxygen, carbon, nitrogen, fluorine, and chlorine and of typical results obtained with metallized propellants such as lithium, boron, beryllium, aluminum, and magnesium.

5.2. CALCULATION OF ADIABATIC FLAME TEMPERATURES AND EQUILIBRIUM COMPOSITIONS

The first step in computing rocket performance is the determination of the adiabatic flame temperature, which is pressure dependent. In Chap. 4 we described two methods of computing equilibrium properties for a system at constant temperature and pressure. Either method can be used to compute adiabatic flame temperatures by the trial and error procedure which we will discuss first. An iterative procedure will be described also for computing adiabatic flame temperatures using the *equilibrium-constant approach*.

It should be clear that for constant pressure, temperature, and stoichiometry of reactants there are many systems that have identical properties for a specified set of combustion product species chosen *a priori*. For example, thermodynamic properties of product species of the systems

$$C_2H_4 + O_2$$

$$2\,CH_2 + O_2$$

$$2\,C_{(s)} + 2\,H_2 + O_2$$

are identical at every fixed temperature and pressure. The adiabatic flame temperature, heat release, or available work of these three systems are all different because each system has a different amount of initial energy. To make the required distinction between different systems we must introduce, therefore, the *conservation of energy equation* to the system of equations used to describe a constant temperature-pressure process in Chap. 4.

The available energy of the propellant

$$h_0 = \sum_{j=1}^{r} n_j (H_T^0)_j \qquad (5.1)$$

where h_0 is the total enthalpy at the initial conditions of the reactants, n_j is the number of moles per gram of propellant of the jth reactant, $(H_T^0)_j$ is the molar enthalpy of the jth reactant at its initial conditions, and r is the number of reactants. The molar enthalpy is given by the expression

$$H_T^0 = \int_0^T C_p \, dT + H_0^0 \qquad (5.2)$$

where H_0^0 is the chemical energy of a substance at a temperature of $0°K$. The procedure for computing the zero-point energy H_0^0 is described in Sec. 5.3.

The total enthalpy h of the s products of reaction per gram of propellant at temperature T is given by the relation

$$h = \sum_{i=1}^{s} \frac{p_i (H_T^0)_i}{A} \qquad (5.3)$$

where p_i is the partial pressure of the ith combustion product and $(H_T^0)_i$ is the molar enthalpy of the ith combustion product. The heat of reaction for any process carried out at constant pressure is equal to the enthalpy change corresponding to the reaction, i.e.,

$$\Delta H_T = h - h_0 \qquad (5.4)$$

The *adiabatic flame temperature* T_c is defined by the condition that

$$\Delta H_T = 0 \qquad (5.5)$$

from which the adiabatic flame temperature T_c is determined by the relation

$$h = h_0 \qquad (5.6)$$

We see, therefore, for adiabatic combustion that $h = h_0$ when the correct temperature and composition of the product species are found. If heat, q, were lost, i.e., $q \neq 0$, in the combustion process as is the case in nonadiabatic combustion, then the total enthalpy h_0 at the initial conditions would be reduced by the amount of heat lost. The *nonadiabatic flame temperature* would be calculated by the relation

$$h_0' = h_0 - q \qquad (5.7)$$

It is a common practice in the calculation of adiabatic flame temperatures to avoid the problem of computing zero-point energies by defining

$$h_0 = \sum_{j=1}^{r} n_j (\Delta H_f^0)_j \qquad (5.8)$$

where $(\Delta H_f^0)_j$ is the heat of formation of the jth reactant at its initial conditions, n_j is the number of moles per gram of propellant of the jth reactant, and h_0 is the total enthalpy at the initial conditions of the reactants. The total enthalpy h of the s products of reaction per gram of propellant at temperature T is given by the relation

$$h = \sum_{i=1}^{s} n_i \left[(\Delta H_f^0)_i + \int_{T_0}^{T} (c_p^0)_i \, dT \right] \qquad (5.9)$$

where T_0 is initial temperature of the ith combustion product. If we assume that the initial reactants are at room temperature, then $T_0 = 298.15°K$, and

$$h = \sum_{i=1}^{s} n_i \left[(\Delta H_f^0)_i + \int_{298.15}^{T} (C_p^0)_i \, dT \right] \qquad (5.10)$$

where $(\Delta H_f^0)_i$ is the heat of formation of the ith combustion species at $298.15°K$ and $\int_{298.15}^{T} (c_p^0)_i \, dT$ is the molar enthalpy change of the ith combustion species between $298.15°K$ and temperature T. The latter is called the *sensible enthalpy* and is represented by the equation

$$H_T^0 - H_{298.15} = \int_{298.15}^{T} (C_p^0) \, dT \qquad (5.11)$$

Combining Eqs. (5.8) and (5.10) we find that the adiabatic flame temperature T_c is determined by the relation that

$$\sum_{i=1}^{s} n_i (\Delta H_f^0)_i - \sum_{j=1}^{r} n_j (\Delta H_f^0)_j = - \sum_{i=1}^{s} n_i (H_T^0 - H_{298.15})_i \qquad (5.12)$$

The negative of the enthalpy change for the reaction in going from $298.15°K$

to the combustion temperature T_c is known as the *available heat*, Q. From Eq. (5.12),

$$Q = -\left[\sum_{i=1}^{s} n_i(\Delta H_f^0)_i - \sum_{j=1}^{r} n_j(\Delta H_f^0)_j \right] \qquad (5.13)$$

and is a function of the combustion temperature, since the composition n_i of the s product species is dependent on the combustion temperature. The available heat will be positive if the enthalpy change for the reaction is negative as is the case for combustion processes. In terms of the available heat Q one can write Eq. (5.12) as

$$Q = \sum_{i=1}^{s} n_i(H_T^0 - H_{298.15})_i \qquad (5.14)$$

or

$$Q = \sum_{i=1}^{s} n_i[(H_T^0 - H_0^0) - (H_{298.15}^0 - H_0^0)]_i \qquad (5.15)$$

where $(H_{298.15}^0 - H_0^0)$ is molar enthalpy change of species i in going from $0°K$ to 298.15 and $(H_T^0 - H_0^0)$ is the molar enthalpy change of species i in going from $0°K$ to the combustion temperature. Sensible enthalpies are tabulated in Appendices 2 through 4 for the important combustion species, free, and in combination with elements in the first three rows of the periodic table.

The typical method of computing adiabatic flame temperature is as follows:

(1) Assume a temperature $T_c = T_c'$ for the adiabatic flame temperature at specified chamber pressure.

(2) Obtain the solution to the system of equations described in Chap. 4 for a constant temperature-pressure process. Either the *equilibrium-constant approach* or the *free energy minimization method* can be used to calculate the equilibrium composition at the assumed temperature T_c'.

(3) Use the calculated composition at the assumed adiabatic flame temperature T_c' to determine Q from Eq. (5.13) or h from Eq. (5.3).

(4a) If Q is used, evaluate the right-hand side of Eq. (5.15). Q represents the heat absorbed when the combustion products are heated from 298.15° to the combustion temperature T_c. At the temperature T_c' the right-hand side of Eq. (5.15) has the value Q'.

(4b) If h is used, evaluate the right-hand side of Eq. (5.6). Since h_0 in Eq. (5.6) is not dependent on the combustion composition, it is necessary to calculate h_0 only once.

(5a) If $Q < Q'$, then the assumed T_c' is too large. If $Q > Q'$, then the assumed T_c' is too small. If $Q = Q'$, then the correct temperature $T_c = T_c'$ has been found.

(5b) If $h > h_0$, then the assumed T_c' is too large. If $h < h_0$, then the assumed T'_c is too small. If $h = h_0$, then the correct temperature $T_c = T'_c$ has been found.

(6) The assumed adiabatic flame temperature is lowered or raised according as $Q > Q'$ or $Q < Q'$ as discussed in step (5a) or $h > h_0$ or $h < h_0$ as discussed in step (5b). In either case a new temperature is assumed and steps (1) through (5) are repeated. Interpolation methods are usually used to arrive at the correct adiabatic flame temperature T_c.

5.3. CALCULATION OF ZERO-POINT ENERGY, H_0^0

It is convenient to take H_0^0 as zero for the atoms. If this procedure is adopted, negative values of H_0^0 will result for some species. Since the absolute values of enthalpy are not measurable but only the differences, one can adopt an arbitrary base for assigning absolute values to the enthalpy of various substances. The only requirement for use of this method is that a *self-consistent* set of H_0^0 values be calculated. For example, consider a chemical system consisting of species H_2, F_2, HF, H, and F. The heats of formation of H_2 and F_2 in the standard state are zero. The heat of formation of HF at $0°K$ is given by the reaction

$$\tfrac{1}{2} H_2 + \tfrac{1}{2} F_2 \longrightarrow HF, \qquad \Delta H_f^0 = -64.17 \text{ kcal/mole}$$

and ΔH_f^0 is defined as

$$(\Delta H_f^0)_{HF} = (H_0^0)_{HF} - \tfrac{1}{2}(H_0^0)_{H_2} - \tfrac{1}{2}(H_0^0)_{F_2}$$

Therefore,

$$(H_0^0)_{HF} = (\Delta H_f^0)_{HF} + \tfrac{1}{2}(H_0^0)_{H_2} + \tfrac{1}{2}(H_0^0)_{F_2} \qquad (5.16)$$

In order to compute $(H_0^0)_{HF}$ we must compute $(H_0^0)_{H_2}$ and $(H_0^0)_{F_2}$. The $(H_0^0)_{H_2}$ and $(H_0^0)_{F_2}$ are calculated from the dissociation reactions

$$H_2 \longrightarrow 2 H, \qquad D_0^0 = 103.242 \text{ kcal/mole}$$

$$F_2 \longrightarrow 2 F, \qquad D_0^0 = 36.714 \text{ kcal/mole}$$

and the heats of dissociation D_0^0 for H_2 and F_2 are defined as

$$(D_0^0)_{H_2} = 2(H_0^0)_H - (H_0^0)_{H_2}$$

$$(D_0^0)_{F_2} = 2(H_0^0)_F - (H_0^0)_{F_2}$$

Therefore,

$$(H_0^0)_{H_2} = 2(H_0^0)_H - (D_0^0)_{H_2} = -(D_0^0)_{H_2}$$

$$(H_0^0)_{F_2} = 2(H_0^0)_F - (D_0^0)_{F_2} = -(D_0^0)_{F_2} \qquad (5.17)$$

since we arbitrarily chose $H_0^0 = 0$ for the atoms H and F. Substituting the values of $(H_0^0)_{H_2}$ and $(H_0^0)_{F_2}$ in Eq. (5.17) into Eq. (5.16) we obtain

$$(H_0^0)_{HF} = (\Delta H_f^0)_{HF} - \tfrac{1}{2}(D_0^0)_{H_2} - \tfrac{1}{2}(D_0^0)_{F_2}$$

$$= -64.17 - \tfrac{1}{2}(103.242) - \tfrac{1}{2}(36.714) = -134.148 \text{ kcal/mole}$$

which is the negative of the heat of dissociation of HF.

The zero-point energies H_0^0 were chosen by Huff *et al.*[7] such that at every temperature for all species, both reactants and products, the absolute enthalpy H_T^0 would be positive. This choice is necessary to avoid the possibility of calculating the logarithm of a negative number when temperature is used as a variable in the iteration method to be discussed in Sec. 5.5.

5.4. CALCULATION OF ENTHALPIES OF REACTANTS

The reactants of the propellant are introduced in the combustion chamber in condensed (liquid or solid) phase at a known temperature which, unless otherwise specified, is either 298.15°K or the normal boiling point, whichever is lower. For example, in a liquid hydrogen-liquid fluorine engine, liquid hydrogen would be injected into the combustion chamber at its boiling point of 20.39°K and liquid fluorine at its boiling point of 85.24°K. For this example, $(H_{20.39}^0)_{H_2(l)}$ and $(H_{85.24}^0)_{F_2(l)}$ are calculated by the following expressions:

$$(H_{20.39}^0)_{H_2(l)} = (H_{20.39}^0 - H_{298.15}^0)_{H_2(g)} + (H_{298.15}^0)_{H_2(g)} + (\Delta H_v)_{H_2}$$

$$(H_{85.24}^0)_{F_2(l)} = (H_{85.24}^0 - H_{298.15}^0)_{F_2(g)} + (H_{298.15}^0)_{F_2(g)} + (\Delta H_v)_{F_2}$$

where

$$(H_{20.39}^0 - H_{298.15}^0)_{H_2(g)} = \int_{298.15}^{20.39} (C_p^0)_{H_2(g)} \, dT$$

and

$$(H_{85.24}^0 - H_{298.15}^0)_{F_2(g)} = \int_{298.15}^{85.24} (C_p^0)_{F_2(g)} \, dT$$

and ΔH_v is the heat of vaporization.

If the reactants are preheated to some temperature T, one must calculate the heat required to preheat each reactant from a temperature T_0 to T by the relation

$$H_T^0 - H_{T_0}^0 = \int_{T_0}^{T} (C_p^0) \, dT \tag{5.18}$$

and the total enthalpy H_T^0 is defined from Eq. (5.18) as

$$H_T^0 = (H_T^0 - H_{T_0}^0) + (H_{T_0}^0) \tag{5.19}$$

The available energy of the propellant [Eq. (5.1)] is the total enthalpy at the initial conditions of the reactants, which in this case corresponds to the reactants being at the preheated temperature.

---

[7] V. Huff, S. Gordon, and V. E. Morrell, *General Method and Thermodynamic Tables for Computation of Equilibrium Composition and Temperatures of Chemical Reactions,* National Advisory Committee for Aeronautics Report 1037 (1951).

5.5. CALCULATION OF TEMPERATURE FOR A CONSTANT-PRESSURE PROCESS

If the *equilibrium-constant approach* is used, one can extend the method described in Chap. 4 to calculate composition and temperature for a constant-pressure process. The equations defining the constant-pressure combustion are the equilibrium relations, conservation of atomic species, conservation of pressure, and conservation of energy. The total enthalpy h in Eq. (5.3) is expanded in a Taylor's series and the results expressed in logarithm form. For a system consisting of only gaseous species we have

$$\sum_{i=1}^{s} p_i (H_T^0)_i \, \Delta \ln p_i = Ah \ln \left(\frac{h_0}{h} \right) \tag{5.20}$$

If there are solids or liquids in the system, h in Eq. (5.3) becomes, upon expansion in a Taylor's series,

$$\sum_{i=1}^{s-p} (H_T^0)_i \, p_i \, \Delta \ln p_i + A \sum_{q=s-p+1}^{s} n_q (H_T^0)_q \, \Delta \ln (An_q) = Ah \ln \left(\frac{h_0}{h} \right) \tag{5.21}$$

The resulting equations for a constant-pressure process are obtained from Eqs. (4.61) through (4.63) and Eq. (5.20) for a system with only gaseous combustion products. If there are condensed species one uses Eqs. (4.80) through (4.83) and Eq. (5.21). In the latter case the zero on the left-hand side of both Eqs. (4.80) and (4.81) is replaced by $(\Delta H/RT)_i \, \Delta \ln T$, as was done in Eq. (4.61), since the process is not a constant-temperature process. The system of equations is used to construct the Crout auxiliary matrix described in Chap. 4. The order of the columns in this matrix is written:

(1) $\Delta \ln p_i$ of the $s - c - p$ gaseous species
(2) $\Delta \ln p_i$ of the c gaseous components chosen as major
(3) $\Delta \ln (An_q)$ of the p condensed species
(4) $\Delta \ln (A)$
(5) Constant terms of the equation

The order of rows in the matrix is:

(1) Equilibrium equations in the same order as the $s - c - p$ gaseous species
(2) m mass balance equations
(3) Equilibrium equations for the p condensed species
(4) Total enthalpy equation
(5) Total pressure equation

The resulting matrix is solved by the Crout method as described in Chap. 4. The equilibrium equations are quite sensitive to changes in temperature. Consequently the iteration method used must have a rigid control on temperature changes permitted in the matrix routine. The *equilibrium-constant approach* requires that the total enthalpies h_0 and h be positive at all temperatures. If this choice is made [see Eqs. (5.20) and (5.21)] one avoids the possibility of divergence due to the evaluation of logarithms of negative numbers.

5.6. CALCULATION OF ISENTROPIC EXPANSION ASSUMING FROZEN AND SHIFTING FLOW

After the adiabatic flame temperature and composition have been determined, one computes the entropy of combustion from the relation

$$S_c = \left[\sum_{i=1}^{s} n_i(S_T^0)_i - \frac{R}{M_g P} \sum_{i=1}^{s-p} p_i \ln p_i \right]_c \qquad (5.22)$$

where M_g is the molecular weight of the gas mixture. In case condensed products are present in the chamber, the assumption is made that the volume of the condensed phase is negligible compared to the gas volume. The over-all average molecular weight M is then the total weight of gaseous and condensed products divided by the moles of gaseous products formed.

The accuracy of this assumption may be illustrated by considering a typical case. The combustion products of liquid oxygen and RP-1 at a temperature of 3660°K have a molecular weight of 23.3 and a density of 5.3×10^{-3} g per cc. Typical condensed phases such as carbon (graphite) or light metal oxides which may be formed will generally have densities of 8 g per cc or greater. The density of the condensed phase will therefore be about 400 times that of the gas. About 80 weight per cent solid present would be required to occupy even one per cent of the volume. Since the gas density chosen in this example is near the upper limit encountered in current rocket practice, the neglect of condensed-phase volume is sufficiently accurate for all practical purposes.

The combustion species are assumed to expand isentropically and adiabatically to an assigned pressure P_e. Since the expansion process is assumed isentropic, the total entropy at the nozzle exit pressure P_e must equal the total entropy in the combustion chamber, and an equation similar to Eq. (5.22) can be written for exit conditions.[8]

$$S_e = \left[\sum_{i=1}^{s} n_i(S_T^0)_i - \frac{R}{M_g P} \sum_{i=1}^{s-p} p_i \ln p_i \right]_e \qquad (5.23)$$

Once the exit pressure has been specified, then by a trial and error procedure one can compute the exit temperature corresponding to P_e and S_c. The procedure is as follows for *frozen flow*:

(1) The combustion species are composed at each exit-nozzle pressure in the same relative proportions as they were in the combustion chamber. The mole fraction of each species at each exit plane is identical to its mole fraction

---

[8] The subscripts c and e stand for chamber and exit conditions, respectively.

in the combustion chamber. We can express Eqs. (5.22) and (5.23) in mole fractions X_i as

$$S_c = \left[\frac{\sum\limits_{i=1}^{s} X_i (S_T^0)_i}{\left(1 - \sum\limits_{q=1}^{p} X_q\right) M_g} - \frac{R}{M_g} \sum\limits_{i=1}^{s-p} X_i \ln X_i - \frac{R}{M_g} \ln P \right]_c \qquad (5.24)$$

$$S_e = \left[\frac{\sum\limits_{i=1}^{s} X_i (S_T^0)_i}{\left(1 - \sum\limits_{q=1}^{p} X_q\right) M_g} - \frac{R}{M_g} \sum\limits_{i=1}^{s-p} X_i \ln X_i - \frac{R}{M_g} \ln P \right]_e \qquad (5.25)$$

(2) The entropy of combustion S_c is computed from Eq. (5.22) or Eq. (5.24). The second and third terms in Eq. (5.25) are computed only once at the specified exit pressure. An exit temperature T_e' is assumed and the first term in Eq. (5.25) is computed. The exit entropy is the difference between the first term computed in Eq. (5.25) and sum of the second and third terms in Eq. (5.25).

(3) If $S_e' > S_c$, then the exit temperature T_e' assumed is too high.
If $S_e' < S_c$, then the exit temperature T_e' assumed is too low.
If $S_e' = S_c$, then $T_e' = T_e$.

(4) The exit temperature T_e' is adjusted according to the criteria stated in step (3), and steps (1) through (3) are repeated. Interpolation methods are used to arrive at the correct exit temperature.

The trial and error procedure for computing exit temperature and composition for shifting flows corresponding to an exit pressure P_e and chamber entropy S_c is as follows:

(1) An exit temperature is assumed for the assigned exit pressure P_e.

(2) The composition of the product species is computed by either the *equilibrium-constant approach* or the *minimization of the energy method* described in Chap. 4.

(3) The exit entropy S_e' is computed from Eq. (5.23).

(4) If $S_e' > S_c$, then the exit temperature T_e' assumed is too high.
If $S_e' < S_c$, then the exit temperature T_e' is too low.
If $S_e' = S_c$, then $T_e' = T_e$.

(5) The exit temperature is lowered if $S_e' > S_c$, and is raised if $S_e' < S_c$, and steps (1) through (4) are repeated. Interpolation methods are used to arrive at the correct exit temperature.

5.7. CALCULATION OF TEMPERATURE FOR A CONSTANT-ENTROPY PROCESS

If the *equilibrium-constant approach* is used, one can extend the method described in Chap. 4 to calculate composition and temperature for a *constant-entropy process.* The equations defining the constant entropy process are equilibrium relations, conservation of atomic species, conservation of pressure, and conservation of entropy. The total entropy S in Eq. (5.23) is expanded in a Taylor's series and the results expressed in logarithm form. For a system consisting of only gaseous species we have

$$AS_e \ln \frac{S_c}{S_e} = \sum_{i=1}^{s} [p_i(S_T^0)_i - Rp_i(1 + \ln p_i)] \Delta \ln p_i - AS_e \Delta \ln (A)$$

$$+ \left(\sum_{i=1}^{s} n_i(C_p^0)_i \right) \Delta \ln T \qquad (5.26)$$

If there are solids and liquids in the system, S in Eq. (5.23) becomes, upon expansion,

$$AS_e \ln \frac{S_c}{S_e} = \sum_{i=1}^{s} [n_i(S_T^0)_i - Rp_i(1 + \ln p_i)] \ln p_i - AS_e \Delta \ln A$$

$$+ \left(\sum_{i=1}^{s} n_i(C_p^0)_i \right) \Delta \ln T \qquad (5.27)$$

The resulting equations for a constant-entropy process are obtained from Eqs. (4.61) through (4.63) and Eq. (5.26) for a system with only gaseous combustion products. If there are condensed species one uses Eqs. (4.80) through (4.83) and Eq. (5.27). In the latter case the zero on the left-hand side of Eqs. (4.80) and (4.81) is replaced by $(\Delta H/RT)\Delta \ln T$ as was done in Eq. (4.61), since the process is not a constant-temperature process. Either system of equations is used to construct the Crout auxiliary matrix described in Chap. 4. The order of the columns in this matrix is written:

   (1) $\Delta \ln p_i$ of the $s - c - p$ gaseous species
   (2) $\Delta \ln p_i$ of the c gaseous components chosen as major
   (3) $\Delta \ln (An_i)$ of the p condensed species   (5.28)
   (4) $\Delta \ln (A)$
   (5) Constant terms of the equation

The order of rows in the matrix is:

   (1) Equilibrium equations in the same order as the $s - c - p$
       gaseous species
   (2) m mass balance equations
   (3) Equilibrium equations for the p condensed species   (5.29)
   (4) Total entropy equation
   (5) Total pressure equation

The resulting matrix is solved by the Crout method as described in Chap. 4. This procedure is used to compute exit temperature and composition when *equilibrium flow* is assumed for the expansion process.

In case the flow during the expansion is assumed frozen, Eq. (5.26) reduces to

$$X_T = \frac{\delta s}{C'} \tag{5.30}$$

since $\Delta \ln P_i$ and $\Delta \ln (A)$ are zero. In Eq. (5.30)

$$X_T = \Delta \ln T \tag{5.31}$$

$$\delta s = M_g P_e S_e \ln \frac{S_c}{S_e} \tag{5.32}$$

$$C' = \frac{A \sum\limits_{i=1}^{s} X_i (C_p^0)_i}{\left(1 - \sum\limits_{q=1}^{p} X_q\right) M_g} \tag{5.33}$$

The rth and $(r + 1)$th approximation to the exit-plane temperature are related by

$$\ln T_e^{(r+1)} = \ln T_e^{(r)} + X_{T_e}^{(r)} \tag{5.34}$$

This iterative method almost always converges, except for cases of discontinuities in thermodynamic data which occur at phase transitions. For frozen systems it is usually assumed that the phase, as well as the composition, should be invariant during the expansion process.

5.8. CALCULATION OF THE ISENTROPIC EXPANSION TO LOCAL SOUND VELOCITY

The velocity of sound of the product species at any point in the nozzle is defined as

$$u^2 = \left(\frac{\partial P}{\partial \rho}\right)_S \tag{5.35}$$

where ρ is the density of the mixture and subscript S represents constant-entropy conditions. The total pressure of system

$$P = \sum_{i=1}^{s-p} p_i \tag{5.36a}$$

and

$$dP = \sum_{i=1}^{s-p} dp_i \tag{5.36b}$$

The density of the mixture, assuming an ideal gas, is

$$\rho = \frac{A}{RT} \tag{5.37}$$

and

$$d\rho = \frac{1}{RT} dA - \frac{A}{RT^2} dT \tag{5.38}$$

Substituting Eqs. (5.38) and (5.36b) into Eq. (5.35) we obtain

$$u^2 = \left(\frac{\partial P}{\partial \rho}\right)_S = \frac{\sum\limits_{i=1}^{s-p} p_i \left(\frac{\partial \ln p_i}{\partial \ln T}\right)_S}{\frac{A}{RT}\left[\left(\frac{\partial \ln A}{\partial \ln T}\right)_S - 1\right]} \tag{5.39}$$

Using the nomenclature of Huff et al.[7] we write

$$u^2 = \frac{RT \sum\limits_{i=1}^{s-p} p_i D_i}{A(D_A - 1)} \tag{5.40}$$

where

$$D_i = \left(\frac{\partial \ln p_i}{\partial \ln T}\right)_S \tag{5.41}$$

$$D_A = \left(\frac{\partial \ln (A)}{\partial \ln T}\right)_S \tag{5.42}$$

To evaluate D_i and D_A for the conditions of chemical equilibrium for an isentropic process, one computes the total differentials of Eqs. (4.60), (4.57), and (5.27). The total differentials of these equations, when expressed in logarithmic variables and divided by $d \ln T$, can be written for gaseous products,

$$\left(\frac{d \ln p_i}{d \ln T}\right) - \sum\limits_{j=1}^{c} \nu_{ij} \left(\frac{d \ln p_j}{d \ln T}\right) = \left(\frac{\Delta H}{RT}\right)_i,$$
$$i = c + 1, c + 2, \ldots, (s - c - p) \tag{5.43}$$

and for condensed products

$$-\sum\limits_{j=1}^{c} \nu_{qj} \left(\frac{d \ln p_j}{d \ln T}\right) = \left(\frac{\Delta H}{RT}\right)_q, \qquad q = 1, 2, \ldots, p \tag{5.44}$$

and for the products of reaction

$$\sum\limits_{i=1}^{s} \bar{a}_{ki} n_i \left(\frac{d \ln n_i}{d \ln T}\right) - A\sigma_K \left(\frac{d \ln A}{d \ln T}\right) = A\sigma_K \frac{d \ln \sigma_K}{d \ln T}, \qquad k = 1, 2, \ldots, m \tag{5.45}$$

$$\sum\limits_{i=1}^{s} S_i' \left(\frac{d \ln n_i}{d \ln T}\right) - AS \frac{d \ln A}{d \ln T} = -\sum\limits_{i=1}^{s} n_i (C_p^0)_i + AS \left(\frac{d \ln S}{d \ln T}\right) \tag{5.46}$$

where

$$S_i' = n_i (S_T^0)_i - Rp_i(1 + \ln p_i) \tag{5.47}$$

Since $d \ln S = 0$, S is a constant and $d \ln \sigma_K = 0$ for $k = 1, 2, \ldots, m$, since σ_K's are constants, the partial derivatives D_i in Eq. (5.41) and D_A in Eq. (5.42) can be substituted for the total derivatives in Eqs. (5.43) through

(5.46). The velocity-of-sound matrix is constructed as follows. The order of the columns in the matrix is written:

(1) D_i of the $s - c - p$ gaseous species
(2) D_i of the c gaseous components chosen as majors
(3) D_i of the p condensed species
(4) D_A
(5) Constant terms of the equation

The order of the rows in this matrix is written:

(1) Equilibrium equations (5.43) in the same order as the $s - c - p$ gaseous species
(2) m mass balance equations (5.45)
(3) Equilibrium equations (5.44) for the p condensed species
(4) Total entropy equation (5.46)

The resulting system of linear equations is solved by the Crout method as described in Chap. 4. This procedure is used to compute the velocity of sound of a gas mixture at any point in the nozzle, assuming equilibrium flow. The solution to the reduced Crout matrix yields D_j of the c components, D_q of the p condensed species, and D_A. The D_i of the $s - c - p$ gaseous species are computed from Eq. (5.43), i.e.,

$$D_i = \sum_{j=1}^{c} \nu_{ij} D_j + \left(\frac{\Delta H}{RT}\right)_i, \qquad i = c + 1, c + 2, \ldots, (s - c - p) \qquad (5.48)$$

Since

$$\gamma = \left(\frac{\partial \ln P}{\partial \ln \rho}\right)_s \qquad (5.49)$$

we have, from Eqs. (5.35) and (5.41), that

$$\gamma = \left(\frac{\partial \ln P}{\partial \ln \rho}\right)_s = \frac{\rho}{P}\left(\frac{\partial P}{\partial \rho}\right)_s = \frac{\sum_{i=1}^{s-p} p_i D_i}{P(D_A - 1)} \qquad (5.50)$$

This calculation of the *velocity of sound* requires that the volume of the condensed species be negligible compared to the volume of the gas and assumes that solids and liquid species are in thermodynamic and velocity equilibrium with the gas.

5.9. CALCULATION OF SPECIFIC HEAT AT CONSTANT PRESSURE

The molar specific heat at constant pressure of a mixture in equilibrium is found from Eq. (5.3).

$$C_p^0 = \frac{A}{n}\left(\frac{\partial h}{\partial T}\right)_p = \frac{1}{nT}\left[\sum_{i=1}^{s}(H_T^0)_i n_i \left(\frac{\partial \ln n_i}{\partial \ln T}\right)_p \right.$$

$$\left. - Ah\left(\frac{\partial \ln A}{\partial \ln T}\right)_p + T\sum_{i=1}^{s} n_i(C_p^0)_i \right] \qquad (5.51)$$

The total differential of the total pressure [Eq. (5.36)] divided by $d \ln T$ at constant pressure is written

$$\sum_{i=1}^{s-p} p_i \left(\frac{d \ln p_i}{d \ln T}\right)_P = 0 \qquad (5.52)$$

The matrix constructed for the *isentropic expansion to an assigned pressure* can be used to construct a specific heat at constant pressure matrix. To do so, one substitutes Eq. (5.52) in place of Eq. (5.46). The matrix is then constructed in the same manner as described in Sec. 5.8. The reduced Crout matrix is solved for $Y_i = (\partial \ln n_i / \partial \ln T)_P$ for the components and $Y_A = (\partial \ln A / \partial \ln T)_P$. The Y_i of the $s - c - p$ gaseous species are computed from Eq. (5.43), i.e.,

$$Y_i = \sum_{j=1}^{c} \nu_{ij} Y_j + \left(\frac{\Delta H}{RT}\right)_i, \qquad i = c+1, c+2, \ldots, (s-c-p) \qquad (5.53)$$

The Y_i's are substituted into Eq. (5.51) to evaluate the molar heat capacity C_p^0 of the mixture.

5.10. CALCULATION OF ISENTROPIC EXPANSION TO AN ASSIGNED MACH NUMBER

The law of the conservation of energy requires that sum of the enthalpy plus kinetic energy is a constant at every point in a nozzle. We write for this sum h^* from Eqs. (5.3) and (5.4) that

$$h^* = [h + \tfrac{1}{2}v^2]_x \qquad (5.54)$$

where v is velocity of flow of the gas, and the variables are evaluated at point x in the nozzle. The *Mach number M* of the flow is

$$M = \frac{v}{u} \qquad (5.55)$$

where u is the velocity of sound of the gas, and combining Eqs. (5.55) and (5.40) we obtain

$$h^* = \frac{\sum_{i=1}^{s} n_i(H_T^0)_i}{A} + \frac{M^2 RT}{A}\frac{\sum_{i=1}^{s} p_i D_i}{2(D_A - 1)} \qquad (5.56)$$

When Eq. (5.56) is expanded in a Taylor's series about the variables and the results are written in logarithm form, one obtains

$$\sum_{i=1}^{s} h_i'' \Delta \ln n_i - Ah^* \Delta \ln A + TC'' \Delta \ln T = Ah^* \ln \frac{h_0}{h^*} \qquad (5.57)$$

where

$$h_i'' = n_i(H_T^0)_i + \frac{M^2 R T p_i D_i}{2(D_A - 1)} \tag{5.58}$$

and

$$C'' = \sum_{i=1}^{s} \left[n_i(C_p^0)_i + \frac{M^2 R T p_i D_i}{2(D_A - 1)} \right] \tag{5.59}$$

The correction equations for an isentropic expansion to an assigned Mach number are Eqs. (4.60), (4.57), (5.27), and (5.57). This matrix is constructed as described in Sec. 5.6, with Eq. (5.57) replacing step (5) in (5.29). To evaluate the elements in Eq. (5.57) it is necessary to evaluate the velocity-of-sound matrix in Sec. 5.7 for the D_i and D_A. The reduced Crout matrix for the isentropic expansion to an assigned Mach number is solved by any matrix method for the composition of the components, the total number of moles in the system, and the temperature. After convergence has been obtained, the total pressure for the assigned Mach number is obtained from Eq. (5.36a).

5.11. DEFINITIONS OF ROCKET PARAMETERS

The combustion product species which are formed in the combustion chamber are expanded adiabatically and isentropically through a nozzle. The rocket receives its propulsive force from the momentum of the ejected combustion product species, which move at supersonic velocities in a direction opposite to that of the rocket. It is shown from the conservation of momentum [9] that the thrust on a rocket motor is

$$F = \left(\frac{1}{2} + \frac{1}{2} \cos \alpha \right) \frac{\dot{W} V_e}{g} + (P_e - P_0) A_e \tag{5.60}$$

where α is the half of the divergence angle of the nozzle, $\dot{W}$ is the total weight flow of the propellant, g is the acceleration-of-gravity constant, P_e is the absolute pressure at the nozzle exit, P_0 is the external atmospheric pressure, and A_e is the cross-sectional area at the nozzle exit. The first term in Eq. (5.60) is called the *momentum thrust* and is the product of propellant flow rate and the velocity of gases at the nozzle exit. The second term in Eq. (5.60) is called the *pressure thrust* and is the product of the cross-sectional area at the nozzle exit and the difference between the static pressure of the gas stream at the nozzle exit and the ambient pressure of the surrounding fluid. If we define the effective exhaust velocity c by the relation

$$c = \left(\frac{1}{2} + \frac{1}{2} \cos \alpha \right) V_e + g(P_e - P_0) \frac{A_e}{\dot{W}} \tag{5.61}$$

[9] F. J. Malina, *J. Franklin Inst.*, **230** (1940), 433.

then Eq. (5.60) can be written as

$$F = \frac{\dot{W}}{g} c \tag{5.62}$$

The maximum thrust is obtained when $P_e = P_0$.[9] The latter condition can be obtained by proper construction of the nozzle. If the divergence angle α of the nozzle is made sufficiently small, Eqs. (5.60) and (5.61) become

$$F = \dot{W}\frac{V_e}{g} + (P_e - P_0)A_e \tag{5.63}$$

$$c = V_e + g(P_e - P_0)\frac{A_e}{\dot{W}} \tag{5.64}$$

If $P_e = P_0$, then Eqs. (5.63) and (5.64) become

$$F = \dot{W}\frac{V_e}{g} = \frac{\dot{W}c}{g} \tag{5.65}$$

$$c = V_e \tag{5.66}$$

We see from Eq. (5.66) that the effective exhaust velocity equals the velocity of the gas at the nozzle exit when the static exit pressure P_e equals the pressure of the surrounding fluid P_0. The effective exhaust velocity can be determined, therefore, from measurements of the rocket thrust and propellant flow rate as shown in Eq. (5.65).

The *specific impulse* or *specific thrust* is one of the most important performance parameters used in rocket technology. The *specific impulse* is defined as the thrust which can be obtained from an *equivalent* rocket which has a propellant flow rate of unity

$$I_s = \frac{F}{\dot{W}} \tag{5.67}$$

I_s is expressed as pounds of thrust per pound second of propellant flow and has the dimensions of *seconds*.

If one combines Eqs. (5.63) and (5.67), the following relation is obtained.

$$I_s = \frac{V_e}{g} + (P_e - P_0)\frac{A_e}{\dot{W}} \tag{5.68}$$

If the exit static pressure P_e is equal to the surrounding fluid pressure P_0, the pressure thrust term in Eq. (5.68) is zero, and the specific thrust in Eq. (5.68) becomes

$$I_s = \frac{V_e}{g} = I_{opt} \tag{5.69}$$

where I_{opt} is the *optimum specific impulse* obtainable for a specified chamber pressure and exit pressure with $P_e = P_0$. A rocket nozzle which is designed to achieve the condition that $P_e = P_0$ is called a rocket nozzle with optimum

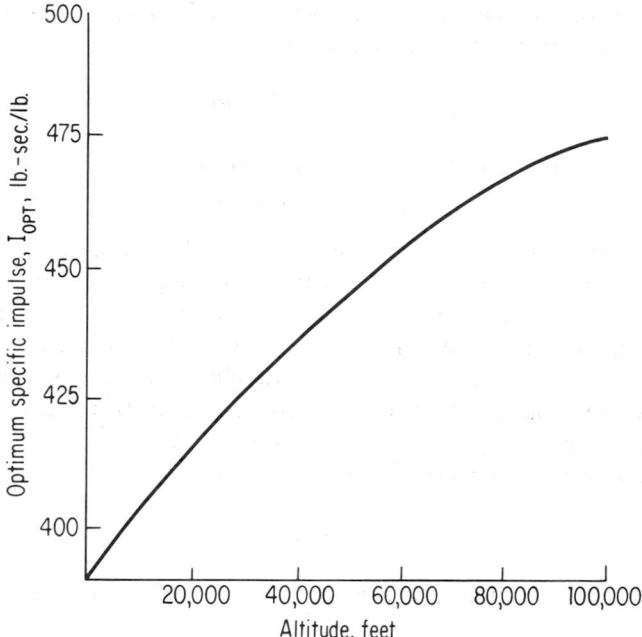

Fig. 5.1 Optimum specific impulse of F_2/H_2 (shifting equilibrium) mixture ratio, M.R. = 20, wt. oxid/wt. fuel; P_c = 1000 psia.

expansion ratio (A_e/A_t). If $P_e < P_0$ the pressure thrust term in Eq. (5.68) is negative and if $P_e > P_0$ it is positive. The former is not desirable for optimum performance of a rocket, since such a rocket would lose thrust. Most rockets are designed such that $P_e = P_0$ or such that $P_e > P_0$. We see from Eq. (5.68) that the thrust of a rocket is dependent upon the external atmosphere pressure, which is dependent upon altitude. Since the fluid pressure of the atmosphere decreases with increasing altitude, the thrust of the rocket increases when the rocket is propelled to high altitudes. When the rocket is propelled to sufficiently high altitudes such that $P_0 = 0$, Eq. (5.68) gives *vacuum specific impulse*

$$I_{vac} = \frac{V_e}{g} + A_e \frac{P_e}{\dot{W}} \tag{5.70}$$

The optimum impulse and vacuum impulse are defined exactly, once the chamber pressure and exit pressure are specified for a given propellant system. Figure 5.1 demonstrates the large increase in specific impulse made possible by designing the rocket nozzle with a variable area ratio. Such a rocket design would vary the area ratio continuously with altitude such that P_e always equals P_0.

The *impulse* or *total impulse* I_t of a rocket is defined as the integral of the thrust F over the duration of operating time t.

$$I_t = \int_0^t F \, dt = \int_0^t I_s \dot{W} \, dt \tag{5.71}$$

If the thrust is constant, Eq. (5.71) is written as

$$I_t = Ft = I_s W \tag{5.72}$$

where W is the total weight of the effective propellant in pounds. The total impulse equation (5.71) is used to calculate the average specific impulse for a solid propellant when it is not possible to measure a flow rate but it is possible to measure thrust F and duration t of thrust or the total propellant weight W. In liquid propellants the flow rate of the propellant can be measured. From Eq. (5.72) we see that *specific impulse can be defined as the amount of impulse imparted to a vehicle per pound of effective propellant.*

The *specific propellant consumption*

$$W_s = \frac{1}{I_s} \tag{5.73}$$

is the propellant flow required to produce one pound of thrust in an equivalent rocket.

5.12. CALCULATION OF ROCKET PARAMETERS USING EXACT THERMODYNAMIC RELATIONS

The following assumptions are made in theoretical rocket performance calculations:

(1) The chamber temperature and composition are fixed by assuming that the material introduced as propellant is transformed adiabatically to certain presumed combustion constituents in amounts fixed by the prescribed stoichiometry, total pressure, and equilibrium coefficients.

(2) Complete combustion, perfect mixing, gas ideality, and negligible velocity at the nozzle entrance are assumed.

(3) The state of the gas throughout expansion in the nozzle is fixed by the entropy of the system, which is presumed to be invariant as the pressure is reduced to the value assigned to the exit plane. The expansion is thus isentropic and one-dimensional.

(4) Effects of friction, divergence angle, heat exchange, and nonequilibrium are not considered.

(5) The liquids and solids are assumed to have negligible volume and to be in kinetic as well as thermal equilibrium with the gas.

(6) Each condensed phase is assumed to have a partial pressure of zero, even when finely divided and suspended in the gas.

Experimental evaluation of performance of rocket engines has indicated that these six assumptions introduce only small errors in calculated values of specific impulse. The assumption of gas ideality introduces a small error of about 1 per cent in the calculated value of the specific impulse. It is necessary to correct for *gas imperfections*[10] at extremely high pressure (in excess of 100 atmospheres for most systems).

Let us consider the computation of specific impulse. It is desired to evaluate the gas flow velocity at the nozzle exit according to Eq. (5.68). The energy equation for an open system according to the first law of thermodynamics for a flow process in gases is

$$dE = dq - P\,dV \qquad (5.74)$$

where E is the internal energy, dq is the heat absorbed by the gas, and V is its volume. We neglect in Eq. (5.74) the frictional work done on the gas. The enthalpy or heat content

$$H = E + PV \qquad (5.75)$$

and upon differentiation becomes

$$dH = dE + P\,dV + V\,dP \qquad (5.76)$$

Combining Eqs. (5.74) and (5.76) we obtain

$$dH = dq + V\,dP \qquad (5.77)$$

The conservation of momentum equation requires

$$P + \rho \frac{u^2}{2} = \text{constant} \qquad (5.78)$$

where ρ is the density of the gas, and u is the gas flow velocity. The conservation of momentum equation becomes, upon differentiation of Eq. (5.78),

$$dP = -\rho u\,du \qquad (5.79)$$

For complete representation of the thermodynamic parameters during the flow process the momentum equation (5.79) and the energy equation (5.77) are combined. We find

$$dH = dq - V\rho u\,du \qquad (5.80)$$

Since the density of the gas $\rho = m/V$, Eq. (5.80) becomes

$$dH = dq - mu\,du \qquad (5.81)$$

where m is the mass of the propellant. Equations (5.74) through (5.81) can be used to treat the thermodynamics of any type of flow process. Since the flow process in the nozzle is assumed adiabatic, $dq = 0$ and Eq. (5.81) can be written

$$dH = -mu\,du \qquad (5.82)$$

---

[10] *Gas imperfections* are deviations of properties of combustion gases from ideal gas behavior.

and upon integration between chamber and nozzle exit becomes

$$u_e = \sqrt{2(h_c - h_e) + u_c^2} \qquad (5.83)$$

where the total mass m of the system is taken as one gram. The velocity u_c at the nozzle entrance position is assumed small compared to that at the exit position. We therefore take $u_c = 0$, and Eq. (5.83) is written

$$u_e = \sqrt{2(h_c - h_e)} \qquad (5.84)$$

We note that the exit velocity [Eq. (5.84)] and therefore the specific impulse [Eq. (5.69)] is the difference between the chamber and exit enthalpies. The adiabatic flame temperature is computed by one of the methods described in Sec. 5.2, and the combustion entropy of the mixture S_c at the chamber temperature T_c is calculated from Eq. (5.22). The expansion of the combustion gases through the nozzle is assumed isentropic, i.e., $dS = 0$; therefore, the combustion entropy S_c and a specified exit plane pressure P_e are required if we are to use one of the methods described in Sec. 5.7 to compute the exit temperature and composition. The exit enthalpy h_e is computed from Eq. (5.3), and upon combining Eqs. (5.84) and (5.69) the specific impulse becomes

$$I_s = \sqrt{\frac{2J}{g}(1800)(h_c - h_e)} \qquad (5.85)$$

where J is the mechanical equivalent of heat and the enthalpies h_c and h_e are expressed as kcal/gram.

Experimental specific impulses as determined by Eq. (5.67) are usually 80 per cent or more of the value computed by Eq. (5.85). When experimental conditions are ideal, and the heat losses to the combustion chamber and nozzle are known, the experimental specific impulses are usually as high as 95 per cent of the computed value. Factors contributing to the loss of energy are (1) loss of heat to the walls of the combustion chamber and nozzle, (2) friction in the nozzle, (3) angle of divergence of the nozzle [see Eq. (5.60)], (4) incomplete combustion, (5) combustion continuing in the nozzle, (6) uncertainty as to the establishment of a state of thermodynamic equilibrium during expansion, and (7) certain shock effects that may arise when the sonic velocity is reached.

The area ratio describes the thrust chamber geometry and is given by

$$\epsilon = \frac{A_e}{A_t} \qquad (5.86)$$

where A_e is the cross-sectional area at the nozzle exit and A_t is the cross-sectional area at the throat. The continuity of mass equation is

$$\rho A u = \dot{W} \qquad (5.87)$$

where ρ is the density of the mixture, A is the cross-sectional area at some point x in the flow, u is the flow velocity of the gas, and $\dot{W}$ is the propellant flow rate. When Eq. (5.87) is substituted into Eq. (5.86) we obtain

$$\epsilon = \frac{A_e}{A_t} = \frac{\rho_t u_t}{\rho_e u_e} \tag{5.88}$$

Therefore, to compute the area ratio we must compute conditions at the throat of the rocket. *The velocity of the gas at the throat is assumed sonic.* Sonic velocity corresponds to a Mach number of unity. We use, therefore, the method described in Sec. 5.8 to calculate the properties at the throat which corresponds to an isentropic expansion to Mach one.

That region of the nozzle with minimum cross-sectional area is called the throat. From Eq. (5.87) it is seen that this condition is met when the product ρu is a maximum. Another accurate way to compute the area $A_t/\dot{W}$ at the throat per unit flow rate of propellant is to calculate the product of ρu at several assumed pressures and temperatures near the throat. An interpolation method is used to locate the pressure at which maximum value of ρu is obtained. The maximum value of ρu, when obtained, can be used to evaluate the area ratio in Eq. (5.88) or the characteristic velocity c^*, described below.

In experimental rocket work, it is convenient to separate the combustion process from the expansion process. The combustion process should determine the capability of the propellant to generate kinetic energy, whereas the expansion process should determine the effectiveness of use of the heat originally available. To distinguish between combustion processes and the expansion processes in a rocket, use is made of two parameters whose variables are expressed in terms of *measurable* quantities. The first parameter, used to measure the effectiveness of the combustion process, is called the *characteristic velocity*, c^*, and is defined by the relation

$$c^* = gP_c \left(\frac{A_t}{\dot{W}}\right) \tag{5.89}$$

The characteristic velocity, c^*, has been the source of much misunderstanding in the rocket literature. The characteristic velocity c^* in Eq. (5.89) states that for a given throat area and chamber pressure, propellants with higher c^* require less flow rate to produce the same chamber pressure.

The second parameter, used to measure the effectiveness of the expansion process, is called the *thrust coefficient*, C_F, and is defined by the relation

$$C_F = \frac{F}{P_c A_t} \tag{5.90}$$

The calculation of the characteristic velocity and the thrust coefficient requires a knowledge of the cross-sectional area at the throat per unit flow rate of propellant. The latter is computed from the continuity of mass equation and the method described in Sec. 5.10 for calculation of parameters at the throat, which we know corresponds to an isentropic expansion to Mach one, or by finding the pressure and temperature at which the product ρu is maximum.

The product of c^* and C_F is the effective exhaust velocity [Eq. (5.65)] when $P_e = P_0$, and we have

$$c^* C_F = I_s g \tag{5.91}$$

so that the thrust coefficient C_F can be computed from the characteristic velocity c^* and the specific impulse. The experimental c^* is less than the theoretical c^* and the experimental C_F is greater than the theoretical C_F. In the theoretical calculations of chamber conditions one assumes complete combustion. This is probably not true; therefore, owing to incomplete combustion in the chamber, the experimental characteristic velocity is lower than the theoretical characteristic velocity. The experimental coefficient of thrust is higher than the theoretical coefficient of thrust, probably because some combustion occurs in the nozzle. Theoretically, therefore, a different characteristic velocity is possible for each of the three types of flow processes described in Sec. 5.1.

5.13. CALCULATION OF ROCKET PARAMETERS USING APPROXIMATE RELATIONS

The rocket parameters described in the previous sections were derived from exact thermodynamic relations. These methods are somewhat more complex than the approximate relations described for computing rocket performance in the rocket literature. In these approximations it is assumed that the heat capacity of the mixture is invariant with temperature. This certainly is not the case. Hence large discrepancies exist between theoretical performance parameters computed from exact thermodynamic relations and those computed with approximate relations even for the frozen flow assumption.

Let us assume that the specific heat of a gas is invariant with temperature; then Eq. (5.85) becomes

$$I_s = \sqrt{\frac{2J(1.8)}{g}} \sqrt{\frac{C_p}{M}(T_c - T_e)} \tag{5.92}$$

where C_p is the heat capacity in calories per mole per degree. The expansion process is assumed adiabatic and isentropic; thus, from Eq. (5.74),

$$dE = -p \, dV \tag{5.93}$$

and for a perfect gas assumed independent of temperature Eq. (5.93) becomes

$$C_V \frac{dT}{T} = -nR \frac{dV}{V} \tag{5.94}$$

or, upon integration,

$$TV^{nR/C_V} = \text{constant} = TV^{\gamma - 1} \tag{5.95}$$

where n is the total number of moles of gas in the system, and $\gamma = C_p/C_V$ and $C_p - C_V = nR$. If the ideal gas law

$$PV = nRT \tag{5.96}$$

is assumed, Eq. (5.95) can be written as

$$TP^{(\gamma-1)/\gamma} = \text{constant} \tag{5.97}$$

The relation in Eq. (5.97) can be used to derive a relation between chamber properties and nozzle exit properties in a nozzle, and one obtains

$$\frac{T_e}{T_c} = \left(\frac{P_e}{P_c}\right)^{(\gamma-1)/\gamma} \tag{5.98}$$

Substitution of Eq. (5.98) into Eq. (5.92) gives

$$I_s = \sqrt{\frac{2J(1.8)}{g}} \sqrt{\frac{\gamma}{\gamma-1} \frac{T_c}{M_c} \left[1 - \left(\frac{P_e}{P_c}\right)^{(\gamma-1)/\gamma}\right]} \tag{5.99}$$

since

$$C_p = \frac{\gamma}{\gamma-1} = \sum_{i=1}^{s} \frac{X_i(C_p^0)_i}{\sum\limits_{q=1}^{p}(1-X_q)} \tag{5.100}$$

The specific impulse equation (5.99) was derived on the following assumptions:

(1) The specific heat of the gas is invariant with temperature.
(2) The expansion process is assumed adiabatic and isentropic.
(3) The perfect gas law is assumed to hold.
(4) The compositions of the combustion species at the nozzle exit are in the same relative proportions as in the combustion chamber since the flow process is assumed *frozen*.

The first assumption is valid only for *inert gases*. The second assumption is not 100 per cent true, since the expansion process is not exactly adiabatic, but heat transfer to the nozzle will introduce only small errors in theoretical specific impulse. The third assumption is valid at high temperatures and low pressures (pressures less than 100 atmospheres) and is certainly applicable to most rocket combustion processes. By definition the fourth assumption is valid for *frozen flow* and is not valid for the assumption of *equilibrium flow*.

In order to compute the specific impulse from Eq. (5.99), one must calculate an *average gamma* of the product gases or an average *specific heat* of the product gases. Since the γ is a state function and varies with temperature, it is questionable as to what "γ" should be used in computing specific impulse. An "average gamma," $\bar{\gamma} = (\gamma_c + \gamma_e)/2$, is computed for the combustion products which are expanded adiabatically from the chamber pressure P_c to the exit pressure P_e. For adiabatic expansion the exit temperature T_e can be expressed in terms of the chamber temperature, the pressure ratio, and the $\bar{\gamma}$. According to Eq. (5.98) we write

$$T_e = T_c \left(\frac{P_e}{P_c}\right)^{(\gamma-1)/\gamma} \tag{5.101}$$

Additional parameters, calculated for rocket engines with the same assumptions as those stated in this section, are

$$c^* = \left(\frac{P_c}{P_t}\right)\left(\frac{T_t}{T_c}\right)^{1/2} \sqrt{\frac{RT_c}{\gamma_t M_t}} \tag{5.102}$$

where

$$\frac{T_t}{T_c} = \frac{2}{\bar{\gamma}_t + 1} \tag{5.103}$$

$$\frac{P_t}{P_c} = \left(\frac{2}{\bar{\gamma}_t + 1}\right)^{\bar{\gamma}_t/(\bar{\gamma}_t - 1)} \tag{5.104}$$

and

$$C_F = \sqrt{\frac{2\bar{\gamma}\gamma_t}{\bar{\gamma} - 1}\left(\frac{2}{\bar{\gamma} + 1}\right)^{(\bar{\gamma}+1)/(\bar{\gamma}-1)}\left[1 - \left(\frac{P_e}{P_c}\right)^{(\bar{\gamma}-1)/\bar{\gamma}}\right]} \tag{5.105}$$

For calculations with gases for which the specific heat varies markedly with temperatures, Eqs. (5.99) through (5.105) are entirely approximate and subject to the choice of a "proper" average γ for the expansion process. For most propellant systems the proper choice of γ presents a problem, especially when these performance parameters are desired as a function of altitude. For example, assuming isentropic flow, values of γ given in Table 5.1 for a liquid fluorine-liquid hydrogen propellant system at the stoichiometric mixture ratio and a chamber pressure of 600 psia (pounds per square inch absolute) show that γ varies quite markedly with temperature from 1.163 to 1.420.

The values of γ depend upon the nature of the system. For a frozen composition system, this variation in γ with temperature results from changes in the internal energy state of the combustion products. For a shifting composition system, γ is not equal to $C_P/(C_P - R)$ because the equilibrium composition is a function of exit pressure and temperature. It can be shown that γ in Eq. (5.50) for a shifting system can be written as

$$\gamma = \frac{\left(\frac{\partial H}{\partial T}\right)_p}{\left(\frac{\partial E}{\partial T}\right)_v}\left[1 - \frac{RT}{P}\left(\frac{\partial N}{\partial V}\right)_T\right] \tag{5.106}$$

where N is the total number of moles in the system.

Table 5.1. VARIATION OF γ WITH
TEMPERATURE FOR BOTH FROZEN AND
EQUILIBRIUM COMPOSITION FOR LIQUID
HYDROGEN WITH LIQUID FLUORINE

Temperature, °K	Frozen γ	Shifting γ
4800	1.327	1.163
4400	1.333	1.155
4000	1.337	1.148
3600	1.343	1.145
3200	1.349	1.153
2800	1.356	1.184
2400	1.366	1.251
2000	1.379	1.311
1600	1.397	1.341
1200	1.420	1.367

For the case of a frozen composition, that is, no chemical reaction in the nozzle, $(\partial N/\partial V)_T$ equals zero and Eq. (5.106) reduces to

$$\gamma = \frac{C_P}{C_P - R} \tag{5.107}$$

With such a variation in γ as indicated in Table 5.1 for frozen and shifting composition systems, it is apparent that the use of an average γ is a rather crude approximation. Further, it may be shown that in case of variation in the value of γ during expansion, there are actually three different average γ values which could be used in the approximate Eq. (5.99) and Eqs. (5.102) through (5.105). These are the average values from chamber to throat, chamber to exit, and at the throat. Suffice it to say at this point that accurate values, for example, of specific impulse can be computed only from the isentropic change in enthalpy between the combustion products in the combustion chamber and the exit plane upon complete expansion in the nozzle, that is, Eq. (5.85). The other performance parameters such as coefficient of thrust, characteristic velocity, and area ratio should be calculated from the procedures described in Sec. 5.12.

5.14. CHAMBER PRESSURE CORRECTIONS

When performance parameters are available for a given system at two different chamber pressures it is possible to correlate the data for chamber pressure effect. The basis of such a correlation is that the values of the parameters I_S, c^*, A_e/A_t, and temperature are linear with the logarithm of the chamber pressure for a given mixture ratio and pressure ratio. Gordon and

Huff[11] showed that it was possible to correlate these parameters for chamber pressure effects according to the following equations and, in general, to the accuracies indicated. In cases where substantial quantities of solids occur, the accuracies may be somewhat poorer than indicated.

$$I = I_1 \left(\frac{P_c}{P_{c,1}}\right)^{n_I} \qquad (\pm 0.06 \text{ per cent}) \qquad (5.108)$$

$$c^* = c_1^* \left(\frac{P_c}{P_{c,1}}\right)^{n_{c^*}} \qquad (\pm 0.07 \text{ per cent}) \qquad (5.109)$$

$$T = T_1 \left(\frac{P_c}{P_{c,1}}\right)^{n_T} \qquad (\pm 0.3 \text{ per cent}) \qquad (5.110)$$

$$\epsilon = \epsilon_1 \left(\frac{P_c}{P_{c,1}}\right)^{n_\epsilon} \qquad (\pm 0.3 \text{ per cent}) \qquad (5.111)$$

The values of the exponents n_I, n_{c^*}, n_T, and n_ϵ are computed from the following relations:

$$n_I = \frac{\log \dfrac{I_2}{I_1}}{\log \dfrac{P_{c,2}}{P_{c,1}}} \qquad (5.112)$$

$$n_{c^*} = \frac{\log \dfrac{c_2^*}{c_1^*}}{\log \dfrac{P_{c,2}}{P_{c,1}}} \qquad (5.113)$$

$$n_T = \frac{\log \dfrac{T_2}{T_1}}{\log \dfrac{P_{c,2}}{P_{c,1}}} \qquad (5.114)$$

$$n_\epsilon = \frac{\log \dfrac{\epsilon_2}{\epsilon_1}}{\log \dfrac{P_{c,2}}{P_{c,1}}} \qquad (5.115)$$

As an illustration of the use of Eqs. (5.108) through (5.115), suppose that it is desired to obtain the values of T_c, I_s, c^*, and A_e/A_t for a combustion pressure of 600 psia and an expansion ratio of 400 at a mixture ratio of 5.665 for the hydrogen-fluorine system. The values of these parameters are as follows.

[11] S. Gordon and V. N. Huff, *Theoretical Performance of Liquid Hydrazine and Liquid Fluorine as a Rocket Propellant*, NACA RME 53E12 (1953).

$P_c = 500$ psia	$P_c = 800$ psia
$T_c = 3371.0°K$	$T_c = 3412.8°K$
$I_s = 427.2$ lb-sec/lb	$I_s = 429.8$ lb-sec/lb
$c^* = 8212$ ft/sec	$c^* = 8254$ ft/sec
$A_e/A_t = 22.62$	$A_e/A_t = 22.74$

Using Eqs. (5.108) through (5.115), the following results are obtained:

$$P_c = 600 \text{ psia}$$
$$T_c = 3387°K$$
$$I_s = 428.2 \text{ lb-sec/lb}$$
$$c^* = 8228 \text{ ft/sec}$$
$$A_e/A_t = 22.67$$

For comparison, the values of these parameters computed directly are:

$$T_c = 3387°K$$
$$I_s = 428.2 \text{ lb-sec/lb}$$
$$c^* = 8228 \text{ ft/sec}$$
$$A_e/A_t = 22.67$$

5.15. ESTIMATION OF THEORETICAL PERFORMANCE DATA

The performance parameters can be represented by the empirical relation

$$y = A + (Bx + C)e^{Dz} \tag{5.116}$$

where x is the *weight mixture ratio* defined as the grams of oxidizer to grams of fuel, and y is any one of the parameters I_s, c^*, or C_F. The empirical fits to these performance parameters with the standard deviation of each fit from the theoretical data are presented in Table 5.2 for a CH_2 fuel-liquid O_2 system at chamber pressures of 400 psia and 350 psia, respectively. The data at 400 psia were taken at mixture ratios from 1.4 to 2.3 and the data at 350 psia from 1.2 to 2.3. The data were taken at an exit pressure of one atmosphere. The numbers in the last column of Table 5.2 indicate that the largest error in any of these performance parameters is at most 0.05 per cent. In general, Eq. (5.116) provides an excellent representation of these performance parameters and should be similarly successful for other propellants.

5.16. AREA RATIO AND ALTITUDE CORRECTIONS

The tabulated performance values in Table 5.4, when used correctly, permit the computation of the effect of area ratio on specific impulse. If one combines Eq. (5.61) and (5.68), the following exact equation for the effect of area ratio on specific impulse can be expressed as

$$I_\epsilon = \lambda I_{opt} + \left(\frac{P_e - P_0}{P_c}\right)\frac{\epsilon c^*}{g} \tag{5.117}$$

Table 5.2. Empirical Fits of Theoretical Performance Data for CH_2/Liquid Oxygen Systems

Parameters (y, x)	P_c (psia)	A	B	C	D	x max	σ_z max	y max	σ_y max	Largest error in curve-fit
I_s, O/F	400	193.893	477.897	−523.903	−0.946260	2.1531	0.0014	259.74	0.01	0.03
c^*, O/F	400	4524.40	10874.4	−12344.7	−1.01740	2.1181	0.0024	5763.3	0.5	1.6
C_F, O/F	400	1.45835	0	−0.194737	−1.46963	..	..	..	..	0.0003
I_s, O/F	350	187.259	471.282	−504.013	−0.934970	2.1390	0.0014	255.48	0.01	0.09
c^*, O/F	350	4395.33	10758.7	−11780.9	−0.987700	2.1075	0.0018	5754.1	0.3	2.6
C_F, O/F	350	1.43435	−0.424240	0.053038	−2.33902	..	..	..	..	0.0004

where $\epsilon = A_e/A_t$ and $\lambda = (\frac{1}{2} + \frac{1}{2}\cos\alpha)$ and subscript I_ϵ is the specific impulse for a specified area ratio. The use of Eq. (5.117) will be illustrated for the data given in Table 5.3 for the hydrogen-fluorine system at 500 psia. For a given mixture ratio and chamber pressure, the parameters I_{opt} and P_e are plotted against area ratio. The plots are given in Figs. 5.2 and 5.3.

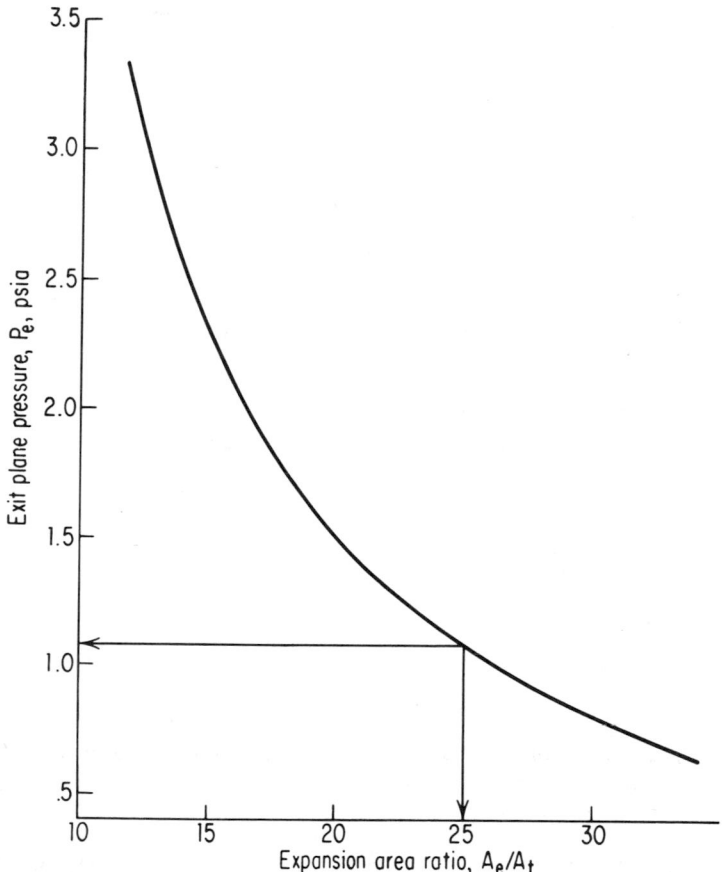

Fig. 5.2 Exit plane pressure as a function of expansion area ratio (frozen equilibrium). H_2—F_2; $P_c = 500$ psia; $O/F = 5.665$.

Suppose that it is desired to obtain the specific impulse at sea level for a combustion pressure of 500 psia, and an expansion ratio of 25 at a mixture ratio of 5.665 and for $\lambda = 1$ (i.e., $\alpha = 0$). The values read from Figs. 5.2 and 5.3 and Table 5.3 for a hydrogen-fluorine system at a mixture ratio of 5.665 and a chamber pressure of 500 psia are:

$$I_{opt} = 429.6, \qquad P_e = 1.08 \text{ psia}, \qquad c^* = 8210.0 \text{ ft/sec}$$

Using these values in Eq. (5.117) with the values of $P_0 = 14.7$ psia at sea level gives $I_\epsilon = 255.8$ sec. At any altitude other than sea level, substitution of the appropriate value for P_0 will yield the corresponding I_ϵ.

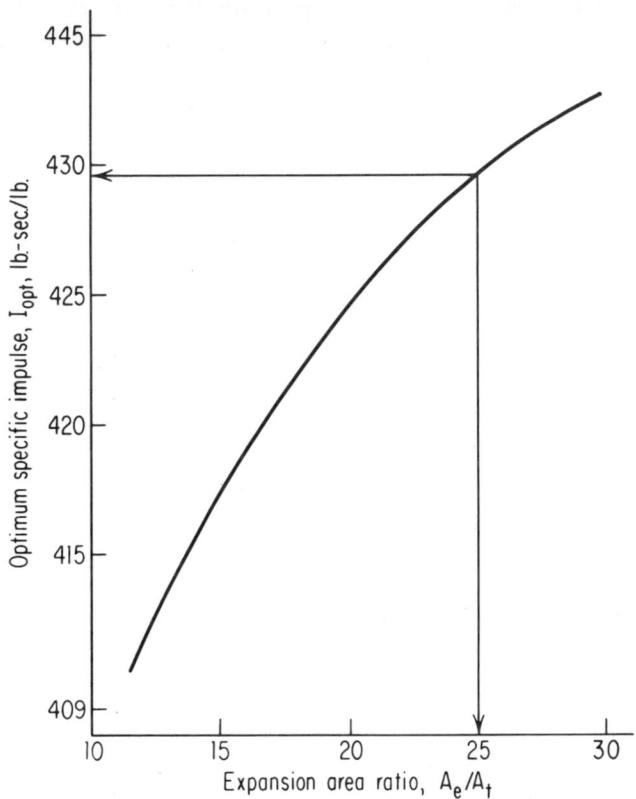

Fig. 5.3 Optimum specific impulse as a function of expansion area ratio (frozen equilibrium). H_2—F_2; $P_c = 500$ psia; $O/F = 5.665$.

Table 5.3. CALCULATED PERFORMANCE OF LIQUID FLUORINE/LIQUID HYDROGEN (FROZEN EQUILIBRIUM)

$P_c = 500$ psia, $O/F = 5.665$,   per cent fuel $= 15.00$, $c^* = 8210$ ft/sec

P_c/P_e	1.0	1.8342†	34.023	100	200	400	600	800
$T(°K)$	3371	2932	1423.0	1061	874	716.8	637.9	587.1
γ	1.294	1.303	1.361	1.385	1.396	1.403	1.405	1.406
ϵ		1.000	4.384	8.904	14.159	22.626	29.821	36.301
C_F		0.711	1.459	1.575	1.630	1.674	1.696	1.709
$I_{opt,sec}$		181.3	372.3	401.9	416.0	427.2	432.7	436.2

† Throat conditions.

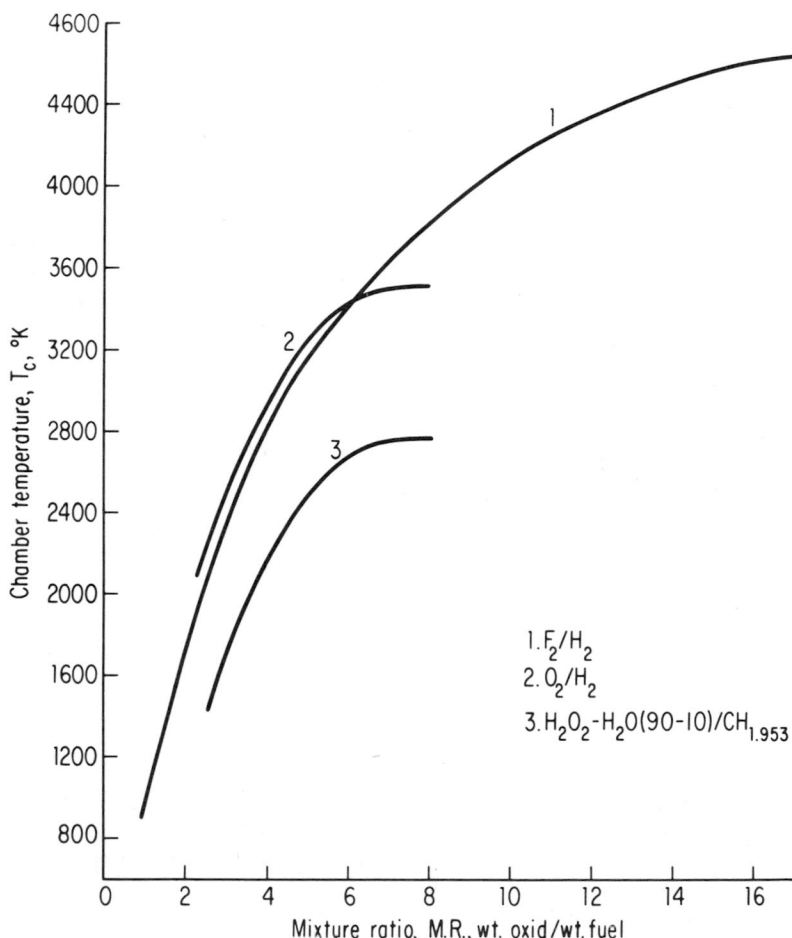

Fig. 5.4 Chamber temperature as a function of mixture ratio. $P_c = 500$ psia.

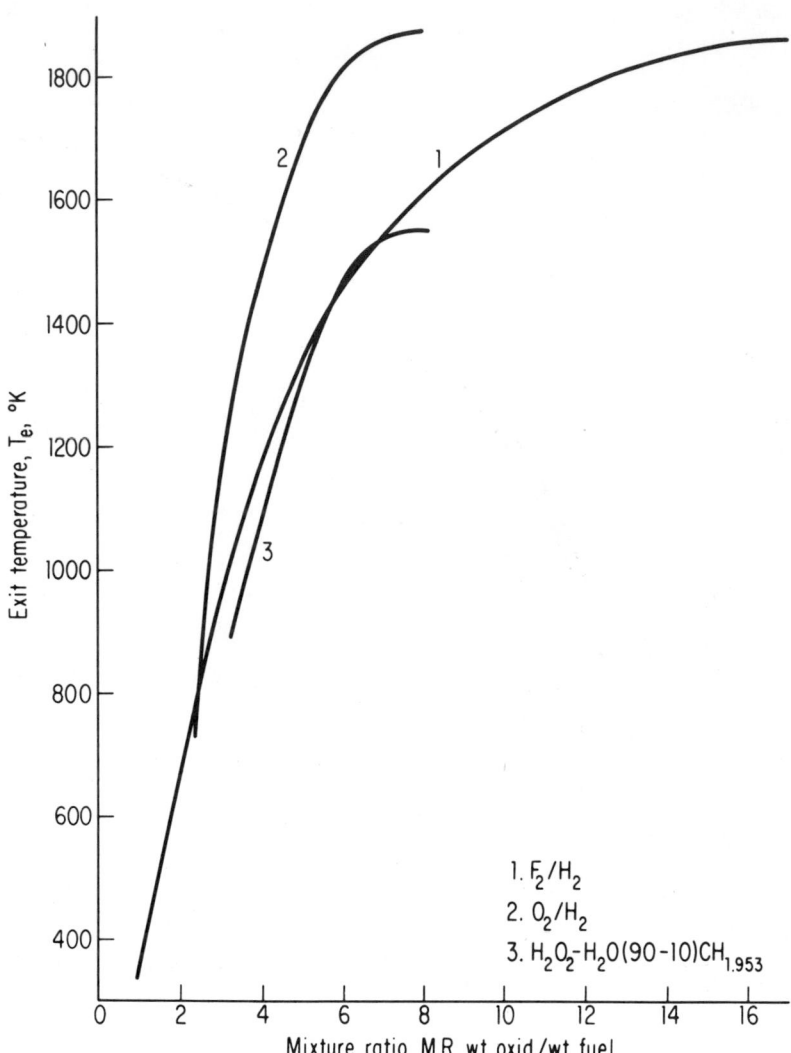

Fig. 5.5 Exit temperature as a function of mixture ratio (frozen equilibrium). $P_c = 500$ psia; $P_e = 14.696$ psia.

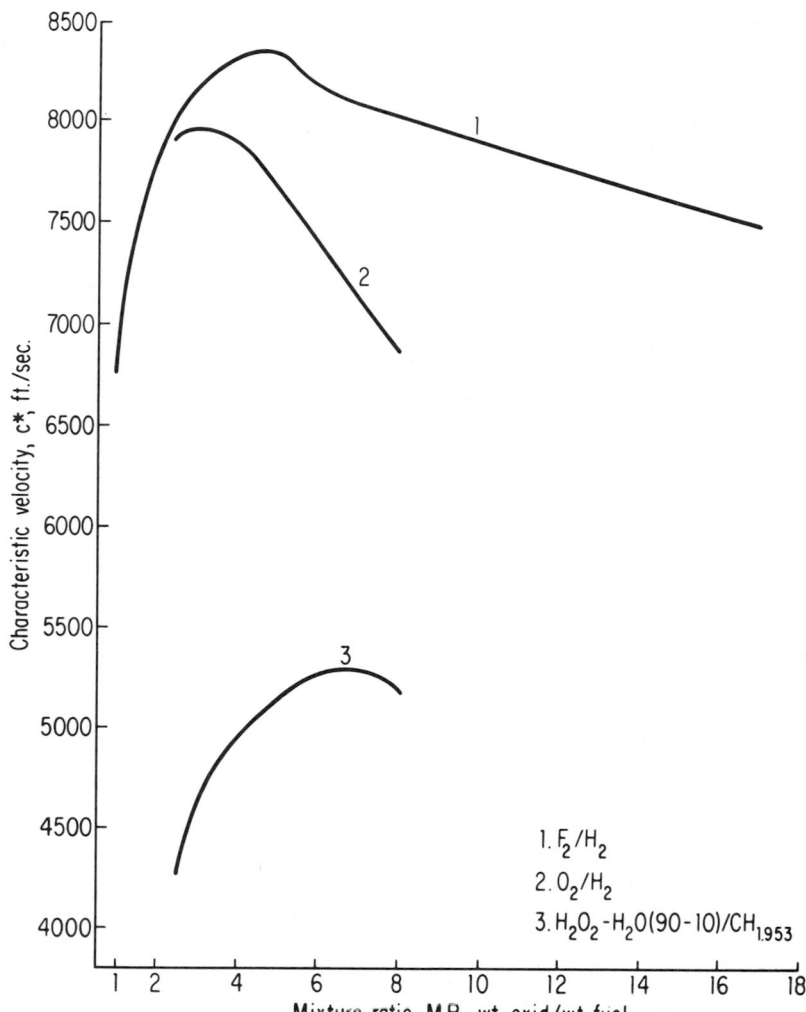

Fig. 5.6 Characteristic velocity as a function of mixture ratio (frozen equilibrium). $P_c = 500$ psia.

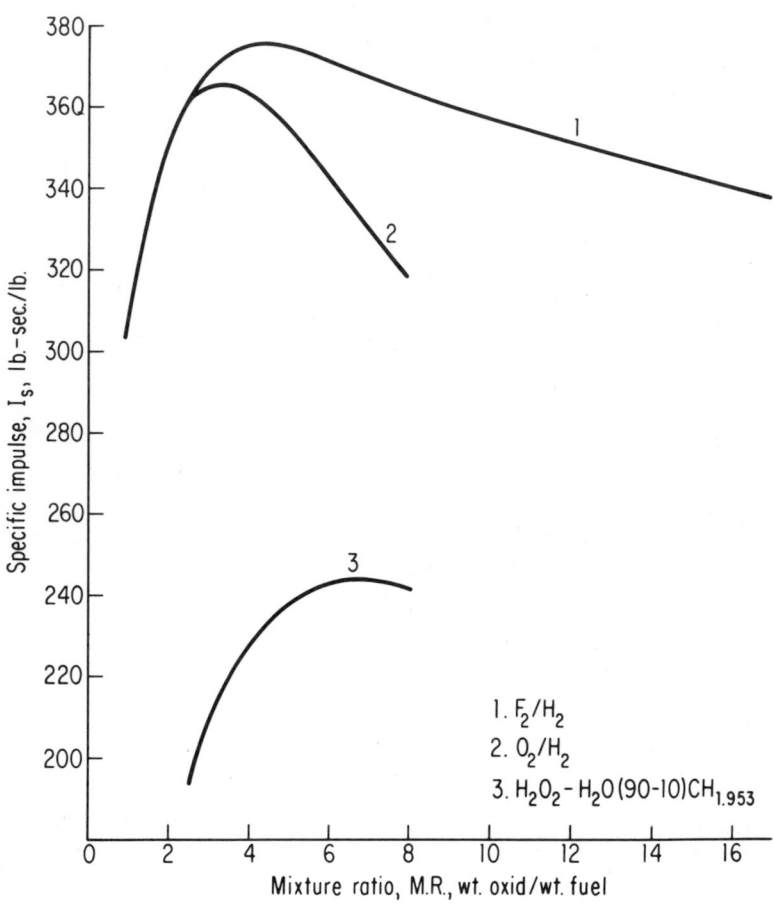

Fig. 5.7 Optimum specific impulse for isentropic expansion to one atmosphere pressure (frozen equilibrium). $P_c = 500$ psia; $P_e = 14.696$ psia.

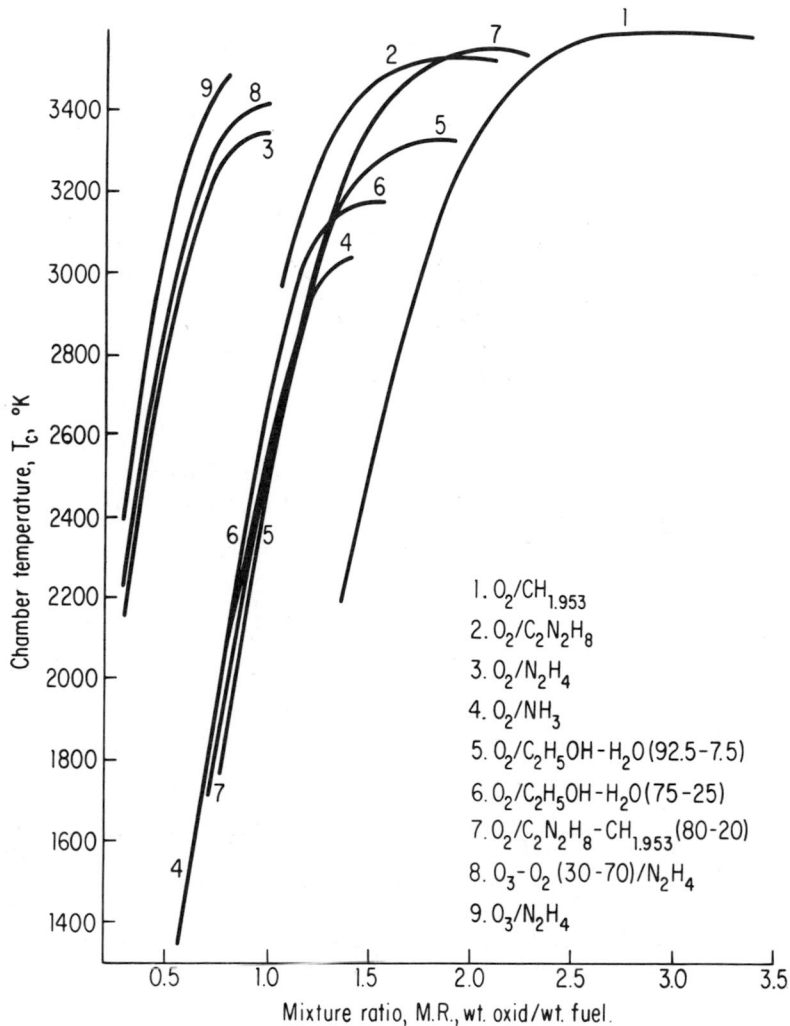

Fig. 5.8 Chamber temperature as a function of mixture ratio. P_c = 500 psia.

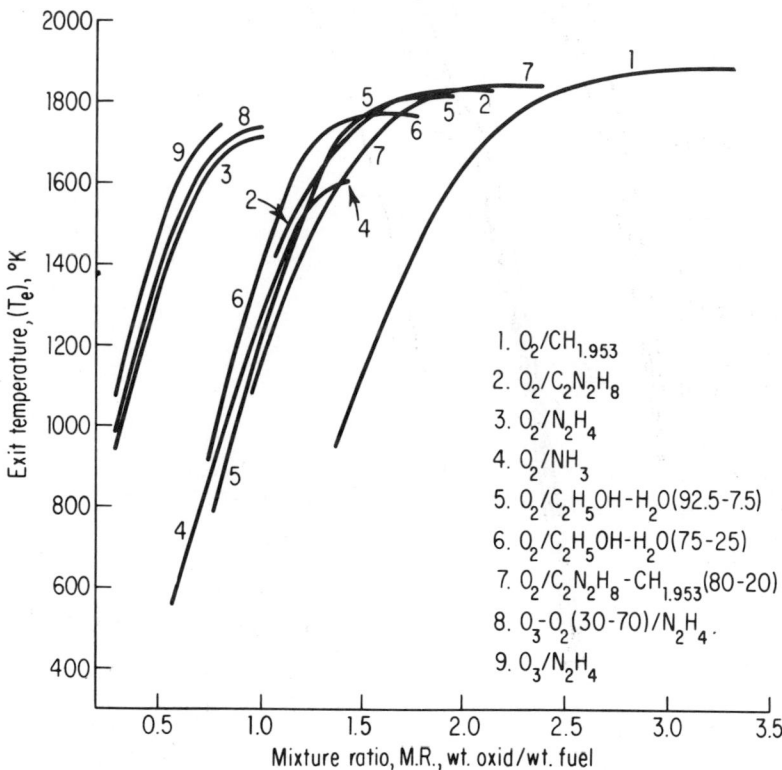

1. $O_2/CH_{1.953}$
2. $O_2/C_2N_2H_8$
3. O_2/N_2H_4
4. O_2/NH_3
5. $O_2/C_2H_5OH-H_2O(92.5-7.5)$
6. $O_2/C_2H_5OH-H_2O(75-25)$
7. $O_2/C_2N_2H_8-CH_{1.953}(80-20)$
8. $O_3-O_2(30-70)/N_2H_4$.
9. O_3/N_2H_4

Fig. 5.9 Exit temperature for isentropic expansion to one atmosphere pressure (frozen equilibrium). $P_c = 500$ psia; $P_e = 14.696$ psia.

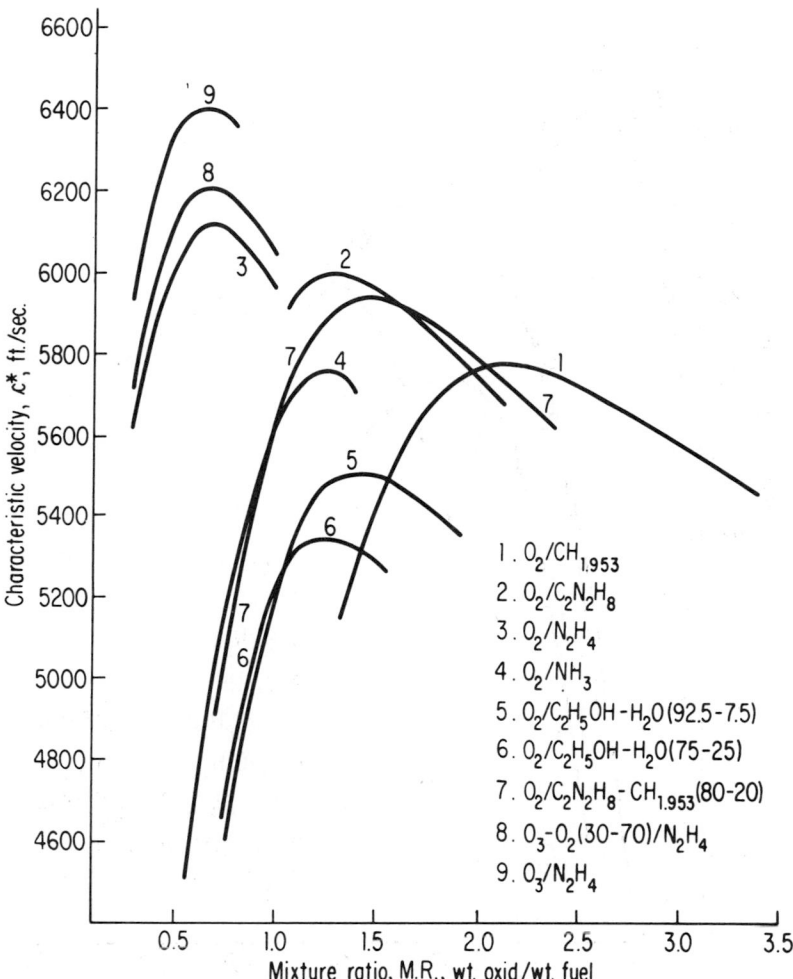

Fig. 5.10 Characteristic velocity as a function of mixture ratio (frozen equilibrium). $P_c = 500$ psia.

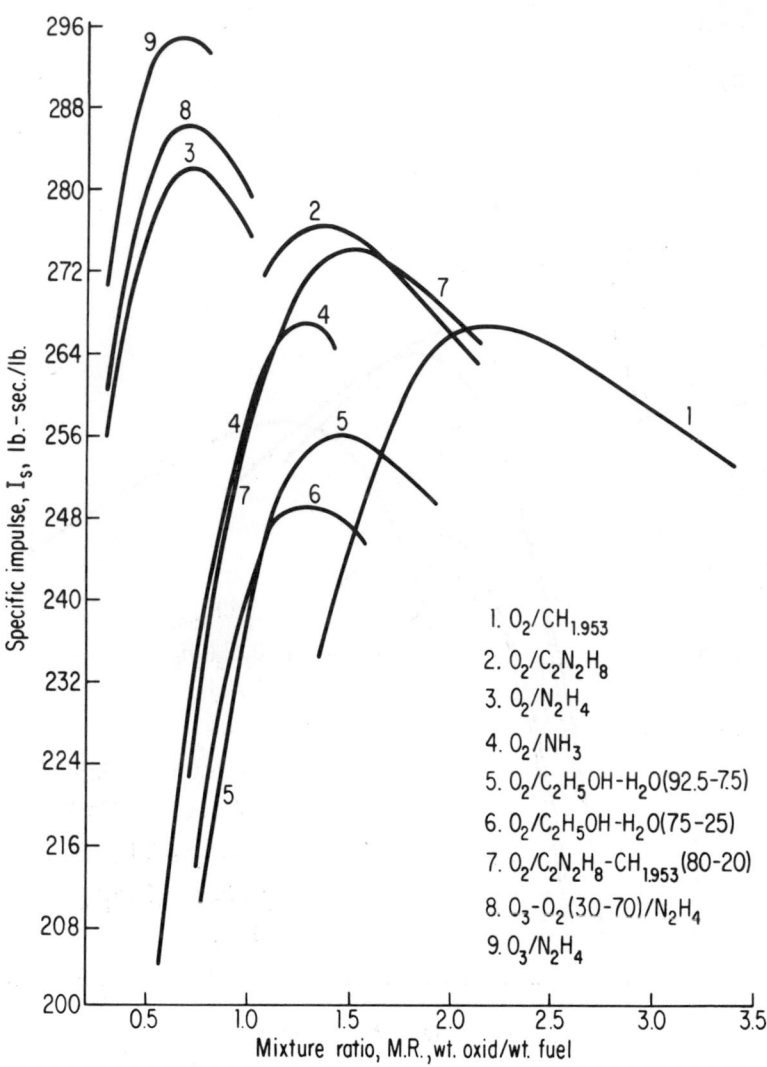

Fig. 5.11 Optimum specific impulse for isentropic expansion to one atmosphere pressure (frozen equilibrium). $P_c = 500$ psia; $P_e = 14.696$ psia.

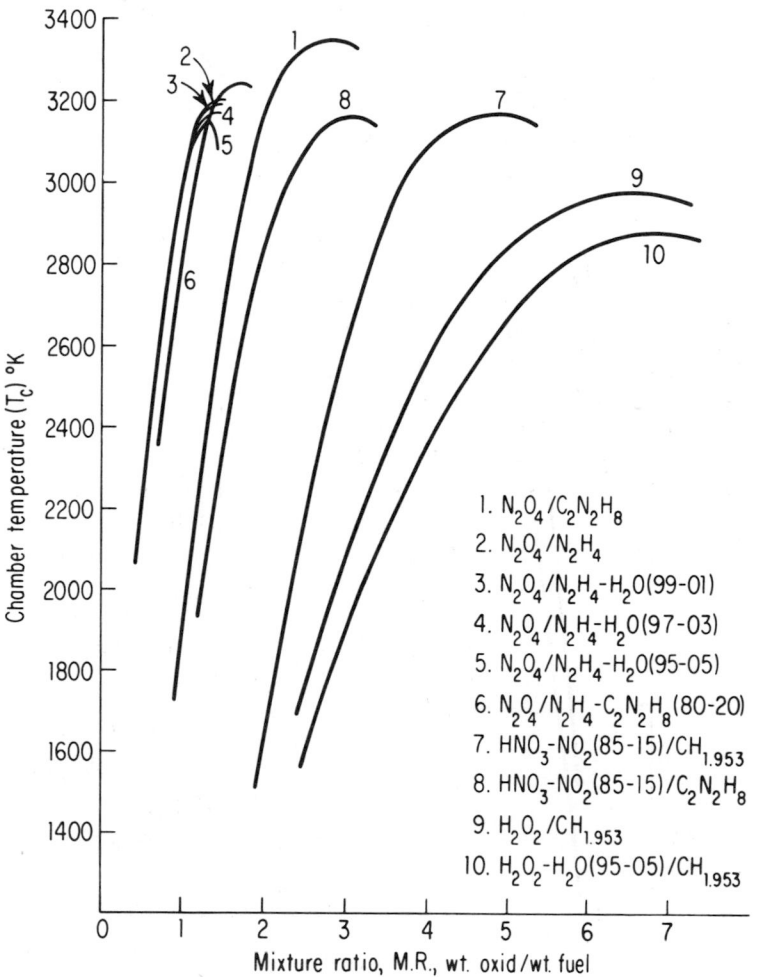

1. $N_2O_4/C_2N_2H_8$
2. N_2O_4/N_2H_4
3. $N_2O_4/N_2H_4-H_2O(99-01)$
4. $N_2O_4/N_2H_4-H_2O(97-03)$
5. $N_2O_4/N_2H_4-H_2O(95-05)$
6. $N_2O_4/N_2H_4-C_2N_2H_8(80-20)$
7. $HNO_3-NO_2(85-15)/CH_{1.953}$
8. $HNO_3-NO_2(85-15)/C_2N_2H_8$
9. $H_2O_2/CH_{1.953}$
10. $H_2O_2-H_2O(95-05)/CH_{1.953}$

Chamber temperature (T_c) °K

Mixture ratio, M.R., wt. oxid/wt. fuel

Fig. 5.12 Chamber temperature as a function of mixture ratio. $P_c = 500$ psia.

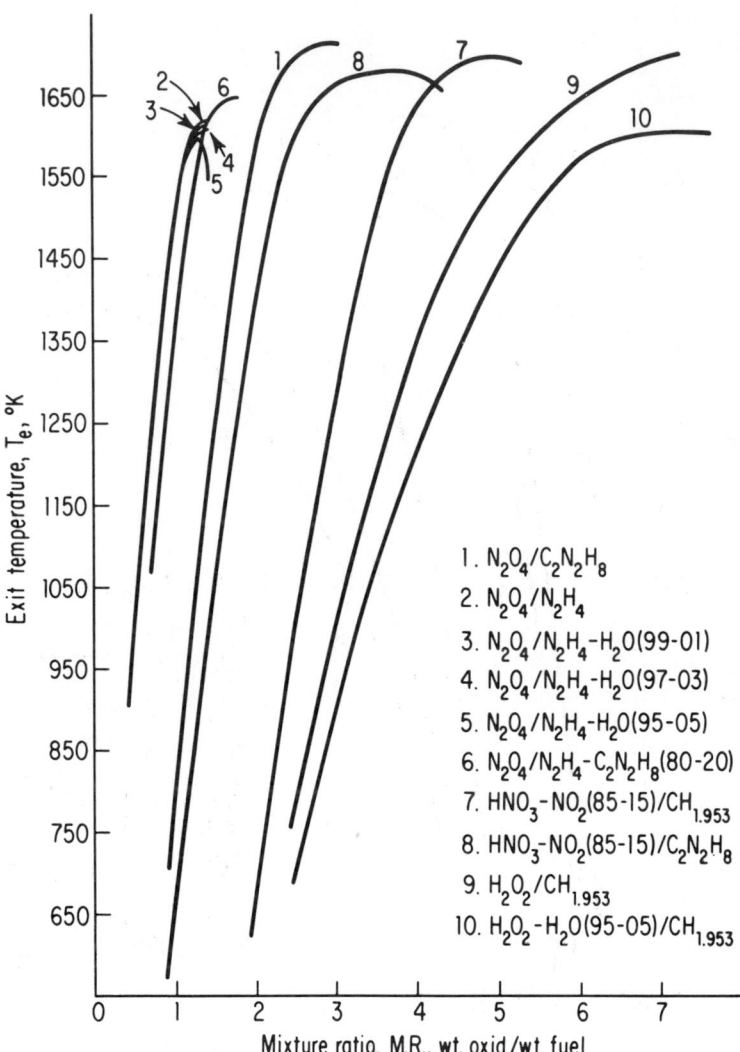

Fig. 5.13 Exit temperature for isentropic expansion to one atmosphere pressure (frozen equilibrium). $P_c = 500$ psia; $P_e = 14.696$ psia.

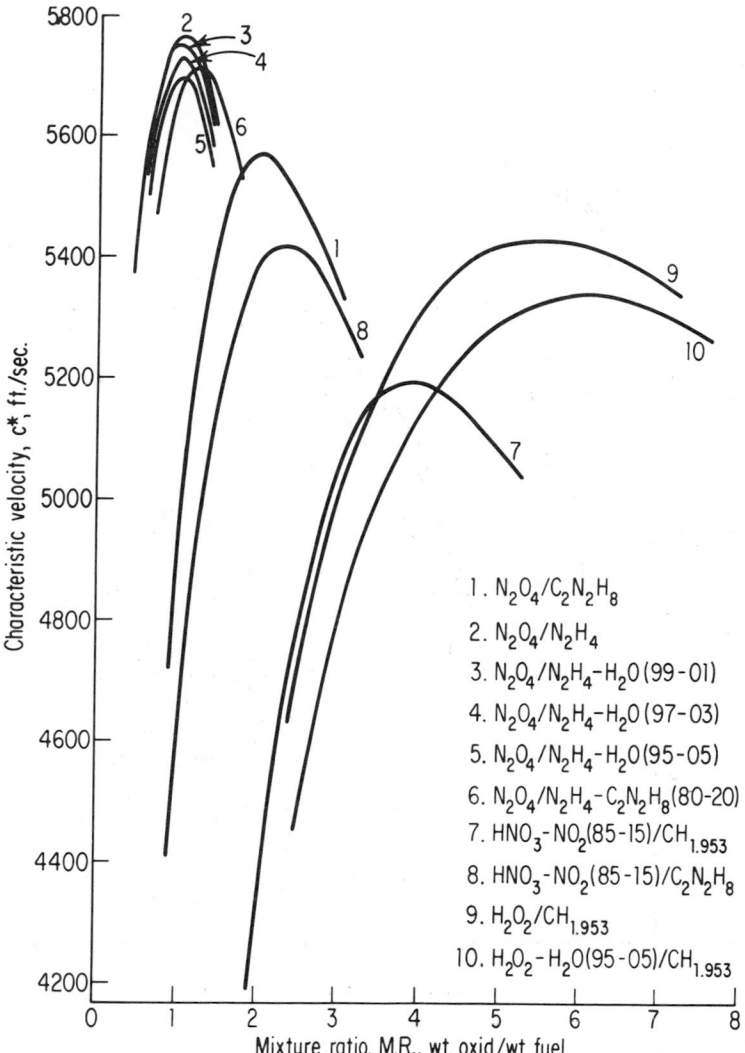

Fig. 5.14 Characteristic velocity as a function of mixture ratio (frozen equilibrium). $P_c = 500$ psia.

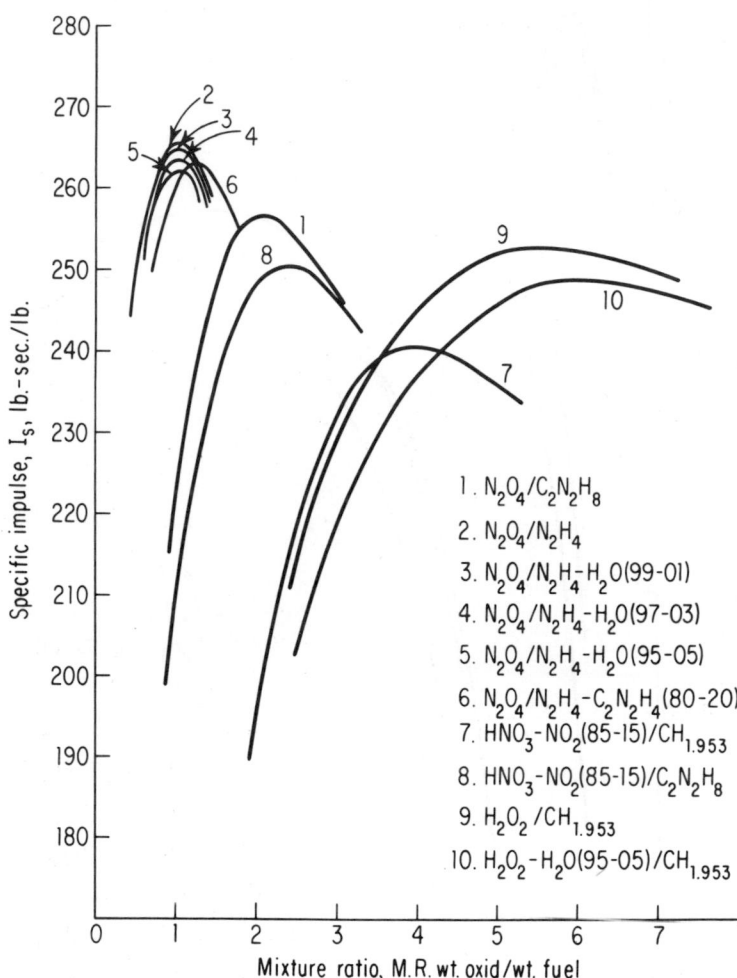

Fig. 5.15 Optimum specific impulse for isentropic expansion to one atmosphere pressure (frozen equilibrium). $P_c = 500$ psia; $P_e = 14.696$ psia.

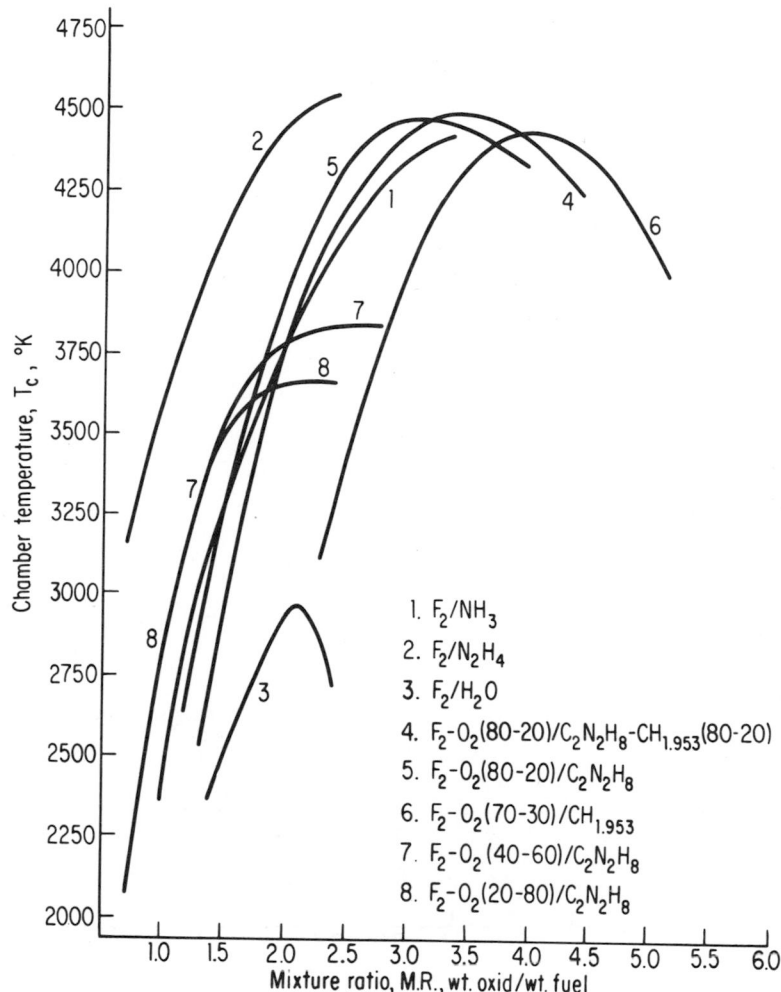

Fig. 5.16 Chamber temperature as a function of mixture ratio. $P_c = 500$ psia.

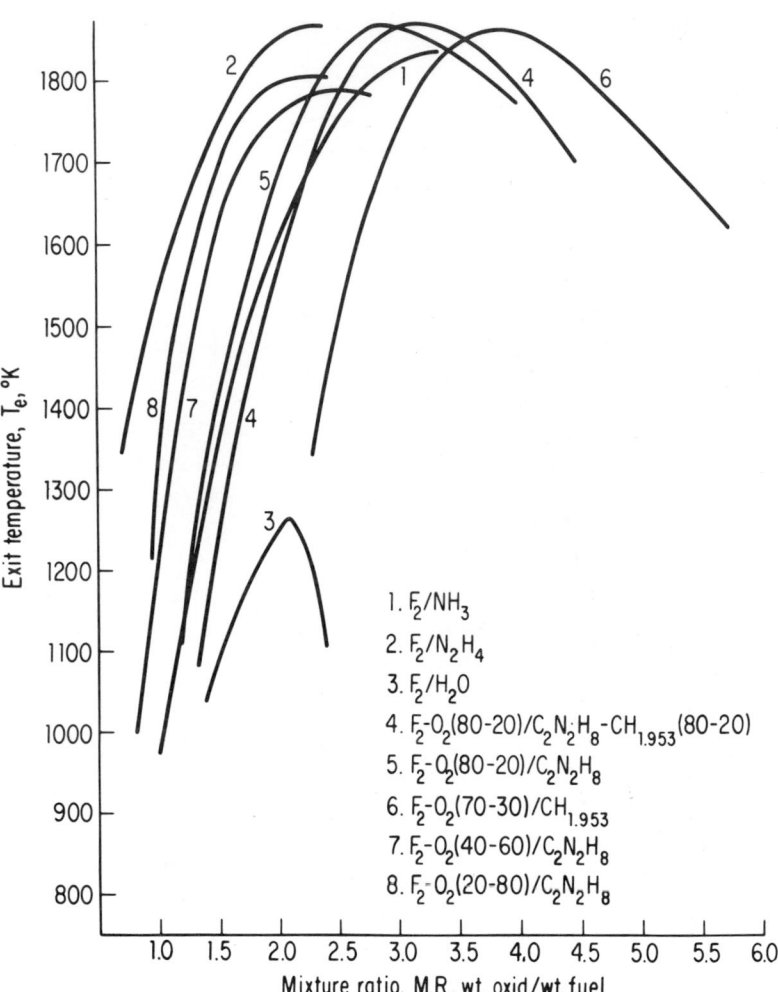

1. F_2/NH_3

2. F_2/N_2H_4

3. F_2/H_2O

4. $F_2\text{-}O_2(80\text{-}20)/C_2N_2H_8\text{-}CH_{1.953}(80\text{-}20)$

5. $F_2\text{-}O_2(80\text{-}20)/C_2N_2H_8$

6. $F_2\text{-}O_2(70\text{-}30)/CH_{1.953}$

7. $F_2\text{-}O_2(40\text{-}60)/C_2N_2H_8$

8. $F_2\text{-}O_2(20\text{-}80)/C_2N_2H_8$

Fig. 5.17 Exit temperature for isentropic expansion to one atmosphere pressure (frozen equilibrium). $P_c = 500$ psia; $P_e = 14.696$ psia.

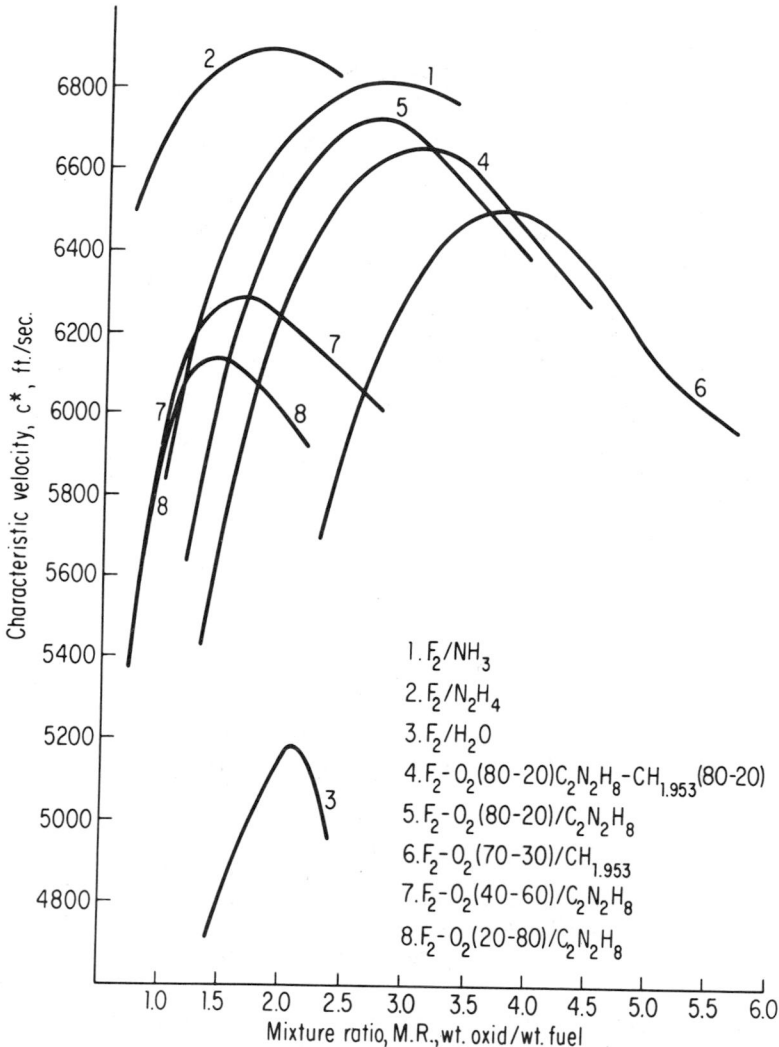

Fig. 5.18 Characteristic velocity as a function of mixture ratio (frozen equilibrium). P_c = 500 psia.

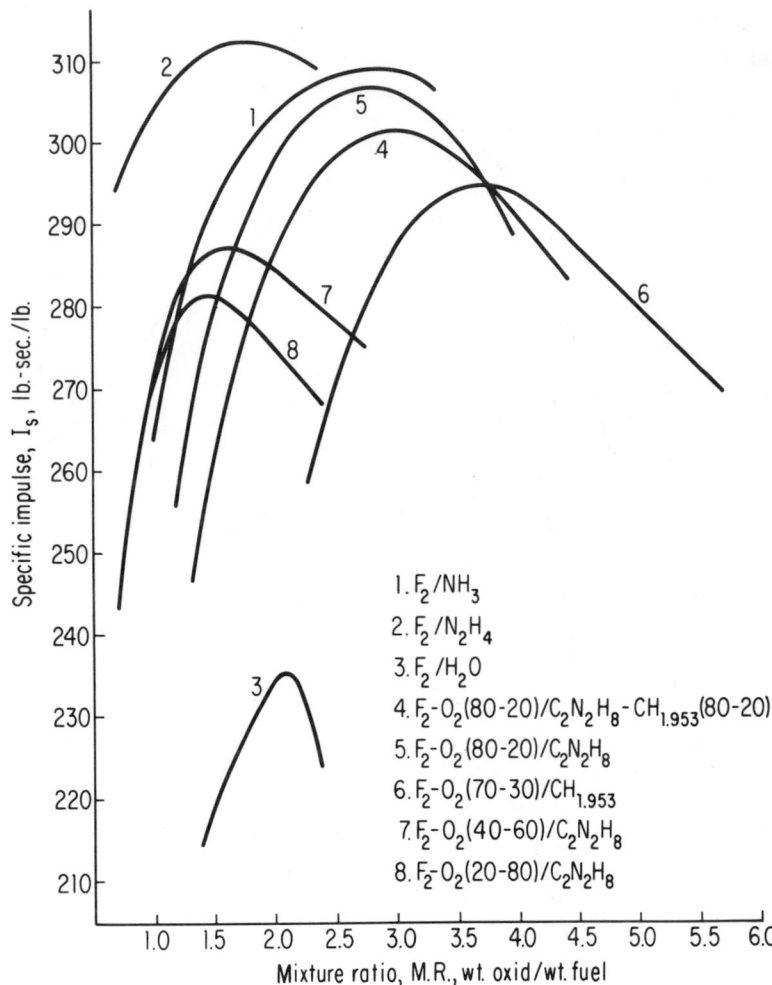

1. F_2/NH_3
2. F_2/N_2H_4
3. F_2/H_2O
4. $F_2\text{-}O_2(80\text{-}20)/C_2N_2H_8\text{-}CH_{1.953}(80\text{-}20)$
5. $F_2\text{-}O_2(80\text{-}20)/C_2N_2H_8$
6. $F_2\text{-}O_2(70\text{-}30)/CH_{1.953}$
7. $F_2\text{-}O_2(40\text{-}60)/C_2N_2H_8$
8. $F_2\text{-}O_2(20\text{-}80)/C_2N_2H_8$

Fig. 5.19 Optimum specific impulse for isentropic expansion to one atmosphere pressure (frozen equilibrium). $P_c = 500$ psia; $P_e = 14.696$ psia.

5.17. REPRESENTATIVE CALCULATIONS

Performance results of several propellant systems[12] containing hydrogen, oxygen, carbon, nitrogen, and fluorine are given in Table 5.4 and in Figs. 5.4 through 5.19. Tables 5.5 throuth 5.7 give typical results obtained with metallized propellants such as lithium, boron, beryllium, and aluminum based on values published by Dobbins.[13]

Each of these propellant combinations has certain desirable characteristics. Practical use of these chemicals as propellants depends on such factors as ease and speed of combustion, propellant density, toxicity, coolant characteristics, and so forth. The qualities needed in a propellant lie outside the scope of this text since our purpose was only to discuss the techniques required to evaluate theoretical performance of chemical propellants. Discussions of the qualities needed in a propellant can be found in standard texts on rocket propulsion.[14]

Table 5.4. CALCULATED PERFORMANCE OF SOME LIQUID PROPELLANTS (FROZEN EQUILIBRIUM)

$$F_2/H_2$$

$P_c = 500$ psia,   O/F $= 4.712$,   per cent fuel $= 17.51$, $c^* = 8276$ ft/sec

P_c/P_e	1.0	1.835†	34.022	100	200	400	800
T, °K	3097	2694	1302	970	798	655	537
γ	1.295	1.304	1.364	1.386	1.395	1.399	1.402
ϵ		1.000	4.368	8.860	14.092	22.532	36.194
C_F		0.711	1.458	1.574	1.628	1.672	1.707
$I_{opt, sec}$		182.8	375.1	404.8	418.9	430.1	439.2

$$O_2/H_2$$

$P_c = 500$ psia,   O/F $= 3.175$,   per cent fuel $= 23.95$, $c^* = 7976$ ft/sec

P_c/P_e	1.0	1.802†	34.022	100	200	400	800
T, °K	2580	2297	1227	951	802	673	562
γ	1.242	1.249	1.299	1.321	1.334	1.344	1.353
ϵ		1.000	4.743	9.941	16.137	26.283	42.906
C_F		0.693	1.475	1.602	1.664	1.715	1.756
$I_{opt, sec}$		171.9	365.6	397.2	412.6	425.2	435.4

[12] R. L. Wilkins and J. D. Weiher, *Propellant Performance Manual*, Rocketdyne Report R-669 (unclassified), Feb. 1959; S. Gordon and R. L. Wilkins, "Theoretical Maximum Performance of Liquid Fluorine—Liquid Oxygen Mixtures with JP-4 Fuel as Rocket Propellants," NACA Report RM E54H09, 1954.

[13] T. O. Dobbins, *Thermodynamics of Rocket Propulsion and Theoretical Evaluation of Some Prototype Propellant Combinations*, Project 3148, TR59-757, Wright Air Development Center, Wright-Patterson Air Force Base, Ohio, 1959.

[14] See, for example, G. P. Sutton, *Rocket Propulsion Elements* (New York: John Wiley & Sons, Inc., 1956), or, B. Kit and D. S. Evered, *Rocket Propellant Handbook* (New York: The Macmillan Company, 1960).

Table 5.4. (cont'd)

90% H_2O_2—10% $H_2O/CH_{1.953}$

$P_c = 500$ psia, O/F = 6.462, per cent fuel = 13.40, $c^* = 5242$ ft/sec

P_c/P_e	1.0	1.767†	34.022	100	200	400	800
T, °K	2735	2496	1514	1242	1087	947	821
γ	1.189	1.192	1.218	1.232	1.242	1.254	1.266
ϵ		1.000	5.263	11.574	19.401	32.614	54.939
C_F		0.675	1.497	1.642	1.715	1.777	1.829
$I_{opt, sec}$		110.0	243.9	267.5	279.5	289.6	298.1

F_2/NH_3

$P_c = 500$ psia, O/F = 3.012, per cent fuel = 24.93, $c^* = 6808$ ft/sec

P_c/P_e	1.0	1.840†	34.022	100	200	400	800
T, °K	4354	3770	1825	1367	1128	925	756
γ	1.306	1.313	1.354	1.377	1.392	1.405	1.415
ϵ		1.000	4.378	8.930	14.229	22.737	36.401
C_F		0.713	1.458	1.574	1.630	1.674	1.709
$I_{opt, sec}$		151.0	308.6	333.1	344.8	354.2	361.7

F_2/N_2H_4

$P_c = 500$ psia, O/F = 1.897, per cent fuel = 34.52, $c^* = 6899$ ft/sec

P_c/P_e	1.0	1.842†	34.022	100	200	400	800
T, °K	4401	3807	1840	1380	1138	935	764
γ	1.308	1.314	1.354	1.376	1.391	1.404	1.414
ϵ		1.000	4.373	8.926	14.230	22.748	36.427
C_F		0.714	1.458	1.574	1.630	1.674	1.709
$I_{opt, sec}$		153.1	312.7	337.6	349.4	358.9	366.5

F_2/H_2O

$P_c = 500$ psia, O/F = 2.1, per cent fuel = 32.26, $c^* = 5186$ ft/sec

P_c/P_e	1.0	1.833†	34.022	100	200	400	800
T, °K	2967	2583	1264	950	786	649	534
γ	1.292	1.300	1.351	1.371	1.380	1.387	1.393
ϵ		1.000	4.415	9.024	14.425	23.165	37.337
C_F		0.710	1.460	1.577	1.633	1.678	1.714
$I_{opt, sec}$		114.4	235.3	254.2	263.3	270.5	276.3

Table 5.4. (cont'd)

$80\% \ F_2 - 20\% \ O_2/80\% \ C_2N_2H_8 - 20\% \ CH_{1.953}$

$P_c = 500$ psia,   O/F = 3.11,   per cent fuel = 24.33, $c^* = 6655$ ft/sec

P_c/P_e	1.0	1.842†	34.022	100	200	400	800
T, °K	4472	3867	1872	1406	1163	956	783
γ	1.310	1.315	1.351	1.371	1.385	1.399	1.410
ϵ		1.000	4.378	8.957	14.302	22.906	36.743
C_F		0.714	1.458	1.575	1.630	1.675	1.710
$I_{opt, sec}$		147.8	301.7	325.7	337.2	346.4	353.8

$80\% \ F_2 - 20\% \ O_2/C_2N_2H_8$

$P_c = 500$ psia,   O/F = 2.78,   per cent fuel = 26.46, $c^* = 6723$ ft/sec

P_c/P_e	1.0	1.841†	34.022	100	200	400	800
T, °K	4450	3849	1866	1403	1160	954	782
γ	1.308	1.314	1.350	1.371	1.385	1.398	1.409
ϵ		1.000	4.385	8.971	14.328	22.950	36.825
C_F		0.714	1.459	1.575	1.631	1.675	1.711
$I_{opt, sec}$		149.2	304.8	329.1	340.7	350.0	357.5

$70\% \ F_2 - 30\% \ O_2/CH_{1.953}$

$P_c = 500$ psia,   O/F = 4.01,   per cent fuel = 19.96, $c^* = 6482$ ft/sec

P_c/P_e	1.0	1.841†	34.022	100	200	400	800
T, °K	4433	3834	1860	1399	1158	954	783
γ	1.309	1.315	1.348	1.368	1.382	1.395	1.406
ϵ		1.000	4.387	8.984	14.363	23.030	37.005
C_F		0.714	1.459	1.575	1.631	1.676	1.711
$I_{opt, sec}$		143.9	293.9	317.3	328.6	337.6	344.8

$40\% \ F_2 - 60\% \ O_2/C_2N_2H_8$

$P_c = 500$ psia,   O/F = 1.663,   per cent fuel = 37.55, $c^* = 6285$ ft/sec

P_c/P_e	1.0	1.813†	34.022	100	200	400	800
T, °K	3645	3217	1686	1306	1102	924	771
γ	1.264	1.268	1.301	1.319	1.333	1.347	1.359
ϵ		1.000	4.676	9.813	15.938	25.951	42.324
C_F		0.700	1.471	1.596	1.658	1.708	1.748
$I_{opt, sec}$		136.7	287.4	311.9	323.9	333.7	341.6

Table 5.4. (cont'd)

$$20\% \text{ F}_2\text{—}80\% \text{ O}_2/\text{C}_2\text{N}_2\text{H}_8$$

$P_c = 500$ psia, $\quad$ O/F $= 1.45$, $\quad$ per cent fuel $= 40.82$, $\quad c^* = 6131$ ft/sec

P_c/P_e	1.0	1.803†	34.022	100	200	400	800
T, °K	3456	3072	1661	1304	1108	937	789
γ	1.248	1.252	1.282	1.300	1.312	1.325	1.339
ϵ		1.000	4.798	10.174	16.640	27.286	44.814
C_F		0.694	1.477	1.606	1.670	1.722	1.765
$I_{opt, sec}$		132.3	281.4	306.1	318.2	328.2	336.4

† Throat conditions.

Table 5.5. THEORETICAL MAXIMUM SHIFTING SPECIFIC IMPULSE[13]

$$p_c = 1000 \text{ psi}, \qquad p_e = 14.696 \text{ psi}$$

Fuel	Oxidizer	Weight per cent oxidizer	Shifting I_s seconds	T_c, °K
H₂	OF₂	85.5	411	3591
	F₂	89	410	3964
	O₂	78	391	2769
	NF₃	93	351	3876
	NO₂ClO₄	83	349	2713
	ClO₃F	84	344	2744
	N₂O₄	84	342	2660
	H₂O₂	88	322	2404
	ClF₃	92	318	3403
	NH₄ClO₄	91	287	2448
N₂H₄	F₂	69	363	4688
	OF₂	60	345	4037
	NF₃	73	322	4242
	O₂	48	313	3409
	NO₂ClO₄	56	295	3363
	ClO₃F	59.5	295	3466
	ClF₃	73	293	3882
	N₂O₄	57	291	3257
	H₂O₂	67	286	2923
	NH₄ClO₄	73	265	2969
CH₂	OF₂	79	350	4650
	F₂	72.5	325	4382
	O₂	73	300	3683
	NF₃	78	287	3781
	ClO₃F	81	280	3722
	NO₂ClO₄	79	278	3586
	H₂O₂	86.5	277	2999
	N₂O₄	80	276	3444
	ClF₃	77	257	3541
	NH₄ClO₄	90.5	252	3016

Table 5.5. (cont'd)

$p_c = 1000$ psi, $p_e = 14.696$ psi

Fuel	Oxidizer	Weight per cent oxidizer	Shifting I_s seconds	T_c, °K
UDMH	OF_2	72	351	4460
	F_2	71	344	4342
	O_2	63	310	3614
	NF_3	76	309	3964
	ClO_3F	73	290	3666
	NO_2ClO_4	70	289	3540
	N_2O_4	72	286	3429
	H_2O_2	81	283	3008
	ClF_3	75	280	3794
	NH_4ClO_4	85	259	3038
C_4N_2	O_2	49	302	4816
	N_2O_4	61	282	4224
	H_2O_2	75	280	3320
	OF_2	68	278	4061
	NO_2ClO_4	61	276	4272
	NH_4ClO_4	80	258	3333
	ClO_3F	62	255	3708
	F_2	85	253	3891
	NF_3	85	232	3680
	ClF_3	87	203	3404
B_5H_9	OF_2	80	367	5169
	F_2	82	360	5101
	O_2	70	327	4518
	NF_3	87	326	4809
	H_2O_2	73	316	3400
	ClO_3F	79	306	4447
	N_2O_4	77	306	4266
	NO_2ClO_4	78	302	4432
	ClF_3	88	290	4487
	NH_4ClO_4	82	285	3484
MgH_2	F_2	72	329	4963
	OF_2	79	305	4516
	NF_3	78	302	4620
	H_2O_2	39	280	3073
	ClF_3	78	275	4465
	O_2	31	270	3076
	NH_4ClO_4	50	266	3073
	N_2O_4	40	265	3073
	NO_2ClO_4	38	263	3114
	ClO_3F	46	260	3237

Table 5.5. (cont'd)

$$p_c = 1000 \text{ psi}, \qquad p_e = 14.696 \text{ psi}$$

Fuel	Oxidizer	Weight per cent oxidizer	Shifting I_s seconds	T_c, °K
AlH$_3$	F$_2$	73.5	353	5317
	OF$_2$	59	333	4406
	H$_2$O$_2$	48	326	3923
	NF$_3$	78	323	4956
	O$_2$	42	318	4299
	N$_2$O$_4$	52	308	4226
	NO$_2$ClO$_4$	49	305	4175
	NH$_4$ClO$_4$	58	302	3837
	ClO$_3$F	50	301	4029
	ClF$_3$	77	291	4593
BeH$_2$	F$_2$	80.5	395	5331
	OF$_2$	67	383	4347
	H$_2$O$_2$	56.5	375	3574
	O$_2$	54.5	371	4138
	NF$_3$	81.5	359	4731
	N$_2$O$_4$	50	351	3403
	NO$_2$ClO$_4$	55	346	3394
	NH$_4$ClO$_4$	62	340	3283
	ClO$_3$F	68	339	4173
	ClF$_3$	81.5	329	4500
LiH	F$_2$	82	363	4886
	OF$_2$	77	337	4093
	NF$_3$	85.5	319	4384
	ClF$_0$	84	293	4109
	ClO$_3$F	76	272	3351
	O$_2$	66	263	3309
	H$_2$O$_2$	81	262	2711
	NO$_2$ClO$_4$	73	258	3292
	NH$_4$ClO$_4$	85	250	2754
	N$_2$O$_4$	74	250	3171

Table 5.6. THEORETICAL MAXIMUM SHIFTING IMPULSE[13]

$$p_c = 1000 \text{ psi}, \qquad p_e = 2.0 \text{ psi}$$

Fuel	Oxidizer	Weight per cent oxidizer	Shifting I_s, seconds	T_c, °K
H_2	OF_2	87	458	3756
	F_2	92	457	4462
	O_2	82	437	3182
	NF_3	94.5	390	4212
	NO_2ClO_4	86	389	3080
	ClO_3F	87	383	3273
	N_2O_4	86	381	2891
	H_2O_2	91	359	2740
	ClF_3	93.5	352	3690
	NH_4ClO_4	92.5	319	2660
N_2H_4	F_2	69	408	4688
	OF_2	63	392	4100
	NF_3	73	357	4242
	O_2	49	355	3425
	NO_2ClO_4	58	333	3375
	ClO_3F	61	333	3478
	N_2O_4	59	329	3262
	ClF_3	73	325	3882
	H_2O_2	68	323	2916
	NH_4ClO_4	73	297	2969
CH_2	OF_2	79	393	4650
	F_2	72.5	371	4382
	O_2	73	344	3683
	NF_3	78	326	3781
	ClO_3F	82	319	3734
	NO_2ClO_4	81	318	3603
	N_2O_4	82	316	3453
	H_2O_2	88	315	2979
	ClF_3	77	291	3541
	NH_4ClO_4	91	287	3001
UDMH	OF_2	75	400	4519
	F_2	71	393	4342
	O_2	65	354	3633
	NF_3	76	348	3964
	ClO_3F	75	329	3686
	NO_2ClO_4	73	328	3567
	N_2O_4	74	325	3433
	H_2O_2	81	321	3008
	ClF_3	75	314	3794
	NH_4ClO_4	86	293	3026

Table 5.6. (cont'd)

$p_c = 1000$ psi, $\quad p_e = 2.0$ psi

Fuel	Oxidizer	Weight per cent oxidizer	Shifting I_s, seconds	T_c, °K
C₄N₂	O₂	52	342	4609
	N₂O₄	64	320	4127
	OF₂	68	320	4061
	H₂O₂	75	319	3320
	NO₂ClO₄	64	313	4168
	NH₄ClO₄	83	293	3264
	F₂	85	292	3891
	ClO₃F	62	289	3708
	NF₃	85	269	3680
	ClF₃	87	235	3404
B₅H₉	OF₂	80	422	5169
	F₂	84	413	5165
	O₂	70	379	4518
	NF₃	88	374	4841
	H₂O₂	73	361	3400
	ClO₃F	79	353	4447
	N₂O₄	79	353	4388
	NO₂ClO₄	79	350	4502
	ClF₃	88	333	4487
	NH₄ClO₄	73	330	3000
MgH₂	F₂	74	379	4991
	OF₂	69	352	4404
	NF₃	78	346	4620
	H₂O₂	42	327	3073
	O₂	33	316	3216
	ClF₃	78	315	4465
	NH₄ClO₄	50	311	3073
	N₂O₄	44	310	3265
	NO₂ClO₄	40	308	3124
	ClO₃F	49	305	3390
AlH₃	F₂	75	405	5346
	OF₂	62	386	4447
	H₂O₂	48	378	3923
	O₂	44	371	4299
	NF₃	81	370	5006
	N₂O₄	52	358	4226
	NO₂ClO₄	51	355	4252
	NH₄ClO₄	58	350	3837
	ClO₃F	55	350	4204
	ClF₃	80	333	4693

Table 5.6. (cont'd)

$p_c = 1000$ psi, $p_e = 2.0$ psi

Fuel	Oxidizer	Weight per cent oxidizer	Shifting I_s, seconds	T_c, °K
BeH$_2$	F$_2$	80.5	453	5331
	OF$_2$	67	445	4347
	H$_2$O$_2$	58	442	3708
	O$_2$	53	436	4004
	NF$_3$	81.5	413	4731
	N$_2$O$_4$	50	411	3403
	NO$_2$ClO$_4$	61	406	3866
	NH$_4$ClO$_4$	62	398	3283
	ClO$_3$F	68	396	4173
	ClF$_3$	81.5	378	4500
LiH	F$_2$	82	410	4886
	OF$_2$	77	386	4093
	NF$_3$	85.5	360	4384
	ClF$_3$	84	330	4109
	ClO$_3$F	76	312	3351
	O$_2$	66	306	3309
	H$_2$O$_2$	81	304	2711
	NO$_2$ClO$_4$	73	299	3292
	NH$_4$ClO$_4$	85	289	2754
	N$_2$O$_4$	74	290	3171

Table 5.7. THEORETICAL MAXIMUM SHIFTING SPECIFIC IMPULSE[13]

$p_c = 1000$ psi, $p_e = 0.2$ psi

Fuel	Oxidizer	Weight per cent oxidizer	Shifting I_s, seconds	T_c, °K
H$_2$	OF$_2$	91	491	4149
	F$_2$	94	489	4809
	O$_2$	84	470	3374
	NO$_2$ClO$_4$	87.5	416	3259
	NF$_3$	94.5	413	4212
	ClO$_3$F	90	409	3502
	N$_2$O$_4$	89	408	3254
	H$_2$O$_2$	92.5	385	2912
	ClF$_3$	95	373	3985
	NH$_4$ClO$_4$	94	340	2883

Table 5.7. (cont'd)

$$p_c = 1000 \text{ psi}, \qquad p_e = 0.2 \text{ psi}$$

Fuel	Oxidizer	Weight per cent oxidizer	Shifting I_s, seconds	T_c, °K
N_2H_4	F_2	69	436	4688
	OF_2	63	424	4100
	O_2	49	384	3425
	NF_3	73	379	4242
	NO_2ClO_4	58	359	3375
	ClO_3F	61	358	3478
	N_2O_4	59	354	3262
	H_2O_2	68	348	2916
	ClF_3	73	345	3882
	NH_4ClO_4	73	318	2969
CH_2	OF_2	79	420	4650
	F_2	74	405	4405
	O_2	75	379	3699
	NF_3	78	352	3781
	NO_2ClO_4	82.5	349	3587
	ClO_3F	85	347	3700
	N_2O_4	82	345	3453
	H_2O_2	88	344	2979
	ClF_3	77	315	3541
	NH_4ClO_4	91	309	3001
UDMH	OF_2	78	435	4510
	F_2	71	426	4342
	O_2	68	388	3626
	NF_3	76	373	3964
	ClO_3F	77	359	3678
	NO_2ClO_4	73	358	3567
	N_2O_4	74	354	3433
	H_2O_2	82	349	2992
	ClF_3	75	337	3794
	NH_4ClO_4	86	316	3026
C_4N_2	O_2	55	374	4475
	OF_2	65	355	4112
	N_2O_4	67	350	4034
	H_2O_2	78	350	3257
	NO_2ClO_4	67	342	4073
	F_2	85	325	3891
	NH_4ClO_4	83	319	3264
	ClO_3F	68	316	3488
	NF_3	85	301	3680
	ClF_3	87	261	3404

Table 5.7. (cont'd)

$$p_c = 1000 \text{ psi}, \qquad p_e = 0.2 \text{ psi}$$

Fuel	Oxidizer	Weight per cent oxidizer	Shifting I_s, seconds	T_c, °K
B_5H_9	OF_2	81.5	466	5215
	F_2	84	460	5165
	O_2	72	421	4620
	NF_3	89	413	4854
	H_2O_2	73	399	3400
	N_2O_4	79	391	4388
	ClO_3F	79	390	4447
	NO_2ClO_4	79	389	4502
	ClF_3	89	368	4543
	NH_4ClO_4	73	370	3000
MgH_2	F_2	74	420	4991
	OF_2	65	394	4337
	NF_3	78	380	4620
	H_2O_2	42	368	3073
	O_2	33	357	3216
	N_2O_4	44	349	3265
	NH_4ClO_4	53	348	3080
	ClF_3	78	347	4465
	NO_2ClO_4	43	346	3288
	ClO_3F	49	343	3390
AlH_3	F_2	77	447	5368
	OF_2	62	431	4447
	H_2O_2	48	424	3923
	O_2	44	416	4374
	NF_3	81	407	5006
	N_2O_4	54	401	4292
	NO_2ClO_4	51	397	4252
	NH_4ClO_4	58	393	3837
	ClO_3F	55	390	4204
	ClF_3	80	367	4693
BeH_2	F_2	79	501	5194
	H_2O_2	61	498	3884
	OF_2	70	497	4527
	O_2	53	492	4004
	N_2O_4	52	462	3446
	NF_3	81.5	456	4731
	NO_2ClO_4	64	456	4132
	NH_4ClO_4	62	446	3283
	ClO_3F	68	446	4173
	ClF_3	81.5	418	4500

Table 5.7. (cont'd)

$$p_c = 1000 \text{ psi}, \qquad p_e = 0.2 \text{ psi}$$

Fuel	Oxidizer	Weight per cent oxidizer	Shifting I_s, seconds	T_c, °K
LiH	F_2	82	445	4886
	OF_2	77	424	4093
	NF_3	85.5	392	4384
	ClF_3	84	360	4109
	ClO_3F	76	345	3351
	O_2	66	342	3309
	H_2O_2	81	341	2711
	NO_2ClO_4	73	333	3292
	NH_4ClO_4	63.5	326	2292
	N_2O_4	74	325	3171

APPENDIX 1

THERMODYNAMIC FUNCTIONS OF A MONOCHROMATIC OSCILLATOR WITH ADDITIONAL FUNCTIONAL REQUIRED FOR ANHARMONIC CORRECTIONS

In this appendix, we give values of ${}^n\phi$ as defined in Eq. (1.216) through (1.226).

Appendix Table 1

u	1φ	2φ	3φ	4φ	5φ	6φ	7φ	8φ	9φ	10φ	11φ
0.200	4.5167	4.9834	9.9999	8.1601	9.8465	19.9871	2.0199	0.6033	0.9967	0.9033	1.7078
0.205	4.3951	4.8610	9.7560	7.9200	9.5990	19.4987	1.9900	0.6060	0.9965	0.9010	1.6855
0.210	4.2794	4.7444	9.5237	7.6915	9.3633	19.0334	1.9611	0.6087	0.9963	0.8987	1.6638
0.215	4.1691	4.6333	9.3022	7.4739	9.1383	18.5898	1.9331	0.6113	0.9962	0.8963	1.6427
0.220	4.0638	4.5272	9.0908	7.2663	8.9234	18.1663	1.9061	0.6140	0.9960	0.8940	1.6221
0.225	3.9632	4.4257	8.8888	7.0681	8.7180	17.7616	1.8799	0.6167	0.9958	0.8917	1.6020
0.230	3.8670	4.3287	8.6956	6.8786	8.5213	17.3744	1.8545	0.6194	0.9956	0.8894	1.5825
0.235	3.7749	4.2358	8.5105	6.6974	8.3329	17.0036	1.8299	0.6221	0.9954	0.8871	1.5634
0.240	3.6866	4.1467	8.3332	6.5239	8.1522	16.6483	1.8061	0.6248	0.9952	0.8848	1.5447
0.245	3.6020	4.0613	8.1631	6.3576	7.9787	16.3074	1.7829	0.6275	0.9950	0.8825	1.5265
0.250	3.5208	3.9792	7.9999	6.1981	7.8121	15.9801	1.7604	0.6302	0.9948	0.8802	1.5087
0.255	3.4428	3.9004	7.8430	6.0449	7.6519	15.6656	1.7385	0.6329	0.9946	0.8779	1.4913
0.260	3.3678	3.8246	7.6922	5.8979	7.4977	15.3631	1.7172	0.6356	0.9944	0.8756	1.4743
0.265	3.2956	3.7516	7.5470	5.7565	7.3492	15.0720	1.6965	0.6383	0.9942	0.8733	1.4576
0.270	3.2262	3.6813	7.4072	5.6204	7.2062	14.7917	1.6764	0.6411	0.9939	0.8711	1.4413
0.275	3.1593	3.6135	7.2726	5.4895	7.0682	14.5215	1.6567	0.6438	0.9937	0.8688	1.4253
0.280	3.0947	3.5482	7.1427	5.3633	6.9350	14.2609	1.6376	0.6465	0.9935	0.8665	1.4097
0.285	3.0325	3.4851	7.0174	5.2417	6.8065	14.0094	1.6189	0.6493	0.9933	0.8643	1.3944
0.290	2.9724	3.4242	6.8964	5.1244	6.6822	13.7665	1.6007	0.6520	0.9930	0.8620	1.3794
0.295	2.9144	3.3654	6.7794	5.0112	6.5621	13.5318	1.5829	0.6547	0.9928	0.8597	1.3647
0.300	2.8583	3.3084	6.6664	4.9019	6.4459	13.3049	1.5656	0.6575	0.9925	0.8575	1.3502
0.305	2.8041	3.2534	6.5571	4.7963	6.3334	13.0854	1.5486	0.6602	0.9923	0.8552	1.3361
0.310	2.7516	3.2001	6.4514	4.6942	6.2245	12.8730	1.5320	0.6630	0.9920	0.8530	1.3222
0.315	2.7008	3.1485	6.3489	4.5955	6.1189	12.6672	1.5158	0.6658	0.9918	0.8508	1.3086
0.320	2.6516	3.0985	6.2497	4.4999	6.0165	12.4678	1.5000	0.6685	0.9915	0.8485	1.2952
0.325	2.6040	3.0500	6.1536	4.4074	5.9172	12.2745	1.4845	0.6713	0.9912	0.8463	1.2820
0.330	2.5578	3.0030	6.0603	4.3178	5.8209	12.0871	1.4693	0.6741	0.9910	0.8441	1.2691
0.335	2.5129	2.9573	5.9698	4.2310	5.7273	11.9052	1.4545	0.6768	0.9907	0.8418	1.2565
0.340	2.4695	2.9130	5.8820	4.1468	5.6364	11.7286	1.4399	0.6796	0.9904	0.8396	1.2440
0.345	2.4272	2.8700	5.7968	4.0651	5.5481	11.5570	1.4257	0.6824	0.9901	0.8374	1.2318
0.350	2.3863	2.8282	5.7139	3.9859	5.4622	11.3903	1.4117	0.6852	0.9899	0.8352	1.2197
0.355	2.3464	2.7875	5.6334	3.9090	5.3787	11.2283	1.3980	0.6880	0.9896	0.8330	1.2079
0.360	2.3077	2.7480	5.5552	3.8344	5.2974	11.0708	1.3846	0.6908	0.9893	0.8308	1.1963
0.365	2.2701	2.7095	5.4791	3.7619	5.2183	10.9175	1.3715	0.6936	0.9890	0.8286	1.1848
0.370	2.2335	2.6721	5.4050	3.6914	5.1412	10.7683	1.3586	0.6964	0.9887	0.8264	1.1736
0.375	2.1978	2.6356	5.3329	3.6229	5.0662	10.6230	1.3459	0.6992	0.9884	0.8242	1.1625
0.380	2.1632	2.6001	5.2627	3.5563	4.9930	10.4816	1.3335	0.7020	0.9881	0.8220	1.1516

u	1ϕ	2ϕ	3ϕ	4ϕ	5ϕ	6ϕ	7ϕ	8ϕ	9ϕ	10ϕ	11ϕ
0.385	2.1294	2.5656	5.1943	3.4915	4.9217	10.3437	1.3213	0.7048	0.9877	0.8198	1.1408
0.390	2.0965	2.5318	5.1277	3.4284	4.8522	10.2094	1.3093	0.7076	0.9874	0.8176	1.1303
0.395	2.0645	2.4990	5.0628	3.3670	4.7843	10.0784	1.2975	0.7105	0.9871	0.8155	1.1199
0.400	2.0332	2.4669	4.9995	3.3073	4.7181	9.9506	1.2859	0.7133	0.9868	0.8133	1.1096
0.405	2.0028	2.4357	4.9377	3.2491	4.6535	9.8260	1.2746	0.7161	0.9864	0.8111	1.0995
0.410	1.9731	2.4051	4.8775	3.1923	4.5904	9.7044	1.2634	0.7190	0.9861	0.8090	1.0896
0.415	1.9441	2.3754	4.8187	3.1371	4.5288	9.5856	1.2524	0.7218	0.9858	0.8068	1.0798
0.420	1.9159	2.3463	4.7613	3.0832	4.4685	9.4697	1.2416	0.7247	0.9854	0.8047	1.0702
0.425	1.8883	2.3178	4.7053	3.0307	4.4097	9.3564	1.2310	0.7275	0.9851	0.8025	1.0607
0.430	1.8613	2.2901	4.6505	2.9794	4.3521	9.2457	1.2205	0.7304	0.9847	0.8004	1.0513
0.435	1.8350	2.2629	4.5970	2.9294	4.2958	9.1375	1.2103	0.7332	0.9844	0.7982	1.0420
0.440	1.8093	2.2364	4.5448	2.8807	4.2408	9.0318	1.2001	0.7361	0.9840	0.7961	1.0329
0.445	1.7842	2.2105	4.4937	2.8330	4.1869	8.9283	1.1902	0.7389	0.9837	0.7939	1.0239
0.450	1.7596	2.1851	4.4437	2.7866	4.1342	8.8272	1.1804	0.7418	0.9833	0.7918	1.0151
0.455	1.7356	2.1603	4.3948	2.7412	4.0827	8.7282	1.1707	0.7447	0.9829	0.7897	1.0063
0.460	1.7121	2.1360	4.3470	2.6968	4.0321	8.6313	1.1612	0.7476	0.9826	0.7876	0.9977
0.465	1.6891	2.1122	4.3003	2.6535	3.9827	8.5365	1.1518	0.7505	0.9822	0.7855	0.9892
0.470	1.6667	2.0889	4.2545	2.6112	3.9342	8.4437	1.1426	0.7533	0.9818	0.7833	0.9808
0.475	1.6447	2.0661	4.2096	2.5698	3.8867	8.3527	1.1335	0.7562	0.9814	0.7812	0.9726
0.480	1.6232	2.0438	4.1658	2.5293	3.8402	8.2636	1.1246	0.7591	0.9810	0.7791	0.9644
0.485	1.6021	2.0219	4.1228	2.4898	3.7945	8.1764	1.1157	0.7620	0.9806	0.7770	0.9563
0.490	1.5815	2.0005	4.0807	2.4511	3.7498	8.0908	1.1070	0.7649	0.9802	0.7749	0.9484
0.495	1.5613	1.9795	4.0394	2.4132	3.7059	8.0070	1.0985	0.7678	0.9798	0.7728	0.9405
0.500	1.5415	1.9588	3.9990	2.3762	3.6629	7.9248	1.0900	0.7707	0.9794	0.7707	0.9328
0.505	1.5221	1.9386	3.9593	2.3400	3.6207	7.8441	1.0817	0.7737	0.9790	0.7687	0.9251
0.510	1.5031	1.9188	3.9205	2.3045	3.5793	7.7651	1.0734	0.7766	0.9786	0.7666	0.9175
0.515	1.4845	1.8994	3.8824	2.2698	3.5386	7.6875	1.0653	0.7795	0.9782	0.7645	0.9101
0.520	1.4662	1.8803	3.8450	2.2358	3.4987	7.6114	1.0573	0.7824	0.9778	0.7624	0.9027
0.525	1.4483	1.8616	3.8083	2.2025	3.4595	7.5366	1.0494	0.7854	0.9773	0.7604	0.8954
0.530	1.4308	1.8432	3.7724	2.1699	3.4210	7.4633	1.0416	0.7883	0.9769	0.7583	0.8882
0.535	1.4135	1.8252	3.7371	2.1371	3.3832	7.3913	1.0339	0.7912	0.9765	0.7562	0.8811
0.540	1.3966	1.8075	3.7024	2.1066	3.3461	7.3206	1.0263	0.7942	0.9761	0.7542	0.8741
0.545	1.3801	1.7901	3.6684	2.0760	3.3096	7.2511	1.0188	0.7971	0.9756	0.7521	0.8671
0.550	1.3638	1.7730	3.6350	2.0459	3.2738	7.1829	1.0114	0.8001	0.9752	0.7501	0.8603
0.555	1.3478	1.7563	3.6022	2.0164	3.2385	7.1158	1.0041	0.8030	0.9747	0.7480	0.8535
0.560	1.3321	1.7398	3.5700	1.9875	3.2039	7.0500	0.9969	0.8060	0.9743	0.7460	0.8468
0.565	1.3167	1.7236	3.5384	1.9592	3.1699	6.9852	0.9898	0.8090	0.9738	0.7440	0.8402
0.570	1.3016	1.7076	3.5073	1.9314	3.1364	6.9216	0.9827	0.8119	0.9734	0.7419	0.8336
0.575	1.2868	1.6920	3.4767	1.9042	3.1035	6.8590	0.9758	0.8149	0.9729	0.7399	0.8271
0.580	1.2722	1.6766	3.4467	1.8775	3.0711	6.7974	0.9689	0.8179	0.9724	0.7379	0.8207
0.585	1.2579	1.6615	3.4172	1.8512	3.0392	6.7369	0.9621	0.8209	0.9720	0.7359	0.8144

Appendix Table 1 (cont'd)

u	1φ	2φ	3φ	4φ	5φ	6φ	7φ	8φ	9φ	10φ	11φ
0.590	1.2438	1.6466	3.3882	1.8255	3.0078	6.6774	0.9554	0.8238	0.9715	0.7338	0.8082
0.595	1.2300	1.6320	3.3596	1.8003	2.9770	6.6188	0.9487	0.8268	0.9710	0.7318	0.8020
0.600	1.2164	1.6176	3.3316	1.7755	2.9466	6.5612	0.9422	0.8298	0.9705	0.7298	0.7959
0.605	1.2030	1.6034	3.3040	1.7511	2.9168	6.5045	0.9357	0.8328	0.9700	0.7278	0.7898
0.610	1.1899	1.5894	3.2769	1.7273	2.8873	6.4487	0.9293	0.8358	0.9696	0.7258	0.7838
0.615	1.1769	1.5757	3.2502	1.7038	2.8584	6.3937	0.9230	0.8388	0.9691	0.7238	0.7779
0.620	1.1642	1.5622	3.2239	1.6808	2.8298	6.3396	0.9167	0.8418	0.9686	0.7218	0.7721
0.625	1.1517	1.5489	3.1980	1.6582	2.8018	6.2864	0.9105	0.8448	0.9681	0.7198	0.7663
0.630	1.1395	1.5358	3.1726	1.6359	2.7741	6.2339	0.9044	0.8479	0.9676	0.7179	0.7606
0.635	1.1274	1.5229	3.1475	1.6141	2.7468	6.1822	0.8984	0.8509	0.9671	0.7159	0.7549
0.640	1.1155	1.5102	3.1229	1.5927	2.7200	6.1313	0.8924	0.8539	0.9666	0.7139	0.7493
0.645	1.1038	1.4977	3.0986	1.5716	2.6935	6.0812	0.8865	0.8569	0.9660	0.7119	0.7437
0.650	1.0923	1.4854	3.0747	1.5509	2.6675	6.0318	0.8806	0.8600	0.9655	0.7100	0.7382
0.655	1.0809	1.4733	3.0512	1.5306	2.6418	5.9831	0.8748	0.8630	0.9650	0.7080	0.7328
0.660	1.0698	1.4613	3.0280	1.5106	2.6164	5.9351	0.8691	0.8660	0.9645	0.7060	0.7274
0.665	1.0588	1.4495	3.0052	1.4909	2.5915	5.8879	0.8634	0.8691	0.9639	0.7041	0.7221
0.670	1.0480	1.4379	2.9827	1.4716	2.5669	5.8412	0.8578	0.8721	0.9634	0.7021	0.7168
0.675	1.0373	1.4265	2.9605	1.4526	2.5426	5.7953	0.8522	0.8752	0.9629	0.7002	0.7116
0.680	1.0268	1.4152	2.9387	1.4339	2.5187	5.7499	0.8467	0.8782	0.9623	0.6982	0.7065
0.685	1.0165	1.4041	2.9171	1.4156	2.4951	5.7053	0.8413	0.8813	0.9618	0.6963	0.7014
0.690	1.0063	1.3931	2.8959	1.3975	2.4718	5.6612	0.8359	0.8844	0.9613	0.6944	0.6963
0.695	0.9963	1.3823	2.8750	1.3797	2.4489	5.6177	0.8306	0.8874	0.9607	0.6924	0.6913
0.700	0.9864	1.3716	2.8544	1.3623	2.4262	5.5748	0.8253	0.8905	0.9601	0.6905	0.6863
0.705	0.9767	1.3611	2.8341	1.3451	2.4039	5.5325	0.8201	0.8936	0.9596	0.6886	0.6814
0.710	0.9671	1.3507	2.8140	1.3282	2.3818	5.4907	0.8149	0.8967	0.9590	0.6867	0.6766
0.715	0.9577	1.3405	2.7943	1.3115	2.3601	5.4495	0.8098	0.8997	0.9585	0.6847	0.6718
0.720	0.9484	1.3304	2.7748	1.2952	2.3386	5.4089	0.8047	0.9028	0.9579	0.6828	0.6670
0.725	0.9392	1.3204	2.7556	1.2791	2.3174	5.3687	0.7997	0.9059	0.9573	0.6809	0.6623
0.730	0.9302	1.3106	2.7366	1.2632	2.2965	5.3291	0.7947	0.9090	0.9568	0.6790	0.6576
0.735	0.9212	1.3009	2.7179	1.2476	2.2759	5.2900	0.7898	0.9121	0.9562	0.6771	0.6530
0.740	0.9125	1.2913	2.6995	1.2322	2.2555	5.2514	0.7849	0.9152	0.9556	0.6752	0.6484
0.745	0.9038	1.2819	2.6813	1.2171	2.2354	5.2133	0.7801	0.9183	0.9550	0.6733	0.6439
0.750	0.8953	1.2726	2.6633	1.2022	2.2156	5.1756	0.7753	0.9214	0.9544	0.6714	0.6394
0.755	0.8868	1.2633	2.6456	1.1876	2.1959	5.1384	0.7706	0.9246	0.9538	0.6696	0.6349
0.760	0.8785	1.2542	2.6281	1.1731	2.1765	5.1017	0.7659	0.9277	0.9532	0.6677	0.6305
0.765	0.8703	1.2453	2.6108	1.1589	2.1575	5.0654	0.7612	0.9308	0.9526	0.6658	0.6261
0.770	0.8622	1.2364	2.5938	1.1449	2.1386	5.0296	0.7566	0.9339	0.9520	0.6639	0.6218
0.775	0.8543	1.2276	2.5769	1.1312	2.1199	4.9942	0.7520	0.9371	0.9514	0.6621	0.6175
0.780	0.8464	1.2190	2.5603	1.1176	2.1015	4.9592	0.7475	0.9402	0.9508	0.6602	0.6132
0.785	0.8386	1.2104	2.5439	1.1042	2.0833	4.9246	0.7430	0.9433	0.9502	0.6583	0.6090

u	1φ	2φ	3φ	4φ	5φ	6φ	7φ	8φ	9φ	10φ	11φ
0.795	0.8234	1.1937	2.5117	1.0781	2.0475	4.8567	0.7342	0.9496	0.9490	0.6546	0.6007
0.800	0.8160	1.1854	2.4959	1.0653	2.0299	4.8233	0.7298	0.9528	0.9483	0.6528	0.5966
0.805	0.8086	1.1773	2.4803	1.0527	2.0126	4.7904	0.7255	0.9559	0.9477	0.6509	0.5926
0.810	0.8013	1.1692	2.4649	1.0403	1.9954	4.7578	0.7212	0.9591	0.9471	0.6491	0.5885
0.815	0.7942	1.1613	2.4497	1.0281	1.9785	4.7255	0.7170	0.9622	0.9464	0.6472	0.5845
0.820	0.7871	1.1534	2.4347	1.0160	1.9617	4.6936	0.7127	0.9654	0.9458	0.6454	0.5806
0.825	0.7801	1.1456	2.4198	1.0041	1.9452	4.6621	0.7086	0.9686	0.9452	0.6436	0.5767
0.830	0.7732	1.1380	2.4051	0.9924	1.9288	4.6309	0.7044	0.9718	0.9445	0.6418	0.5728
0.835	0.7664	1.1304	2.3906	0.9809	1.9126	4.6001	0.7003	0.9749	0.9439	0.6399	0.5689
0.840	0.7597	1.1229	2.3763	0.9695	1.8966	4.5696	0.6962	0.9781	0.9432	0.6381	0.5651
0.845	0.7530	1.1155	2.3621	0.9583	1.8808	4.5395	0.6922	0.9813	0.9426	0.6363	0.5613
0.850	0.7465	1.1081	2.3481	0.9473	1.8651	4.5096	0.6882	0.9845	0.9419	0.6345	0.5576
0.855	0.7400	1.1009	2.3343	0.9364	1.8497	4.4801	0.6842	0.9877	0.9412	0.6327	0.5539
0.860	0.7336	1.0937	2.3206	0.9256	1.8344	4.4509	0.6803	0.9909	0.9406	0.6309	0.5502
0.865	0.7273	1.0866	2.3071	0.9150	1.8192	4.4221	0.6764	0.9941	0.9399	0.6291	0.5465
0.870	0.7210	1.0796	2.2937	0.9046	1.8043	4.3935	0.6725	0.9973	0.9392	0.6273	0.5429
0.875	0.7149	1.0726	2.2805	0.8943	1.7895	4.3652	0.6687	1.0005	0.9386	0.6255	0.5393
0.880	0.7088	1.0658	2.2674	0.8841	1.7748	4.3372	0.6649	1.0037	0.9379	0.6237	0.5358
0.885	0.7027	1.0590	2.2545	0.8741	1.7604	4.3095	0.6611	1.0069	0.9372	0.6219	0.5322
0.890	0.6968	1.0523	2.2417	0.8642	1.7460	4.2821	0.6574	1.0102	0.9365	0.6202	0.5287
0.895	0.6909	1.0456	2.2290	0.8545	1.7319	4.2549	0.6536	1.0134	0.9358	0.6184	0.5253
0.900	0.6851	1.0391	2.2165	0.8449	1.7179	4.2281	0.6500	1.0166	0.9351	0.6166	0.5218
0.905	0.6794	1.0325	2.2042	0.8354	1.7040	4.2015	0.6463	1.0198	0.9345	0.6148	0.5184
0.910	0.6737	1.0261	2.1919	0.8261	1.6903	4.1751	0.6427	1.0231	0.9338	0.6131	0.5150
0.915	0.6681	1.0197	2.1798	0.8168	1.6767	4.1491	0.6391	1.0263	0.9331	0.6113	0.5117
0.920	0.6626	1.0134	2.1678	0.8077	1.6632	4.1233	0.6355	1.0296	0.9324	0.6096	0.5084
0.925	0.6571	1.0072	2.1560	0.7988	1.6499	4.0977	0.6320	1.0328	0.9316	0.6078	0.5051
0.930	0.6517	1.0010	2.1443	0.7899	1.6368	4.0724	0.6285	1.0361	0.9309	0.6061	0.5018
0.935	0.6463	0.9949	2.1327	0.7812	1.6237	4.0473	0.6250	1.0393	0.9302	0.6043	0.4985
0.940	0.6410	0.9888	2.1212	0.7725	1.6108	4.0225	0.6215	1.0426	0.9295	0.6026	0.4953
0.945	0.6358	0.9828	2.1098	0.7640	1.5981	3.9979	0.6181	1.0458	0.9288	0.6008	0.4921
0.950	0.6306	0.9769	2.0986	0.7556	1.5855	3.9735	0.6147	1.0491	0.9281	0.5991	0.4890
0.955	0.6255	0.9710	2.0875	0.7473	1.5729	3.9494	0.6113	1.0524	0.9273	0.5974	0.4858
0.960	0.6205	0.9652	2.0765	0.7392	1.5606	3.9255	0.6079	1.0556	0.9266	0.5956	0.4827
0.965	0.6155	0.9595	2.0656	0.7311	1.5483	3.9018	0.6046	1.0589	0.9259	0.5939	0.4796
0.970	0.6105	0.9538	2.0548	0.7231	1.5362	3.8783	0.6013	1.0622	0.9251	0.5922	0.4766
0.975	0.6056	0.9481	2.0441	0.7152	1.5242	3.8551	0.5980	1.0655	0.9244	0.5905	0.4735
0.980	0.6008	0.9425	2.0335	0.7075	1.5123	3.8320	0.5948	1.0688	0.9237	0.5888	0.4705
0.985	0.5960	0.9370	2.0231	0.6998	1.5005	3.8092	0.5915	1.0721	0.9229	0.5871	0.4675
0.990	0.5913	0.9315	2.0127	0.6922	1.4888	3.7866	0.5883	1.0754	0.9222	0.5854	0.4645
0.995	0.5866	0.9261	2.0025	0.6848	1.4773	3.7642	0.5851	1.0787	0.9214	0.5837	0.4616

Appendix Table 1 (cont'd)

u	1φ	2φ	3φ	4φ	5φ	6φ	7φ	8φ	9φ	10φ	11φ
1.000	0.5820	0.9207	1.9923	0.6774	1.4658	3.7420	0.5820	1.0820	0.9207	0.5820	0.4587
1.005	0.5774	0.9153	1.9822	0.6701	1.4545	3.7199	0.5788	1.0853	0.9199	0.5803	0.4558
1.010	0.5729	0.9101	1.9723	0.6629	1.4433	3.6981	0.5757	1.0886	0.9192	0.5786	0.4529
1.015	0.5684	0.9048	1.9624	0.6558	1.4322	3.6765	0.5726	1.0919	0.9184	0.5769	0.4500
1.020	0.5640	0.8996	1.9526	0.6488	1.4212	3.6550	0.5696	1.0952	0.9176	0.5752	0.4472
1.025	0.5596	0.8945	1.9430	0.6419	1.4103	3.6337	0.5665	1.0986	0.9169	0.5736	0.4444
1.030	0.5552	0.8894	1.9334	0.6351	1.3995	3.6127	0.5635	1.1019	0.9161	0.5719	0.4416
1.035	0.5509	0.8844	1.9239	0.6283	1.3888	3.5918	0.5605	1.1052	0.9153	0.5702	0.4389
1.040	0.5467	0.8794	1.9145	0.6216	1.3782	3.5710	0.5575	1.1085	0.9145	0.5685	0.4361
1.045	0.5425	0.8744	1.9051	0.6150	1.3677	3.5505	0.5545	1.1119	0.9138	0.5669	0.4334
1.050	0.5383	0.8695	1.8959	0.6085	1.3573	3.5301	0.5516	1.1152	0.9130	0.5652	0.4307
1.055	0.5342	0.8646	1.8868	0.6021	1.3470	3.5099	0.5487	1.1186	0.9122	0.5636	0.4280
1.060	0.5301	0.8598	1.8777	0.5958	1.3368	3.4898	0.5458	1.1219	0.9114	0.5619	0.4253
1.065	0.5261	0.8550	1.8687	0.5895	1.3267	3.4700	0.5429	1.1253	0.9106	0.5603	0.4227
1.070	0.5221	0.8503	1.8598	0.5833	1.3167	3.4503	0.5401	1.1286	0.9098	0.5586	0.4201
1.075	0.5181	0.8456	1.8510	0.5772	1.3068	3.4307	0.5372	1.1320	0.9090	0.5570	0.4175
1.080	0.5142	0.8409	1.8423	0.5712	1.2969	3.4113	0.5344	1.1354	0.9082	0.5554	0.4149
1.085	0.5104	0.8363	1.8336	0.5652	1.2872	3.3921	0.5316	1.1387	0.9074	0.5537	0.4123
1.090	0.5065	0.8317	1.8250	0.5593	1.2775	3.3730	0.5288	1.1421	0.9066	0.5521	0.4098
1.095	0.5027	0.8272	1.8165	0.5535	1.2680	3.3541	0.5261	1.1455	0.9058	0.5505	0.4073
1.100	0.4990	0.8227	1.8081	0.5477	1.2585	3.3353	0.5233	1.1489	0.9050	0.5489	0.4048
1.105	0.4952	0.8183	1.7997	0.5420	1.2491	3.3167	0.5206	1.1522	0.9042	0.5472	0.4023
1.110	0.4916	0.8138	1.7915	0.5364	1.2398	3.2982	0.5179	1.1556	0.9034	0.5456	0.3998
1.115	0.4879	0.8094	1.7832	0.5309	1.2306	3.2798	0.5152	1.1590	0.9025	0.5440	0.3974
1.120	0.4843	0.8051	1.7751	0.5254	1.2214	3.2616	0.5125	1.1624	0.9017	0.5424	0.3949
1.125	0.4807	0.8008	1.7670	0.5200	1.2123	3.2436	0.5099	1.1658	0.9009	0.5408	0.3925
1.130	0.4772	0.7965	1.7590	0.5146	1.2033	3.2257	0.5072	1.1692	0.9001	0.5392	0.3901
1.135	0.4737	0.7923	1.7511	0.5093	1.1944	3.2079	0.5046	1.1726	0.8992	0.5376	0.3878
1.140	0.4702	0.7881	1.7432	0.5041	1.1856	3.1902	0.5020	1.1760	0.8984	0.5360	0.3854
1.145	0.4668	0.7839	1.7354	0.4989	1.1769	3.1727	0.4995	1.1794	0.8976	0.5344	0.3831
1.150	0.4634	0.7798	1.7277	0.4938	1.1682	3.1554	0.4969	1.1829	0.8967	0.5329	0.3807
1.155	0.4600	0.7756	1.7200	0.4887	1.1596	3.1381	0.4943	1.1863	0.8959	0.5313	0.3784
1.160	0.4566	0.7716	1.7124	0.4838	1.1510	3.1210	0.4918	1.1897	0.8950	0.5297	0.3761
1.165	0.4533	0.7675	1.7049	0.4788	1.1426	3.1040	0.4893	1.1931	0.8942	0.5281	0.3739
1.170	0.4500	0.7635	1.6974	0.4739	1.1342	3.0871	0.4868	1.1966	0.8933	0.5266	0.3716
1.175	0.4468	0.7596	1.6900	0.4691	1.1259	3.0704	0.4843	1.2000	0.8925	0.5250	0.3694
1.180	0.4436	0.7556	1.6826	0.4644	1.1177	3.0538	0.4819	1.2034	0.8916	0.5234	0.3671
1.185	0.4404	0.7517	1.6753	0.4597	1.1095	3.0373	0.4794	1.2069	0.8908	0.5219	0.3649
1.190	0.4372	0.7478	1.6681	0.4550	1.1014	3.0209	0.4770	1.2103	0.8899	0.5203	0.3627
1.195	0.4341	0.7440	1.6609	0.4504	1.0934	3.0046	0.4746	1.2138	0.8890	0.5188	0.3605

u	1ϕ	2ϕ	3ϕ	4ϕ	5ϕ	6ϕ	7ϕ	8ϕ	9ϕ	10ϕ	11ϕ
1.205	0.4279	0.7363	1.6467	0.4414	1.0775	2.9724	0.4698	1.2207	0.8873	0.5157	0.3562
1.210	0.4249	0.7326	1.6397	0.4369	1.0697	2.9565	0.4674	1.2241	0.8864	0.5141	0.3541
1.215	0.4219	0.7289	1.6328	0.4325	1.0619	2.9407	0.4650	1.2276	0.8856	0.5126	0.3520
1.220	0.4189	0.7251	1.6259	0.4282	1.0542	2.9250	0.4627	1.2311	0.8847	0.5111	0.3499
1.225	0.4159	0.7215	1.6190	0.4239	1.0466	2.9094	0.4604	1.2345	0.8838	0.5095	0.3478
1.230	0.4130	0.7178	1.6122	0.4196	1.0390	2.8939	0.4581	1.2380	0.8829	0.5080	0.3457
1.235	0.4101	0.7142	1.6055	0.4154	1.0315	2.8786	0.4558	1.2415	0.8820	0.5065	0.3437
1.240	0.4072	0.7106	1.5988	0.4113	1.0240	2.8633	0.4535	1.2450	0.8811	0.5050	0.3416
1.245	0.4044	0.7070	1.5922	0.4072	1.0167	2.8482	0.4512	1.2485	0.8803	0.5035	0.3396
1.250	0.4016	0.7035	1.5856	0.4031	1.0093	2.8331	0.4489	1.2519	0.8794	0.5019	0.3376
1.255	0.3987	0.7000	1.5791	0.3991	1.0021	2.8181	0.4467	1.2554	0.8785	0.5004	0.3356
1.260	0.3960	0.6965	1.5726	0.3951	0.9949	2.8033	0.4445	1.2589	0.8776	0.4989	0.3336
1.265	0.3932	0.6930	1.5661	0.3912	0.9877	2.7885	0.4423	1.2624	0.8767	0.4974	0.3316
1.270	0.3905	0.6896	1.5597	0.3873	0.9806	2.7739	0.4401	1.2659	0.8758	0.4959	0.3297
1.275	0.3878	0.6862	1.5534	0.3835	0.9736	2.7593	0.4379	1.2694	0.8749	0.4944	0.3277
1.280	0.3851	0.6828	1.5471	0.3797	0.9666	2.7449	0.4357	1.2729	0.8740	0.4929	0.3258
1.285	0.3825	0.6794	1.5409	0.3759	0.9597	2.7305	0.4335	1.2765	0.8731	0.4915	0.3239
1.290	0.3798	0.6761	1.5347	0.3722	0.9528	2.7163	0.4314	1.2800	0.8721	0.4900	0.3220
1.295	0.3772	0.6728	1.5285	0.3685	0.9460	2.7021	0.4293	1.2835	0.8712	0.4885	0.3201
1.300	0.3746	0.6695	1.5224	0.3649	0.9393	2.6880	0.4271	1.2870	0.8703	0.4870	0.3182
1.305	0.3721	0.6662	1.5163	0.3613	0.9326	2.6740	0.4250	1.2905	0.8694	0.4855	0.3163
1.310	0.3695	0.6630	1.5103	0.3578	0.9259	2.6601	0.4229	1.2941	0.8685	0.4841	0.3145
1.315	0.3670	0.6597	1.5043	0.3542	0.9193	2.6463	0.4209	1.2976	0.8676	0.4826	0.3126
1.320	0.3645	0.6565	1.4984	0.3508	0.9128	2.6326	0.4188	1.3012	0.8666	0.4812	0.3108
1.325	0.3620	0.6534	1.4925	0.3473	0.9063	2.6190	0.4167	1.3047	0.8657	0.4797	0.3090
1.330	0.3596	0.6502	1.4867	0.3439	0.8999	2.6054	0.4147	1.3082	0.8648	0.4782	0.3072
1.335	0.3571	0.6471	1.4809	0.3406	0.8935	2.5920	0.4127	1.3118	0.8638	0.4768	0.3054
1.340	0.3547	0.6440	1.4751	0.3372	0.8872	2.5786	0.4106	1.3153	0.8629	0.4753	0.3036
1.345	0.3523	0.6409	1.4694	0.3339	0.8809	2.5653	0.4086	1.3189	0.8620	0.4739	0.3018
1.350	0.3500	0.6378	1.4637	0.3307	0.8746	2.5521	0.4066	1.3225	0.8610	0.4725	0.3001
1.355	0.3476	0.6347	1.4580	0.3275	0.8684	2.5390	0.4046	1.3260	0.8601	0.4710	0.2983
1.360	0.3453	0.6317	1.4524	0.3243	0.8623	2.5259	0.4027	1.3296	0.8591	0.4696	0.2966
1.365	0.3430	0.6287	1.4469	0.3211	0.8562	2.5130	0.4007	1.3332	0.8582	0.4682	0.2949
1.370	0.3407	0.6257	1.4413	0.3180	0.8502	2.5001	0.3987	1.3367	0.8572	0.4667	0.2932
1.375	0.3384	0.6228	1.4358	0.3149	0.8442	2.4873	0.3968	1.3403	0.8563	0.4653	0.2915
1.380	0.3361	0.6198	1.4304	0.3119	0.8382	2.4746	0.3949	1.3439	0.8553	0.4639	0.2898
1.385	0.3339	0.6169	1.4250	0.3088	0.8323	2.4619	0.3930	1.3475	0.8544	0.4625	0.2881
1.390	0.3317	0.6140	1.4196	0.3059	0.8264	2.4493	0.3911	1.3511	0.8534	0.4611	0.2864
1.395	0.3295	0.6111	1.4142	0.3029	0.8206	2.4368	0.3892	1.3546	0.8525	0.4596	0.2848
1.400	0.3273	0.6082	1.4089	0.3000	0.8149	2.4244	0.3873	1.3582	0.8515	0.4582	0.2832
1.405	0.3251	0.6054	1.4037	0.2971	0.8091	2.4121	0.3854	1.3618	0.8505	0.4568	0.2815

Appendix Table 1 (cont'd)

u	1φ	2φ	3φ	4φ	5φ	6φ	7φ	8φ	9φ	10φ	11φ
1.410	0.3230	0.6025	1.3984	0.2942	0.8035	2.3998	0.3835	1.3654	0.8496	0.4554	0.2799
1.415	0.3209	0.5997	1.3932	0.2914	0.7978	2.3876	0.3817	1.3690	0.8486	0.4540	0.2783
1.420	0.3188	0.5969	1.3880	0.2886	0.7922	2.3755	0.3799	1.3726	0.8476	0.4526	0.2767
1.425	0.3167	0.5942	1.3829	0.2858	0.7867	2.3635	0.3780	1.3763	0.8467	0.4513	0.2751
1.430	0.3146	0.5914	1.3778	0.2831	0.7812	2.3515	0.3762	1.3799	0.8457	0.4499	0.2735
1.435	0.3125	0.5887	1.3727	0.2803	0.7757	2.3396	0.3744	1.3835	0.8447	0.4485	0.2720
1.440	0.3105	0.5859	1.3677	0.2776	0.7703	2.3277	0.3726	1.3871	0.8437	0.4471	0.2704
1.445	0.3085	0.5832	1.3627	0.2750	0.7649	2.3160	0.3708	1.3907	0.8428	0.4457	0.2689
1.450	0.3065	0.5805	1.3577	0.2724	0.7595	2.3043	0.3690	1.3944	0.8418	0.4444	0.2673
1.455	0.3045	0.5779	1.3528	0.2697	0.7542	2.2926	0.3673	1.3980	0.8408	0.4430	0.2658
1.460	0.3025	0.5752	1.3479	0.2672	0.7489	2.2811	0.3655	1.4016	0.8398	0.4416	0.2643
1.465	0.3005	0.5726	1.3430	0.2646	0.7437	2.2696	0.3637	1.4053	0.8388	0.4403	0.2628
1.470	0.2986	0.5700	1.3381	0.2621	0.7385	2.2581	0.3620	1.4089	0.8378	0.4389	0.2613
1.475	0.2966	0.5673	1.3333	0.2596	0.7334	2.2468	0.3603	1.4126	0.8368	0.4376	0.2598
1.480	0.2947	0.5648	1.3285	0.2571	0.7283	2.2355	0.3586	1.4162	0.8358	0.4362	0.2583
1.485	0.2928	0.5622	1.3238	0.2547	0.7232	2.2242	0.3568	1.4199	0.8348	0.4349	0.2568
1.490	0.2909	0.5596	1.3191	0.2523	0.7182	2.2130	0.3551	1.4235	0.8339	0.4335	0.2554
1.495	0.2891	0.5571	1.3144	0.2499	0.7132	2.2019	0.3534	1.4272	0.8329	0.4322	0.2539
1.500	0.2872	0.5546	1.3097	0.2475	0.7082	2.1909	0.3518	1.4308	0.8318	0.4308	0.2525
1.505	0.2854	0.5521	1.3051	0.2451	0.7033	2.1799	0.3501	1.4345	0.8308	0.4295	0.2511
1.510	0.2835	0.5496	1.3004	0.2428	0.6984	2.1690	0.3484	1.4382	0.8298	0.4282	0.2496
1.515	0.2817	0.5471	1.2959	0.2405	0.6935	2.1581	0.3468	1.4418	0.8288	0.4268	0.2482
1.520	0.2799	0.5446	1.2913	0.2382	0.6887	2.1473	0.3451	1.4455	0.8278	0.4255	0.2468
1.525	0.2782	0.5422	1.2868	0.2360	0.6839	2.1366	0.3435	1.4492	0.8268	0.4242	0.2454
1.530	0.2764	0.5397	1.2823	0.2337	0.6792	2.1259	0.3419	1.4529	0.8258	0.4229	0.2440
1.535	0.2746	0.5373	1.2778	0.2315	0.6745	2.1153	0.3402	1.4565	0.8248	0.4215	0.2427
1.540	0.2729	0.5349	1.2733	0.2294	0.6698	2.1047	0.3386	1.4602	0.8238	0.4202	0.2413
1.545	0.2712	0.5325	1.2689	0.2272	0.6652	2.0942	0.3370	1.4639	0.8227	0.4189	0.2399
1.550	0.2694	0.5301	1.2645	0.2250	0.6606	2.0837	0.3354	1.4676	0.8217	0.4176	0.2386
1.555	0.2677	0.5278	1.2602	0.2229	0.6560	2.0733	0.3339	1.4713	0.8207	0.4163	0.2372
1.560	0.2660	0.5254	1.2558	0.2208	0.6514	2.0630	0.3323	1.4750	0.8197	0.4150	0.2359
1.565	0.2644	0.5231	1.2515	0.2187	0.6469	2.0527	0.3307	1.4787	0.8187	0.4137	0.2346
1.570	0.2627	0.5208	1.2472	0.2167	0.6425	2.0425	0.3292	1.4824	0.8176	0.4124	0.2333
1.575	0.2610	0.5185	1.2429	0.2147	0.6380	2.0323	0.3276	1.4861	0.8166	0.4111	0.2319
1.580	0.2594	0.5162	1.2387	0.2126	0.6336	2.0222	0.3261	1.4899	0.8156	0.4099	0.2306
1.585	0.2578	0.5139	1.2345	0.2106	0.6292	2.0121	0.3245	1.4936	0.8145	0.4086	0.2293
1.590	0.2562	0.5116	1.2303	0.2087	0.6249	2.0021	0.3230	1.4973	0.8135	0.4073	0.2281
1.595	0.2546	0.5094	1.2261	0.2067	0.6206	1.9922	0.3215	1.5010	0.8125	0.4060	0.2268
1.600	0.2530	0.5071	1.2220	0.2048	0.6163	1.9823	0.3200	1.5048	0.8114	0.4048	0.2255
1.605	0.2514	0.5049	1.2178	0.2029	0.6120	1.9724	0.3185	1.5085	0.8104	0.4035	0.2243

u	1φ	2φ	3φ	4φ	5φ	6φ	7φ	8φ	9φ	10φ	11φ
1.615	0.2483	0.5005	1.2097	0.1991	0.6036	1.9529	0.3155	1.5160	0.8083	0.4010	0.2218
1.620	0.2467	0.4983	1.2056	0.1972	0.5995	1.9432	0.3140	1.5197	0.8073	0.3997	0.2205
1.625	0.2452	0.4961	1.2016	0.1954	0.5953	1.9335	0.3126	1.5234	0.8062	0.3984	0.2193
1.630	0.2437	0.4940	1.1976	0.1936	0.5912	1.9240	0.3111	1.5272	0.8052	0.3972	0.2181
1.635	0.2422	0.4918	1.1936	0.1918	0.5871	1.9144	0.3096	1.5309	0.8041	0.3959	0.2169
1.640	0.2407	0.4897	1.1896	0.1900	0.5831	1.9049	0.3082	1.5347	0.8031	0.3947	0.2156
1.645	0.2392	0.4875	1.1857	0.1882	0.5791	1.8955	0.3068	1.5384	0.8020	0.3934	0.2144
1.650	0.2377	0.4854	1.1817	0.1865	0.5751	1.8861	0.3053	1.5422	0.8010	0.3922	0.2133
1.655	0.2362	0.4833	1.1778	0.1847	0.5711	1.8767	0.3039	1.5460	0.7999	0.3910	0.2121
1.660	0.2348	0.4812	1.1740	0.1830	0.5672	1.8674	0.3025	1.5497	0.7989	0.3897	0.2109
1.665	0.2333	0.4792	1.1701	0.1813	0.5633	1.8582	0.3011	1.5535	0.7978	0.3885	0.2097
1.670	0.2319	0.4771	1.1663	0.1796	0.5594	1.8490	0.2997	1.5573	0.7967	0.3873	0.2086
1.675	0.2305	0.4750	1.1624	0.1780	0.5556	1.8398	0.2983	1.5611	0.7957	0.3861	0.2074
1.680	0.2291	0.4730	1.1586	0.1763	0.5518	1.8307	0.2969	1.5648	0.7946	0.3848	0.2063
1.685	0.2277	0.4709	1.1549	0.1747	0.5480	1.8217	0.2955	1.5686	0.7935	0.3836	0.2051
1.690	0.2263	0.4689	1.1511	0.1731	0.5442	1.8127	0.2942	1.5724	0.7925	0.3824	0.2040
1.695	0.2249	0.4669	1.1474	0.1714	0.5405	1.8037	0.2928	1.5762	0.7914	0.3812	0.2028
1.700	0.2235	0.4649	1.1437	0.1699	0.5368	1.7948	0.2914	1.5800	0.7903	0.3800	0.2017
1.705	0.2222	0.4629	1.1400	0.1683	0.5331	1.7859	0.2901	1.5838	0.7893	0.3788	0.2006
1.710	0.2208	0.4609	1.1363	0.1667	0.5294	1.7771	0.2887	1.5876	0.7882	0.3776	0.1995
1.715	0.2195	0.4590	1.1326	0.1652	0.5258	1.7683	0.2874	1.5914	0.7871	0.3764	0.1984
1.720	0.2181	0.4570	1.1290	0.1637	0.5222	1.7595	0.2861	1.5952	0.7861	0.3752	0.1973
1.725	0.2168	0.4551	1.1254	0.1622	0.5186	1.7508	0.2847	1.5990	0.7850	0.3740	0.1962
1.730	0.2155	0.4531	1.1217	0.1607	0.5150	1.7422	0.2834	1.6028	0.7839	0.3728	0.1951
1.735	0.2142	0.4512	1.1182	0.1592	0.5115	1.7336	0.2821	1.6066	0.7828	0.3716	0.1941
1.740	0.2129	0.4493	1.1146	0.1577	0.5080	1.7250	0.2808	1.6104	0.7817	0.3704	0.1930
1.745	0.2116	0.4474	1.1110	0.1563	0.5045	1.7165	0.2795	1.6142	0.7807	0.3692	0.1919
1.750	0.2103	0.4455	1.1075	0.1548	0.5010	1.7080	0.2782	1.6181	0.7796	0.3681	0.1909
1.755	0.2091	0.4436	1.1040	0.1534	0.4976	1.6995	0.2769	1.6219	0.7785	0.3669	0.1898
1.760	0.2078	0.4417	1.1005	0.1520	0.4942	1.6911	0.2757	1.6257	0.7774	0.3657	0.1888
1.765	0.2065	0.4398	1.0970	0.1506	0.4908	1.6828	0.2744	1.6296	0.7763	0.3646	0.1878
1.770	0.2053	0.4380	1.0936	0.1492	0.4874	1.6745	0.2731	1.6334	0.7752	0.3634	0.1867
1.775	0.2041	0.4361	1.0901	0.1478	0.4841	1.6662	0.2719	1.6372	0.7742	0.3622	0.1857
1.780	0.2028	0.4343	1.0867	0.1465	0.4808	1.6579	0.2706	1.6411	0.7731	0.3611	0.1847
1.785	0.2016	0.4325	1.0833	0.1451	0.4775	1.6498	0.2694	1.6449	0.7720	0.3599	0.1837
1.790	0.2004	0.4307	1.0799	0.1438	0.4742	1.6416	0.2681	1.6488	0.7709	0.3588	0.1827
1.795	0.1992	0.4289	1.0765	0.1425	0.4710	1.6335	0.2669	1.6526	0.7698	0.3576	0.1817
1.800	0.1980	0.4271	1.0731	0.1412	0.4677	1.6254	0.2657	1.6565	0.7687	0.3565	0.1807
1.805	0.1969	0.4253	1.0698	0.1399	0.4645	1.6174	0.2645	1.6603	0.7676	0.3553	0.1797
1.810	0.1957	0.4235	1.0665	0.1386	0.4613	1.6094	0.2633	1.6642	0.7665	0.3542	0.1787
1.815	0.1945	0.4217	1.0632	0.1373	0.4582	1.6014	0.2621	1.6680	0.7654	0.3530	0.1777

Appendix Table 1 (cont'd)

u	1φ	2φ	3φ	4φ	5φ	6φ	7φ	8φ	9φ	10φ	11φ
1.820	0.1934	0.4199	1.0599	0.1361	0.4550	1.5935	0.2608	1.6719	0.7643	0.3519	0.1768
1.825	0.1922	0.4182	1.0566	0.1348	0.4519	1.5856	0.2597	1.6758	0.7632	0.3508	0.1758
1.830	0.1911	0.4164	1.0533	0.1336	0.4488	1.5778	0.2585	1.6796	0.7621	0.3496	0.1748
1.835	0.1899	0.4147	1.0501	0.1324	0.4458	1.5700	0.2573	1.6835	0.7610	0.3485	0.1739
1.840	0.1888	0.4130	1.0468	0.1312	0.4427	1.5622	0.2561	1.6874	0.7599	0.3474	0.1729
1.845	0.1877	0.4113	1.0436	0.1300	0.4397	1.5545	0.2549	1.6913	0.7588	0.3463	0.1720
1.850	0.1866	0.4096	1.0404	0.1288	0.4367	1.5468	0.2538	1.6952	0.7577	0.3452	0.1711
1.855	0.1855	0.4079	1.0372	0.1276	0.4337	1.5391	0.2526	1.6990	0.7566	0.3440	0.1701
1.860	0.1844	0.4062	1.0340	0.1265	0.4307	1.5315	0.2515	1.7029	0.7555	0.3429	0.1692
1.865	0.1833	0.4045	1.0309	0.1253	0.4278	1.5239	0.2503	1.7068	0.7544	0.3418	0.1683
1.870	0.1822	0.4028	1.0277	0.1242	0.4248	1.5164	0.2492	1.7107	0.7532	0.3407	0.1674
1.875	0.1811	0.4011	1.0246	0.1230	0.4219	1.5089	0.2480	1.7146	0.7521	0.3396	0.1665
1.880	0.1801	0.3995	1.0215	0.1219	0.4190	1.5014	0.2469	1.7185	0.7510	0.3385	0.1656
1.885	0.1790	0.3978	1.0184	0.1208	0.4162	1.4940	0.2458	1.7224	0.7499	0.3374	0.1647
1.890	0.1780	0.3962	1.0153	0.1197	0.4133	1.4866	0.2446	1.7263	0.7488	0.3363	0.1638
1.895	0.1769	0.3946	1.0122	0.1186	0.4105	1.4792	0.2435	1.7302	0.7477	0.3352	0.1629
1.900	0.1759	0.3929	1.0092	0.1175	0.4077	1.4719	0.2424	1.7342	0.7466	0.3342	0.1620
1.905	0.1748	0.3913	1.0061	0.1165	0.4049	1.4646	0.2413	1.7381	0.7455	0.3331	0.1611
1.910	0.1738	0.3897	1.0031	0.1154	0.4021	1.4573	0.2402	1.7420	0.7443	0.3320	0.1603
1.915	0.1728	0.3881	1.0001	0.1144	0.3994	1.4501	0.2391	1.7459	0.7432	0.3309	0.1594
1.920	0.1718	0.3865	0.9971	0.1133	0.3966	1.4429	0.2380	1.7498	0.7421	0.3298	0.1585
1.925	0.1708	0.3849	0.9941	0.1123	0.3939	1.4357	0.2370	1.7538	0.7410	0.3288	0.1577
1.930	0.1698	0.3833	0.9911	0.1113	0.3912	1.4286	0.2359	1.7577	0.7399	0.3277	0.1568
1.935	0.1688	0.3818	0.9881	0.1103	0.3885	1.4215	0.2348	1.7616	0.7387	0.3266	0.1560
1.940	0.1678	0.3802	0.9852	0.1093	0.3859	1.4145	0.2337	1.7656	0.7376	0.3256	0.1551
1.945	0.1668	0.3787	0.9822	0.1083	0.3832	1.4075	0.2327	1.7695	0.7365	0.3245	0.1543
1.950	0.1659	0.3771	0.9793	0.1073	0.3806	1.4005	0.2316	1.7735	0.7354	0.3235	0.1535
1.955	0.1649	0.3756	0.9764	0.1063	0.3780	1.3935	0.2306	1.7774	0.7342	0.3224	0.1526
1.960	0.1640	0.3740	0.9735	0.1054	0.3754	1.3866	0.2295	1.7813	0.7331	0.3213	0.1518
1.965	0.1630	0.3725	0.9706	0.1044	0.3728	1.3797	0.2285	1.7853	0.7320	0.3203	0.1510
1.970	0.1621	0.3710	0.9677	0.1035	0.3703	1.3728	0.2275	1.7893	0.7308	0.3193	0.1502
1.975	0.1611	0.3695	0.9649	0.1025	0.3677	1.3660	0.2264	1.7932	0.7297	0.3182	0.1494
1.980	0.1602	0.3680	0.9620	0.1016	0.3652	1.3592	0.2254	1.7972	0.7286	0.3172	0.1486
1.985	0.1593	0.3665	0.9592	0.1007	0.3627	1.3524	0.2244	1.8011	0.7275	0.3161	0.1478
1.990	0.1583	0.3650	0.9563	0.0998	0.3602	1.3457	0.2234	1.8051	0.7263	0.3151	0.1470
1.995	0.1574	0.3635	0.9535	0.0989	0.3578	1.3390	0.2224	1.8091	0.7252	0.3141	0.1462
2.000	0.1565	0.3620	0.9507	0.0980	0.3553	1.3323	0.2213	1.8130	0.7241	0.3130	0.1454
2.005	0.1556	0.3606	0.9479	0.0971	0.3529	1.3257	0.2203	1.8170	0.7229	0.3120	0.1446
2.010	0.1547	0.3591	0.9451	0.0962	0.3505	1.3191	0.2194	1.8210	0.7218	0.3110	0.1439
2.015	0.1538	0.3576	0.9424	0.0954	0.3481	1.3125	0.2184	1.8250	0.7207	0.3100	0.1431

u	1ϕ	2ϕ	3ϕ	4ϕ	5ϕ	6ϕ	7ϕ	8ϕ	9ϕ	10ϕ	11ϕ
2.025	0.1521	0.3548	0.9369	0.0937	0.3433	1.2995	0.2164	1.8329	0.7184	0.3079	0.1416
2.030	0.1512	0.3533	0.9341	0.0928	0.3410	1.2930	0.2154	1.8369	0.7172	0.3069	0.1408
2.035	0.1503	0.3519	0.9314	0.0920	0.3386	1.2865	0.2144	1.8409	0.7161	0.3059	0.1400
2.040	0.1495	0.3505	0.9287	0.0911	0.3363	1.2801	0.2135	1.8449	0.7150	0.3049	0.1393
2.045	0.1486	0.3491	0.9260	0.0903	0.3340	1.2737	0.2125	1.8489	0.7138	0.3039	0.1385
2.050	0.1478	0.3477	0.9233	0.0895	0.3317	1.2673	0.2116	1.8529	0.7127	0.3029	0.1378
2.055	0.1469	0.3463	0.9206	0.0887	0.3294	1.2610	0.2106	1.8569	0.7116	0.3019	0.1371
2.060	0.1461	0.3449	0.9180	0.0879	0.3272	1.2547	0.2097	1.8609	0.7104	0.3009	0.1363
2.065	0.1452	0.3435	0.9153	0.0871	0.3249	1.2484	0.2087	1.8649	0.7093	0.2999	0.1356
2.070	0.1444	0.3421	0.9126	0.0863	0.3227	1.2422	0.2078	1.8689	0.7081	0.2989	0.1349
2.075	0.1436	0.3407	0.9100	0.0856	0.3205	1.2359	0.2068	1.8729	0.7070	0.2979	0.1342
2.080	0.1428	0.3393	0.9074	0.0848	0.3183	1.2297	0.2059	1.8770	0.7058	0.2970	0.1335
2.085	0.1420	0.3380	0.9048	0.0840	0.3161	1.2236	0.2050	1.8810	0.7047	0.2960	0.1327
2.090	0.1411	0.3366	0.9022	0.0833	0.3139	1.2175	0.2041	1.8850	0.7036	0.2950	0.1320
2.095	0.1403	0.3353	0.8996	0.0825	0.3118	1.2113	0.2031	1.8890	0.7024	0.2940	0.1313
2.100	0.1395	0.3339	0.8970	0.0818	0.3096	1.2053	0.2022	1.8930	0.7013	0.2930	0.1306
2.105	0.1388	0.3326	0.8944	0.0811	0.3075	1.1992	0.2013	1.8971	0.7001	0.2921	0.1299
2.110	0.1380	0.3313	0.8918	0.0803	0.3054	1.1932	0.2004	1.9011	0.6990	0.2911	0.1292
2.115	0.1372	0.3299	0.8893	0.0796	0.3033	1.1872	0.1995	1.9051	0.6978	0.2901	0.1286
2.120	0.1364	0.3286	0.8867	0.0789	0.3012	1.1812	0.1986	1.9092	0.6967	0.2892	0.1279
2.125	0.1356	0.3273	0.8842	0.0782	0.2992	1.1753	0.1977	1.9132	0.6955	0.2882	0.1272
2.130	0.1349	0.3260	0.8817	0.0775	0.2971	1.1694	0.1968	1.9173	0.6944	0.2873	0.1265
2.135	0.1341	0.3247	0.8792	0.0768	0.2951	1.1635	0.1959	1.9213	0.6932	0.2863	0.1258
2.140	0.1333	0.3234	0.8767	0.0761	0.2930	1.1576	0.1951	1.9254	0.6921	0.2854	0.1252
2.145	0.1326	0.3221	0.8742	0.0754	0.2910	1.1518	0.1942	1.9294	0.6909	0.2844	0.1245
2.150	0.1318	0.3208	0.8717	0.0747	0.2890	1.1460	0.1933	1.9335	0.6898	0.2835	0.1238
2.155	0.1311	0.3196	0.8692	0.0741	0.2870	1.1402	0.1925	1.9375	0.6886	0.2825	0.1232
2.160	0.1304	0.3183	0.8667	0.0734	0.2851	1.1345	0.1916	1.9416	0.6875	0.2816	0.1225
2.165	0.1296	0.3170	0.8643	0.0728	0.2831	1.1288	0.1907	1.9456	0.6863	0.2806	0.1219
2.170	0.1289	0.3158	0.8618	0.0721	0.2812	1.1231	0.1899	1.9497	0.6852	0.2797	0.1212
2.175	0.1282	0.3145	0.8594	0.0715	0.2792	1.1174	0.1890	1.9538	0.6840	0.2788	0.1206
2.180	0.1274	0.3132	0.8569	0.0708	0.2773	1.1118	0.1882	1.9578	0.6829	0.2778	0.1200
2.185	0.1267	0.3120	0.8545	0.0702	0.2754	1.1061	0.1873	1.9619	0.6817	0.2769	0.1193
2.190	0.1260	0.3108	0.8521	0.0696	0.2735	1.1005	0.1865	1.9660	0.6806	0.2760	0.1187
2.195	0.1253	0.3095	0.8497	0.0689	0.2716	1.0950	0.1857	1.9701	0.6794	0.2751	0.1181
2.200	0.1246	0.3083	0.8473	0.0683	0.2698	1.0894	0.1848	1.9741	0.6783	0.2741	0.1174
2.205	0.1239	0.3071	0.8449	0.0677	0.2679	1.0839	0.1840	1.9782	0.6771	0.2732	0.1168
2.210	0.1232	0.3059	0.8425	0.0671	0.2661	1.0784	0.1832	1.9823	0.6760	0.2723	0.1162
2.215	0.1225	0.3047	0.8402	0.0665	0.2642	1.0730	0.1824	1.9864	0.6748	0.2714	0.1156
2.220	0.1218	0.3034	0.8378	0.0659	0.2624	1.0675	0.1815	1.9905	0.6737	0.2705	0.1150
2.225	0.1212	0.3022	0.8355	0.0653	0.2606	1.0621	0.1807	1.9946	0.6725	0.2696	0.1144

Appendix Table 1 (cont'd)

u	1ϕ	2ϕ	3ϕ	4ϕ	5ϕ	6ϕ	7ϕ	8ϕ	9ϕ	10ϕ	11ϕ
2.230	0.1205	0.3011	0.8331	0.0647	0.2588	1.0567	0.1799	1.9987	0.6713	0.2687	0.1138
2.235	0.1198	0.2999	0.8308	0.0642	0.2570	1.0513	0.1791	2.0028	0.6702	0.2678	0.1132
2.240	0.1191	0.2987	0.8285	0.0636	0.2552	1.0460	0.1783	2.0069	0.6690	0.2669	0.1126
2.245	0.1185	0.2975	0.8261	0.0630	0.2535	1.0407	0.1775	2.0110	0.6679	0.2660	0.1120
2.250	0.1178	0.2963	0.8238	0.0625	0.2517	1.0354	0.1767	2.0151	0.6667	0.2651	0.1114
2.255	0.1172	0.2952	0.8215	0.0619	0.2500	1.0301	0.1759	2.0192	0.6656	0.2642	0.1108
2.260	0.1165	0.2940	0.8192	0.0614	0.2483	1.0249	0.1752	2.0233	0.6644	0.2633	0.1102
2.265	0.1159	0.2928	0.8169	0.0608	0.2466	1.0197	0.1744	2.0274	0.6633	0.2624	0.1096
2.270	0.1152	0.2917	0.8147	0.0603	0.2449	1.0145	0.1736	2.0315	0.6621	0.2615	0.1090
2.275	0.1146	0.2905	0.8124	0.0597	0.2432	1.0093	0.1728	2.0357	0.6609	0.2607	0.1085
2.280	0.1139	0.2894	0.8101	0.0592	0.2415	1.0041	0.1720	2.0398	0.6598	0.2598	0.1079
2.285	0.1133	0.2882	0.8079	0.0587	0.2398	0.9990	0.1713	2.0439	0.6586	0.2589	0.1073
2.290	0.1127	0.2871	0.8056	0.0581	0.2382	0.9939	0.1705	2.0480	0.6575	0.2580	0.1068
2.295	0.1121	0.2860	0.8034	0.0576	0.2365	0.9888	0.1698	2.0522	0.6563	0.2572	0.1062
2.300	0.1114	0.2848	0.8012	0.0571	0.2349	0.9838	0.1690	2.0563	0.6552	0.2563	0.1056
2.305	0.1108	0.2837	0.7989	0.0566	0.2333	0.9787	0.1682	2.0604	0.6540	0.2554	0.1051
2.310	0.1102	0.2826	0.7967	0.0561	0.2317	0.9737	0.1675	2.0646	0.6528	0.2546	0.1045
2.315	0.1096	0.2815	0.7945	0.0556	0.2301	0.9687	0.1667	2.0687	0.6517	0.2537	0.1040
2.320	0.1090	0.2804	0.7923	0.0551	0.2285	0.9638	0.1660	2.0728	0.6505	0.2528	0.1034
2.325	0.1084	0.2793	0.7901	0.0546	0.2269	0.9588	0.1653	2.0770	0.6494	0.2520	0.1029
2.330	0.1078	0.2782	0.7879	0.0541	0.2253	0.9539	0.1645	2.0811	0.6482	0.2511	0.1024
2.335	0.1072	0.2771	0.7858	0.0537	0.2238	0.9490	0.1638	2.0853	0.6471	0.2503	0.1018
2.340	0.1066	0.2760	0.7836	0.0532	0.2222	0.9441	0.1631	2.0894	0.6459	0.2494	0.1013
2.345	0.1060	0.2749	0.7814	0.0527	0.2207	0.9393	0.1623	2.0936	0.6447	0.2486	0.1008
2.350	0.1054	0.2739	0.7793	0.0522	0.2192	0.9345	0.1616	2.0977	0.6436	0.2477	0.1002
2.355	0.1048	0.2728	0.7771	0.0518	0.2176	0.9297	0.1609	2.1019	0.6424	0.2469	0.0997
2.360	0.1043	0.2717	0.7750	0.0513	0.2161	0.9249	0.1602	2.1061	0.6413	0.2461	0.0992
2.365	0.1037	0.2707	0.7729	0.0509	0.2146	0.9201	0.1595	2.1102	0.6401	0.2452	0.0987
2.370	0.1031	0.2696	0.7707	0.0504	0.2131	0.9154	0.1588	2.1144	0.6389	0.2444	0.0981
2.375	0.1026	0.2685	0.7686	0.0500	0.2117	0.9107	0.1580	2.1186	0.6378	0.2436	0.0976
2.380	0.1020	0.2675	0.7665	0.0495	0.2102	0.9060	0.1573	2.1227	0.6366	0.2427	0.0971
2.385	0.1014	0.2664	0.7644	0.0491	0.2087	0.9013	0.1566	2.1269	0.6355	0.2419	0.0966
2.390	0.1009	0.2654	0.7623	0.0486	0.2073	0.8966	0.1559	2.1311	0.6343	0.2411	0.0961
2.395	0.1003	0.2644	0.7602	0.0482	0.2059	0.8920	0.1553	2.1353	0.6332	0.2403	0.0956
2.400	0.0998	0.2633	0.7581	0.0478	0.2044	0.8874	0.1546	2.1394	0.6320	0.2394	0.0951
2.405	0.0992	0.2623	0.7560	0.0474	0.2030	0.8828	0.1539	2.1436	0.6308	0.2386	0.0946
2.410	0.0987	0.2613	0.7540	0.0469	0.2016	0.8782	0.1532	2.1478	0.6297	0.2378	0.0941
2.415	0.0981	0.2603	0.7519	0.0465	0.2002	0.8737	0.1525	2.1520	0.6285	0.2370	0.0936
2.420	0.0976	0.2592	0.7498	0.0461	0.1988	0.8691	0.1518	2.1562	0.6274	0.2362	0.0931
2.425	0.0971	0.2582	0.7478	0.0457	0.1974	0.8646	0.1512	2.1604	0.6262	0.2354	0.0926
2.430	0.0965	0.2572	0.7457	0.0453	0.1961	0.8602	0.1505	2.1646	0.6251	0.2346	0.0922

u	1φ	2φ	3φ	4φ	5φ	6φ	7φ	8φ	9φ	10φ	11φ
2.435	0.0960	0.2562	0.7437	0.0449	0.1947	0.8557	0.1498	2.1688	0.6239	0.2338	0.0917
2.440	0.0955	0.2552	0.7417	0.0445	0.1934	0.8512	0.1491	2.1730	0.6227	0.2330	0.0912
2.445	0.0950	0.2542	0.7396	0.0441	0.1920	0.8468	0.1485	2.1772	0.6216	0.2322	0.0907
2.450	0.0944	0.2532	0.7376	0.0437	0.1907	0.8424	0.1478	2.1814	0.6204	0.2314	0.0902
2.455	0.0939	0.2523	0.7356	0.0433	0.1894	0.8380	0.1472	2.1856	0.6193	0.2306	0.0898
2.460	0.0934	0.2513	0.7336	0.0429	0.1880	0.8337	0.1465	2.1898	0.6181	0.2298	0.0893
2.465	0.0929	0.2503	0.7316	0.0426	0.1867	0.8293	0.1459	2.1940	0.6170	0.2290	0.0888
2.470	0.0924	0.2493	0.7296	0.0422	0.1854	0.8250	0.1452	2.1982	0.6158	0.2282	0.0884
2.475	0.0919	0.2483	0.7276	0.0418	0.1841	0.8207	0.1446	2.2024	0.6147	0.2274	0.0879
2.480	0.0914	0.2474	0.7257	0.0414	0.1829	0.8164	0.1439	2.2067	0.6135	0.2267	0.0875
2.485	0.0909	0.2464	0.7237	0.0411	0.1816	0.8122	0.1433	2.2109	0.6124	0.2259	0.0870
2.490	0.0904	0.2455	0.7217	0.0407	0.1803	0.8079	0.1427	2.2151	0.6112	0.2251	0.0865
2.495	0.0899	0.2445	0.7197	0.0403	0.1791	0.8037	0.1420	2.2193	0.6100	0.2243	0.0861
2.500	0.0894	0.2436	0.7178	0.0400	0.1778	0.7995	0.1414	2.2236	0.6089	0.2236	0.0857
2.505	0.0889	0.2426	0.7158	0.0396	0.1766	0.7953	0.1408	2.2278	0.6077	0.2228	0.0852
2.510	0.0885	0.2417	0.7139	0.0393	0.1753	0.7911	0.1401	2.2320	0.6066	0.2220	0.0848
2.515	0.0880	0.2407	0.7120	0.0389	0.1741	0.7870	0.1395	2.2363	0.6054	0.2213	0.0843
2.520	0.0875	0.2398	0.7100	0.0386	0.1729	0.7829	0.1389	2.2405	0.6043	0.2205	0.0839
2.525	0.0870	0.2389	0.7081	0.0382	0.1717	0.7787	0.1383	2.2447	0.6031	0.2197	0.0834
2.530	0.0866	0.2379	0.7062	0.0379	0.1705	0.7747	0.1377	2.2490	0.6020	0.2190	0.0830
2.535	0.0861	0.2370	0.7043	0.0376	0.1693	0.7706	0.1371	2.2532	0.6008	0.2182	0.0826
2.540	0.0856	0.2361	0.7024	0.0372	0.1681	0.7665	0.1365	2.2575	0.5997	0.2175	0.0822
2.545	0.0852	0.2352	0.7005	0.0369	0.1670	0.7625	0.1358	2.2617	0.5985	0.2167	0.0817
2.550	0.0847	0.2343	0.6986	0.0366	0.1658	0.7585	0.1352	2.2660	0.5974	0.2160	0.0813
2.555	0.0842	0.2334	0.6967	0.0363	0.1646	0.7545	0.1346	2.2702	0.5962	0.2152	0.0809
2.560	0.0838	0.2324	0.6948	0.0359	0.1635	0.7505	0.1341	2.2745	0.5951	0.2145	0.0805
2.565	0.0833	0.2315	0.6929	0.0356	0.1623	0.7466	0.1335	2.2787	0.5939	0.2137	0.0800
2.570	0.0829	0.2307	0.6910	0.0353	0.1612	0.7426	0.1329	2.2830	0.5928	0.2130	0.0796
2.575	0.0824	0.2298	0.6892	0.0350	0.1601	0.7387	0.1323	2.2873	0.5916	0.2123	0.0792
2.580	0.0820	0.2289	0.6873	0.0347	0.1590	0.7348	0.1317	2.2915	0.5905	0.2115	0.0788
2.585	0.0815	0.2280	0.6854	0.0344	0.1578	0.7309	0.1311	2.2958	0.5893	0.2108	0.0784
2.590	0.0811	0.2271	0.6836	0.0341	0.1567	0.7270	0.1305	2.3001	0.5882	0.2101	0.0780
2.595	0.0807	0.2262	0.6817	0.0338	0.1556	0.7232	0.1299	2.3043	0.5870	0.2093	0.0776
2.600	0.0802	0.2253	0.6799	0.0335	0.1546	0.7194	0.1294	2.3086	0.5859	0.2086	0.0772
2.605	0.0798	0.2245	0.6781	0.0332	0.1535	0.7156	0.1288	2.3129	0.5847	0.2079	0.0768
2.610	0.0794	0.2236	0.6762	0.0329	0.1524	0.7118	0.1282	2.3172	0.5836	0.2072	0.0764
2.615	0.0789	0.2227	0.6744	0.0326	0.1513	0.7080	0.1277	2.3214	0.5825	0.2064	0.0760
2.620	0.0785	0.2219	0.6726	0.0323	0.1503	0.7042	0.1271	2.3257	0.5813	0.2057	0.0756
2.625	0.0781	0.2210	0.6708	0.0320	0.1492	0.7005	0.1265	2.3300	0.5802	0.2050	0.0752
2.630	0.0777	0.2202	0.6690	0.0317	0.1482	0.6968	0.1260	2.3343	0.5790	0.2043	0.0748
2.635	0.0773	0.2193	0.6672	0.0315	0.1471	0.6931	0.1254	2.3386	0.5779	0.2036	0.0744

Appendix Table 1 (cont'd)

u	1φ	2φ	3φ	4φ	5φ	6φ	7φ	8φ	9φ	10φ	11φ
2.640	0.0768	0.2185	0.6654	0.0312	0.1461	0.6894	0.1249	2.3429	0.5767	0.2029	0.0740
2.645	0.0764	0.2176	0.6636	0.0309	0.1451	0.6857	0.1243	2.3472	0.5756	0.2022	0.0737
2.650	0.0760	0.2168	0.6618	0.0306	0.1441	0.6820	0.1238	2.3515	0.5745	0.2015	0.0733
2.655	0.0756	0.2159	0.6600	0.0304	0.1430	0.6784	0.1232	2.3558	0.5733	0.2008	0.0729
2.660	0.0752	0.2151	0.6582	0.0301	0.1420	0.6748	0.1227	2.3601	0.5722	0.2001	0.0725
2.665	0.0748	0.2143	0.6565	0.0298	0.1410	0.6712	0.1221	2.3644	0.5710	0.1994	0.0721
2.670	0.0744	0.2134	0.6547	0.0296	0.1400	0.6676	0.1216	2.3687	0.5699	0.1987	0.0718
2.675	0.0740	0.2126	0.6529	0.0293	0.1391	0.6640	0.1210	2.3730	0.5688	0.1980	0.0714
2.680	0.0736	0.2118	0.6512	0.0290	0.1381	0.6605	0.1205	2.3773	0.5676	0.1973	0.0710
2.685	0.0732	0.2110	0.6494	0.0288	0.1371	0.6569	0.1200	2.3816	0.5665	0.1966	0.0707
2.690	0.0728	0.2102	0.6477	0.0285	0.1361	0.6534	0.1194	2.3859	0.5653	0.1959	0.0703
2.695	0.0724	0.2094	0.6459	0.0283	0.1352	0.6499	0.1189	2.3902	0.5642	0.1952	0.0699
2.700	0.0720	0.2085	0.6442	0.0280	0.1342	0.6464	0.1184	2.3945	0.5631	0.1945	0.0696
2.705	0.0717	0.2077	0.6425	0.0278	0.1333	0.6429	0.1179	2.3988	0.5619	0.1938	0.0692
2.710	0.0713	0.2069	0.6407	0.0275	0.1324	0.6395	0.1173	2.4032	0.5608	0.1932	0.0689
2.715	0.0709	0.2061	0.6390	0.0273	0.1314	0.6361	0.1168	2.4075	0.5597	0.1925	0.0685
2.720	0.0705	0.2053	0.6373	0.0271	0.1305	0.6326	0.1163	2.4118	0.5585	0.1918	0.0681
2.725	0.0701	0.2045	0.6356	0.0268	0.1296	0.6292	0.1158	2.4161	0.5574	0.1911	0.0678
2.730	0.0698	0.2038	0.6339	0.0266	0.1287	0.6258	0.1153	2.4205	0.5563	0.1905	0.0674
2.735	0.0694	0.2030	0.6322	0.0263	0.1278	0.6225	0.1148	2.4248	0.5551	0.1898	0.0671
2.740	0.0690	0.2022	0.6305	0.0261	0.1269	0.6191	0.1143	2.4291	0.5540	0.1891	0.0667
2.745	0.0687	0.2014	0.6288	0.0259	0.1260	0.6158	0.1138	2.4335	0.5529	0.1885	0.0664
2.750	0.0683	0.2006	0.6271	0.0257	0.1251	0.6124	0.1133	2.4378	0.5517	0.1878	0.0661
2.755	0.0679	0.1999	0.6254	0.0254	0.1242	0.6091	0.1128	2.4421	0.5506	0.1871	0.0657
2.760	0.0676	0.1991	0.6237	0.0252	0.1233	0.6058	0.1123	2.4465	0.5495	0.1865	0.0654
2.765	0.0672	0.1983	0.6221	0.0250	0.1224	0.6026	0.1118	2.4508	0.5484	0.1858	0.0650
2.770	0.0669	0.1976	0.6204	0.0248	0.1216	0.5993	0.1113	2.4552	0.5472	0.1852	0.0647
2.775	0.0665	0.1968	0.6187	0.0245	0.1207	0.5961	0.1108	2.4595	0.5461	0.1845	0.0644
2.780	0.0661	0.1960	0.6171	0.0243	0.1199	0.5928	0.1103	2.4639	0.5450	0.1839	0.0640
2.785	0.0658	0.1953	0.6154	0.0241	0.1190	0.5896	0.1098	2.4682	0.5439	0.1832	0.0637
2.790	0.0654	0.1945	0.6138	0.0239	0.1182	0.5864	0.1093	2.4726	0.5427	0.1826	0.0634
2.795	0.0651	0.1938	0.6121	0.0237	0.1173	0.5832	0.1088	2.4769	0.5416	0.1819	0.0631
2.800	0.0647	0.1930	0.6105	0.0235	0.1165	0.5801	0.1083	2.4813	0.5405	0.1813	0.0627
2.805	0.0644	0.1923	0.6088	0.0233	0.1157	0.5769	0.1079	2.4857	0.5394	0.1807	0.0624
2.810	0.0641	0.1915	0.6072	0.0231	0.1149	0.5738	0.1074	2.4900	0.5382	0.1800	0.0621
2.815	0.0637	0.1908	0.6056	0.0229	0.1140	0.5706	0.1069	2.4944	0.5371	0.1794	0.0618
2.820	0.0634	0.1901	0.6040	0.0227	0.1132	0.5675	0.1064	2.4987	0.5360	0.1787	0.0615
2.825	0.0630	0.1893	0.6023	0.0225	0.1124	0.5644	0.1060	2.5031	0.5349	0.1781	0.0611
2.830	0.0627	0.1886	0.6007	0.0223	0.1116	0.5614	0.1055	2.5075	0.5338	0.1775	0.0608
2.835	0.0624	0.1879	0.5991	0.0221	0.1108	0.5583	0.1050	2.5119	0.5327	0.1769	0.0605
2.8	0.0621	0.1872	0.5975	0.0219	0.1101	0.5552	0.1046	2.5162	0.5315	0.1762	0.0602

222

u	1φ	2φ	3φ	4φ	5φ	6φ	7φ	8φ	9φ	10φ	11φ
2.845	0.0617	0.1864	0.5959	0.0217	0.1093	0.5522	0.1041	2.5206	0.5304	0.1756	0.0599
2.850	0.0614	0.1857	0.5943	0.0215	0.1085	0.5492	0.1036	2.5250	0.5293	0.1750	0.0596
2.855	0.0611	0.1850	0.5927	0.0213	0.1077	0.5462	0.1032	2.5294	0.5282	0.1744	0.0593
2.860	0.0607	0.1843	0.5911	0.0211	0.1070	0.5432	0.1027	2.5337	0.5271	0.1737	0.0590
2.865	0.0604	0.1836	0.5895	0.0209	0.1062	0.5402	0.1023	2.5381	0.5260	0.1731	0.0587
2.870	0.0601	0.1829	0.5879	0.0207	0.1055	0.5373	0.1018	2.5425	0.5249	0.1725	0.0584
2.875	0.0598	0.1822	0.5864	0.0206	0.1047	0.5343	0.1014	2.5469	0.5237	0.1719	0.0581
2.880	0.0595	0.1815	0.5848	0.0204	0.1040	0.5314	0.1009	2.5513	0.5226	0.1713	0.0578
2.885	0.0592	0.1808	0.5832	0.0202	0.1032	0.5285	0.1005	2.5557	0.5215	0.1707	0.0575
2.890	0.0588	0.1801	0.5817	0.0200	0.1025	0.5255	0.1000	2.5601	0.5204	0.1701	0.0572
2.895	0.0585	0.1794	0.5801	0.0198	0.1018	0.5227	0.0996	2.5645	0.5193	0.1695	0.0569
2.900	0.0582	0.1787	0.5785	0.0197	0.1010	0.5198	0.0992	2.5689	0.5182	0.1689	0.0566
2.905	0.0579	0.1780	0.5770	0.0195	0.1003	0.5169	0.0987	2.5733	0.5171	0.1683	0.0563
2.910	0.0576	0.1773	0.5754	0.0193	0.0996	0.5141	0.0983	2.5777	0.5160	0.1677	0.0560
2.915	0.0573	0.1766	0.5739	0.0191	0.0989	0.5112	0.0978	2.5821	0.5149	0.1671	0.0557
2.920	0.0570	0.1760	0.5724	0.0190	0.0982	0.5084	0.0974	2.5865	0.5138	0.1665	0.0554
2.925	0.0567	0.1753	0.5708	0.0188	0.0975	0.5056	0.0970	2.5909	0.5127	0.1659	0.0552
2.930	0.0564	0.1746	0.5693	0.0186	0.0968	0.5028	0.0966	2.5953	0.5116	0.1653	0.0549
2.935	0.0561	0.1739	0.5678	0.0185	0.0961	0.5000	0.0961	2.5997	0.5105	0.1647	0.0546
2.940	0.0558	0.1733	0.5662	0.0183	0.0954	0.4973	0.0957	2.6041	0.5094	0.1641	0.0543
2.945	0.0555	0.1726	0.5647	0.0182	0.0947	0.4945	0.0953	2.6085	0.5083	0.1635	0.0540
2.950	0.0552	0.1719	0.5632	0.0180	0.0941	0.4918	0.0949	2.6129	0.5072	0.1629	0.0538
2.955	0.0549	0.1713	0.5617	0.0178	0.0934	0.4890	0.0944	2.6173	0.5061	0.1623	0.0535
2.960	0.0547	0.1706	0.5602	0.0177	0.0927	0.4863	0.0940	2.6218	0.5050	0.1618	0.0532
2.965	0.0544	0.1700	0.5587	0.0175	0.0921	0.4836	0.0936	2.6262	0.5039	0.1612	0.0529
2.970	0.0541	0.1693	0.5572	0.0174	0.0914	0.4809	0.0932	2.6306	0.5028	0.1606	0.0527
2.975	0.0538	0.1686	0.5557	0.0172	0.0907	0.4783	0.0928	2.6350	0.5017	0.1600	0.0524
2.980	0.0535	0.1680	0.5542	0.0171	0.0901	0.4756	0.0924	2.6395	0.5006	0.1595	0.0521
2.985	0.0532	0.1673	0.5527	0.0169	0.0894	0.4729	0.0920	2.6439	0.4995	0.1589	0.0519
2.990	0.0530	0.1667	0.5512	0.0168	0.0888	0.4703	0.0916	2.6483	0.4984	0.1583	0.0516
2.995	0.0527	0.1661	0.5498	0.0166	0.0882	0.4677	0.0912	2.6528	0.4974	0.1578	0.0513
3.000	0.0524	0.1654	0.5483	0.0165	0.0875	0.4651	0.0908	2.6572	0.4963	0.1572	0.0511
3.005	0.0521	0.1648	0.5468	0.0163	0.0869	0.4625	0.0904	2.6616	0.4952	0.1566	0.0508
3.010	0.0518	0.1642	0.5453	0.0162	0.0863	0.4599	0.0900	2.6661	0.4941	0.1561	0.0505
3.015	0.0516	0.1635	0.5439	0.0160	0.0857	0.4573	0.0896	2.6705	0.4930	0.1555	0.0503
3.020	0.0513	0.1629	0.5424	0.0159	0.0851	0.4548	0.0892	2.6749	0.4919	0.1549	0.0500
3.025	0.0510	0.1623	0.5409	0.0158	0.0844	0.4522	0.0888	2.6794	0.4908	0.1544	0.0498
3.030	0.0508	0.1616	0.5395	0.0156	0.0838	0.4497	0.0884	2.6838	0.4898	0.1538	0.0495
3.035	0.0505	0.1610	0.5380	0.0155	0.0832	0.4472	0.0880	2.6883	0.4887	0.1533	0.0493
3.040	0.0502	0.1604	0.5366	0.0153	0.0826	0.4447	0.0876	2.6927	0.4876	0.1527	0.0490
3.045	0.0500	0.1598	0.5352	0.0152	0.0820	0.4422	0.0872	2.6972	0.4865	0.1522	0.0488

Appendix Table 1 (cont'd)

u	1ϕ	2ϕ	3ϕ	4ϕ	5ϕ	6ϕ	7ϕ	8ϕ	9ϕ	10ϕ	11ϕ
3.050	0.0497	0.1592	0.5337	0.0151	0.0815	0.4397	0.0868	2.7016	0.4854	0.1516	0.0485
3.055	0.0495	0.1586	0.5323	0.0149	0.0809	0.4372	0.0864	2.7061	0.4844	0.1511	0.0483
3.060	0.0492	0.1579	0.5308	0.0148	0.0803	0.4348	0.0861	2.7105	0.4833	0.1505	0.0480
3.065	0.0489	0.1573	0.5294	0.0147	0.0797	0.4323	0.0857	2.7150	0.4822	0.1500	0.0478
3.070	0.0487	0.1567	0.5280	0.0146	0.0791	0.4299	0.0853	2.7195	0.4811	0.1495	0.0475
3.075	0.0484	0.1561	0.5266	0.0144	0.0786	0.4275	0.0849	2.7239	0.4801	0.1489	0.0473
3.080	0.0482	0.1555	0.5252	0.0143	0.0780	0.4251	0.0845	2.7284	0.4790	0.1484	0.0470
3.085	0.0479	0.1549	0.5237	0.0142	0.0774	0.4227	0.0842	2.7328	0.4779	0.1478	0.0468
3.090	0.0477	0.1543	0.5223	0.0140	0.0769	0.4203	0.0838	2.7373	0.4769	0.1473	0.0466
3.095	0.0474	0.1537	0.5209	0.0139	0.0763	0.4179	0.0834	2.7418	0.4758	0.1468	0.0463
3.100	0.0472	0.1531	0.5195	0.0138	0.0758	0.4155	0.0831	2.7462	0.4747	0.1462	0.0461
3.105	0.0469	0.1525	0.5181	0.0137	0.0752	0.4132	0.0827	2.7507	0.4737	0.1457	0.0459
3.110	0.0467	0.1520	0.5167	0.0136	0.0747	0.4109	0.0823	2.7552	0.4726	0.1452	0.0456
3.115	0.0464	0.1514	0.5153	0.0134	0.0742	0.4085	0.0820	2.7597	0.4715	0.1447	0.0454
3.120	0.0462	0.1508	0.5139	0.0133	0.0736	0.4062	0.0816	2.7641	0.4705	0.1441	0.0452
3.125	0.0460	0.1502	0.5126	0.0132	0.0731	0.4039	0.0812	2.7686	0.4694	0.1436	0.0449
3.130	0.0457	0.1496	0.5112	0.0131	0.0726	0.4016	0.0809	2.7731	0.4684	0.1431	0.0447
3.135	0.0455	0.1491	0.5098	0.0130	0.0720	0.3993	0.0805	2.7776	0.4673	0.1426	0.0445
3.140	0.0452	0.1485	0.5084	0.0129	0.0715	0.3971	0.0802	2.7821	0.4662	0.1421	0.0442
3.145	0.0450	0.1479	0.5071	0.0127	0.0710	0.3948	0.0798	2.7865	0.4652	0.1415	0.0440
3.150	0.0448	0.1473	0.5057	0.0126	0.0705	0.3926	0.0795	2.7910	0.4641	0.1410	0.0438
3.155	0.0445	0.1468	0.5043	0.0125	0.0700	0.3903	0.0791	2.7955	0.4631	0.1405	0.0436
3.160	0.0443	0.1462	0.5030	0.0124	0.0695	0.3881	0.0788	2.8000	0.4620	0.1400	0.0434
3.165	0.0441	0.1456	0.5016	0.0123	0.0690	0.3859	0.0784	2.8045	0.4610	0.1395	0.0431
3.170	0.0438	0.1451	0.5002	0.0122	0.0685	0.3837	0.0781	2.8090	0.4599	0.1390	0.0429
3.175	0.0436	0.1445	0.4989	0.0121	0.0680	0.3815	0.0777	2.8135	0.4589	0.1385	0.0427
3.180	0.0434	0.1440	0.4975	0.0120	0.0675	0.3793	0.0774	2.8180	0.4578	0.1380	0.0425
3.185	0.0432	0.1434	0.4962	0.0119	0.0670	0.3772	0.0770	2.8225	0.4568	0.1375	0.0423
3.190	0.0429	0.1429	0.4949	0.0118	0.0665	0.3750	0.0767	2.8270	0.4557	0.1370	0.0420
3.195	0.0427	0.1423	0.4935	0.0117	0.0660	0.3729	0.0764	2.8315	0.4547	0.1365	0.0418
3.200	0.0425	0.1418	0.4922	0.0116	0.0656	0.3707	0.0760	2.8360	0.4536	0.1360	0.0416
3.205	0.0423	0.1412	0.4909	0.0115	0.0651	0.3686	0.0757	2.8405	0.4526	0.1355	0.0414
3.210	0.0421	0.1407	0.4895	0.0114	0.0646	0.3665	0.0753	2.8450	0.4515	0.1350	0.0412
3.215	0.0418	0.1401	0.4882	0.0113	0.0641	0.3644	0.0750	2.8495	0.4505	0.1345	0.0410
3.220	0.0416	0.1396	0.4869	0.0112	0.0637	0.3623	0.0747	2.8540	0.4495	0.1340	0.0408
3.225	0.0414	0.1390	0.4856	0.0111	0.0632	0.3602	0.0744	2.8585	0.4484	0.1335	0.0406
3.230	0.0412	0.1385	0.4842	0.0110	0.0627	0.3581	0.0740	2.8630	0.4474	0.1330	0.0404
3.235	0.0410	0.1380	0.4829	0.0109	0.0623	0.3561	0.0737	2.8675	0.4464	0.1325	0.0402
3.240	0.0408	0.1374	0.4816	0.0108	0.0618	0.3540	0.0734	2.8721	0.4453	0.1321	0.0400
3.245	0.0405	0.1369	0.4803	0.0107	0.0614	0.3520	0.0730	2.8766	0.4443	0.1316	0.0397
3.250	0.0403	0.1364	0.4790	0.0106	0.0609	0.3500	0.0727	2.8811	0.4433	0.1311	0.0395

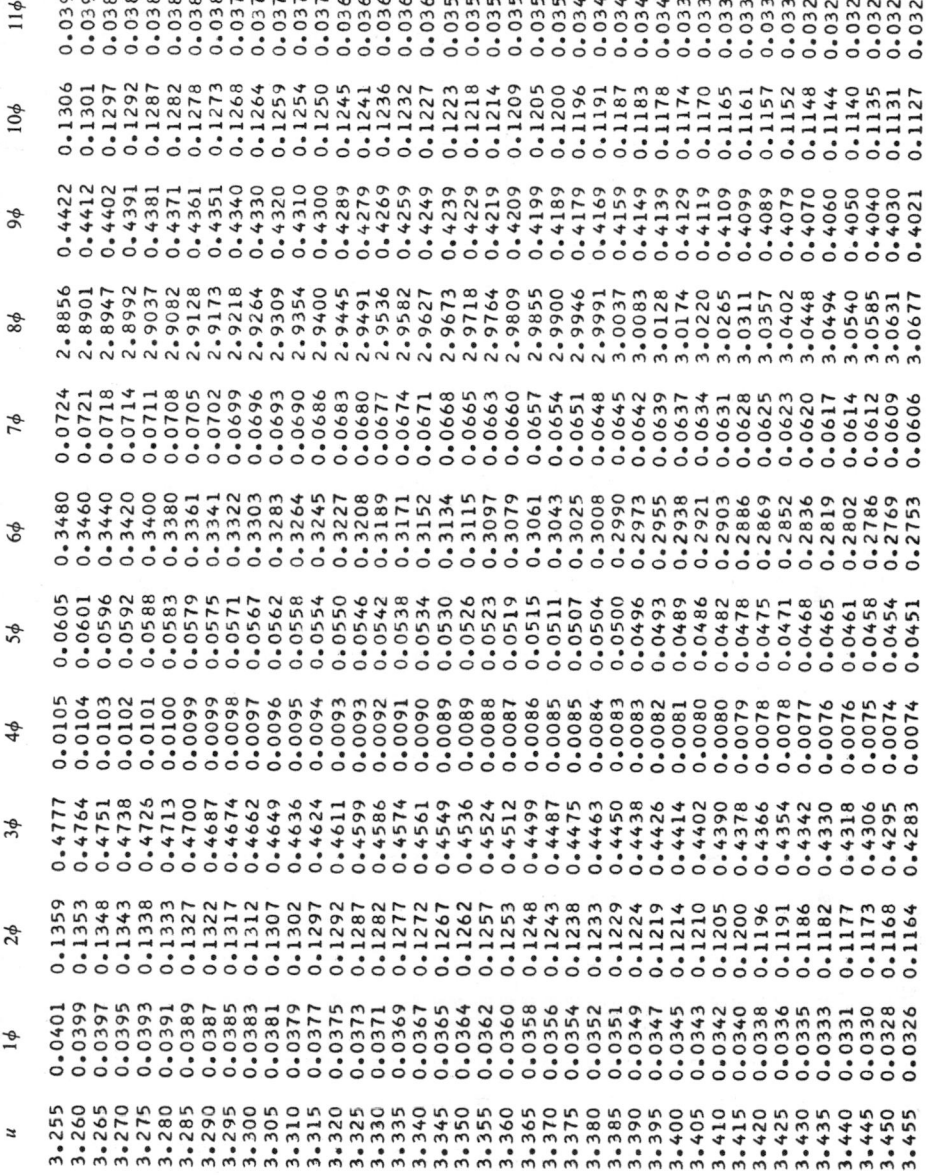

u	1ϕ	2ϕ	3ϕ	4ϕ	5ϕ	6ϕ	7ϕ	8ϕ	9ϕ	10ϕ	11ϕ
3.255	0.0401	0.1359	0.4777	0.0105	0.0605	0.3480	0.0724	2.8856	0.4422	0.1306	0.0393
3.260	0.0399	0.1353	0.4764	0.0104	0.0601	0.3460	0.0721	2.8901	0.4412	0.1301	0.0391
3.265	0.0397	0.1348	0.4751	0.0103	0.0596	0.3440	0.0718	2.8947	0.4402	0.1297	0.0389
3.270	0.0395	0.1343	0.4738	0.0102	0.0592	0.3420	0.0714	2.8992	0.4391	0.1292	0.0387
3.275	0.0393	0.1338	0.4726	0.0101	0.0588	0.3400	0.0711	2.9037	0.4381	0.1287	0.0386
3.280	0.0391	0.1333	0.4713	0.0100	0.0583	0.3380	0.0708	2.9082	0.4371	0.1282	0.0384
3.285	0.0389	0.1327	0.4700	0.0099	0.0579	0.3361	0.0705	2.9128	0.4361	0.1278	0.0382
3.290	0.0387	0.1322	0.4687	0.0099	0.0575	0.3341	0.0702	2.9173	0.4351	0.1273	0.0380
3.295	0.0385	0.1317	0.4674	0.0098	0.0571	0.3322	0.0699	2.9218	0.4340	0.1268	0.0378
3.300	0.0383	0.1312	0.4662	0.0097	0.0567	0.3303	0.0696	2.9264	0.4330	0.1264	0.0376
3.305	0.0381	0.1307	0.4649	0.0096	0.0562	0.3283	0.0693	2.9309	0.4320	0.1259	0.0374
3.310	0.0379	0.1302	0.4636	0.0095	0.0558	0.3264	0.0690	2.9354	0.4310	0.1254	0.0372
3.315	0.0377	0.1297	0.4624	0.0094	0.0554	0.3245	0.0686	2.9400	0.4300	0.1250	0.0370
3.320	0.0375	0.1292	0.4611	0.0093	0.0550	0.3227	0.0683	2.9445	0.4289	0.1245	0.0368
3.325	0.0373	0.1287	0.4599	0.0093	0.0546	0.3208	0.0680	2.9491	0.4279	0.1241	0.0366
3.330	0.0371	0.1282	0.4586	0.0092	0.0542	0.3189	0.0677	2.9536	0.4269	0.1236	0.0364
3.335	0.0369	0.1277	0.4574	0.0091	0.0538	0.3171	0.0674	2.9582	0.4259	0.1232	0.0363
3.340	0.0367	0.1272	0.4561	0.0090	0.0534	0.3152	0.0671	2.9627	0.4249	0.1227	0.0361
3.345	0.0365	0.1267	0.4549	0.0089	0.0530	0.3134	0.0668	2.9673	0.4239	0.1223	0.0359
3.350	0.0364	0.1262	0.4536	0.0089	0.0526	0.3115	0.0665	2.9718	0.4229	0.1218	0.0357
3.355	0.0362	0.1257	0.4524	0.0088	0.0523	0.3097	0.0663	2.9764	0.4219	0.1214	0.0355
3.360	0.0360	0.1253	0.4512	0.0087	0.0519	0.3079	0.0660	2.9809	0.4209	0.1209	0.0354
3.365	0.0358	0.1248	0.4499	0.0086	0.0515	0.3061	0.0657	2.9855	0.4199	0.1205	0.0352
3.370	0.0356	0.1243	0.4487	0.0085	0.0511	0.3043	0.0654	2.9900	0.4189	0.1200	0.0350
3.375	0.0354	0.1238	0.4475	0.0085	0.0507	0.3025	0.0651	2.9946	0.4179	0.1196	0.0348
3.380	0.0352	0.1233	0.4463	0.0084	0.0504	0.3008	0.0648	2.9991	0.4169	0.1191	0.0346
3.385	0.0351	0.1229	0.4450	0.0083	0.0500	0.2990	0.0645	3.0037	0.4159	0.1187	0.0345
3.390	0.0349	0.1224	0.4438	0.0083	0.0496	0.2973	0.0642	3.0083	0.4149	0.1183	0.0343
3.395	0.0347	0.1219	0.4426	0.0082	0.0493	0.2955	0.0639	3.0128	0.4139	0.1178	0.0341
3.400	0.0345	0.1214	0.4414	0.0081	0.0489	0.2938	0.0637	3.0174	0.4129	0.1174	0.0339
3.405	0.0343	0.1210	0.4402	0.0080	0.0486	0.2921	0.0634	3.0220	0.4119	0.1170	0.0338
3.410	0.0342	0.1205	0.4390	0.0080	0.0482	0.2903	0.0631	3.0265	0.4109	0.1165	0.0336
3.415	0.0340	0.1200	0.4378	0.0079	0.0478	0.2886	0.0628	3.0311	0.4099	0.1161	0.0334
3.420	0.0338	0.1196	0.4366	0.0078	0.0475	0.2869	0.0625	3.0357	0.4089	0.1157	0.0333
3.425	0.0336	0.1191	0.4354	0.0078	0.0471	0.2852	0.0623	3.0402	0.4079	0.1152	0.0331
3.430	0.0335	0.1186	0.4342	0.0077	0.0468	0.2836	0.0620	3.0448	0.4070	0.1148	0.0329
3.435	0.0333	0.1182	0.4330	0.0076	0.0465	0.2819	0.0617	3.0494	0.4060	0.1144	0.0328
3.440	0.0331	0.1177	0.4318	0.0076	0.0461	0.2802	0.0614	3.0540	0.4050	0.1140	0.0326
3.445	0.0330	0.1173	0.4306	0.0075	0.0458	0.2786	0.0612	3.0585	0.4040	0.1135	0.0324
3.450	0.0328	0.1168	0.4295	0.0074	0.0454	0.2769	0.0609	3.0631	0.4030	0.1131	0.0323
3.455	0.0326	0.1164	0.4283	0.0074	0.0451	0.2753	0.0606	3.0677	0.4021	0.1127	0.0321

Appendix Table 1 (cont'd)

u	1φ	2φ	3φ	4φ	5φ	6φ	7φ	8φ	9φ	10φ	11φ
3.460	0.0324	0.1159	0.4271	0.0073	0.0448	0.2737	0.0604	3.0723	0.4011	0.1123	0.0319
3.465	0.0323	0.1155	0.4259	0.0072	0.0444	0.2720	0.0601	3.0769	0.4001	0.1119	0.0318
3.470	0.0321	0.1150	0.4248	0.0072	0.0441	0.2704	0.0598	3.0814	0.3991	0.1114	0.0316
3.475	0.0320	0.1146	0.4236	0.0071	0.0438	0.2688	0.0596	3.0860	0.3982	0.1110	0.0315
3.480	0.0318	0.1141	0.4224	0.0070	0.0435	0.2672	0.0593	3.0906	0.3972	0.1106	0.0313
3.485	0.0316	0.1137	0.4213	0.0070	0.0431	0.2657	0.0590	3.0952	0.3962	0.1102	0.0311
3.490	0.0315	0.1133	0.4201	0.0069	0.0428	0.2641	0.0588	3.0998	0.3952	0.1098	0.0310
3.495	0.0313	0.1128	0.4190	0.0068	0.0425	0.2625	0.0585	3.1044	0.3943	0.1094	0.0308
3.500	0.0311	0.1124	0.4178	0.0067	0.0422	0.2610	0.0583	3.1090	0.3933	0.1090	0.0307
3.505	0.0310	0.1119	0.4167	0.0067	0.0419	0.2594	0.0580	3.1136	0.3923	0.1086	0.0305
3.510	0.0308	0.1115	0.4155	0.0067	0.0416	0.2579	0.0577	3.1182	0.3914	0.1082	0.0304
3.515	0.0307	0.1111	0.4144	0.0066	0.0413	0.2563	0.0575	3.1228	0.3904	0.1078	0.0302
3.520	0.0305	0.1106	0.4132	0.0065	0.0410	0.2548	0.0572	3.1274	0.3895	0.1074	0.0300
3.525	0.0303	0.1102	0.4121	0.0065	0.0407	0.2533	0.0570	3.1320	0.3885	0.1070	0.0299
3.530	0.0302	0.1098	0.4109	0.0064	0.0404	0.2518	0.0567	3.1366	0.3875	0.1066	0.0297
3.535	0.0300	0.1094	0.4098	0.0064	0.0401	0.2503	0.0565	3.1412	0.3866	0.1062	0.0296
3.540	0.0299	0.1089	0.4087	0.0063	0.0398	0.2488	0.0562	3.1458	0.3856	0.1058	0.0294
3.545	0.0297	0.1085	0.4076	0.0063	0.0395	0.2473	0.0560	3.1504	0.3847	0.1054	0.0293
3.550	0.0296	0.1081	0.4064	0.0062	0.0392	0.2458	0.0557	3.1550	0.3837	0.1050	0.0291
3.555	0.0294	0.1077	0.4053	0.0062	0.0389	0.2443	0.0555	3.1596	0.3828	0.1046	0.0290
3.560	0.0293	0.1073	0.4042	0.0061	0.0386	0.2429	0.0552	3.1642	0.3818	0.1042	0.0289
3.565	0.0291	0.1068	0.4031	0.0060	0.0383	0.2414	0.0550	3.1688	0.3809	0.1038	0.0287
3.570	0.0290	0.1064	0.4020	0.0060	0.0380	0.2400	0.0547	3.1734	0.3799	0.1034	0.0286
3.575	0.0288	0.1060	0.4008	0.0059	0.0378	0.2385	0.0545	3.1780	0.3790	0.1030	0.0284
3.580	0.0287	0.1056	0.3997	0.0059	0.0375	0.2371	0.0543	3.1827	0.3780	0.1027	0.0283
3.585	0.0285	0.1052	0.3986	0.0058	0.0372	0.2357	0.0540	3.1873	0.3771	0.1023	0.0281
3.590	0.0284	0.1048	0.3975	0.0058	0.0369	0.2343	0.0538	3.1919	0.3762	0.1019	0.0280
3.595	0.0282	0.1044	0.3964	0.0057	0.0366	0.2329	0.0535	3.1965	0.3752	0.1015	0.0278
3.600	0.0281	0.1040	0.3953	0.0057	0.0364	0.2315	0.0533	3.2011	0.3743	0.1011	0.0277
3.605	0.0279	0.1036	0.3942	0.0056	0.0361	0.2301	0.0531	3.2057	0.3734	0.1007	0.0276
3.610	0.0278	0.1032	0.3931	0.0056	0.0358	0.2287	0.0528	3.2104	0.3724	0.1004	0.0274
3.615	0.0277	0.1028	0.3920	0.0055	0.0356	0.2273	0.0526	3.2150	0.3715	0.1000	0.0273
3.620	0.0275	0.1024	0.3909	0.0055	0.0353	0.2259	0.0524	3.2196	0.3706	0.0996	0.0271
3.625	0.0274	0.1020	0.3899	0.0054	0.0350	0.2246	0.0521	3.2242	0.3696	0.0992	0.0270
3.630	0.0272	0.1016	0.3888	0.0054	0.0348	0.2232	0.0519	3.2289	0.3687	0.0989	0.0269
3.635	0.0271	0.1012	0.3877	0.0053	0.0345	0.2219	0.0517	3.2335	0.3678	0.0985	0.0267
3.640	0.0270	0.1008	0.3866	0.0053	0.0343	0.2205	0.0514	3.2381	0.3668	0.0981	0.0266
3.645	0.0268	0.1004	0.3855	0.0052	0.0340	0.2192	0.0512	3.2428	0.3659	0.0978	0.0265
3.650	0.0267	0.1000	0.3845	0.0052	0.0338	0.2179	0.0510	3.2474	0.3650	0.0974	0.0263
3.655	0.0265	0.0996	0.3834	0.0052	0.0335	0.2165	0.0508	3.2520	0.3641	0.0970	0.0262

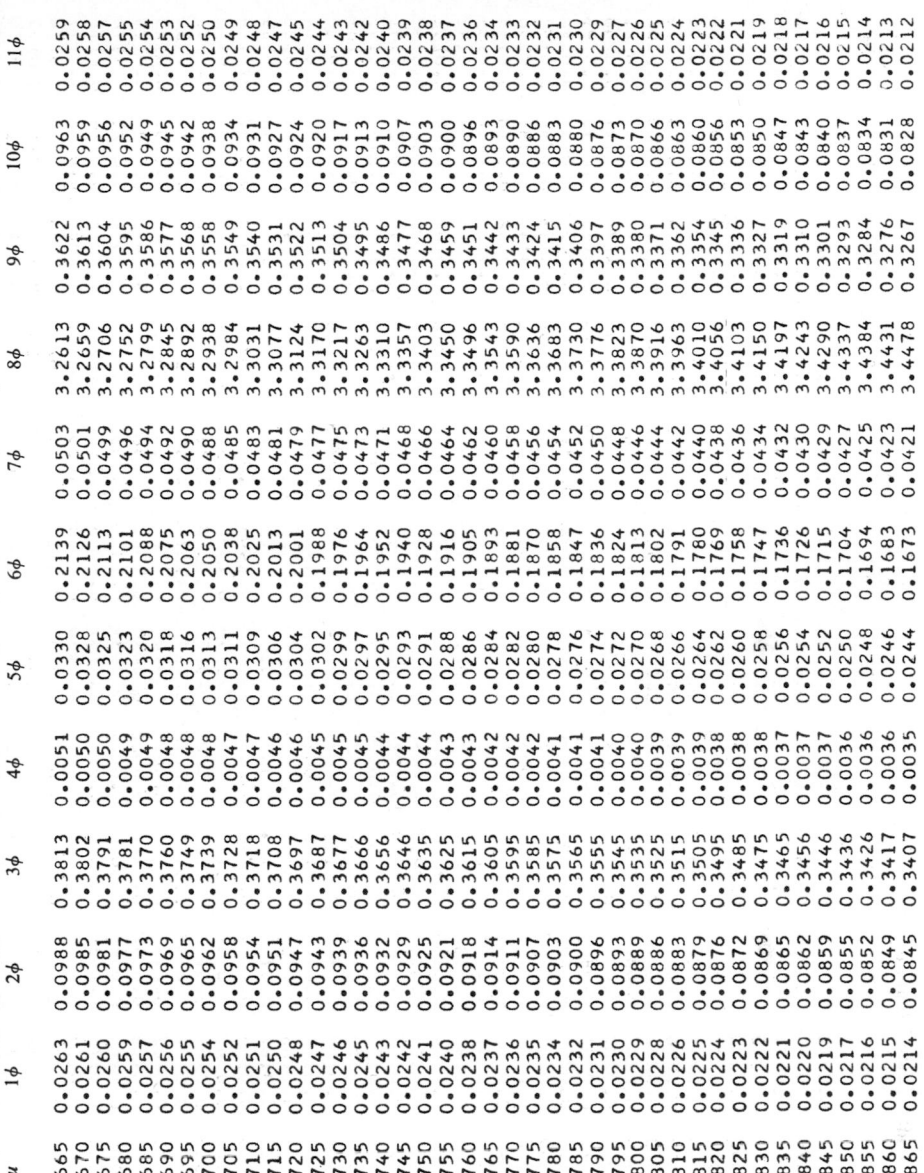

u	1φ	2φ	3φ	4φ	5φ	6φ	7φ	8φ	9φ	10φ	11φ
3.665	0.0263	0.0988	0.3813	0.0051	0.0330	0.2139	0.0503	3.2613	0.3622	0.0963	0.0259
3.670	0.0261	0.0985	0.3802	0.0050	0.0328	0.2126	0.0501	3.2659	0.3613	0.0959	0.0258
3.675	0.0260	0.0981	0.3791	0.0050	0.0325	0.2113	0.0499	3.2706	0.3604	0.0956	0.0257
3.680	0.0259	0.0977	0.3781	0.0049	0.0323	0.2101	0.0496	3.2752	0.3595	0.0952	0.0255
3.685	0.0257	0.0973	0.3770	0.0049	0.0320	0.2088	0.0494	3.2799	0.3586	0.0949	0.0254
3.690	0.0256	0.0969	0.3760	0.0048	0.0318	0.2075	0.0492	3.2845	0.3577	0.0945	0.0253
3.695	0.0255	0.0965	0.3749	0.0048	0.0316	0.2063	0.0490	3.2892	0.3568	0.0942	0.0252
3.700	0.0254	0.0962	0.3739	0.0048	0.0313	0.2050	0.0488	3.2938	0.3558	0.0938	0.0250
3.705	0.0252	0.0958	0.3728	0.0047	0.0311	0.2038	0.0485	3.2984	0.3549	0.0934	0.0249
3.710	0.0251	0.0954	0.3718	0.0047	0.0309	0.2025	0.0483	3.3031	0.3540	0.0931	0.0248
3.715	0.0250	0.0951	0.3708	0.0046	0.0306	0.2013	0.0481	3.3077	0.3531	0.0927	0.0247
3.720	0.0248	0.0947	0.3697	0.0046	0.0304	0.2001	0.0479	3.3124	0.3522	0.0924	0.0245
3.725	0.0247	0.0943	0.3687	0.0045	0.0302	0.1988	0.0477	3.3170	0.3513	0.0920	0.0244
3.730	0.0246	0.0939	0.3677	0.0045	0.0299	0.1976	0.0475	3.3217	0.3504	0.0917	0.0243
3.735	0.0245	0.0936	0.3666	0.0045	0.0297	0.1964	0.0473	3.3263	0.3495	0.0913	0.0242
3.740	0.0243	0.0932	0.3656	0.0044	0.0295	0.1952	0.0471	3.3310	0.3486	0.0910	0.0240
3.745	0.0242	0.0929	0.3646	0.0044	0.0293	0.1940	0.0468	3.3357	0.3477	0.0907	0.0239
3.750	0.0241	0.0925	0.3635	0.0044	0.0291	0.1928	0.0466	3.3403	0.3468	0.0903	0.0238
3.755	0.0240	0.0921	0.3625	0.0043	0.0288	0.1916	0.0464	3.3450	0.3459	0.0900	0.0237
3.760	0.0238	0.0918	0.3615	0.0043	0.0286	0.1905	0.0462	3.3496	0.3451	0.0896	0.0236
3.765	0.0237	0.0914	0.3605	0.0042	0.0284	0.1893	0.0460	3.3543	0.3442	0.0893	0.0234
3.770	0.0236	0.0911	0.3595	0.0042	0.0282	0.1881	0.0458	3.3590	0.3433	0.0890	0.0233
3.775	0.0235	0.0907	0.3585	0.0042	0.0280	0.1870	0.0456	3.3636	0.3424	0.0886	0.0232
3.780	0.0234	0.0903	0.3575	0.0041	0.0278	0.1858	0.0454	3.3683	0.3415	0.0883	0.0231
3.785	0.0232	0.0900	0.3565	0.0041	0.0276	0.1847	0.0452	3.3730	0.3406	0.0880	0.0230
3.790	0.0231	0.0896	0.3555	0.0041	0.0274	0.1836	0.0450	3.3776	0.3397	0.0876	0.0229
3.795	0.0230	0.0893	0.3545	0.0040	0.0272	0.1824	0.0448	3.3823	0.3389	0.0873	0.0227
3.800	0.0229	0.0889	0.3535	0.0040	0.0270	0.1813	0.0446	3.3870	0.3380	0.0870	0.0226
3.805	0.0228	0.0886	0.3525	0.0039	0.0268	0.1802	0.0444	3.3916	0.3371	0.0866	0.0225
3.810	0.0226	0.0883	0.3515	0.0039	0.0266	0.1791	0.0442	3.3963	0.3362	0.0863	0.0224
3.815	0.0225	0.0879	0.3505	0.0038	0.0264	0.1780	0.0440	3.4010	0.3354	0.0860	0.0223
3.820	0.0224	0.0876	0.3495	0.0038	0.0262	0.1769	0.0438	3.4056	0.3345	0.0856	0.0222
3.825	0.0223	0.0872	0.3485	0.0038	0.0260	0.1758	0.0436	3.4103	0.3336	0.0853	0.0221
3.830	0.0222	0.0869	0.3475	0.0038	0.0258	0.1747	0.0434	3.4150	0.3327	0.0850	0.0219
3.835	0.0221	0.0865	0.3465	0.0037	0.0256	0.1736	0.0432	3.4197	0.3319	0.0847	0.0218
3.840	0.0220	0.0862	0.3456	0.0037	0.0254	0.1726	0.0430	3.4243	0.3310	0.0843	0.0217
3.845	0.0219	0.0859	0.3446	0.0037	0.0252	0.1715	0.0429	3.4290	0.3301	0.0840	0.0216
3.850	0.0217	0.0855	0.3436	0.0036	0.0250	0.1704	0.0427	3.4337	0.3293	0.0837	0.0215
3.855	0.0216	0.0852	0.3426	0.0036	0.0248	0.1694	0.0425	3.4384	0.3284	0.0834	0.0214
3.860	0.0215	0.0849	0.3417	0.0036	0.0246	0.1683	0.0423	3.4431	0.3276	0.0831	0.0213
3.865	0.0214	0.0845	0.3407	0.0035	0.0244	0.1673	0.0421	3.4478	0.3267	0.0828	0.0212

Appendix Table 1 (cont'd)

u	1φ	2φ	3φ	4φ	5φ	6φ	7φ	8φ	9φ	10φ	11φ
3.870	0.0213	0.0842	0.3397	0.0035	0.0243	0.1662	0.0419	3.4524	0.3258	0.0824	0.0211
3.875	0.0212	0.0839	0.3388	0.0035	0.0241	0.1652	0.0417	3.4571	0.3250	0.0821	0.0210
3.880	0.0211	0.0835	0.3378	0.0035	0.0239	0.1642	0.0415	3.4618	0.3241	0.0818	0.0209
3.885	0.0210	0.0832	0.3368	0.0034	0.0237	0.1632	0.0414	3.4665	0.3233	0.0815	0.0208
3.890	0.0209	0.0829	0.3359	0.0034	0.0235	0.1621	0.0412	3.4712	0.3224	0.0812	0.0207
3.895	0.0208	0.0826	0.3349	0.0034	0.0234	0.1611	0.0410	3.4759	0.3216	0.0809	0.0206
3.900	0.0207	0.0822	0.3340	0.0034	0.0232	0.1601	0.0408	3.4806	0.3207	0.0806	0.0204
3.905	0.0206	0.0819	0.3330	0.0033	0.0230	0.1591	0.0406	3.4853	0.3199	0.0803	0.0203
3.910	0.0205	0.0816	0.3321	0.0033	0.0228	0.1582	0.0404	3.4900	0.3190	0.0800	0.0202
3.915	0.0203	0.0813	0.3311	0.0032	0.0227	0.1572	0.0403	3.4947	0.3182	0.0797	0.0201
3.920	0.0202	0.0810	0.3302	0.0032	0.0225	0.1562	0.0401	3.4994	0.3174	0.0794	0.0200
3.925	0.0201	0.0806	0.3293	0.0032	0.0223	0.1552	0.0399	3.5040	0.3165	0.0790	0.0199
3.930	0.0200	0.0803	0.3283	0.0032	0.0221	0.1542	0.0397	3.5087	0.3157	0.0787	0.0198
3.935	0.0199	0.0800	0.3274	0.0031	0.0220	0.1533	0.0395	3.5134	0.3148	0.0784	0.0197
3.940	0.0198	0.0797	0.3265	0.0031	0.0218	0.1523	0.0394	3.5181	0.3140	0.0781	0.0196
3.945	0.0197	0.0794	0.3255	0.0031	0.0216	0.1514	0.0392	3.5228	0.3132	0.0778	0.0195
3.950	0.0196	0.0791	0.3246	0.0030	0.0215	0.1504	0.0390	3.5275	0.3123	0.0775	0.0194
3.955	0.0195	0.0788	0.3237	0.0030	0.0213	0.1495	0.0388	3.5323	0.3115	0.0773	0.0193
3.960	0.0194	0.0785	0.3227	0.0030	0.0212	0.1485	0.0387	3.5370	0.3107	0.0770	0.0192
3.965	0.0193	0.0781	0.3218	0.0030	0.0210	0.1476	0.0385	3.5417	0.3098	0.0767	0.0192
3.970	0.0192	0.0778	0.3209	0.0029	0.0208	0.1467	0.0383	3.5464	0.3090	0.0764	0.0191
3.975	0.0191	0.0775	0.3200	0.0029	0.0207	0.1458	0.0382	3.5511	0.3082	0.0761	0.0190
3.980	0.0190	0.0772	0.3191	0.0029	0.0205	0.1449	0.0380	3.5558	0.3074	0.0758	0.0189
3.985	0.0189	0.0769	0.3182	0.0029	0.0204	0.1439	0.0378	3.5605	0.3065	0.0755	0.0188
3.990	0.0188	0.0766	0.3172	0.0028	0.0202	0.1430	0.0376	3.5652	0.3057	0.0752	0.0187
3.995	0.0188	0.0763	0.3163	0.0028	0.0201	0.1421	0.0375	3.5699	0.3049	0.0749	0.0186
4.000	0.0187	0.0760	0.3154	0.0028	0.0199	0.1412	0.0373	3.5746	0.3041	0.0746	0.0186
4.005	0.0186	0.0757	0.3145	0.0028	0.0198	0.1404	0.0371	3.5793	0.3033	0.0743	0.0185
4.010	0.0185	0.0754	0.3136	0.0027	0.0196	0.1395	0.0370	3.5841	0.3025	0.0741	0.0184
4.015	0.0184	0.0751	0.3127	0.0027	0.0195	0.1386	0.0368	3.5888	0.3016	0.0738	0.0183
4.020	0.0183	0.0748	0.3118	0.0027	0.0193	0.1377	0.0367	3.5935	0.3008	0.0735	0.0182
4.025	0.0182	0.0745	0.3109	0.0027	0.0192	0.1369	0.0365	3.5982	0.3000	0.0732	0.0181
4.030	0.0181	0.0742	0.3100	0.0026	0.0190	0.1360	0.0363	3.6029	0.2992	0.0729	0.0180
4.035	0.0180	0.0740	0.3092	0.0026	0.0189	0.1351	0.0362	3.6076	0.2984	0.0726	0.0179
4.040	0.0179	0.0737	0.3083	0.0026	0.0187	0.1343	0.0360	3.6124	0.2976	0.0724	0.0178
4.045	0.0178	0.0734	0.3074	0.0026	0.0186	0.1334	0.0358	3.6171	0.2968	0.0721	0.0178
4.050	0.0177	0.0731	0.3065	0.0025	0.0184	0.1326	0.0357	3.6218	0.2960	0.0718	0.0177
4.055	0.0176	0.0728	0.3056	0.0025	0.0183	0.1317	0.0355	3.6265	0.2952	0.0715	0.0175
4.060	0.0176	0.0725	0.3047	0.0025	0.0182	0.1309	0.0354	3.6313	0.2944	0.0713	0.0174
4.065	0.0175	0.0722	0.3039	0.0025	0.0180	0.1301	0.0352	3.6360	0.2936	0.0710	0.0173

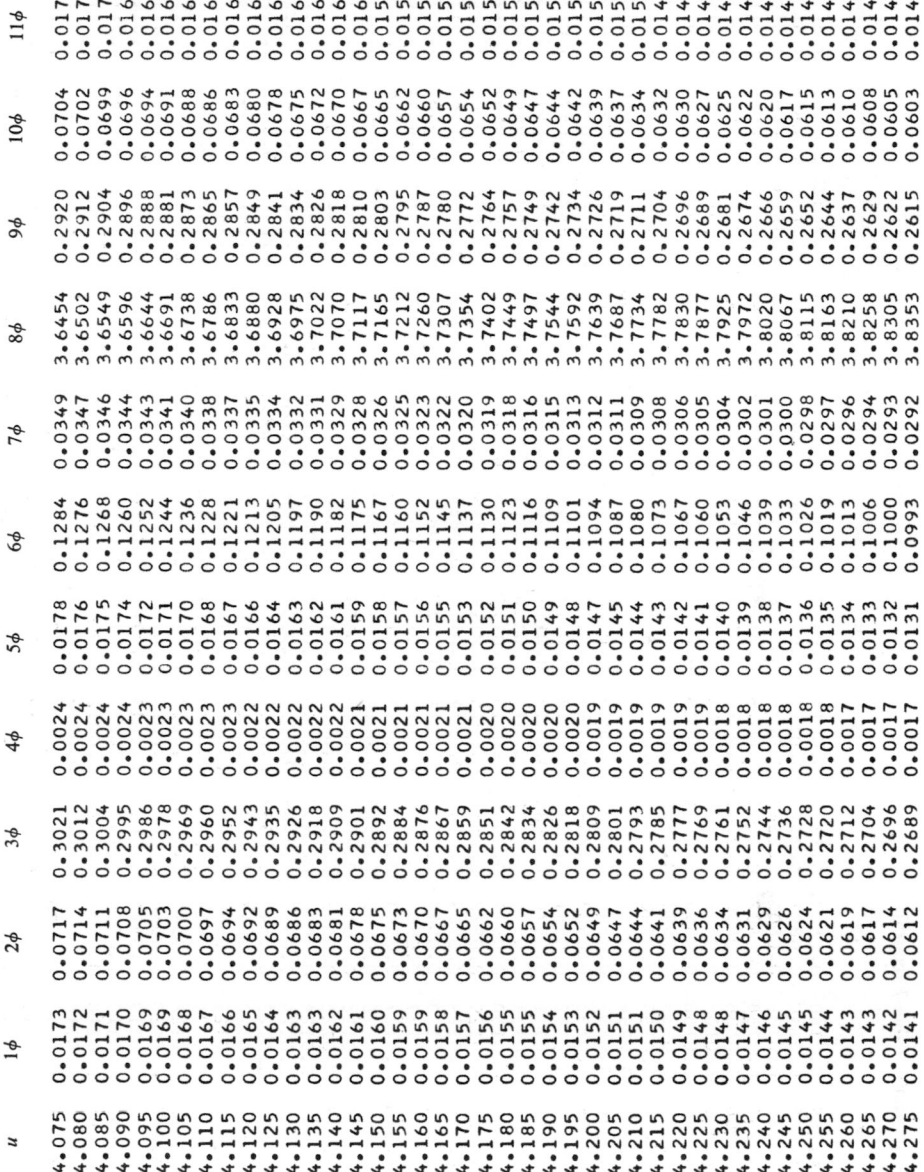

u	1ϕ	2ϕ	3ϕ	4ϕ	5ϕ	6ϕ	7ϕ	8ϕ	9ϕ	10ϕ	11ϕ
4.075	0.0173	0.0717	0.3021	0.0024	0.0178	0.1284	0.0349	3.6454	0.2920	0.0704	0.0171
4.080	0.0172	0.0714	0.3012	0.0024	0.0176	0.1276	0.0347	3.6502	0.2912	0.0702	0.0171
4.085	0.0171	0.0711	0.3004	0.0024	0.0175	0.1268	0.0346	3.6549	0.2904	0.0699	0.0170
4.090	0.0170	0.0708	0.2995	0.0024	0.0174	0.1260	0.0344	3.6596	0.2896	0.0696	0.0169
4.095	0.0169	0.0705	0.2986	0.0023	0.0172	0.1252	0.0343	3.6644	0.2888	0.0694	0.0168
4.100	0.0169	0.0703	0.2978	0.0023	0.0171	0.1244	0.0341	3.6691	0.2881	0.0691	0.0167
4.105	0.0168	0.0700	0.2969	0.0023	0.0171	0.1236	0.0340	3.6738	0.2873	0.0688	0.0166
4.110	0.0167	0.0697	0.2960	0.0023	0.0168	0.1228	0.0338	3.6786	0.2865	0.0686	0.0166
4.115	0.0166	0.0694	0.2952	0.0023	0.0167	0.1221	0.0337	3.6833	0.2857	0.0683	0.0165
4.120	0.0165	0.0692	0.2943	0.0022	0.0166	0.1213	0.0335	3.6880	0.2849	0.0680	0.0164
4.125	0.0164	0.0689	0.2935	0.0022	0.0164	0.1205	0.0334	3.6928	0.2841	0.0678	0.0163
4.130	0.0163	0.0686	0.2926	0.0022	0.0163	0.1197	0.0332	3.6975	0.2834	0.0675	0.0162
4.135	0.0163	0.0683	0.2918	0.0022	0.0162	0.1190	0.0331	3.7022	0.2826	0.0672	0.0161
4.140	0.0162	0.0681	0.2909	0.0022	0.0161	0.1182	0.0329	3.7070	0.2818	0.0670	0.0161
4.145	0.0161	0.0678	0.2901	0.0021	0.0159	0.1175	0.0328	3.7117	0.2810	0.0667	0.0160
4.150	0.0160	0.0675	0.2892	0.0021	0.0158	0.1167	0.0326	3.7165	0.2803	0.0665	0.0160
4.155	0.0159	0.0673	0.2884	0.0021	0.0157	0.1160	0.0325	3.7212	0.2795	0.0662	0.0159
4.160	0.0159	0.0670	0.2876	0.0021	0.0156	0.1152	0.0323	3.7260	0.2787	0.0660	0.0158
4.165	0.0158	0.0667	0.2867	0.0021	0.0155	0.1145	0.0322	3.7307	0.2780	0.0657	0.0157
4.170	0.0157	0.0665	0.2859	0.0021	0.0153	0.1137	0.0320	3.7354	0.2772	0.0654	0.0156
4.175	0.0156	0.0662	0.2851	0.0020	0.0152	0.1130	0.0319	3.7402	0.2764	0.0652	0.0155
4.180	0.0155	0.0660	0.2842	0.0020	0.0151	0.1123	0.0318	3.7449	0.2757	0.0649	0.0154
4.185	0.0155	0.0657	0.2834	0.0020	0.0150	0.1116	0.0316	3.7497	0.2749	0.0647	0.0153
4.190	0.0154	0.0654	0.2826	0.0020	0.0149	0.1109	0.0315	3.7544	0.2742	0.0644	0.0153
4.195	0.0153	0.0652	0.2818	0.0020	0.0148	0.1101	0.0313	3.7592	0.2734	0.0642	0.0152
4.200	0.0152	0.0649	0.2809	0.0019	0.0147	0.1094	0.0312	3.7639	0.2726	0.0639	0.0151
4.205	0.0151	0.0647	0.2801	0.0019	0.0145	0.1087	0.0311	3.7687	0.2719	0.0637	0.0151
4.210	0.0151	0.0644	0.2793	0.0019	0.0144	0.1080	0.0309	3.7734	0.2711	0.0634	0.0150
4.215	0.0150	0.0641	0.2785	0.0019	0.0143	0.1073	0.0308	3.7782	0.2704	0.0632	0.0149
4.220	0.0149	0.0639	0.2777	0.0019	0.0142	0.1067	0.0306	3.7830	0.2696	0.0630	0.0148
4.225	0.0148	0.0636	0.2769	0.0018	0.0141	0.1060	0.0305	3.7877	0.2689	0.0627	0.0147
4.230	0.0148	0.0634	0.2761	0.0018	0.0140	0.1053	0.0304	3.7925	0.2681	0.0625	0.0147
4.235	0.0147	0.0631	0.2752	0.0018	0.0139	0.1046	0.0302	3.7972	0.2674	0.0622	0.0146
4.240	0.0146	0.0629	0.2744	0.0018	0.0138	0.1039	0.0301	3.8020	0.2666	0.0620	0.0145
4.245	0.0145	0.0626	0.2736	0.0018	0.0137	0.1033	0.0300	3.8067	0.2659	0.0617	0.0144
4.250	0.0145	0.0624	0.2728	0.0018	0.0136	0.1026	0.0298	3.8115	0.2652	0.0615	0.0144
4.255	0.0144	0.0621	0.2720	0.0018	0.0135	0.1019	0.0297	3.8163	0.2644	0.0613	0.0143
4.260	0.0143	0.0619	0.2712	0.0017	0.0134	0.1013	0.0296	3.8210	0.2637	0.0610	0.0142
4.265	0.0143	0.0617	0.2704	0.0017	0.0133	0.1006	0.0294	3.8258	0.2629	0.0608	0.0142
4.270	0.0142	0.0614	0.2696	0.0017	0.0132	0.1000	0.0293	3.8305	0.2622	0.0605	0.0141
4.275	0.0141	0.0612	0.2689	0.0017	0.0131	0.0993	0.0292	3.8353	0.2615	0.0603	0.0140

Appendix Table 1 (cont'd)

u	1ϕ	2ϕ	3ϕ	4ϕ	5ϕ	6ϕ	7ϕ	8ϕ	9ϕ	10ϕ	11ϕ
4.280	0.0140	0.0609	0.2681	0.0017	0.0130	0.0987	0.0290	3.8401	0.2607	0.0601	0.0139
4.285	0.0140	0.0607	0.2673	0.0017	0.0129	0.0980	0.0289	3.8448	0.2600	0.0598	0.0139
4.290	0.0139	0.0604	0.2665	0.0017	0.0128	0.0974	0.0288	3.8496	0.2593	0.0596	0.0138
4.295	0.0138	0.0602	0.2657	0.0016	0.0127	0.0968	0.0287	3.8544	0.2586	0.0594	0.0137
4.300	0.0138	0.0600	0.2649	0.0016	0.0126	0.0961	0.0285	3.8591	0.2578	0.0591	0.0137
4.305	0.0137	0.0597	0.2641	0.0016	0.0125	0.0955	0.0284	3.8639	0.2571	0.0589	0.0136
4.310	0.0136	0.0595	0.2634	0.0016	0.0124	0.0949	0.0283	3.8687	0.2564	0.0587	0.0135
4.315	0.0135	0.0593	0.2626	0.0016	0.0123	0.0943	0.0281	3.8735	0.2557	0.0585	0.0135
4.320	0.0135	0.0590	0.2618	0.0016	0.0122	0.0937	0.0280	3.8782	0.2549	0.0582	0.0134
4.325	0.0134	0.0588	0.2610	0.0016	0.0121	0.0931	0.0279	3.8830	0.2542	0.0580	0.0133
4.330	0.0133	0.0585	0.2603	0.0015	0.0120	0.0925	0.0278	3.8878	0.2535	0.0578	0.0133
4.335	0.0133	0.0583	0.2595	0.0015	0.0119	0.0919	0.0276	3.8926	0.2528	0.0576	0.0132
4.340	0.0132	0.0581	0.2587	0.0015	0.0118	0.0913	0.0275	3.8973	0.2521	0.0573	0.0131
4.345	0.0131	0.0579	0.2580	0.0015	0.0117	0.0907	0.0274	3.9021	0.2514	0.0571	0.0131
4.350	0.0131	0.0576	0.2572	0.0015	0.0116	0.0901	0.0273	3.9069	0.2507	0.0569	0.0130
4.355	0.0130	0.0574	0.2565	0.0015	0.0115	0.0895	0.0271	3.9117	0.2499	0.0567	0.0130
4.360	0.0129	0.0572	0.2557	0.0015	0.0114	0.0889	0.0270	3.9164	0.2492	0.0564	0.0129
4.365	0.0129	0.0569	0.2549	0.0014	0.0114	0.0883	0.0269	3.9212	0.2485	0.0562	0.0128
4.370	0.0128	0.0567	0.2542	0.0014	0.0113	0.0877	0.0268	3.9260	0.2478	0.0560	0.0127
4.375	0.0127	0.0565	0.2534	0.0014	0.0112	0.0872	0.0267	3.9308	0.2471	0.0558	0.0127
4.380	0.0127	0.0563	0.2527	0.0014	0.0111	0.0866	0.0265	3.9356	0.2464	0.0556	0.0126
4.385	0.0126	0.0560	0.2519	0.0014	0.0110	0.0860	0.0264	3.9403	0.2457	0.0553	0.0125
4.390	0.0126	0.0558	0.2512	0.0014	0.0109	0.0855	0.0263	3.9451	0.2450	0.0551	0.0125
4.395	0.0125	0.0556	0.2504	0.0014	0.0108	0.0849	0.0262	3.9499	0.2443	0.0549	0.0124
4.400	0.0124	0.0554	0.2497	0.0014	0.0108	0.0844	0.0261	3.9547	0.2436	0.0547	0.0124
4.405	0.0124	0.0552	0.2489	0.0013	0.0107	0.0838	0.0260	3.9595	0.2429	0.0545	0.0123
4.410	0.0123	0.0549	0.2482	0.0013	0.0106	0.0833	0.0258	3.9643	0.2422	0.0543	0.0122
4.415	0.0123	0.0547	0.2475	0.0013	0.0105	0.0827	0.0257	3.9691	0.2416	0.0541	0.0122
4.420	0.0122	0.0545	0.2467	0.0013	0.0104	0.0822	0.0256	3.9738	0.2409	0.0538	0.0121
4.425	0.0122	0.0543	0.2460	0.0013	0.0103	0.0816	0.0255	3.9786	0.2402	0.0536	0.0120
4.430	0.0121	0.0541	0.2453	0.0013	0.0103	0.0811	0.0254	3.9834	0.2395	0.0534	0.0120
4.435	0.0121	0.0538	0.2445	0.0013	0.0102	0.0806	0.0253	3.9882	0.2388	0.0532	0.0119
4.440	0.0120	0.0536	0.2438	0.0013	0.0101	0.0800	0.0252	3.9930	0.2381	0.0530	0.0119
4.445	0.0119	0.0534	0.2431	0.0013	0.0100	0.0795	0.0250	3.9978	0.2374	0.0528	0.0118
4.450	0.0119	0.0532	0.2424	0.0012	0.0099	0.0790	0.0249	4.0026	0.2368	0.0526	0.0117
4.455	0.0118	0.0530	0.2416	0.0012	0.0099	0.0785	0.0248	4.0074	0.2361	0.0524	0.0117
4.460	0.0117	0.0528	0.2409	0.0012	0.0098	0.0779	0.0247	4.0122	0.2354	0.0522	0.0116
4.465	0.0116	0.0526	0.2402	0.0012	0.0097	0.0774	0.0246	4.0170	0.2347	0.0520	0.0116
4.470	0.0116	0.0524	0.2395	0.0012	0.0096	0.0769	0.0245	4.0218	0.2341	0.0518	0.0115
4.475	0.0115	0.0522	0.2388	0.0012	0.0096	0.0764	0.0244	4.0266	0.2334	0.0516	0.0115

u	1ϕ	2ϕ	3ϕ	4ϕ	5ϕ	6ϕ	7ϕ	8ϕ	9ϕ	10ϕ	11ϕ
4.485	0.0114	0.0517	0.2373	0.0012	0.0094	0.0754	0.0242	4.0362	0.2320	0.0512	0.0113
4.490	0.0113	0.0515	0.2366	0.0012	0.0093	0.0749	0.0240	4.0410	0.2314	0.0510	0.0113
4.495	0.0113	0.0513	0.2359	0.0011	0.0093	0.0744	0.0239	4.0458	0.2307	0.0508	0.0112
4.500	0.0112	0.0511	0.2352	0.0011	0.0092	0.0739	0.0238	4.0506	0.2300	0.0506	0.0112
4.505	0.0112	0.0509	0.2345	0.0011	0.0091	0.0734	0.0237	4.0554	0.2294	0.0504	0.0111
4.510	0.0111	0.0507	0.2338	0.0011	0.0091	0.0730	0.0236	4.0602	0.2287	0.0502	0.0111
4.515	0.0111	0.0505	0.2331	0.0011	0.0090	0.0725	0.0235	4.0650	0.2281	0.0500	0.0110
4.520	0.0110	0.0503	0.2324	0.0011	0.0089	0.0720	0.0234	4.0698	0.2274	0.0498	0.0109
4.525	0.0110	0.0501	0.2317	0.0011	0.0088	0.0715	0.0233	4.0746	0.2267	0.0496	0.0109
4.530	0.0110	0.0499	0.2310	0.0011	0.0088	0.0710	0.0232	4.0794	0.2261	0.0494	0.0108
4.535	0.0109	0.0497	0.2303	0.0011	0.0087	0.0706	0.0231	4.0842	0.2254	0.0492	0.0108
4.540	0.0108	0.0495	0.2296	0.0011	0.0087	0.0701	0.0230	4.0890	0.2248	0.0490	0.0107
4.545	0.0107	0.0493	0.2289	0.0010	0.0086	0.0696	0.0229	4.0938	0.2241	0.0488	0.0107
4.550	0.0107	0.0491	0.2282	0.0010	0.0086	0.0692	0.0228	4.0986	0.2235	0.0486	0.0106
4.555	0.0106	0.0489	0.2276	0.0010	0.0085	0.0687	0.0227	4.1034	0.2228	0.0484	0.0106
4.560	0.0106	0.0487	0.2269	0.0010	0.0084	0.0683	0.0226	4.1082	0.2222	0.0482	0.0105
4.565	0.0105	0.0485	0.2262	0.0010	0.0084	0.0678	0.0225	4.1130	0.2215	0.0480	0.0105
4.570	0.0105	0.0483	0.2255	0.0010	0.0083	0.0674	0.0224	4.1178	0.2209	0.0478	0.0104
4.575	0.0104	0.0481	0.2248	0.0010	0.0082	0.0669	0.0223	4.1226	0.2202	0.0476	0.0104
4.580	0.0104	0.0479	0.2241	0.0010	0.0082	0.0665	0.0222	4.1275	0.2196	0.0475	0.0103
4.585	0.0103	0.0478	0.2235	0.0010	0.0081	0.0660	0.0221	4.1323	0.2190	0.0473	0.0103
4.590	0.0103	0.0476	0.2228	0.0010	0.0081	0.0656	0.0220	4.1371	0.2183	0.0471	0.0102
4.595	0.0102	0.0474	0.2221	0.0010	0.0080	0.0651	0.0219	4.1419	0.2177	0.0469	0.0102
4.600	0.0102	0.0472	0.2214	0.0009	0.0079	0.0647	0.0218	4.1467	0.2170	0.0467	0.0101
4.605	0.0101	0.0470	0.2208	0.0009	0.0078	0.0643	0.0217	4.1515	0.2164	0.0465	0.0101
4.610	0.0101	0.0468	0.2201	0.0009	0.0077	0.0638	0.0216	4.1563	0.2158	0.0463	0.0100
4.615	0.0100	0.0466	0.2194	0.0009	0.0077	0.0634	0.0215	4.1612	0.2151	0.0462	0.0100
4.620	0.0100	0.0464	0.2188	0.0009	0.0076	0.0630	0.0214	4.1660	0.2145	0.0460	0.0099
4.625	0.0099	0.0462	0.2181	0.0009	0.0076	0.0626	0.0213	4.1708	0.2139	0.0458	0.0099
4.630	0.0099	0.0461	0.2175	0.0009	0.0075	0.0622	0.0212	4.1756	0.2133	0.0456	0.0098
4.635	0.0098	0.0459	0.2168	0.0009	0.0074	0.0617	0.0211	4.1804	0.2126	0.0454	0.0098
4.640	0.0098	0.0457	0.2161	0.0009	0.0074	0.0613	0.0210	4.1852	0.2120	0.0452	0.0097
4.645	0.0097	0.0455	0.2155	0.0009	0.0073	0.0609	0.0209	4.1901	0.2114	0.0451	0.0097
4.650	0.0097	0.0453	0.2148	0.0009	0.0073	0.0605	0.0208	4.1949	0.2108	0.0449	0.0096
4.655	0.0096	0.0451	0.2142	0.0009	0.0072	0.0601	0.0207	4.1997	0.2101	0.0447	0.0096
4.660	0.0096	0.0450	0.2135	0.0009	0.0072	0.0597	0.0206	4.2045	0.2095	0.0445	0.0095
4.665	0.0095	0.0448	0.2129	0.0008	0.0071	0.0593	0.0205	4.2094	0.2089	0.0444	0.0095
4.670	0.0095	0.0446	0.2122	0.0008	0.0070	0.0589	0.0204	4.2142	0.2083	0.0442	0.0094
4.675	0.0094	0.0444	0.2116	0.0008	0.0070	0.0585	0.0203	4.2190	0.2077	0.0440	0.0094
4.680	0.0094	0.0442	0.2109	0.0008	0.0069	0.0581	0.0203	4.2238	0.2071	0.0438	0.0093
4.685	0.0093	0.0441	0.2103	0.0008	0.0069	0.0577	0.0202	4.2287	0.2064	0.0437	0.0093

Appendix Table 1 (cont'd)

u	1ϕ	2ϕ	3ϕ	4ϕ	5ϕ	6ϕ	7ϕ	8ϕ	9ϕ	10ϕ	11ϕ
4.690	0.0093	0.0439	0.2097	0.0008	0.0068	0.0573	0.0201	4.2335	0.2058	0.0435	0.0092
4.695	0.0093	0.0437	0.2090	0.0008	0.0068	0.0569	0.0200	4.2383	0.2052	0.0433	0.0092
4.700	0.0092	0.0435	0.2084	0.0008	0.0067	0.0566	0.0199	4.2431	0.2046	0.0431	0.0091
4.705	0.0091	0.0434	0.2077	0.0008	0.0067	0.0562	0.0198	4.2480	0.2040	0.0430	0.0091
4.710	0.0091	0.0432	0.2071	0.0008	0.0066	0.0558	0.0197	4.2528	0.2034	0.0428	0.0090
4.715	0.0090	0.0430	0.2065	0.0008	0.0066	0.0554	0.0197	4.2576	0.2028	0.0426	0.0090
4.720	0.0090	0.0428	0.2058	0.0008	0.0065	0.0551	0.0195	4.2625	0.2022	0.0425	0.0090
4.725	0.0090	0.0427	0.2052	0.0008	0.0065	0.0547	0.0195	4.2673	0.2016	0.0423	0.0089
4.730	0.0089	0.0425	0.2046	0.0008	0.0064	0.0543	0.0194	4.2721	0.2010	0.0421	0.0089
4.735	0.0089	0.0423	0.2040	0.0007	0.0064	0.0540	0.0193	4.2770	0.2004	0.0420	0.0088
4.740	0.0088	0.0422	0.2033	0.0007	0.0063	0.0536	0.0192	4.2818	0.1998	0.0418	0.0088
4.745	0.0088	0.0420	0.2027	0.0007	0.0063	0.0532	0.0191	4.2866	0.1992	0.0416	0.0087
4.750	0.0087	0.0418	0.2021	0.0007	0.0062	0.0529	0.0190	4.2915	0.1986	0.0415	0.0087
4.755	0.0087	0.0416	0.2015	0.0007	0.0062	0.0525	0.0189	4.2963	0.1980	0.0413	0.0086
4.760	0.0086	0.0415	0.2009	0.0007	0.0061	0.0522	0.0188	4.3011	0.1974	0.0411	0.0086
4.765	0.0086	0.0413	0.2002	0.0007	0.0061	0.0518	0.0188	4.3060	0.1969	0.0410	0.0086
4.770	0.0086	0.0411	0.1996	0.0007	0.0060	0.0515	0.0187	4.3108	0.1963	0.0408	0.0085
4.775	0.0085	0.0410	0.1990	0.0007	0.0060	0.0511	0.0186	4.3156	0.1957	0.0406	0.0085
4.780	0.0085	0.0408	0.1984	0.0007	0.0059	0.0508	0.0185	4.3205	0.1951	0.0405	0.0084
4.785	0.0084	0.0407	0.1978	0.0007	0.0059	0.0504	0.0184	4.3253	0.1945	0.0403	0.0084
4.790	0.0084	0.0405	0.1972	0.0007	0.0058	0.0501	0.0183	4.3302	0.1939	0.0402	0.0083
4.795	0.0083	0.0403	0.1966	0.0007	0.0058	0.0497	0.0183	4.3350	0.1934	0.0400	0.0083
4.800	0.0083	0.0402	0.1960	0.0007	0.0057	0.0494	0.0182	4.3398	0.1928	0.0398	0.0083
4.805	0.0083	0.0400	0.1954	0.0007	0.0057	0.0491	0.0181	4.3447	0.1922	0.0397	0.0082
4.810	0.0082	0.0398	0.1948	0.0006	0.0056	0.0487	0.0180	4.3495	0.1916	0.0395	0.0082
4.815	0.0082	0.0397	0.1942	0.0006	0.0056	0.0484	0.0179	4.3544	0.1910	0.0394	0.0081
4.820	0.0082	0.0395	0.1936	0.0006	0.0056	0.0481	0.0179	4.3592	0.1905	0.0392	0.0081
4.825	0.0081	0.0394	0.1930	0.0006	0.0055	0.0477	0.0178	4.3640	0.1899	0.0390	0.0081
4.830	0.0081	0.0392	0.1924	0.0006	0.0055	0.0474	0.0177	4.3689	0.1893	0.0389	0.0080
4.835	0.0080	0.0390	0.1918	0.0006	0.0054	0.0471	0.0176	4.3737	0.1888	0.0387	0.0080
4.840	0.0080	0.0389	0.1912	0.0006	0.0054	0.0468	0.0175	4.3786	0.1882	0.0386	0.0079
4.845	0.0079	0.0387	0.1906	0.0006	0.0053	0.0465	0.0175	4.3834	0.1876	0.0384	0.0079
4.850	0.0079	0.0386	0.1900	0.0006	0.0053	0.0461	0.0174	4.3883	0.1871	0.0383	0.0079
4.855	0.0079	0.0384	0.1894	0.0006	0.0053	0.0458	0.0173	4.3931	0.1865	0.0381	0.0078
4.860	0.0078	0.0383	0.1888	0.0006	0.0052	0.0455	0.0172	4.3980	0.1859	0.0380	0.0078
4.865	0.0078	0.0381	0.1883	0.0006	0.0052	0.0452	0.0171	4.4028	0.1854	0.0378	0.0077
4.870	0.0077	0.0379	0.1877	0.0006	0.0051	0.0449	0.0171	4.4077	0.1848	0.0377	0.0077
4.875	0.0077	0.0378	0.1871	0.0006	0.0051	0.0446	0.0170	4.4125	0.1843	0.0375	0.0077
4.880	0.0077	0.0376	0.1865	0.0006	0.0051	0.0443	0.0169	4.4174	0.1837	0.0374	0.0076
4.885	0.0076	0.0375	0.1859	0.0006	0.0050	0.0440	0.0168	4.4222	0.1831	0.0372	0.0076

u	1φ	2φ	3φ	4φ	5φ	6φ	7φ	8φ	9φ	10φ	11φ
4.895	0.0075	0.0372	0.1848	0.0006	0.0049	0.0434	0.0167	4.4319	0.1820	0.0369	0.0075
4.900	0.0075	0.0370	0.1842	0.0006	0.0049	0.0431	0.0166	4.4368	0.1815	0.0368	0.0075
4.905	0.0075	0.0369	0.1836	0.0005	0.0049	0.0428	0.0165	4.4416	0.1809	0.0366	0.0074
4.910	0.0074	0.0367	0.1831	0.0005	0.0048	0.0425	0.0164	4.4465	0.1804	0.0365	0.0074
4.915	0.0074	0.0366	0.1825	0.0005	0.0048	0.0422	0.0163	4.4513	0.1798	0.0363	0.0074
4.920	0.0074	0.0364	0.1819	0.0005	0.0047	0.0419	0.0163	4.4562	0.1793	0.0362	0.0073
4.925	0.0073	0.0363	0.1814	0.0005	0.0047	0.0416	0.0162	4.4610	0.1787	0.0360	0.0073
4.930	0.0073	0.0361	0.1808	0.0005	0.0047	0.0413	0.0162	4.4659	0.1782	0.0359	0.0073
4.935	0.0072	0.0360	0.1802	0.0005	0.0046	0.0411	0.0161	4.4707	0.1777	0.0357	0.0072
4.940	0.0072	0.0359	0.1797	0.0005	0.0046	0.0408	0.0160	4.4756	0.1771	0.0356	0.0072
4.945	0.0072	0.0357	0.1791	0.0005	0.0046	0.0405	0.0159	4.4805	0.1766	0.0355	0.0071
4.950	0.0071	0.0356	0.1786	0.0005	0.0045	0.0402	0.0159	4.4853	0.1760	0.0353	0.0071
4.955	0.0071	0.0354	0.1780	0.0005	0.0045	0.0399	0.0158	4.4902	0.1755	0.0352	0.0071
4.960	0.0071	0.0353	0.1774	0.0005	0.0044	0.0397	0.0157	4.4950	0.1750	0.0350	0.0070
4.965	0.0070	0.0351	0.1769	0.0005	0.0044	0.0394	0.0157	4.4999	0.1744	0.0349	0.0070
4.970	0.0070	0.0350	0.1763	0.0005	0.0044	0.0391	0.0156	4.5047	0.1739	0.0347	0.0070
4.975	0.0070	0.0348	0.1758	0.0005	0.0043	0.0389	0.0155	4.5096	0.1734	0.0346	0.0069
4.980	0.0069	0.0347	0.1752	0.0005	0.0043	0.0386	0.0154	4.5145	0.1728	0.0345	0.0069
4.985	0.0069	0.0346	0.1747	0.0005	0.0043	0.0383	0.0154	4.5193	0.1723	0.0343	0.0069
4.990	0.0069	0.0344	0.1741	0.0005	0.0042	0.0381	0.0153	4.5242	0.1718	0.0342	0.0068
4.995	0.0068	0.0343	0.1736	0.0005	0.0042	0.0378	0.0152	4.5291	0.1713	0.0341	0.0068
5.000	0.0068	0.0341	0.1731	0.0005	0.0042	0.0375	0.0152	4.5339	0.1707	0.0339	0.0068
5.050	0.0065	0.0328	0.1677	0.0004	0.0039	0.0350	0.0145	4.5826	0.1656	0.0326	0.0064
5.100	0.0061	0.0315	0.1625	0.0004	0.0036	0.0327	0.0139	4.6313	0.1605	0.0313	0.0061
5.150	0.0058	0.0302	0.1574	0.0004	0.0033	0.0305	0.0132	4.6800	0.1556	0.0300	0.0058
5.200	0.0055	0.0290	0.1525	0.0003	0.0030	0.0284	0.0126	4.7288	0.1508	0.0288	0.0055
5.250	0.0053	0.0278	0.1477	0.0003	0.0028	0.0265	0.0121	4.7777	0.1462	0.0277	0.0053
5.300	0.0050	0.0267	0.1430	0.0003	0.0026	0.0247	0.0115	4.8266	0.1416	0.0266	0.0050
5.350	0.0048	0.0256	0.1385	0.0002	0.0024	0.0230	0.0110	4.8755	0.1372	0.0255	0.0048
5.400	0.0045	0.0246	0.1341	0.0002	0.0022	0.0214	0.0105	4.9245	0.1329	0.0245	0.0045
5.450	0.0043	0.0236	0.1298	0.0002	0.0020	0.0199	0.0101	4.9735	0.1287	0.0235	0.0043
5.500	0.0041	0.0227	0.1257	0.0002	0.0019	0.0186	0.0096	5.0226	0.1246	0.0226	0.0041
5.550	0.0039	0.0217	0.1216	0.0002	0.0017	0.0173	0.0092	5.0717	0.1207	0.0217	0.0039
5.600	0.0037	0.0209	0.1177	0.0002	0.0016	0.0161	0.0088	5.1208	0.1168	0.0208	0.0037
5.650	0.0035	0.0200	0.1139	0.0001	0.0015	0.0149	0.0084	5.1699	0.1131	0.0199	0.0035
5.700	0.0034	0.0192	0.1102	0.0001	0.0013	0.0139	0.0080	5.2191	0.1094	0.0191	0.0034
5.750	0.0032	0.0184	0.1066	0.0001	0.0012	0.0129	0.0073	5.2684	0.1059	0.0184	0.0032
5.800	0.0030	0.0177	0.1031	0.0001	0.0011	0.0120	0.0070	5.3176	0.1025	0.0176	0.0030
5.850	0.0029	0.0169	0.0997	0.0001	0.0010	0.0112	0.0070	5.3669	0.0991	0.0169	0.0029
5.900	0.0027	0.0163	0.0964	0.0001	0.0010	0.0104	0.0067	5.4162	0.0959	0.0162	0.0027
5.950	0.0026	0.0156	0.0932	0.0001	0.0009	0.0096	0.0064	5.4655	0.0927	0.0155	0.0026

Appendix Table 1 (cont'd)

u	1φ	2φ	3φ	4φ	5φ	6φ	7φ	8φ	9φ	10φ	11φ
6.000	0.0025	0.0149	0.0901	0.0001	0.0008	0.0090	0.0061	5.5149	0.0897	0.0149	0.0025
6.050	0.0024	0.0143	0.0871	0.0001	0.0008	0.0083	0.0058	5.5643	0.0867	0.0143	0.0024
6.100	0.0022	0.0137	0.0842	0.0001	0.0007	0.0077	0.0056	5.6137	0.0838	0.0137	0.0022
6.150	0.0021	0.0132	0.0814	0.0001	0.0006	0.0072	0.0053	5.6631	0.0810	0.0131	0.0021
6.200	0.0020	0.0126	0.0786	0.0001	0.0006	0.0067	0.0051	5.7126	0.0783	0.0126	0.0020
6.250	0.0019	0.0121	0.0760	0.0000	0.0005	0.0062	0.0048	5.7621	0.0757	0.0121	0.0019
6.300	0.0018	0.0116	0.0734	0.0000	0.0005	0.0057	0.0046	5.8116	0.0732	0.0116	0.0018
6.350	0.0017	0.0111	0.0709	0.0000	0.0005	0.0053	0.0044	5.8611	0.0707	0.0111	0.0017
6.400	0.0017	0.0107	0.0685	0.0000	0.0004	0.0049	0.0042	5.9107	0.0683	0.0107	0.0017
6.450	0.0016	0.0102	0.0662	0.0000	0.0004	0.0046	0.0040	5.9602	0.0660	0.0102	0.0016
6.500	0.0015	0.0098	0.0639	0.0000	0.0004	0.0042	0.0038	6.0098	0.0637	0.0098	0.0015
6.550	0.0014	0.0094	0.0617	0.0000	0.0003	0.0039	0.0037	6.0594	0.0615	0.0094	0.0014
6.600	0.0014	0.0090	0.0596	0.0000	0.0003	0.0036	0.0035	6.1090	0.0594	0.0090	0.0014
6.650	0.0013	0.0086	0.0575	0.0000	0.0003	0.0034	0.0033	6.1586	0.0574	0.0086	0.0013
6.700	0.0012	0.0083	0.0555	0.0000	0.0003	0.0031	0.0032	6.2083	0.0554	0.0083	0.0012
6.750	0.0012	0.0079	0.0536	0.0000	0.0002	0.0029	0.0030	6.2579	0.0535	0.0079	0.0012
6.800	0.0011	0.0076	0.0517	0.0000	0.0002	0.0027	0.0029	6.3076	0.0516	0.0076	0.0011
6.850	0.0011	0.0073	0.0499	0.0000	0.0002	0.0025	0.0028	6.3573	0.0498	0.0073	0.0011
6.900	0.0010	0.0070	0.0482	0.0000	0.0002	0.0023	0.0026	6.4070	0.0481	0.0070	0.0010
6.950	0.0010	0.0067	0.0465	0.0000	0.0002	0.0021	0.0025	6.4567	0.0464	0.0067	0.0010
7.000	0.0009	0.0064	0.0448	0.0000	0.0002	0.0020	0.0024	6.5064	0.0448	0.0064	0.0009
7.050	0.0009	0.0061	0.0433	0.0000	0.0001	0.0018	0.0023	6.5561	0.0432	0.0061	0.0009
7.100	0.0008	0.0059	0.0417	0.0000	0.0001	0.0017	0.0022	6.6059	0.0417	0.0059	0.0008
7.150	0.0008	0.0056	0.0403	0.0000	0.0001	0.0016	0.0021	6.6556	0.0402	0.0056	0.0008
7.200	0.0007	0.0054	0.0388	0.0000	0.0001	0.0014	0.0020	6.7054	0.0388	0.0054	0.0007
7.250	0.0007	0.0052	0.0374	0.0000	0.0001	0.0013	0.0019	6.7552	0.0374	0.0052	0.0007
7.300	0.0007	0.0049	0.0361	0.0000	0.0001	0.0012	0.0018	6.8049	0.0360	0.0049	0.0007
7.350	0.0006	0.0047	0.0348	0.0000	0.0001	0.0011	0.0017	6.8547	0.0348	0.0047	0.0006
7.400	0.0006	0.0045	0.0336	0.0000	0.0001	0.0011	0.0016	6.9045	0.0335	0.0045	0.0006
7.450	0.0006	0.0043	0.0323	0.0000	0.0001	0.0010	0.0016	6.9543	0.0323	0.0043	0.0006
7.500	0.0006	0.0042	0.0312	0.0000	0.0001	0.0009	0.0015	7.0041	0.0311	0.0042	0.0006
7.550	0.0005	0.0040	0.0301	0.0000	0.0001	0.0008	0.0014	7.0540	0.0300	0.0040	0.0005
7.600	0.0005	0.0038	0.0290	0.0000	0.0001	0.0008	0.0014	7.1038	0.0289	0.0038	0.0005
7.650	0.0005	0.0036	0.0279	0.0000	0.0000	0.0007	0.0013	7.1536	0.0279	0.0036	0.0005
7.700	0.0004	0.0035	0.0269	0.0000	0.0000	0.0007	0.0013	7.2035	0.0269	0.0035	0.0004
7.750	0.0004	0.0033	0.0259	0.0000	0.0000	0.0006	0.0012	7.2533	0.0259	0.0033	0.0004
7.800	0.0004	0.0032	0.0250	0.0000	0.0000	0.0006	0.0011	7.3032	0.0249	0.0032	0.0004
7.850	0.0004	0.0031	0.0241	0.0000	0.0000	0.0005	0.0011	7.3531	0.0240	0.0031	0.0004
7.900	0.0004	0.0029	0.0232	0.0000	0.0000	0.0004	0.0010	7.4029	0.0232	0.0029	0.0004
7.950	0.0004	0.0028	0.0223	0.0000	0.0000	0.0004	0.0010	7.4528	0.0223	0.0028	0.0003

u	1ϕ	2ϕ	3ϕ	4ϕ	5ϕ	6ϕ	7ϕ	8ϕ	9ϕ	10ϕ	11ϕ
8.050	0.0003	0.0026	0.0207	0.0000	0.0000	0.0004	0.0009	7.5526	0.0207	0.0026	0.0003
8.100	0.0003	0.0025	0.0199	0.0000	0.0000	0.0003	0.0009	7.6025	0.0199	0.0025	0.0003
8.150	0.0003	0.0024	0.0192	0.0000	0.0000	0.0003	0.0008	7.6524	0.0192	0.0024	0.0003
8.200	0.0003	0.0023	0.0185	0.0000	0.0000	0.0003	0.0008	7.7023	0.0185	0.0023	0.0003
8.250	0.0002	0.0022	0.0178	0.0000	0.0000	0.0003	0.0007	7.7522	0.0178	0.0022	0.0003
8.300	0.0002	0.0021	0.0171	0.0000	0.0000	0.0002	0.0007	7.8021	0.0171	0.0021	0.0002
8.350	0.0002	0.0020	0.0165	0.0000	0.0000	0.0002	0.0007	7.8520	0.0165	0.0020	0.0002
8.400	0.0002	0.0019	0.0159	0.0000	0.0000	0.0002	0.0006	7.9019	0.0159	0.0019	0.0002
8.450	0.0002	0.0018	0.0153	0.0000	0.0000	0.0002	0.0006	7.9518	0.0153	0.0018	0.0002
8.500	0.0002	0.0017	0.0147	0.0000	0.0000	0.0002	0.0006	8.0017	0.0147	0.0017	0.0002
8.550	0.0002	0.0017	0.0142	0.0000	0.0000	0.0002	0.0005	8.0517	0.0142	0.0017	0.0002
8.600	0.0002	0.0016	0.0136	0.0000	0.0000	0.0002	0.0005	8.1016	0.0136	0.0016	0.0002
8.650	0.0002	0.0015	0.0131	0.0000	0.0000	0.0001	0.0005	8.1515	0.0131	0.0015	0.0002
8.700	0.0002	0.0014	0.0126	0.0000	0.0000	0.0001	0.0005	8.2014	0.0126	0.0014	0.0002
8.750	0.0002	0.0014	0.0121	0.0000	0.0000	0.0001	0.0004	8.2514	0.0121	0.0014	0.0002
8.800	0.0002	0.0013	0.0117	0.0000	0.0000	0.0001	0.0004	8.3013	0.0117	0.0013	0.0002
8.850	0.0001	0.0013	0.0112	0.0000	0.0000	0.0001	0.0004	8.3513	0.0112	0.0013	0.0002
8.900	0.0001	0.0012	0.0108	0.0000	0.0000	0.0001	0.0004	8.4012	0.0108	0.0012	0.0001
8.950	0.0001	0.0012	0.0104	0.0000	0.0000	0.0001	0.0004	8.4512	0.0104	0.0012	0.0001
9.000	0.0001	0.0011	0.0100	0.0000	0.0000	0.0001	0.0004	8.5011	0.0100	0.0011	0.0001
9.050	0.0001	0.0011	0.0096	0.0000	0.0000	0.0001	0.0004	8.5511	0.0096	0.0011	0.0001
9.100	0.0001	0.0010	0.0093	0.0000	0.0000	0.0001	0.0003	8.6010	0.0092	0.0010	0.0001
9.150	0.0001	0.0010	0.0089	0.0000	0.0000	0.0001	0.0003	8.6510	0.0089	0.0010	0.0001
9.200	0.0001	0.0009	0.0086	0.0000	0.0000	0.0001	0.0003	8.7009	0.0086	0.0009	0.0001
9.250	0.0001	0.0009	0.0082	0.0000	0.0000	0.0001	0.0003	8.7509	0.0082	0.0009	0.0001
9.300	0.0001	0.0008	0.0079	0.0000	0.0000	0.0000	0.0003	8.8008	0.0079	0.0008	0.0001
9.350	0.0001	0.0008	0.0076	0.0000	0.0000	0.0000	0.0003	8.8508	0.0076	0.0008	0.0001
9.400	0.0001	0.0008	0.0073	0.0000	0.0000	0.0000	0.0002	8.9008	0.0073	0.0008	0.0001
9.450	0.0001	0.0007	0.0070	0.0000	0.0000	0.0000	0.0002	8.9507	0.0070	0.0007	0.0001
9.500	0.0001	0.0007	0.0068	0.0000	0.0000	0.0000	0.0002	9.0007	0.0068	0.0007	0.0001
9.550	0.0001	0.0007	0.0065	0.0000	0.0000	0.0000	0.0002	9.0507	0.0065	0.0007	0.0001
9.600	0.0001	0.0007	0.0062	0.0000	0.0000	0.0000	0.0002	9.1007	0.0062	0.0007	0.0001
9.650	0.0001	0.0006	0.0060	0.0000	0.0000	0.0000	0.0002	9.1506	0.0060	0.0006	0.0001
9.700	0.0001	0.0006	0.0058	0.0000	0.0000	0.0000	0.0002	9.2006	0.0058	0.0006	0.0001
9.750	0.0001	0.0006	0.0055	0.0000	0.0000	0.0000	0.0002	9.2506	0.0055	0.0006	0.0001
9.800	0.0001	0.0005	0.0053	0.0000	0.0000	0.0000	0.0002	9.3005	0.0053	0.0005	0.0001
9.850	0.0001	0.0005	0.0051	0.0000	0.0000	0.0000	0.0002	9.3505	0.0051	0.0005	0.0001
9.900	0.0000	0.0005	0.0049	0.0000	0.0000	0.0000	0.0002	9.4005	0.0049	0.0005	0.0001
9.950	0.0000	0.0005	0.0047	0.0000	0.0000	0.0000	0.0002	9.4505	0.0047	0.0005	0.0000
10.000	0.0000	0.0005	0.0045	0.0000	0.0000	0.0000	0.0001	9.5005	0.0045	0.0005	0.0000
10.050	0.0000	0.0004	0.0044	0.0000	0.0000	0.0000	0.0001	9.5504	0.0044	0.0004	0.0000

u	1φ	2φ	3φ	4φ	5φ	6φ	7φ	8φ	9φ	10φ	11φ
10.100	0.0000	0.0004	0.0042	0.0000	0.0000	0.0000	0.0001	9.6004	0.0042	0.0004	0.0000
10.150	0.0000	0.0004	0.0040	0.0000	0.0000	0.0000	0.0001	9.6504	0.0040	0.0004	0.0000
10.200	0.0000	0.0004	0.0039	0.0000	0.0000	0.0000	0.0001	9.7004	0.0039	0.0004	0.0000
10.250	0.0000	0.0004	0.0037	0.0000	0.0000	0.0000	0.0001	9.7504	0.0037	0.0004	0.0000
10.300	0.0000	0.0003	0.0036	0.0000	0.0000	0.0000	0.0001	9.8003	0.0036	0.0003	0.0000
10.350	0.0000	0.0003	0.0034	0.0000	0.0000	0.0000	0.0001	9.8503	0.0034	0.0003	0.0000
10.400	0.0000	0.0003	0.0033	0.0000	0.0000	0.0000	0.0001	9.9003	0.0033	0.0003	0.0000
10.450	0.0000	0.0003	0.0032	0.0000	0.0000	0.0000	0.0001	9.9503	0.0033	0.0003	0.0000
10.500	0.0000	0.0003	0.0030	0.0000	0.0000	0.0000	0.0001	10.0003	0.0032	0.0003	0.0000
10.550	0.0000	0.0003	0.0029	0.0000	0.0000	0.0000	0.0001	10.0503	0.0030	0.0003	0.0000
10.600	0.0000	0.0003	0.0028	0.0000	0.0000	0.0000	0.0001	10.1003	0.0029	0.0003	0.0000
10.650	0.0000	0.0003	0.0027	0.0000	0.0000	0.0000	0.0001	10.1503	0.0028	0.0003	0.0000
10.700	0.0000	0.0002	0.0026	0.0000	0.0000	0.0000	0.0001	10.2002	0.0027	0.0002	0.0000
10.750	0.0000	0.0002	0.0025	0.0000	0.0000	0.0000	0.0001	10.2502	0.0026	0.0002	0.0000
10.800	0.0000	0.0002	0.0024	0.0000	0.0000	0.0000	0.0001	10.3002	0.0025	0.0002	0.0000
10.850	0.0000	0.0002	0.0023	0.0000	0.0000	0.0000	0.0001	10.3502	0.0024	0.0002	0.0000
10.900	0.0000	0.0002	0.0022	0.0000	0.0000	0.0000	0.0001	10.4002	0.0023	0.0002	0.0000
10.950	0.0000	0.0002	0.0021	0.0000	0.0000	0.0000	0.0001	10.4502	0.0022	0.0002	0.0000
11.000	0.0000	0.0002	0.0020	0.0000	0.0000	0.0000	0.0001	10.5002	0.0021	0.0002	0.0000
11.050	0.0000	0.0002	0.0019	0.0000	0.0000	0.0000	0.0000	10.5502	0.0020	0.0002	0.0000
11.100	0.0000	0.0002	0.0019	0.0000	0.0000	0.0000	0.0000	10.6002	0.0019	0.0002	0.0000
11.150	0.0000	0.0002	0.0018	0.0000	0.0000	0.0000	0.0000	10.6502	0.0019	0.0002	0.0000
11.200	0.0000	0.0002	0.0017	0.0000	0.0000	0.0000	0.0000	10.7002	0.0018	0.0002	0.0000
11.250	0.0000	0.0001	0.0016	0.0000	0.0000	0.0000	0.0000	10.7501	0.0017	0.0001	0.0000
11.300	0.0000	0.0001	0.0016	0.0000	0.0000	0.0000	0.0000	10.8001	0.0016	0.0001	0.0000
11.350	0.0000	0.0001	0.0015	0.0000	0.0000	0.0000	0.0000	10.8501	0.0016	0.0001	0.0000
11.400	0.0000	0.0001	0.0015	0.0000	0.0000	0.0000	0.0000	10.9001	0.0015	0.0001	0.0000
11.450	0.0000	0.0001	0.0014	0.0000	0.0000	0.0000	0.0000	10.9501	0.0015	0.0001	0.0000
11.500	0.0000	0.0001	0.0013	0.0000	0.0000	0.0000	0.0000	11.0001	0.0014	0.0001	0.0000
11.550	0.0000	0.0001	0.0013	0.0000	0.0000	0.0000	0.0000	11.0501	0.0013	0.0001	0.0000
11.600	0.0000	0.0001	0.0012	0.0000	0.0000	0.0000	0.0000	11.1001	0.0013	0.0001	0.0000
11.650	0.0000	0.0001	0.0012	0.0000	0.0000	0.0000	0.0000	11.1501	0.0012	0.0001	0.0000
11.700	0.0000	0.0001	0.0011	0.0000	0.0000	0.0000	0.0000	11.2001	0.0012	0.0001	0.0000
11.750	0.0000	0.0001	0.0011	0.0000	0.0000	0.0000	0.0000	11.2501	0.0011	0.0001	0.0000
11.800	0.0000	0.0001	0.0010	0.0000	0.0000	0.0000	0.0000	11.3001	0.0011	0.0001	0.0000
11.850	0.0000	0.0001	0.0010	0.0000	0.0000	0.0000	0.0000	11.3501	0.0010	0.0001	0.0000
11.900	0.0000	0.0001	0.0010	0.0000	0.0000	0.0000	0.0000	11.4001	0.0010	0.0001	0.0000
11.950	0.0000	0.0001	0.0009	0.0000	0.0000	0.0000	0.0000	11.4501	0.0009	0.0001	0.0000
12.000	0.0000	0.0001	0.0009	0.0000	0.0000	0.0000	0.0000	11.5001	0.0009	0.0001	0.0000
12.050	0.0000	0.0001	0.0008	0.0000			0.0000	11.5501	0.0008	0.0001	0.0000

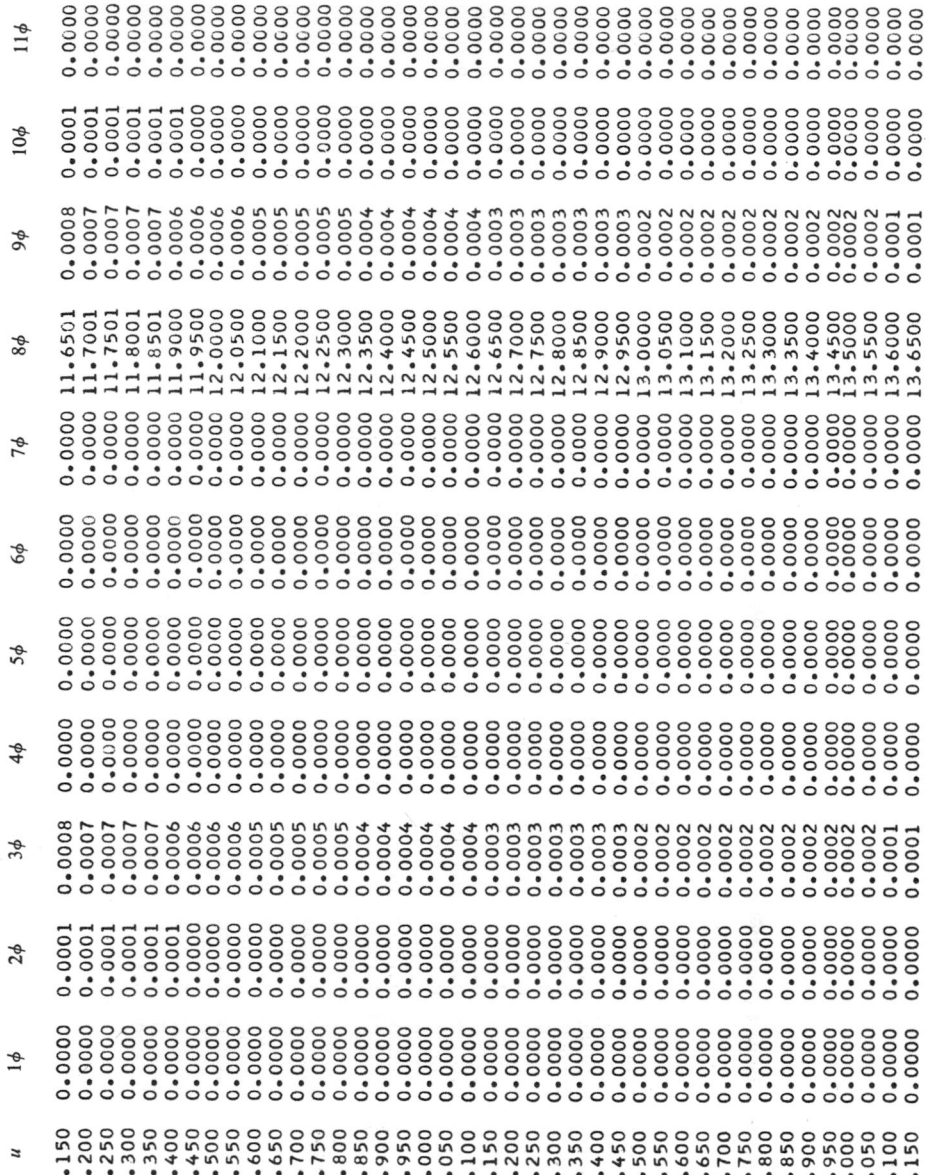

u	1φ	2φ	3φ	4φ	5φ	6φ	7φ	8φ	9φ	10φ	11φ
12.150	0.0000	0.0001	0.0008	0.0000	0.0000	0.0000	0.0000	11.6501	0.0008	0.0001	0.0000
12.200	0.0000	0.0001	0.0007	0.0000	0.0000	0.0000	0.0000	11.7001	0.0007	0.0001	0.0000
12.250	0.0000	0.0001	0.0007	0.0000	0.0000	0.0000	0.0000	11.7501	0.0007	0.0001	0.0000
12.300	0.0000	0.0001	0.0007	0.0000	0.0000	0.0000	0.0000	11.8001	0.0007	0.0001	0.0000
12.350	0.0000	0.0001	0.0007	0.0000	0.0000	0.0000	0.0000	11.8501	0.0007	0.0001	0.0000
12.400	0.0000	0.0001	0.0006	0.0000	0.0000	0.0000	0.0000	11.9000	0.0006	0.0001	0.0000
12.450	0.0000	0.0000	0.0006	0.0000	0.0000	0.0000	0.0000	11.9500	0.0006	0.0000	0.0000
12.500	0.0000	0.0000	0.0006	0.0000	0.0000	0.0000	0.0000	12.0000	0.0006	0.0000	0.0000
12.550	0.0000	0.0000	0.0006	0.0000	0.0000	0.0000	0.0000	12.0500	0.0006	0.0000	0.0000
12.600	0.0000	0.0000	0.0005	0.0000	0.0000	0.0000	0.0000	12.1000	0.0005	0.0000	0.0000
12.650	0.0000	0.0000	0.0005	0.0000	0.0000	0.0000	0.0000	12.1500	0.0005	0.0000	0.0000
12.700	0.0000	0.0000	0.0005	0.0000	0.0000	0.0000	0.0000	12.2000	0.0005	0.0000	0.0000
12.750	0.0000	0.0000	0.0005	0.0000	0.0000	0.0000	0.0000	12.2500	0.0005	0.0000	0.0000
12.800	0.0000	0.0000	0.0005	0.0000	0.0000	0.0000	0.0000	12.3000	0.0005	0.0000	0.0000
12.850	0.0000	0.0000	0.0004	0.0000	0.0000	0.0000	0.0000	12.3500	0.0004	0.0000	0.0000
12.900	0.0000	0.0000	0.0004	0.0000	0.0000	0.0000	0.0000	12.4000	0.0004	0.0000	0.0000
12.950	0.0000	0.0000	0.0004	0.0000	0.0000	0.0000	0.0000	12.4500	0.0004	0.0000	0.0000
13.000	0.0000	0.0000	0.0004	0.0000	0.0000	0.0000	0.0000	12.5000	0.0004	0.0000	0.0000
13.050	0.0000	0.0000	0.0004	0.0000	0.0000	0.0000	0.0000	12.5500	0.0004	0.0000	0.0000
13.100	0.0000	0.0000	0.0003	0.0000	0.0000	0.0000	0.0000	12.6000	0.0003	0.0000	0.0000
13.150	0.0000	0.0000	0.0003	0.0000	0.0000	0.0000	0.0000	12.6500	0.0003	0.0000	0.0000
13.200	0.0000	0.0000	0.0003	0.0000	0.0000	0.0000	0.0000	12.7000	0.0003	0.0000	0.0000
13.250	0.0000	0.0000	0.0003	0.0000	0.0000	0.0000	0.0000	12.7500	0.0003	0.0000	0.0000
13.300	0.0000	0.0000	0.0003	0.0000	0.0000	0.0000	0.0000	12.8000	0.0003	0.0000	0.0000
13.350	0.0000	0.0000	0.0003	0.0000	0.0000	0.0000	0.0000	12.8500	0.0003	0.0000	0.0000
13.400	0.0000	0.0000	0.0002	0.0000	0.0000	0.0000	0.0000	12.9000	0.0002	0.0000	0.0000
13.450	0.0000	0.0000	0.0002	0.0000	0.0000	0.0000	0.0000	12.9500	0.0002	0.0000	0.0000
13.500	0.0000	0.0000	0.0002	0.0000	0.0000	0.0000	0.0000	13.0000	0.0002	0.0000	0.0000
13.550	0.0000	0.0000	0.0002	0.0000	0.0000	0.0000	0.0000	13.0500	0.0002	0.0000	0.0000
13.600	0.0000	0.0000	0.0002	0.0000	0.0000	0.0000	0.0000	13.1000	0.0002	0.0000	0.0000
13.650	0.0000	0.0000	0.0002	0.0000	0.0000	0.0000	0.0000	13.1500	0.0002	0.0000	0.0000
13.700	0.0000	0.0000	0.0002	0.0000	0.0000	0.0000	0.0000	13.2000	0.0002	0.0000	0.0000
13.750	0.0000	0.0000	0.0002	0.0000	0.0000	0.0000	0.0000	13.2500	0.0002	0.0000	0.0000
13.800	0.0000	0.0000	0.0002	0.0000	0.0000	0.0000	0.0000	13.3000	0.0002	0.0000	0.0000
13.850	0.0000	0.0000	0.0002	0.0000	0.0000	0.0000	0.0000	13.3500	0.0002	0.0000	0.0000
13.900	0.0000	0.0000	0.0002	0.0000	0.0000	0.0000	0.0000	13.4000	0.0002	0.0000	0.0000
13.950	0.0000	0.0000	0.0002	0.0000	0.0000	0.0000	0.0000	13.4500	0.0002	0.0000	0.0000
14.000	0.0000	0.0000	0.0002	0.0000	0.0000	0.0000	0.0000	13.5000	0.0002	0.0000	0.0000
14.050	0.0000	0.0000	0.0002	0.0000	0.0000	0.0000	0.0000	13.5500	0.0002	0.0000	0.0000
14.100	0.0000	0.0000	0.0001	0.0000	0.0000	0.0000	0.0000	13.6000	0.0001	0.0000	0.0000
14.150	0.0000	0.0000	0.0001	0.0000	0.0000	0.0000	0.0000	13.6500	0.0001	0.0000	0.0000

Appendix Table 1 (cont'd)

u	1φ	2φ	3φ	4φ	5φ	6φ	7φ	8φ	9φ	10φ	11φ
14.200	0.0000	0.0000	0.0001	0.0000	0.0000	0.0000	0.0000	13.7000	0.0001	0.0000	0.0000
14.250	0.0000	0.0000	0.0001	0.0000	0.0000	0.0000	0.0000	13.7500	0.0001	0.0000	0.0000
14.300	0.0000	0.0000	0.0001	0.0000	0.0000	0.0000	0.0000	13.8000	0.0001	0.0000	0.0000
14.350	0.0000	0.0000	0.0001	0.0000	0.0000	0.0000	0.0000	13.8500	0.0001	0.0000	0.0000
14.400	0.0000	0.0000	0.0001	0.0000	0.0000	0.0000	0.0000	13.9000	0.0001	0.0000	0.0000
14.450	0.0000	0.0000	0.0001	0.0000	0.0000	0.0000	0.0000	13.9500	0.0001	0.0000	0.0000
14.500	0.0000	0.0000	0.0001	0.0000	0.0000	0.0000	0.0000	14.0000	0.0001	0.0000	0.0000
14.550	0.0000	0.0000	0.0001	0.0000	0.0000	0.0000	0.0000	14.0500	0.0001	0.0000	0.0000
14.600	0.0000	0.0000	0.0001	0.0000	0.0000	0.0000	0.0000	14.1000	0.0001	0.0000	0.0000
14.650	0.0000	0.0000	0.0001	0.0000	0.0000	0.0000	0.0000	14.1500	0.0001	0.0000	0.0000
14.700	0.0000	0.0000	0.0001	0.0000	0.0000	0.0000	0.0000	14.2000	0.0001	0.0000	0.0000
14.750	0.0000	0.0000	0.0001	0.0000	0.0000	0.0000	0.0000	14.2500	0.0001	0.0000	0.0000
14.800	0.0000	0.0000	0.0001	0.0000	0.0000	0.0000	0.0000	14.3000	0.0001	0.0000	0.0000
14.850	0.0000	0.0000	0.0001	0.0000	0.0000	0.0000	0.0000	14.3500	0.0001	0.0000	0.0000
14.900	0.0000	0.0000	0.0001	0.0000	0.0000	0.0000	0.0000	14.4000	0.0001	0.0000	0.0000
14.950	0.0000	0.0000	0.0001	0.0000	0.0000	0.0000	0.0000	14.4500	0.0001	0.0000	0.0000
15.000	0.0000	0.0000	0.0001	0.0000	0.0000	0.0000	0.0000	14.5000	0.0001	0.0000	0.0000
15.050	0.0000	0.0000	0.0001	0.0000	0.0000	0.0000	0.0000	14.5500	0.0001	0.0000	0.0000
15.100	0.0000	0.0000	0.0001	0.0000	0.0000	0.0000	0.0000	14.6000	0.0001	0.0000	0.0000
15.150	0.0000	0.0000	0.0001	0.0000	0.0000	0.0000	0.0000	14.6500	0.0001	0.0000	0.0000
15.200	0.0000	0.0000	0.0001	0.0000	0.0000	0.0000	0.0000	14.7000	0.0001	0.0000	0.0000
15.250	0.0000	0.0000	0.0001	0.0000	0.0000	0.0000	0.0000	14.7500	0.0001	0.0000	0.0000
15.300	0.0000	0.0000	0.0001	0.0000	0.0000	0.0000	0.0000	14.8000	0.0001	0.0000	0.0000
15.350	0.0000	0.0000	0.0001	0.0000	0.0000	0.0000	0.0000	14.8500	0.0001	0.0000	0.0000
15.400	0.0000	0.0000	0.0000	0.0000	0.0000	0.0000	0.0000	14.9000	0.0000	0.0000	0.0000
15.450	0.0000	0.0000	0.0000	0.0000	0.0000	0.0000	0.0000	14.9500	0.0000	0.0000	0.0000

APPENDIX 2

THERMODYNAMIC PROPERTIES OF SOME ATOMIC SPECIES IN THE IDEAL GAS STATE

In this appendix we tabulate the thermodynamic properties of atomic species in the first three rows of the periodic chart. This data was computed using all the energy levels listed in Moore.* For a discussion of the method of calculation, read Section (1.2.1).

* C. E. Moore, *Atomic Energy Levels I* (Washington, D.C.: U.S. Government Printing Office, 1949).

Appendix 2.1   THERMODYNAMIC PROPERTIES OF AL GAS

T	C_P^0	$(H^0-H_0^0)_T$	$-(F^0-H_0^0)/T$	S_T^0
DEG-K	CAL/MOLE DEG-K	KCAL/MOLE	CAL/MOLE DEG-K	CAL/MOLE DEG-K
100	6.021	0.588	27.462	33.344
200	5.290	1.145	31.507	37.231
273.15	5.141	1.525	33.270	38.855
298.15	5.113	1.654	33.757	39.304
400	5.047	2.171	35.369	40.795
500	5.018	2.674	36.571	41.918
600	5.002	3.175	37.541	42.832
700	4.993	3.674	38.353	43.602
800	4.987	4.173	39.052	44.268
900	4.983	4.672	39.665	44.855
1000	4.980	5.170	40.210	45.380
1100	4.978	5.668	40.702	45.855
1200	4.976	6.166	41.150	46.288
1300	4.975	6.663	41.561	46.686
1400	4.974	7.161	41.940	47.055
1500	4.973	7.658	42.293	47.398
1600	4.973	8.155	42.622	47.719
1700	4.972	8.653	42.931	48.020
1800	4.972	9.150	43.221	48.305
1900	4.971	9.647	43.496	48.573
2000	4.971	10.144	43.756	48.828
2100	4.971	10.641	44.004	49.071
2200	4.971	11.138	44.239	49.302
2300	4.970	11.635	44.464	49.523
2400	4.970	12.132	44.680	49.735
2500	4.970	12.629	44.886	49.938
2600	4.970	13.126	45.084	50.132
2700	4.970	13.623	45.274	50.320
2800	4.970	14.120	45.458	50.501
2900	4.970	14.617	45.635	50.675
3000	4.971	15.114	45.806	50.844
3200	4.972	16.109	46.131	51.165
3400	4.975	17.103	46.436	51.466
3600	4.979	18.099	46.723	51.751
3800	4.986	19.095	46.995	52.020
4000	4.996	20.093	47.253	52.276
4200	5.010	21.094	47.498	52.520
4400	5.030	22.098	47.731	52.754
4600	5.055	23.106	47.955	52.978
4800	5.089	24.121	48.168	53.193
5000	5.131	25.142	48.374	53.402
5200	5.182	26.173	48.571	53.604
5400	5.245	27.216	48.761	53.801
5600	5.320	28.272	48.944	53.993
5800	5.408	29.345	49.122	54.181
6000	5.510	30.436	49.293	54.366

Appendix 2.2   THERMODYNAMIC PROPERTIES OF AR GAS

T	C_P^0	$(H - H_0^0)_T$	$-(F^0 -H_0^0)/T$	S_T^0
DEG-K	CAL/MOLE DEG-K	KCAL/MOLE	CAL/MOLE DEG-K	CAL/MOLE DEG-K
100	4.968	0.497	26.516	31.484
200	4.968	0.994	29.960	34.928
273.15	4.968	1.357	31.508	36.477
298.15	4.968	1.481	31.944	36.912
400	4.968	1.987	33.403	38.372
500	4.968	2.484	34.512	39.480
600	4.968	2.981	35.418	40.386
700	4.968	3.478	36.184	41.152
800	4.968	3.974	36.847	41.815
900	4.968	4.471	37.432	42.400
1000	4.968	4.968	37.956	42.924
1100	4.968	5.465	38.429	43.397
1200	4.968	5.962	38.862	43.830
1300	4.968	6.459	39.259	44.227
1400	4.968	6.955	39.627	44.595
1500	4.968	7.452	39.970	44.938
1600	4.968	7.949	40.291	45.259
1700	4.968	8.446	40.592	45.560
1800	4.968	8.943	40.876	45.844
1900	4.968	9.439	41.145	46.113
2000	4.968	9.936	41.399	46.367
2100	4.968	10.433	41.642	46.610
2200	4.968	10.930	41.873	46.841
2300	4.968	11.427	42.094	47.062
2400	4.968	11.923	42.305	47.273
2500	4.968	12.420	42.508	47.476
2600	4.968	12.917	42.703	47.671
2700	4.968	13.414	42.890	47.858
2800	4.968	13.911	43.071	48.039
2900	4.968	14.408	43.245	48.213
3000	4.968	14.904	43.414	48.382
3200	4.968	15.898	43.734	48.703
3400	4.968	16.892	44.036	49.004
3600	4.968	17.885	44.320	49.288
3800	4.968	18.879	44.588	49.556
4000	4.968	19.872	44.843	49.811
4200	4.968	20.866	45.085	50.054
4400	4.968	21.860	45.317	50.285
4600	4.968	22.853	45.537	50.505
4800	4.968	23.847	45.749	50.717
5000	4.968	24.841	45.952	50.920
5200	4.968	25.834	46.146	51.115
5400	4.968	26.828	46.334	51.302
5600	4.968	27.821	46.515	51.483
5800	4.968	28.815	46.689	51.657
6000	4.968	29.809	46.857	51.826

Appendix 2.3   THERMODYNAMIC PROPERTIES OF B GAS

T	C_P^0	$(H^0 - H_0^0)$	$-(F^0 - H_0^0)/T$	S_T^0
DEG-K	CAL/MOLE DEG-K	KCAL/MOLE	CAL/MOLE DEG-K	CAL/MOLE DEG-K
100	4.993	0.525	25.962	31.211
200	4.974	1.023	29.549	34.664
273.15	4.971	1.387	31.137	36.214
298.15	4.971	1.511	31.581	36.649
400	4.970	2.017	33.067	38.110
500	4.969	2.514	34.190	39.218
600	4.969	3.011	35.106	40.124
700	4.969	3.508	35.879	40.890
800	4.968	4.005	36.548	41.554
900	4.968	4.502	37.137	42.139
1000	4.968	4.998	37.664	42.662
1100	4.968	5.495	38.140	43.136
1200	4.968	5.992	38.575	43.568
1300	4.968	6.489	38.974	43.966
1400	4.968	6.986	39.344	44.334
1500	4.968	7.483	39.689	44.677
1600	4.968	7.979	40.010	44.998
1700	4.968	8.476	40.313	45.299
1800	4.968	8.973	40.598	45.583
1900	4.968	9.470	40.867	45.851
2000	4.968	9.967	41.123	46.106
2100	4.968	10.463	41.366	46.349
2200	4.968	10.960	41.598	46.580
2300	4.968	11.457	41.819	46.801
2400	4.968	11.954	42.031	47.012
2500	4.968	12.451	42.234	47.215
2600	4.968	12.948	42.430	47.410
2700	4.968	13.444	42.618	47.597
2800	4.968	13.941	42.799	47.778
2900	4.969	14.438	42.974	47.952
3000	4.969	14.935	43.142	48.121
3200	4.970	15.929	43.464	48.441
3400	4.971	16.923	43.765	48.743
3600	4.973	17.917	44.050	49.027
3800	4.977	18.912	44.319	49.296
4000	4.982	19.908	44.574	49.551
4200	4.988	20.905	44.817	49.794
4400	4.997	21.904	45.049	50.027
4600	5.008	22.904	45.270	50.249
4800	5.022	23.907	45.482	50.463
5000	5.039	24.913	45.685	50.668
5200	5.058	25.923	45.881	50.866
5400	5.081	26.937	46.069	51.057
5600	5.107	27.955	46.250	51.242
5800	5.136	28.980	46.426	51.422
6000	5.168	30.010	46.595	51.597

THERMODYNAMIC PROPERTIES OF BE GAS

T	C_P^0	$(H^0 - H_0^0)$	$-(F^0 - H_0^0)/T$	S_T^0
DEG-K	CAL/MOLE DEG-K	KCAL/MOLE	CAL/MOLE DEG-K	CAL/MOLE DEG-K
100	4.968	0.497	22.150	27.118
200	4.968	0.994	25.593	30.561
273.15	4.968	1.357	27.142	32.110
298.15	4.968	1.481	27.577	32.545
400	4.968	1.987	29.037	34.005
500	4.968	2.484	30.145	35.114
600	4.968	2.981	31.051	36.019
700	4.968	3.478	31.817	36.785
800	4.968	3.974	32.480	37.449
900	4.968	4.471	33.066	38.034
1000	4.968	4.968	33.589	38.557
1100	4.968	5.465	34.063	39.031
1200	4.968	5.962	34.495	39.463
1300	4.968	6.459	34.893	39.861
1400	4.968	6.955	35.261	40.229
1500	4.968	7.452	35.603	40.572
1600	4.968	7.949	35.924	40.892
1700	4.968	8.446	36.225	41.193
1800	4.968	8.943	36.509	41.477
1900	4.968	9.439	36.778	41.746
2000	4.969	9.936	37.033	42.001
2100	4.969	10.433	37.275	42.243
2200	4.970	10.930	37.506	42.474
2300	4.972	11.427	37.727	42.695
2400	4.974	11.925	37.939	42.907
2500	4.977	12.422	38.141	43.110
2600	4.982	12.920	38.336	43.306
2700	4.988	13.419	38.524	43.494
2800	4.997	13.918	38.705	43.675
2900	5.007	14.418	38.879	43.851
3000	5.021	14.919	39.048	44.021
3200	5.057	15.927	39.369	44.346
3400	5.109	16.943	39.671	44.654
3600	5.179	17.972	39.956	44.948
3800	5.268	19.016	40.226	45.230
4000	5.378	20.080	40.483	45.503
4200	5.508	21.169	40.728	45.768
4400	5.658	22.285	40.963	46.028
4600	5.828	23.433	41.189	46.283
4800	6.014	24.617	41.407	46.535
5000	6.215	25.840	41.617	46.785
5200	6.428	27.104	41.820	47.033
5400	6.649	28.411	42.018	47.279
5600	6.877	29.764	42.210	47.525
5800	7.108	31.163	42.398	47.771
6000	7.339	32.607	42.581	48.015

Appendix 2.5   THERMODYNAMIC PROPERTIES OF C GAS

T	C_P^0	$(H^0 - H_0^0)/T$	$-(F^0 - H_0^0)/T$	S_T^0
DEG-K	CAL/MOLE DEG-K	KCAL/MOLE	CAL/MOLE DEG-K	CAL/MOLE DEG-K
100	5.085	0.570	26.580	32.283
200	4.997	1.073	30.406	35.770
273.15	4.983	1.438	32.061	37.325
298.15	4.981	1.562	32.521	37.761
400	4.975	2.069	34.051	39.224
500	4.973	2.567	35.201	40.334
600	4.971	3.064	36.134	41.240
700	4.970	3.561	36.920	42.006
800	4.970	4.058	37.598	42.670
900	4.970	4.555	38.195	43.255
1000	4.969	5.052	38.727	43.779
1100	4.969	5.549	39.208	44.253
1200	4.970	6.046	39.647	44.685
1300	4.971	6.543	40.050	45.083
1400	4.972	7.040	40.423	45.451
1500	4.975	7.537	40.770	45.794
1600	4.978	8.035	41.094	46.116
1700	4.984	8.533	41.398	46.418
1800	4.990	9.032	41.685	46.703
1900	4.998	9.531	41.956	46.973
2000	5.008	10.031	42.214	47.229
2100	5.019	10.533	42.458	47.474
2200	5.032	11.035	42.692	47.708
2300	5.046	11.539	42.915	47.932
2400	5.061	12.044	43.128	48.147
2500	5.077	12.551	43.333	48.354
2600	5.094	13.060	43.530	48.553
2700	5.112	13.570	43.720	48.746
2800	5.130	14.082	43.903	48.932
2900	5.149	14.596	44.079	49.112
3000	5.168	15.112	44.250	49.287
3200	5.206	16.149	44.575	49.622
3400	5.243	17.194	44.881	49.938
3600	5.279	18.246	45.171	50.239
3800	5.313	19.305	45.445	50.525
4000	5.345	20.371	45.706	50.799
4200	5.375	21.443	45.955	51.060
4400	5.402	22.521	46.193	51.311
4600	5.426	23.604	46.420	51.552
4800	5.448	24.691	46.639	51.783
5000	5.468	25.783	46.849	52.006
5200	5.486	26.878	47.052	52.221
5400	5.502	27.977	47.247	52.428
5600	5.516	29.079	47.436	52.628
5800	5.529	30.183	47.618	52.822
6000	5.540	31.290	47.795	53.010

Appendix 2.6 THERMODYNAMIC PROPERTIES OF CL GAS

T	C_P^0	$(H^0 - H_0^0)_T$	$-(F^0 - H_0^0)/T$	S_T^0
DEG-K	CAL/MOLE DEG-K	KCAL/MOLE	CAL/MOLE DEG-K	CAL/MOLE DEG-K
100	4.969	0.497	28.987	33.955
200	5.039	0.996	32.433	37.412
273.15	5.173	1.369	33.989	39.001
298.15	5.220	1.499	34.429	39.456
400	5.371	2.039	35.916	41.014
500	5.436	2.580	37.060	42.220
600	5.445	3.124	38.006	43.213
700	5.423	3.668	38.811	44.051
800	5.389	4.209	39.512	44.773
900	5.351	4.746	40.133	45.406
1000	5.313	5.279	40.688	45.967
1100	5.279	5.809	41.192	46.472
1200	5.248	6.335	41.651	46.930
1300	5.220	6.858	42.074	47.349
1400	5.196	7.379	42.464	47.735
1500	5.175	7.898	42.828	48.093
1600	5.156	8.414	43.167	48.426
1700	5.139	8.929	43.486	48.738
1800	5.125	9.442	43.786	49.032
1900	5.112	9.954	44.069	49.308
2000	5.100	10.464	44.338	49.570
2100	5.090	10.974	44.593	49.819
2200	5.081	11.482	44.836	50.055
2300	5.073	11.990	45.068	50.281
2400	5.066	12.497	45.290	50.497
2500	5.059	13.003	45.502	50.703
2600	5.053	13.509	45.706	50.902
2700	5.048	14.014	45.902	51.092
2800	5.043	14.518	46.091	51.276
2900	5.038	15.022	46.273	51.453
3000	5.034	15.526	46.448	51.623
3200	5.027	16.532	46.782	51.948
3400	5.021	17.537	47.095	52.253
3600	5.016	18.541	47.389	52.539
3800	5.011	19.543	47.668	52.811
4000	5.007	20.545	47.931	53.067
4200	5.004	21.546	48.182	53.312
4400	5.001	22.547	48.420	53.544
4600	4.998	23.546	48.648	53.767
4800	4.996	24.546	48.866	53.979
5000	4.994	25.545	49.074	54.183
5200	4.992	26.543	49.275	54.379
5400	4.990	27.542	49.467	54.567
5600	4.989	28.540	49.652	54.749
5800	4.988	29.537	49.831	54.924
6000	4.986	30.535	50.004	55.093

Appendix 2.7 THERMODYNAMIC PROPERTIES OF E- GAS

T	C_P^0	$(H^0 - H_0^0)$	$-(F^0 - H_0^0)/T$	S^0
DEG-K	CAL/MOLE DEG-K	KCAL/MOLE	CAL/MOLE DEG-K	CAL/MOLE DEG-K
100	4.968	0.497	-5.407	-0.439
200	4.968	0.994	-1.963	3.005
273.15	4.968	1.357	-0.415	4.553
298.15	4.968	1.481	0.020	4.988
400	4.968	1.987	1.480	6.448
500	4.968	2.484	2.589	7.557
600	4.968	2.981	3.495	8.463
700	4.968	3.478	4.261	9.229
800	4.968	3.974	4.924	9.892
900	4.968	4.471	5.509	10.477
1000	4.968	4.968	6.033	11.001
1100	4.968	5.465	6.506	11.474
1200	4.968	5.962	6.938	11.906
1300	4.968	6.459	7.336	12.304
1400	4.968	6.955	7.704	12.672
1500	4.968	7.452	8.047	13.015
1600	4.968	7.949	8.368	13.336
1700	4.968	8.446	8.669	13.637
1800	4.968	8.943	8.953	13.921
1900	4.968	9.439	9.221	14.189
2000	4.968	9.936	9.476	14.444
2100	4.968	10.433	9.719	14.687
2200	4.968	10.930	9.950	14.918
2300	4.968	11.427	10.171	15.139
2400	4.968	11.923	10.382	15.350
2500	4.968	12.420	10.585	15.553
2600	4.968	12.917	10.780	15.748
2700	4.968	13.414	10.967	15.935
2800	4.968	13.911	11.148	16.116
2900	4.968	14.408	11.322	16.290
3000	4.968	14.904	11.491	16.459
3200	4.968	15.898	11.811	16.779
3400	4.968	16.892	12.112	17.081
3600	4.968	17.885	12.396	17.365
3800	4.968	18.879	12.665	17.633
4000	4.968	19.872	12.920	17.888
4200	4.968	20.866	13.162	18.130
4400	4.968	21.860	13.393	18.361
4600	4.968	22.853	13.614	18.582
4800	4.968	23.847	13.826	18.794
5000	4.968	24.841	14.028	18.997
5200	4.968	25.834	14.223	19.191
5400	4.968	26.828	14.411	19.379
5600	4.968	27.821	14.591	19.560
5800	4.968	28.815	14.766	19.734
6000	4.968	29.809	14.934	19.902

Appendix 2.8 THERMODYNAMIC PROPERTIES OF F GAS

T	C_P^0	$(H^0 - H_0^0)$	$-(F^0 - H_0^0)/T$	S_T^0
DEG-K	CAL/MOLE DEG-K	KCAL/MOLE	CAL/MOLE DEG-K	CAL/MOLE DEG-K
100	5.068	0.499	27.130	32.116
200	5.403	1.024	30.625	35.747
273.15	5.445	1.422	32.235	37.440
298.15	5.437	1.558	32.691	37.917
400	5.361	2.108	34.235	39.505
500	5.282	2.640	35.412	40.693
600	5.218	3.165	36.374	41.650
700	5.169	3.684	37.187	42.450
800	5.133	4.199	37.889	43.138
900	5.105	4.711	38.506	43.741
1000	5.083	5.221	39.057	44.277
1100	5.066	5.728	39.554	44.761
1200	5.052	6.234	40.006	45.201
1300	5.041	6.738	40.422	45.605
1400	5.032	7.242	40.806	45.978
1500	5.025	7.745	41.162	46.325
1600	5.018	8.247	41.495	46.649
1700	5.013	8.749	41.807	46.953
1800	5.009	9.250	42.101	47.240
1900	5.005	9.750	42.379	47.511
2000	5.001	10.251	42.642	47.767
2100	4.998	10.751	42.892	48.011
2200	4.996	11.250	43.130	48.244
2300	4.994	11.750	43.357	48.466
2400	4.992	12.249	43.574	48.678
2500	4.990	12.748	43.783	48.882
2600	4.988	13.247	43.983	49.078
2700	4.987	13.746	44.175	49.266
2800	4.986	14.244	44.360	49.447
2900	4.985	14.743	44.538	49.622
3000	4.984	15.241	44.711	49.791
3200	4.982	16.238	45.038	50.113
3400	4.980	17.234	45.346	50.415
3600	4.979	18.230	45.635	50.699
3800	4.978	19.226	45.909	50.968
4000	4.977	20.221	46.168	51.224
4200	4.976	21.216	46.415	51.466
4400	4.975	22.212	46.650	51.698
4600	4.975	23.207	46.874	51.919
4800	4.974	24.202	47.089	52.131
5000	4.974	25.196	47.295	52.334
5200	4.973	26.191	47.492	52.529
5400	4.973	27.186	47.682	52.717
5600	4.973	28.180	47.865	52.898
5800	4.972	29.175	48.042	53.072
6000	4.972	30.169	48.212	53.241

Appendix 2.9   THERMODYNAMIC PROPERTIES OF H   GAS

T	C_P^0	$(H^0 - H_0^0)/T$	$-(F^0 - H_0^0)/T$	S_T^0
DEG-K	CAL/MOLE DEG-K	KCAL/MOLE	CAL/MOLE DEG-K	CAL/MOLE DEG-K
100	4.968	0.497	16.997	21.965
200	4.968	0.994	20.440	25.409
273.15	4.968	1.357	21.989	26.957
298.15	4.968	1.481	22.424	27.392
400	4.968	1.987	23.884	28.852
500	4.968	2.484	24.993	29.961
600	4.968	2.981	25.898	30.867
700	4.968	3.478	26.664	31.632
800	4.968	3.974	27.328	32.296
900	4.968	4.471	27.913	32.881
1000	4.968	4.968	28.436	33.404
1100	4.968	5.465	28.910	33.878
1200	4.968	5.962	29.342	34.310
1300	4.968	6.459	29.740	34.708
1400	4.968	6.955	30.108	35.076
1500	4.968	7.452	30.451	35.419
1600	4.968	7.949	30.771	35.739
1700	4.968	8.446	31.073	36.041
1800	4.968	8.943	31.357	36.325
1900	4.968	9.439	31.625	36.593
2000	4.968	9.936	31.880	36.848
2100	4.968	10.433	32.122	37.090
2200	4.968	10.930	32.353	37.322
2300	4.968	11.427	32.574	37.542
2400	4.968	11.923	32.786	37.754
2500	4.968	12.420	32.989	37.957
2600	4.968	12.917	33.183	38.152
2700	4.968	13.414	33.371	38.339
2800	4.968	13.911	33.552	38.520
2900	4.968	14.408	33.726	38.694
3000	4.968	14.904	33.894	38.862
3200	4.968	15.898	34.215	39.183
3400	4.968	16.892	34.516	39.484
3600	4.968	17.885	34.800	39.768
3800	4.968	18.879	35.069	40.037
4000	4.968	19.872	35.324	40.292
4200	4.968	20.866	35.566	40.534
4400	4.968	21.860	35.797	40.765
4600	4.968	22.853	36.018	40.986
4800	4.968	23.847	36.229	41.198
5000	4.968	24.841	36.432	41.400
5200	4.968	25.834	36.627	41.595
5400	4.968	26.828	36.815	41.783
5600	4.968	27.821	36.995	41.963
5800	4.968	28.815	37.170	42.138
6000	4.968	29.809	37.338	42.306

Appendix 2.10 THERMODYNAMIC PROPERTIES OF HE GAS

T	C_P^0	$(H^0 - H_0^0)_T$	$-(F^0 - H_0^0)/T$	S_T^0
DEG-K	CAL/MOLE DEG-K	KCAL/MOLE	CAL/MOLE DEG-K	CAL/MOLE DEG-K
100	4.968	0.497	19.730	24.698
200	4.968	0.994	23.174	28.142
273.15	4.968	1.357	24.722	29.691
298.15	4.968	1.481	25.157	30.126
400	4.968	1.987	26.617	31.586
500	4.968	2.484	27.726	32.694
600	4.968	2.981	28.632	33.600
700	4.968	3.478	29.398	34.366
800	4.968	3.974	30.061	35.029
900	4.968	4.471	30.646	35.614
1000	4.968	4.968	31.170	36.138
1100	4.968	5.465	31.643	36.611
1200	4.968	5.962	32.076	37.044
1300	4.968	6.459	32.473	37.441
1400	4.968	6.955	32.841	37.809
1500	4.968	7.452	33.184	38.152
1600	4.968	7.949	33.505	38.473
1700	4.968	8.446	33.806	38.774
1800	4.968	8.943	34.090	39.058
1900	4.968	9.439	34.359	39.327
2000	4.968	9.936	34.613	39.581
2100	4.968	10.433	34.856	39.824
2200	4.968	10.930	35.087	40.055
2300	4.968	11.427	35.308	40.276
2400	4.968	11.923	35.519	40.487
2500	4.968	12.420	35.722	40.690
2600	4.968	12.917	35.917	40.885
2700	4.968	13.414	36.104	41.072
2800	4.968	13.911	36.285	41.253
2900	4.968	14.408	36.459	41.427
3000	4.968	14.904	36.628	41.596
3200	4.968	15.898	36.948	41.917
3400	4.968	16.892	37.250	42.218
3600	4.968	17.885	37.534	42.502
3800	4.968	18.879	37.802	42.770
4000	4.968	19.872	38.057	43.025
4200	4.968	20.866	38.299	43.268
4400	4.968	21.860	38.531	43.499
4600	4.968	22.853	38.751	43.719
4800	4.968	23.847	38.963	43.931
5000	4.968	24.841	39.166	44.134
5200	4.968	25.834	39.360	44.329
5400	4.968	26.828	39.548	44.516
5600	4.968	27.821	39.729	44.697
5800	4.968	28.815	39.903	44.871
6000	4.968	29.809	40.071	45.040

Appendix 2.11   THERMODYNAMIC PROPERTIES OF LI GAS

T	C_p^0	$(H^0 - H_0^0)$	$-(F^0 - H_0^0)/T$	S_T^0
DEG-K	CAL/MOLE DEG-K	KCAL/MOLE	CAL/MOLE DEG-K	CAL/MOLE DEG-K
100	4.968	0.497	22.748	27.716
200	4.968	0.994	26.192	31.160
273.15	4.968	1.357	27.740	32.708
298.15	4.968	1.481	28.175	33.143
400	4.968	1.987	29.635	34.603
500	4.968	2.484	30.744	35.712
600	4.968	2.981	31.650	36.618
700	4.968	3.478	32.415	37.384
800	4.968	3.974	33.079	38.047
900	4.968	4.471	33.664	38.632
1000	4.968	4.968	34.187	39.156
1100	4.968	5.465	34.661	39.629
1200	4.968	5.962	35.093	40.061
1300	4.968	6.459	35.491	40.459
1400	4.968	6.955	35.859	40.827
1500	4.969	7.452	36.202	41.170
1600	4.970	7.949	36.522	41.491
1700	4.971	8.446	36.824	41.792
1800	4.974	8.943	37.108	42.076
1900	4.978	9.441	37.376	42.345
2000	4.983	9.939	37.631	42.601
2100	4.991	10.438	37.874	42.844
2200	5.001	10.937	38.105	43.076
2300	5.014	11.438	38.326	43.299
2400	5.031	11.940	38.538	43.513
2500	5.051	12.444	38.741	43.719
2600	5.074	12.951	38.936	43.917
2700	5.102	13.459	39.124	44.109
2800	5.134	13.971	39.306	44.295
2900	5.169	14.486	39.481	44.476
3000	5.209	15.005	39.650	44.652
3200	5.300	16.056	39.973	44.991
3400	5.407	17.126	40.278	45.315
3600	5.529	18.220	40.567	45.628
3800	5.666	19.339	40.841	45.930
4000	5.818	20.487	41.103	46.225
4200	5.987	21.667	41.354	46.513
4400	6.175	22.883	41.595	46.795
4600	6.385	24.139	41.827	47.075
4800	6.621	25.439	42.051	47.351
5000	6.887	26.789	42.269	47.627
5200	7.186	28.196	42.480	47.903
5400	7.523	29.666	42.686	48.180
5600	7.901	31.208	42.887	48.460
5800	8.322	32.830	43.084	48.745
6000	8.787	34.540	43.278	49.035

T	C_P^0	$(H^0 - H_0^0)$	$-(F^0 - H_0^0)/T$	S_T^0
DEG-K	CAL/MOLE DEG-K	KCAL/MOLE	CAL/MOLE DEG-K	CAL/MOLE DEG-K
100	4.968	0.497	25.108	30.077
200	4.968	0.994	28.552	33.520
273.15	4.968	1.357	30.101	35.069
298.15	4.968	1.481	30.536	35.504
400	4.968	1.987	31.996	36.964
500	4.968	2.484	33.104	38.072
600	4.968	2.981	34.010	38.978
700	4.968	3.478	34.776	39.744
800	4.968	3.974	35.439	40.407
900	4.968	4.471	36.025	40.993
1000	4.968	4.968	36.548	41.516
1100	4.968	5.465	37.021	41.990
1200	4.968	5.962	37.454	42.422
1300	4.968	6.459	37.851	42.820
1400	4.968	6.955	38.220	43.188
1500	4.968	7.452	38.562	43.530
1600	4.968	7.949	38.883	43.851
1700	4.968	8.446	39.184	44.152
1800	4.968	8.943	39.468	44.436
1900	4.968	9.439	39.737	44.705
2000	4.969	9.936	39.992	44.960
2100	4.969	10.433	40.234	45.202
2200	4.970	10.930	40.465	45.433
2300	4.972	11.427	40.686	45.654
2400	4.974	11.925	40.897	45.866
2500	4.978	12.422	41.100	46.069
2600	4.983	12.920	41.295	46.264
2700	4.989	13.419	41.483	46.453
2800	4.998	13.918	41.663	46.634
2900	5.009	14.418	41.838	46.810
3000	5.023	14.920	42.007	46.980
3200	5.060	15.928	42.328	47.305
3400	5.114	16.945	42.630	47.613
3600	5.186	17.975	42.915	47.908
3800	5.278	19.021	43.185	48.190
4000	5.392	20.088	43.442	48.464
4200	5.528	21.179	43.688	48.730
4400	5.687	22.300	43.923	48.991
4600	5.867	23.455	44.149	49.248
4800	6.068	24.649	44.366	49.502
5000	6.290	25.884	44.577	49.754
5200	6.531	27.166	44.781	50.005
5400	6.791	28.498	44.979	50.256
5600	7.070	29.883	45.172	50.508
5800	7.368	31.327	45.360	50.762
6000	7.685	32.832	45.545	51.017

Appendix 2.13   THERMODYNAMIC PROPERTIES OF N GAS

T	C_P^0	$(H^0 - H_0^0)$	$-(F^0 - H_0^0)/T$	S_T^0
DEG-K	CAL/MOLE DEG-K	KCAL/MOLE	CAL/MOLE DEG-K	CAL/MOLE DEG-K
100	4.968	0.497	26.219	31.187
200	4.968	0.994	29.663	34.631
273.15	4.968	1.357	31.211	36.179
298.15	4.968	1.481	31.646	36.614
400	4.968	1.987	33.106	38.074
500	4.968	2.484	34.215	39.183
600	4.968	2.981	35.121	40.089
700	4.968	3.478	35.886	40.855
800	4.968	3.974	36.550	41.518
900	4.968	4.471	37.135	42.103
1000	4.968	4.968	37.658	42.627
1100	4.968	5.465	38.132	43.100
1200	4.968	5.962	38.564	43.532
1300	4.968	6.459	38.962	43.930
1400	4.968	6.955	39.330	44.298
1500	4.968	7.452	39.673	44.641
1600	4.968	7.949	39.993	44.962
1700	4.968	8.446	40.295	45.263
1800	4.968	8.943	40.579	45.547
1900	4.969	9.440	40.847	45.815
2000	4.969	9.936	41.102	46.070
2100	4.970	10.433	41.344	46.313
2200	4.971	10.930	41.576	46.544
2300	4.972	11.428	41.796	46.765
2400	4.975	11.925	42.008	46.977
2500	4.978	12.422	42.211	47.180
2600	4.982	12.920	42.406	47.375
2700	4.987	13.419	42.593	47.563
2800	4.993	13.918	42.774	47.745
2900	5.001	14.418	42.948	47.920
3000	5.010	14.918	43.117	48.090
3200	5.035	15.922	43.438	48.414
3400	5.066	16.932	43.740	48.720
3600	5.107	17.950	44.025	49.011
3800	5.155	18.976	44.294	49.288
4000	5.213	20.012	44.551	49.554
4200	5.278	21.061	44.795	49.810
4400	5.351	22.124	45.029	50.057
4600	5.431	23.202	45.253	50.296
4800	5.517	24.297	45.468	50.529
5000	5.608	25.409	45.675	50.756
5200	5.702	26.540	45.874	50.978
5400	5.800	27.690	46.067	51.195
5600	5.900	28.860	46.254	51.408
5800	6.000	30.050	46.436	51.617
6000	6.100	31.260	46.612	51.822

Appendix 2.14   THERMODYNAMIC PROPERTIES OF O GAS

T	C_p^0	$(H_T^0 - H_0^0)$	$-(F_T^0 - H_0^0)/T$	S_T^0
DEG-K	CAL/MOLE DEG-K	KCAL/MOLE	CAL/MOLE DEG-K	CAL/MOLE DEG-K
100	5.666	0.527	27.191	32.466
200	5.434	1.085	30.915	36.340
273.15	5.275	1.476	32.604	38.008
298.15	5.237	1.607	33.077	38.468
400	5.135	2.135	34.654	39.991
500	5.081	2.646	35.840	41.131
600	5.049	3.152	36.801	42.054
700	5.029	3.656	37.608	42.831
800	5.015	4.158	38.304	43.501
900	5.006	4.659	38.915	44.092
1000	4.999	5.159	39.459	44.619
1100	4.994	5.659	39.950	45.095
1200	4.990	6.158	40.397	45.529
1300	4.987	6.657	40.808	45.928
1400	4.984	7.155	41.187	46.298
1500	4.982	7.654	41.539	46.642
1600	4.981	8.152	41.868	46.963
1700	4.979	8.650	42.177	47.265
1800	4.979	9.148	42.468	47.550
1900	4.978	9.646	42.742	47.819
2000	4.978	10.143	43.002	48.074
2100	4.978	10.641	43.250	48.317
2200	4.979	11.139	43.485	48.549
2300	4.980	11.637	43.710	48.770
2400	4.981	12.135	43.926	48.982
2500	4.984	12.633	44.132	49.185
2600	4.986	13.132	44.330	49.381
2700	4.990	13.630	44.521	49.569
2800	4.994	14.130	44.704	49.751
2900	4.999	14.629	44.881	49.926
3000	5.004	15.129	45.052	50.096
3200	5.017	16.132	45.378	50.419
3400	5.033	17.136	45.683	50.723
3600	5.050	18.145	45.971	51.012
3800	5.070	19.157	46.244	51.285
4000	5.091	20.173	46.503	51.546
4200	5.114	21.193	46.749	51.795
4400	5.138	22.219	46.984	52.033
4600	5.162	23.248	47.208	52.262
4800	5.186	24.283	47.423	52.482
5000	5.210	25.323	47.630	52.695
5200	5.234	26.367	47.829	52.899
5400	5.258	27.417	48.020	53.097
5600	5.280	28.470	48.205	53.289
5800	5.302	29.529	48.383	53.475
6000	5.323	30.591	48.556	53.655

Appendix 2.15 THERMODYNAMIC PROPERTIES OF P GAS

T	C_P^0	$(H^0 - H_0^0)$	$-(F^0-H_0^0)/T$	S_T^0
DEG-K	CAL/MOLE DEG-K	KCAL/MOLE	CAL/MOLE DEG-K	CAL/MOLE DEG-K
100	4.968	0.497	28.584	33.552
200	4.968	0.994	32.028	36.996
273.15	4.968	1.357	33.577	38.545
298.15	4.968	1.481	34.012	38.980
400	4.968	1.987	35.472	40.440
500	4.968	2.484	36.580	41.548
600	4.968	2.981	37.486	42.454
700	4.968	3.478	38.252	43.220
800	4.968	3.975	38.915	43.883
900	4.968	4.471	39.500	44.469
1000	4.968	4.968	40.024	44.992
1100	4.969	5.465	40.497	45.466
1200	4.969	5.962	40.930	45.898
1300	4.971	6.459	41.327	46.296
1400	4.974	6.956	41.696	46.664
1500	4.979	7.454	42.038	47.008
1600	4.987	7.952	42.359	47.329
1700	4.999	8.451	42.660	47.632
1800	5.015	8.952	42.945	47.918
1900	5.036	9.454	43.214	48.190
2000	5.062	9.959	43.469	48.449
2100	5.094	10.467	43.712	48.696
2200	5.132	10.978	43.944	48.934
2300	5.176	11.494	44.166	49.163
2400	5.226	12.014	44.379	49.384
2500	5.281	12.539	44.583	49.599
2600	5.341	13.070	44.780	49.807
2700	5.405	13.607	44.970	50.010
2800	5.474	14.151	45.154	50.208
2900	5.546	14.702	45.331	50.401
3000	5.621	15.260	45.504	50.590
3200	5.778	16.400	45.833	50.958
3400	5.939	17.572	46.145	51.313
3600	6.100	18.776	46.442	51.657
3800	6.257	20.011	46.725	51.991
4000	6.407	21.278	46.997	52.316
4200	6.547	22.574	47.257	52.632
4400	6.676	23.896	47.509	52.940
4600	6.791	25.243	47.751	53.239
4800	6.893	26.612	47.986	53.530
5000	6.980	27.999	48.214	53.813
5200	7.053	29.403	48.434	54.089
5400	7.113	30.820	48.649	54.356
5600	7.160	32.247	48.857	54.616
5800	7.195	33.683	49.060	54.868
6000	7.219	35.125	49.258	55.112

THERMODYNAMIC PROPERTIES OF S GAS

T	C_P^0	$(H^0 - H_0^0)_T$	$-(F^0 - H_0^0)/T$	S_T^0
DEG-K	CAL/MOLE DEG-K	KCAL/MOLE	CAL/MOLE DEG-K	CAL/MOLE DEG-K
100	5.104	0.499	29.135	34.127
200	5.590	1.037	32.648	37.831
273.15	5.668	1.450	34.284	39.590
298.15	5.659	1.591	34.750	40.086
400	5.553	2.163	36.330	41.736
500	5.436	2.712	37.538	42.962
600	5.340	3.250	38.527	43.944
700	5.266	3.781	39.361	44.762
800	5.211	4.304	40.081	45.461
900	5.169	4.823	40.713	46.072
1000	5.136	5.338	41.277	46.615
1100	5.112	5.851	41.785	47.104
1200	5.093	6.361	42.247	47.547
1300	5.079	6.869	42.670	47.955
1400	5.069	7.377	43.061	48.331
1500	5.064	7.883	43.424	48.680
1600	5.062	8.390	43.763	49.007
1700	5.063	8.896	44.081	49.314
1800	5.068	9.402	44.380	49.603
1900	5.075	9.910	44.662	49.877
2000	5.085	10.418	44.929	50.138
2100	5.097	10.927	45.183	50.386
2200	5.112	11.437	45.425	50.624
2300	5.127	11.949	45.656	50.851
2400	5.144	12.463	45.877	51.070
2500	5.162	12.978	46.089	51.280
2600	5.181	13.495	46.293	51.483
2700	5.200	14.014	46.489	51.679
2800	5.219	14.535	46.677	51.869
2900	5.239	15.058	46.860	52.052
3000	5.258	15.583	47.036	52.230
3200	5.295	16.638	47.371	52.570
3400	5.331	17.701	47.686	52.893
3600	5.363	18.770	47.984	53.198
3800	5.392	19.846	48.266	53.489
4000	5.418	20.927	48.534	53.766
4200	5.441	22.013	48.790	54.031
4400	5.461	23.103	49.034	54.285
4600	5.477	24.197	49.268	54.528
4800	5.491	25.294	49.492	54.761
5000	5.502	26.394	49.707	54.986
5200	5.511	27.495	49.914	55.202
5400	5.518	28.598	50.114	55.410
5600	5.523	29.702	50.307	55.611
5800	5.526	30.807	50.493	55.804
6000	5.528	31.912	50.673	55.992

T	C_P^0	$(H^0 - H_0^0)$	$-(F^0 - H_0^0)/T$	S_T^0
DEG-K	CAL/MOLE DEG-K	KCAL/MOLE	CAL/MOLE DEG-K	CAL/MOLE DEG-K
100	6.698	0.655	27.096	33.646
200	5.688	1.268	31.595	37.933
273.15	5.382	1.671	33.537	39.654
298.15	5.319	1.805	34.070	40.123
400	5.166	2.338	35.818	41.662
500	5.095	2.850	37.105	42.806
600	5.056	3.358	38.135	43.731
700	5.033	3.862	38.991	44.508
800	5.019	4.365	39.724	45.180
900	5.012	4.866	40.364	45.770
1000	5.012	5.367	40.931	46.298
1100	5.017	5.869	41.441	46.776
1200	5.027	6.371	41.904	47.213
1300	5.043	6.874	42.328	47.616
1400	5.063	7.379	42.719	47.990
1500	5.087	7.887	43.083	48.341
1600	5.113	8.397	43.422	48.670
1700	5.142	8.910	43.740	48.981
1800	5.172	9.425	44.039	49.275
1900	5.202	9.944	44.322	49.556
2000	5.232	10.466	44.590	49.823
2100	5.261	10.990	44.846	50.079
2200	5.289	11.518	45.089	50.325
2300	5.316	12.048	45.322	50.560
2400	5.341	12.581	45.545	50.787
2500	5.364	13.116	45.759	51.006
2600	5.386	13.654	45.965	51.216
2700	5.406	14.193	46.163	51.420
2800	5.424	14.735	46.355	51.617
2900	5.440	15.278	46.539	51.808
3000	5.454	15.823	46.718	51.992
3200	5.478	16.916	47.059	52.345
3400	5.495	18.013	47.380	52.678
3600	5.508	19.114	47.683	52.992
3800	5.516	20.216	47.970	53.290
4000	5.521	21.320	48.243	53.573
4200	5.522	22.424	48.504	53.843
4400	5.522	23.529	48.752	54.100
4600	5.520	24.633	48.990	54.345
4800	5.517	25.737	49.218	54.580
5000	5.513	26.840	49.437	54.805
5200	5.510	27.942	49.648	55.021
5400	5.508	29.044	49.851	55.229
5600	5.507	30.146	50.046	55.429
5800	5.509	31.247	50.235	55.623
6000	5.514	32.349	50.418	55.810

APPENDIX 3

THERMODYNAMIC PROPERTIES OF SOME DIATOMIC SPECIES IN THE IDEAL GAS STATE

In this appendix we tabulate thermodynamic properties of diatomic species which consist of elements in the first three rows of the periodic chart. This data was computed using all of the molecular data listed in Table (1.5). For a discussion of the method of calculation read Section (1.3.1).

Appendix 3.1 THERMODYNAMIC PROPERTIES OF AlBr GAS

T	C_P^0	$(H_T^0 - H_0^0)$	$-(F_T^0 - H_0^0)/T$	S_T^0
DEG-K	CAL/MOLE DEG-K	KCAL/MOLE	CAL/MOLE DEG-K	CAL/MOLE DEG-K
100	7.223	0.701	41.619	48.625
200	8.090	1.469	46.571	53.919
273.15	8.431	2.075	48.900	56.496
298.15	8.507	2.287	49.568	57.238
400	8.709	3.165	51.858	59.770
500	8.815	4.041	53.643	61.725
600	8.881	4.926	55.128	63.339
700	8.926	5.817	56.402	64.711
800	8.959	6.711	57.517	65.905
900	8.986	7.608	58.508	66.962
1000	9.009	8.508	59.402	67.910
1100	9.028	9.410	60.215	68.770
1200	9.046	10.314	60.961	69.556
1300	9.062	11.219	61.651	70.281
1400	9.078	12.126	62.291	70.953
1500	9.092	13.035	62.890	71.580
1600	9.106	13.945	63.452	72.167
1700	9.120	14.856	63.981	72.720
1800	9.133	15.769	64.481	73.241
1900	9.146	16.683	64.955	73.735
2000	9.159	17.598	65.406	74.205
2100	9.171	18.514	65.836	74.652
2200	9.184	19.432	66.246	75.079
2300	9.196	20.351	66.639	75.488
2400	9.208	21.271	67.016	75.879
2500	9.220	22.193	67.378	76.255
2600	9.232	23.115	67.727	76.617
2700	9.244	24.039	68.062	76.966
2800	9.256	24.964	68.386	77.302
2900	9.268	25.891	68.699	77.627
3000	9.280	26.818	69.002	77.942
3200	9.303	28.676	69.580	78.541
3400	9.327	30.539	70.124	79.106
3600	9.350	32.407	70.638	79.640
3800	9.373	34.279	71.125	80.146
4000	9.396	36.156	71.588	80.627
4200	9.420	38.038	72.030	81.086
4400	9.443	39.924	72.451	81.525
4600	9.466	41.815	72.855	81.945
4800	9.489	43.710	73.242	82.349
5000	9.512	45.611	73.614	82.736
5200	9.535	47.515	73.972	83.110
5400	9.558	49.424	74.318	83.470
5600	9.581	51.338	74.651	83.818
5800	9.604	53.257	74.973	84.155
6000	9.627	55.180	75.284	84.481

Appendix 3.2   THERMODYNAMIC PROPERTIES OF ALCL GAS

T	C_P^0	$(H^0 - H_0^0)$	$-(F^0 - H_0^0)/T$	S_T^0
DEG-K	CAL/MOLE DEG-K	KCAL/MOLE	CAL/MOLE DEG-K	CAL/MOLE DEG-K
100	7.056	0.697	39.179	46.150
200	7.776	1.437	44.065	51.252
273.15	8.183	2.022	46.337	53.741
298.15	8.284	2.228	46.989	54.462
400	8.561	3.087	49.221	56.939
500	8.713	3.952	50.964	58.867
600	8.807	4.828	52.418	60.465
700	8.871	5.712	53.667	61.828
800	8.918	6.602	54.763	63.015
900	8.954	7.496	55.740	64.068
1000	8.984	8.392	56.620	65.013
1100	9.009	9.292	57.423	65.870
1200	9.030	10.194	58.160	66.655
1300	9.050	11.098	58.842	67.379
1400	9.068	12.004	59.476	68.050
1500	9.085	12.912	60.069	68.676
1600	9.101	13.821	60.625	69.263
1700	9.117	14.732	61.150	69.816
1800	9.131	15.644	61.646	70.337
1900	9.146	16.558	62.116	70.831
2000	9.160	17.474	62.564	71.301
2100	9.173	18.390	62.991	71.748
2200	9.187	19.308	63.398	72.175
2300	9.200	20.228	63.789	72.584
2400	9.213	21.148	64.164	72.975
2500	9.226	22.070	64.524	73.352
2600	9.239	22.993	64.870	73.714
2700	9.251	23.918	65.204	74.063
2800	9.264	24.844	65.527	74.399
2900	9.277	25.771	65.838	74.725
3000	9.289	26.699	66.140	75.039
3200	9.314	28.559	66.715	75.640
3400	9.338	30.424	67.257	76.205
3600	9.363	32.295	67.769	76.740
3800	9.387	34.170	68.254	77.246
4000	9.411	36.049	68.716	77.728
4200	9.435	37.934	69.156	78.188
4400	9.459	39.823	69.577	78.628
4600	9.483	41.718	69.980	79.049
4800	9.507	43.617	70.366	79.453
5000	9.531	45.521	70.737	79.841
5200	9.555	47.429	71.095	80.216
5400	9.579	49.343	71.439	80.577
5600	9.603	51.261	71.772	80.926
5800	9.627	53.184	72.093	81.263
6000	9.651	55.112	72.405	81.590

Appendix 3.3   THERMODYNAMIC PROPERTIES OF ALF GAS

T	C_P^0	$(H^0 - H_0^0)$	$-(F^0 - H_0^0)/T$	S_T^0
DEG-K	CAL/MOLE DEG-K	KCAL/MOLE	CAL/MOLE DEG-K	CAL/MOLE DEG-K
100	6.960	0.696	36.625	43.582
200	7.179	1.399	41.454	48.449
273.15	7.516	1.936	43.647	50.736
298.15	7.632	2.126	44.269	51.399
400	8.031	2.924	46.390	53.701
500	8.302	3.742	48.040	55.524
600	8.485	4.582	49.418	57.055
700	8.613	5.437	50.606	58.373
800	8.705	6.303	51.650	59.530
900	8.774	7.177	52.584	60.559
1000	8.827	8.058	53.429	61.486
1100	8.870	8.943	54.200	62.330
1200	8.906	9.831	54.910	63.103
1300	8.935	10.723	55.568	63.817
1400	8.961	11.618	56.181	64.480
1500	8.984	12.516	56.756	65.099
1600	9.004	13.415	57.295	65.680
1700	9.022	14.316	57.805	66.226
1800	9.039	15.219	58.287	66.742
1900	9.055	16.124	58.745	67.232
2000	9.070	17.030	59.181	67.696
2100	9.084	17.938	59.597	68.139
2200	9.097	18.847	59.995	68.562
2300	9.110	19.758	60.377	68.967
2400	9.123	20.669	60.743	69.355
2500	9.135	21.582	61.095	69.727
2600	9.146	22.496	61.434	70.086
2700	9.158	23.411	61.760	70.431
2800	9.169	24.328	62.076	70.765
2900	9.180	25.245	62.381	71.087
3000	9.191	26.164	62.677	71.398
3200	9.212	28.004	63.241	71.992
3400	9.232	29.848	63.772	72.551
3600	9.252	31.697	64.274	73.079
3800	9.272	33.549	64.751	73.580
4000	9.292	35.406	65.205	74.056
4200	9.311	37.266	65.637	74.510
4400	9.331	39.130	66.050	74.943
4600	9.350	40.998	66.446	75.359
4800	9.369	42.870	66.826	75.757
5000	9.388	44.746	67.191	76.140
5200	9.406	46.625	67.542	76.508
5400	9.425	48.508	67.881	76.864
5600	9.444	50.395	68.208	77.207
5800	9.462	52.286	68.524	77.539
6000	9.481	54.180	68.830	77.860

Appendix 3.4   THERMODYNAMIC PROPERTIES OF ALH   GAS

T	C_P^0	$(H^0 - H_0^0)_T$	$-(F^0 - H_0^0)_T/T$	S_T^0
DEG-K	CAL/MOLE DEG-K	KCAL/MOLE	CAL/MOLE DEG-K	CAL/MOLE DEG-K
100	6.961	0.696	30.301	37.259
200	6.968	1.392	35.125	42.086
273.15	6.998	1.903	37.295	44.261
298.15	7.020	2.078	37.906	44.875
400	7.180	2.800	39.957	46.958
500	7.409	3.529	41.525	48.584
600	7.651	4.282	42.819	49.956
700	7.874	5.059	43.926	51.153
800	8.068	5.856	44.897	52.217
900	8.233	6.671	45.764	53.177
1000	8.371	7.502	46.550	54.052
1100	8.487	8.345	47.269	54.855
1200	8.586	9.199	47.933	55.598
1300	8.671	10.062	48.549	56.289
1400	8.744	10.932	49.125	56.934
1500	8.808	11.810	49.666	57.540
1600	8.865	12.694	50.176	58.110
1700	8.915	13.583	50.659	58.649
1800	8.961	14.477	51.117	59.160
1900	9.003	15.375	51.553	59.645
2000	9.041	16.277	51.970	60.108
2100	9.077	17.183	52.368	60.550
2200	9.110	18.092	52.749	60.973
2300	9.141	19.005	53.116	61.379
2400	9.170	19.920	53.468	61.768
2500	9.198	20.839	53.808	62.143
2600	9.225	21.760	54.135	62.505
2700	9.251	22.684	54.452	62.853
2800	9.275	23.610	54.758	63.190
2900	9.299	24.539	55.054	63.516
3000	9.322	25.470	55.342	63.832
3200	9.367	27.339	55.891	64.435
3400	9.409	29.216	56.411	65.004
3600	9.450	31.102	56.903	65.543
3800	9.489	32.996	57.372	66.055
4000	9.528	34.898	57.818	66.543
4200	9.565	36.807	58.245	67.008
4400	9.602	38.724	58.653	67.454
4600	9.639	40.648	59.045	67.882
4800	9.674	42.579	59.422	68.293
5000	9.710	44.518	59.785	68.688
5200	9.745	46.463	60.135	69.070
5400	9.780	48.416	60.472	69.438
5600	9.814	50.375	60.799	69.795
5800	9.848	52.341	61.115	70.140
6000	9.882	54.314	61.422	70.474

Appendix 3.5   THERMODYNAMIC PROPERTIES OF ALH+ GAS

T	C_P^0	$(H^0 - H_0^0)$	$-(F^0 - H_0^0)/T$	S_T^0
DEG-K	CAL/MOLE DEG-K	KCAL/MOLE	CAL/MOLE DEG-K	CAL/MOLE DEG-K
100	6.961	0.696	31.597	38.556
200	6.970	1.392	36.421	43.383
273.15	7.004	1.903	38.592	45.559
298.15	7.028	2.079	39.202	46.174
400	7.198	2.802	41.255	48.260
500	7.436	3.533	42.824	49.891
600	7.685	4.290	44.120	51.269
700	7.912	5.070	45.229	52.471
800	8.108	5.871	46.202	53.541
900	8.272	6.690	47.072	54.505
1000	8.409	7.524	47.860	55.384
1100	8.524	8.371	48.581	56.191
1200	8.622	9.229	49.247	56.937
1300	8.705	10.095	49.865	57.631
1400	8.777	10.969	50.443	58.279
1500	8.840	11.850	50.986	58.886
1600	8.895	12.737	51.498	59.459
1700	8.945	13.629	51.982	59.999
1800	8.990	14.526	52.442	60.512
1900	9.031	15.427	52.880	60.999
2000	9.069	16.332	53.297	61.464
2100	9.105	17.241	53.697	61.907
2200	9.138	18.153	54.080	62.331
2300	9.169	19.068	54.448	62.738
2400	9.198	19.987	54.801	63.129
2500	9.226	20.908	55.142	63.505
2600	9.253	21.832	55.471	63.867
2700	9.278	22.758	55.788	64.217
2800	9.303	23.687	56.095	64.555
2900	9.327	24.619	56.392	64.882
3000	9.351	25.553	56.681	65.198
3200	9.396	27.427	57.232	65.803
3400	9.439	29.311	57.753	66.374
3600	9.480	31.203	58.247	66.915
3800	9.521	33.103	58.717	67.429
4000	9.560	35.011	59.165	67.918
4200	9.599	36.927	59.593	68.385
4400	9.637	38.851	60.003	68.833
4600	9.674	40.782	60.396	69.262
4800	9.711	42.720	60.774	69.674
5000	9.748	44.666	61.138	70.072
5200	9.784	46.620	61.489	70.455
5400	9.820	48.580	61.828	70.825
5600	9.856	50.548	62.156	71.182
5800	9.891	52.522	62.473	71.529
6000	9.927	54.504	62.781	71.865

Appendix 3.6   THERMODYNAMIC PROPERTIES OF ALN   GAS

T	C_P^0	$(H^0 - H_0^0)$	$-(F^0 - H_0^0)/T$	S_T^0
DEG-K	CAL/MOLE DEG-K	KCAL/MOLE	CAL/MOLE DEG-K	CAL/MOLE DEG-K
100	6.959	0.696	39.601	46.558
200	7.130	1.397	44.428	51.413
273.15	7.438	1.929	46.616	53.679
298.15	7.550	2.117	47.236	54.336
400	7.952	2.907	49.345	56.613
500	8.238	3.718	50.985	58.420
600	8.437	4.552	52.354	59.941
700	8.578	5.403	53.534	61.253
800	8.681	6.266	54.572	62.405
900	8.759	7.138	55.501	63.432
1000	8.820	8.017	56.341	64.358
1100	8.869	8.902	57.109	65.201
1200	8.910	9.791	57.816	65.975
1300	8.944	10.684	58.471	66.690
1400	8.974	11.580	59.082	67.353
1500	9.001	12.479	59.655	67.974
1600	9.025	13.380	60.193	68.555
1700	9.047	14.283	60.701	69.103
1800	9.067	15.189	61.182	69.621
1900	9.085	16.097	61.639	70.111
2000	9.103	17.006	62.075	70.578
2100	9.120	17.917	62.490	71.022
2200	9.136	18.830	62.888	71.447
2300	9.151	19.744	63.269	71.853
2400	9.166	20.660	63.635	72.243
2500	9.180	21.578	63.987	72.618
2600	9.195	22.496	64.326	72.978
2700	9.208	23.417	64.653	73.325
2800	9.222	24.338	64.968	73.660
2900	9.235	25.261	65.274	73.984
3000	9.248	26.185	65.569	74.298
3200	9.274	28.037	66.134	74.895
3400	9.299	29.894	66.666	75.458
3600	9.323	31.757	67.169	75.990
3800	9.347	33.624	67.647	76.495
4000	9.371	35.496	68.101	76.975
4200	9.395	37.372	68.535	77.433
4400	9.418	39.254	68.949	77.871
4600	9.442	41.140	69.346	78.290
4800	9.465	43.030	69.728	78.692
5000	9.488	44.926	70.094	79.079
5200	9.511	46.826	70.447	79.452
5400	9.534	48.730	70.787	79.811
5600	9.557	50.639	71.115	80.158
5800	9.580	52.553	71.433	80.494
6000	9.602	54.471	71.741	80.819

Appendix 3.7 THERMODYNAMIC PROPERTIES OF ALO GAS

T	C_P^0	$(H^0 - H_0^0)$	$-(F^0 - H_0^0)/T$	S_T^0
DEG-K	CAL/MOLE DEG-K	KCAL/MOLE	CAL/MOLE DEG-K	CAL/MOLE DEG-K
100	6.957	0.696	37.504	44.460
200	7.052	1.394	42.328	49.298
273.15	7.285	1.918	44.507	51.528
298.15	7.382	2.101	45.123	52.170
400	7.766	2.873	47.212	54.394
500	8.067	3.665	48.830	56.161
600	8.288	4.484	50.180	57.652
700	8.449	5.321	51.341	58.943
800	8.568	6.172	52.364	60.079
900	8.658	7.034	53.279	61.094
1000	8.728	7.903	54.107	62.010
1100	8.784	8.779	54.864	62.844
1200	8.829	9.659	55.561	63.610
1300	8.867	10.544	56.208	64.319
1400	8.899	11.433	56.811	64.977
1500	8.927	12.324	57.376	65.592
1600	8.951	13.218	57.908	66.169
1700	8.973	14.114	58.410	66.712
1800	8.993	15.012	58.885	67.226
1900	9.011	15.913	59.337	67.712
2000	9.028	16.814	59.768	68.175
2100	9.043	17.718	60.179	68.616
2200	9.058	18.623	60.572	69.037
2300	9.071	19.530	60.949	69.440
2400	9.085	20.437	61.311	69.826
2500	9.097	21.346	61.659	70.197
2600	9.109	22.257	61.994	70.554
2700	9.121	23.168	62.317	70.898
2800	9.132	24.081	62.630	71.230
2900	9.143	24.995	62.932	71.551
3000	9.154	25.909	63.225	71.861
3200	9.175	27.742	63.783	72.452
3400	9.195	29.579	64.309	73.009
3600	9.214	31.420	64.808	73.535
3800	9.233	33.265	65.280	74.034
4000	9.252	35.114	65.730	74.508
4200	9.270	36.966	66.159	74.960
4400	9.288	38.822	66.569	75.392
4600	9.306	40.681	66.961	75.805
4800	9.324	42.544	67.338	76.201
5000	9.342	44.411	67.700	76.582
5200	9.359	46.281	68.049	76.949
5400	9.377	48.154	68.385	77.303
5600	9.394	50.031	68.710	77.644
5800	9.411	51.912	69.024	77.974
6000	9.428	53.796	69.327	78.293

Appendix 3.8 THERMODYNAMIC PROPERTIES OF ALS GAS

T	C_P^0	$(H^0 - H_0^0)$	$-(F^0 - H_0^0)/T$	S_T^0
DEG-K	CAL/MOLE DEG-K	KCAL/MOLE	CAL/MOLE DEG-K	CAL/MOLE DEG-K
100	6.974	0.696	40.096	47.054
200	7.389	1.410	44.938	51.987
273.15	7.797	1.966	47.156	54.352
298.15	7.916	2.162	47.788	55.040
400	8.280	2.988	49.951	57.422
500	8.500	3.828	51.638	59.295
600	8.640	4.686	53.048	60.858
700	8.735	5.555	54.262	62.197
800	8.802	6.432	55.328	63.368
900	8.853	7.315	56.281	64.408
1000	8.892	8.202	57.141	65.343
1100	8.923	9.093	57.926	66.192
1200	8.950	9.986	58.647	66.969
1300	8.973	10.883	59.315	67.687
1400	8.992	11.781	59.937	68.352
1500	9.010	12.681	60.519	68.973
1600	9.026	13.583	61.066	69.555
1700	9.041	14.486	61.582	70.103
1800	9.055	15.391	62.070	70.620
1900	9.068	16.297	62.533	71.110
2000	9.081	17.205	62.973	71.576
2100	9.093	18.113	63.394	72.019
2200	9.104	19.023	63.795	72.442
2300	9.115	19.934	64.180	72.847
2400	9.126	20.846	64.549	73.235
2500	9.137	21.759	64.904	73.608
2600	9.147	22.673	65.246	73.967
2700	9.157	23.589	65.575	74.312
2800	9.167	24.505	65.893	74.645
2900	9.177	25.422	66.201	74.967
3000	9.187	26.340	66.498	75.278
3200	9.206	28.180	67.066	75.872
3400	9.225	30.023	67.600	76.431
3600	9.244	31.870	68.106	76.958
3800	9.262	33.720	68.585	77.459
4000	9.281	35.575	69.041	77.934
4200	9.299	37.433	69.475	78.388
4400	9.317	39.294	69.890	78.821
4600	9.335	41.160	70.287	79.235
4800	9.353	43.028	70.669	79.633
5000	9.371	44.901	71.035	80.015
5200	9.389	46.777	71.387	80.383
5400	9.406	48.656	71.727	80.737
5600	9.424	50.539	72.055	81.080
5800	9.442	52.426	72.372	81.411
6000	9.459	54.316	72.679	81.731

Appendix 3.9   THERMODYNAMIC PROPERTIES OF BBR GAS

T	C_P^0	$(H^0 - H_0^0)$	$-(F^0 - H_0^0)/T$	S_T^0
DEG-K	CAL/MOLE DEG-K	KCAL/MOLE	CAL/MOLE DEG-K	CAL/MOLE DEG-K
100	6.969	0.696	38.888	45.846
200	7.330	1.407	43.725	50.758
273.15	7.726	1.958	45.936	53.103
298.15	7.846	2.152	46.566	53.785
400	8.223	2.972	48.717	56.147
500	8.457	3.807	50.395	58.009
600	8.609	4.661	51.798	59.565
700	8.712	5.527	53.005	60.901
800	8.786	6.402	54.067	62.069
900	8.841	7.284	55.014	63.107
1000	8.885	8.170	55.871	64.041
1100	8.919	9.060	56.653	64.890
1200	8.949	9.954	57.372	65.667
1300	8.973	10.850	58.038	66.384
1400	8.995	11.748	58.659	67.050
1500	9.015	12.649	59.239	67.671
1600	9.033	13.551	59.784	68.254
1700	9.049	14.455	60.299	68.802
1800	9.064	15.361	60.786	69.320
1900	9.079	16.268	61.248	69.810
2000	9.092	17.177	61.688	70.276
2100	9.105	18.086	62.107	70.720
2200	9.118	18.998	62.509	71.144
2300	9.130	19.910	62.893	71.549
2400	9.142	20.824	63.262	71.938
2500	9.154	21.738	63.616	72.312
2600	9.165	22.654	63.958	72.671
2700	9.176	23.571	64.287	73.017
2800	9.187	24.490	64.605	73.351
2900	9.198	25.409	64.912	73.674
3000	9.209	26.329	65.209	73.986
3200	9.230	28.173	65.776	74.581
3400	9.250	30.021	66.311	75.141
3600	9.271	31.873	66.816	75.670
3800	9.291	33.729	67.296	76.172
4000	9.311	35.590	67.751	76.649
4200	9.331	37.454	68.186	77.104
4400	9.351	39.322	68.601	77.538
4600	9.370	41.194	68.999	77.954
4800	9.390	43.070	69.381	78.353
5000	9.409	44.950	69.747	78.737
5200	9.429	46.834	70.100	79.107
5400	9.448	48.721	70.440	79.463
5600	9.467	50.613	70.769	79.807
5800	9.486	52.508	71.086	80.139
6000	9.506	54.407	71.393	80.461

THERMODYNAMIC PROPERTIES OF BCL   GAS

T	C_P^0	$(H^0 - H_T^0)$	$-(F^0 - H_T^0)/T$	S_T^0
DEG-K	CAL/MOLE DEG-K	KCAL/MOLE	CAL/MOLE DEG-K	CAL/MOLE DEG-K
100	6.959	0.696	36.221	43.177
200	7.144	1.398	41.048	48.036
273.15	7.461	1.931	43.237	50.308
298.15	7.574	2.119	43.858	50.967
400	7.974	2.912	45.971	53.251
500	8.254	3.725	47.614	55.063
600	8.447	4.560	48.985	56.586
700	8.583	5.412	50.167	57.899
800	8.681	6.276	51.207	59.052
900	8.755	7.147	52.137	60.078
1000	8.813	8.026	52.978	61.004
1100	8.859	8.910	53.747	61.846
1200	8.896	9.797	54.454	62.619
1300	8.928	10.689	55.110	63.332
1400	8.956	11.583	55.721	63.995
1500	8.980	12.480	56.294	64.613
1600	9.002	13.379	56.832	65.194
1700	9.021	14.280	57.340	65.740
1800	9.039	15.183	57.821	66.256
1900	9.056	16.088	58.278	66.745
2000	9.072	16.994	58.713	67.210
2100	9.086	17.902	59.128	67.653
2200	9.100	18.811	59.526	68.076
2300	9.114	19.722	59.906	68.481
2400	9.127	20.634	60.272	68.869
2500	9.140	21.548	60.623	69.242
2600	9.152	22.462	60.962	69.601
2700	9.164	23.378	61.288	69.946
2800	9.175	24.295	61.603	70.280
2900	9.187	25.213	61.908	70.602
3000	9.198	26.132	62.203	70.914
3200	9.220	27.974	62.766	71.508
3400	9.242	29.820	63.297	72.068
3600	9.263	31.671	63.799	72.596
3800	9.283	33.525	64.275	73.098
4000	9.304	35.384	64.729	73.575
4200	9.324	37.247	65.161	74.029
4400	9.344	39.114	65.574	74.463
4600	9.364	40.984	65.969	74.879
4800	9.384	42.859	66.349	75.278
5000	9.403	44.738	66.714	75.661
5200	9.423	46.620	67.065	76.031
5400	9.442	48.507	67.404	76.387
5600	9.462	50.397	67.731	76.730
5800	9.481	52.292	68.047	77.063
6000	9.500	54.190	68.353	77.384

Appendix 3.11   THERMODYNAMIC PROPERTIES OF BF   GAS

T	C_P^0	$(H^0 - H_0^0)$	$-(F^0 - H_0^0)/T$	S_T^0
DEG-K	CAL/MOLE DEG-K	KCAL/MOLE	CAL/MOLE DEG-K	CAL/MOLE DEG-K
100	6.957	0.696	33.337	40.293
200	6.969	1.392	38.159	45.117
273.15	7.035	1.903	40.329	47.297
298.15	7.076	2.080	40.939	47.914
400	7.315	2.812	42.996	50.025
500	7.589	3.557	44.573	51.687
600	7.840	4.329	45.879	53.093
700	8.049	5.123	46.999	54.318
800	8.218	5.937	47.983	55.404
900	8.354	6.766	48.862	56.380
1000	8.463	7.607	49.659	57.266
1100	8.551	8.458	50.388	58.077
1200	8.624	9.317	51.060	58.824
1300	8.685	10.182	51.685	59.517
1400	8.736	11.053	52.267	60.163
1500	8.779	11.929	52.814	60.767
1600	8.817	12.809	53.329	61.335
1700	8.850	13.692	53.816	61.870
1800	8.880	14.579	54.278	62.377
1900	8.906	15.468	54.717	62.858
2000	8.929	16.360	55.135	63.315
2100	8.951	17.254	55.535	63.751
2200	8.970	18.150	55.918	64.168
2300	8.989	19.048	56.286	64.567
2400	9.006	19.948	56.639	64.950
2500	9.021	20.849	56.979	65.318
2600	9.036	21.752	57.306	65.672
2700	9.050	22.656	57.622	66.014
2800	9.064	23.562	57.928	66.343
2900	9.077	24.469	58.224	66.661
3000	9.089	25.377	58.510	66.969
3200	9.112	27.198	59.057	67.557
3400	9.134	29.022	59.574	68.110
3600	9.155	30.851	60.063	68.632
3800	9.175	32.684	60.527	69.128
4000	9.194	34.521	60.969	69.599
4200	9.212	36.362	61.390	70.048
4400	9.230	38.206	61.794	70.477
4600	9.248	40.054	62.180	70.888
4800	9.265	41.905	62.551	71.282
5000	9.282	43.760	62.908	71.660
5200	9.298	45.618	63.252	72.024
5400	9.315	47.479	63.583	72.376
5600	9.331	49.343	63.903	72.715
5800	9.347	51.211	64.213	73.042
6000	9.363	53.082	64.513	73.360

Appendix 3.12 THERMODYNAMIC PROPERTIES OF BH GAS

T	C_P^0	$(H^0 - H_0^0)$	$-(F^0 - H_0^0)/T$	S_T^0
DEG-K	CAL/MOLE DEG-K	KCAL/MOLE	CAL/MOLE DEG-K	CAL/MOLE DEG-K
100	6.955	0.696	26.482	33.437
200	6.965	1.392	31.308	38.268
273.15	6.971	1.902	33.477	40.440
298.15	6.974	2.076	34.087	41.050
400	7.014	2.788	36.134	43.104
500	7.109	3.494	37.691	44.679
600	7.253	4.211	38.968	45.987
700	7.423	4.945	40.053	47.117
800	7.600	5.696	41.000	48.120
900	7.771	6.465	41.842	49.025
1000	7.928	7.250	42.602	49.852
1100	8.069	8.050	43.296	50.615
1200	8.196	8.863	43.936	51.322
1300	8.307	9.689	44.530	51.983
1400	8.407	10.524	45.085	52.602
1500	8.495	11.369	45.605	53.185
1600	8.573	12.223	46.097	53.736
1700	8.643	13.084	46.561	54.258
1800	8.707	13.951	47.003	54.754
1900	8.764	14.825	47.423	55.226
2000	8.816	15.704	47.825	55.677
2100	8.864	16.588	48.209	56.108
2200	8.908	17.477	48.578	56.522
2300	8.949	18.370	48.932	56.918
2400	8.987	19.266	49.272	57.300
2500	9.023	20.167	49.601	57.668
2600	9.056	21.071	49.918	58.022
2700	9.088	21.978	50.225	58.365
2800	9.117	22.888	50.521	58.696
2900	9.146	23.802	50.809	59.016
3000	9.173	24.718	51.087	59.327
3200	9.224	26.557	51.621	59.920
3400	9.272	28.407	52.126	60.481
3600	9.316	30.266	52.605	61.012
3800	9.359	32.133	53.061	61.517
4000	9.399	34.009	53.496	61.998
4200	9.438	35.893	53.912	62.458
4400	9.475	37.784	54.310	62.898
4600	9.512	39.683	54.693	63.320
4800	9.547	41.589	55.061	63.725
5000	9.582	43.502	55.415	64.116
5200	9.616	45.422	55.757	64.492
5400	9.650	47.348	56.087	64.856
5600	9.682	49.282	56.407	65.207
5800	9.715	51.221	56.716	65.548
6000	9.747	53.168	57.016	65.877

T	C_P^0	$(H^0 - H_0^0)$	$-(F^0 - H_0^0)/T$	S_T^0
DEG-K	CAL/MOLE DEG-K	KCAL/MOLE	CAL/MOLE DEG-K	CAL/MOLE DEG-K
100	6.957	0.696	36.161	43.117
200	6.964	1.391	40.983	47.940
273.15	7.008	1.902	43.152	50.116
298.15	7.039	2.078	43.762	50.731
400	7.237	2.804	45.815	52.825
500	7.489	3.540	47.386	54.466
600	7.735	4.301	48.685	55.854
700	7.949	5.086	49.797	57.063
800	8.127	5.890	50.774	58.136
900	8.272	6.710	51.646	59.102
1000	8.390	7.544	52.436	59.980
1100	8.487	8.388	53.159	60.784
1200	8.568	9.241	53.826	61.527
1300	8.635	10.101	54.445	62.215
1400	8.692	10.967	55.023	62.857
1500	8.740	11.839	55.566	63.458
1600	8.783	12.715	56.077	64.024
1700	8.819	13.595	56.560	64.558
1800	8.852	14.479	57.019	65.063
1900	8.881	15.365	57.455	65.542
2000	8.907	16.255	57.871	65.998
2100	8.931	17.147	58.268	66.433
2200	8.953	18.041	58.649	66.849
2300	8.973	18.937	59.014	67.248
2400	8.991	19.835	59.365	67.630
2500	9.008	20.735	59.703	67.997
2600	9.025	21.637	60.029	68.351
2700	9.040	22.540	60.344	68.692
2800	9.055	23.445	60.648	69.021
2900	9.068	24.351	60.942	69.339
3000	9.082	25.259	61.227	69.647
3200	9.107	27.078	61.772	70.233
3400	9.130	28.901	62.286	70.786
3600	9.152	30.730	62.773	71.309
3800	9.173	32.562	63.235	71.804
4000	9.193	34.399	63.675	72.275
4200	9.212	36.239	64.096	72.724
4400	9.231	38.083	64.498	73.153
4600	9.249	39.931	64.883	73.564
4800	9.267	41.783	65.253	73.958
5000	9.285	43.638	65.609	74.337
5200	9.302	45.497	65.952	74.701
5400	9.319	47.359	66.282	75.052
5600	9.336	49.225	66.602	75.392
5800	9.352	51.093	66.910	75.720
6000	9.369	52.966	67.209	76.037

Appendix 3.14 THERMODYNAMIC PROPERTIES OF BO GAS

T	C_P^0	$(H^0 - H_T^0)$	$-(F^0 - H_T^0)/T$	S_T^0
DEG-K	CAL/MOLE DEG-K	KCAL/MOLE	CAL/MOLE DEG-K	CAL/MOLE DEG-K
100	6.956	0.696	34.070	41.026
200	6.958	1.391	38.891	45.848
273.15	6.969	1.901	41.060	48.018
298.15	6.979	2.075	41.669	48.629
400	7.071	2.790	43.716	50.690
500	7.235	3.505	45.276	52.285
600	7.434	4.238	46.558	53.621
700	7.634	4.991	47.652	54.782
800	7.818	5.764	48.609	55.814
900	7.978	6.554	49.462	56.744
1000	8.115	7.359	50.233	57.592
1100	8.232	8.176	50.938	58.371
1200	8.330	9.005	51.588	59.092
1300	8.414	9.842	52.191	59.762
1400	8.485	10.687	52.755	60.388
1500	8.546	11.539	53.283	60.976
1600	8.599	12.396	53.782	61.529
1700	8.645	13.258	54.253	62.052
1800	8.685	14.125	54.700	62.547
1900	8.721	14.995	55.125	63.018
2000	8.752	15.869	55.531	63.466
2100	8.780	16.746	55.919	63.893
2200	8.805	17.625	56.291	64.303
2300	8.828	18.507	56.648	64.694
2400	8.849	19.390	56.991	65.071
2500	8.868	20.276	57.322	65.432
2600	8.885	21.164	57.640	65.780
2700	8.902	22.053	57.948	66.116
2800	8.917	22.944	58.246	66.440
2900	8.931	23.837	58.534	66.753
3000	8.944	24.730	58.813	67.056
3200	8.967	26.521	59.346	67.634
3400	8.989	28.317	59.850	68.178
3600	9.008	30.117	60.327	68.693
3800	9.026	31.920	60.780	69.180
4000	9.043	33.727	61.212	69.644
4200	9.058	35.537	61.624	70.085
4400	9.073	37.350	62.018	70.507
4600	9.086	39.166	62.396	70.911
4800	9.100	40.985	62.759	71.298
5000	9.112	42.806	63.108	71.669
5200	9.125	44.630	63.444	72.027
5400	9.137	46.456	63.769	72.372
5600	9.148	48.284	64.082	72.704
5800	9.159	50.115	64.385	73.025
6000	9.170	51.948	64.678	73.336

Appendix 3.15   THERMODYNAMIC PROPERTIES OF BS   GAS

T	C_P^0	$(H^0 - H_0^0)$	$-(F^0 - H_0^0)/T$	S_T^0
DEG-K	CAL/MOLE DEG-K	KCAL/MOLE	CAL/MOLE DEG-K	CAL/MOLE DEG-K
100	6.957	0.696	37.070	44.026
200	6.991	1.392	41.892	48.853
273.15	7.125	1.908	44.065	51.049
298.15	7.193	2.087	44.677	51.676
400	7.515	2.835	46.745	53.834
500	7.816	3.602	48.339	55.544
600	8.060	4.397	49.663	56.991
700	8.248	5.213	50.802	58.249
800	8.392	6.045	51.804	59.360
900	8.503	6.890	52.700	60.355
1000	8.589	7.745	53.511	61.256
1100	8.658	8.607	54.253	62.078
1200	8.714	9.476	54.937	62.833
1300	8.760	10.350	55.571	63.533
1400	8.799	11.228	56.164	64.183
1500	8.832	12.109	56.719	64.792
1600	8.860	12.994	57.241	65.363
1700	8.884	13.881	57.735	65.900
1800	8.906	14.771	58.203	66.409
1900	8.926	15.662	58.648	66.891
2000	8.943	16.556	59.071	67.349
2100	8.959	17.451	59.476	67.786
2200	8.974	18.348	59.863	68.203
2300	8.987	19.246	60.235	68.602
2400	9.000	20.145	60.591	68.985
2500	9.012	21.046	60.934	69.353
2600	9.023	21.947	61.265	69.706
2700	9.033	22.850	61.584	70.047
2800	9.044	23.754	61.892	70.376
2900	9.053	24.659	62.190	70.693
3000	9.062	25.565	62.479	71.000
3200	9.080	27.379	63.030	71.586
3400	9.097	29.197	63.550	72.137
3600	9.112	31.017	64.041	72.657
3800	9.127	32.841	64.508	73.150
4000	9.142	34.668	64.952	73.619
4200	9.156	36.498	65.375	74.065
4400	9.170	38.331	65.780	74.491
4600	9.183	40.166	66.168	74.899
4800	9.196	42.004	66.540	75.290
5000	9.209	43.845	66.897	75.666
5200	9.222	45.688	67.241	76.028
5400	9.235	47.534	67.573	76.376
5600	9.248	49.382	67.894	76.712
5800	9.260	51.233	68.203	77.037
6000	9.272	53.086	68.503	77.351

Appendix 3.16   THERMODYNAMIC PROPERTIES OF B2   GAS

T	C_P^0	$(H^0 - H_0^0)/T$	$-(F^0 - H_0^0)/T$	S_T^0
DEG-K	CAL/MOLE DEG-K	KCAL/MOLE	CAL/MOLE DEG-K	CAL/MOLE DEG-K
100	6.958	0.696	33.625	40.582
200	7.026	1.393	38.449	45.416
273.15	7.223	1.914	40.625	47.632
298.15	7.310	2.095	41.240	48.268
400	7.680	2.859	43.321	50.469
500	7.988	3.643	44.931	52.217
600	8.223	4.454	46.271	53.695
700	8.398	5.286	47.425	54.976
800	8.529	6.132	48.441	56.106
900	8.630	6.990	49.350	57.117
1000	8.709	7.857	50.173	58.031
1100	8.773	8.732	50.926	58.864
1200	8.825	9.612	51.620	59.629
1300	8.869	10.496	52.263	60.337
1400	8.906	11.385	52.864	60.996
1500	8.939	12.277	53.427	61.612
1600	8.967	13.173	53.957	62.190
1700	8.993	14.071	54.457	62.734
1800	9.017	14.971	54.931	63.249
1900	9.038	15.874	55.382	63.737
2000	9.058	16.779	55.811	64.201
2100	9.077	17.686	56.222	64.643
2200	9.094	18.594	56.614	65.066
2300	9.111	19.504	56.990	65.471
2400	9.127	20.416	57.352	65.859
2500	9.142	21.330	57.700	66.232
2600	9.157	22.245	58.035	66.590
2700	9.171	23.161	58.358	66.936
2800	9.185	24.079	58.670	67.270
2900	9.199	24.998	58.973	67.593
3000	9.212	25.919	59.265	67.905
3200	9.238	27.764	59.824	68.500
3400	9.263	29.614	60.351	69.061
3600	9.287	31.469	60.850	69.591
3800	9.310	33.328	61.323	70.094
4000	9.334	35.193	61.774	70.572
4200	9.357	37.062	62.204	71.028
4400	9.379	38.935	62.615	71.464
4600	9.402	40.814	63.009	71.881
4800	9.424	42.696	63.387	72.282
5000	9.446	44.583	63.750	72.667
5200	9.468	46.474	64.100	73.038
5400	9.489	48.370	64.438	73.395
5600	9.511	50.270	64.764	73.741
5800	9.532	52.174	65.079	74.075
6000	9.554	54.083	65.385	74.399

Appendix 3.17   THERMODYNAMIC PROPERTIES OF BECL GAS

T	C_P^0	$(H^0 - H_T^0)$	$-(F^0 - H_T^0)/T$	S_T^0
DEG-K	CAL/MOLE DEG-K	KCAL/MOLE	CAL/MOLE DEG-K	CAL/MOLE DEG-K
100	6.959	0.696	37.254	44.210
200	7.138	1.397	42.081	49.068
273.15	7.450	1.931	44.269	51.337
298.15	7.563	2.118	44.890	51.995
400	7.963	2.910	47.001	54.276
500	8.245	3.721	48.643	56.085
600	8.439	4.556	50.013	57.606
700	8.576	5.407	51.194	58.918
800	8.676	6.270	52.233	60.070
900	8.751	7.141	53.162	61.097
1000	8.809	8.020	54.002	62.022
1100	8.856	8.903	54.770	62.864
1200	8.894	9.790	55.477	63.636
1300	8.926	10.681	56.133	64.349
1400	8.954	11.576	56.743	65.012
1500	8.978	12.472	57.315	65.630
1600	9.000	13.371	57.853	66.210
1700	9.020	14.272	58.361	66.757
1800	9.038	15.175	58.842	67.273
1900	9.055	16.080	59.299	67.762
2000	9.071	16.986	59.734	68.227
2100	9.086	17.894	60.149	68.670
2200	9.100	18.803	60.546	69.093
2300	9.114	19.714	60.926	69.497
2400	9.127	20.626	61.292	69.886
2500	9.139	21.539	61.643	70.258
2600	9.152	22.454	61.981	70.617
2700	9.164	23.369	62.307	70.963
2800	9.175	24.286	62.623	71.296
2900	9.187	25.205	62.927	71.618
3000	9.198	26.124	63.222	71.930
3200	9.220	27.966	63.785	72.524
3400	9.242	29.812	64.316	73.084
3600	9.263	31.662	64.818	73.613
3800	9.284	33.517	65.294	74.114
4000	9.304	35.376	65.747	74.591
4200	9.324	37.239	66.179	75.045
4400	9.344	39.105	66.592	75.480
4600	9.364	40.976	66.988	75.895
4800	9.384	42.851	67.367	76.294
5000	9.404	44.730	67.732	76.678
5200	9.423	46.613	68.083	77.047
5400	9.443	48.499	68.422	77.403
5600	9.462	50.390	68.749	77.747
5800	9.482	52.284	69.065	78.079
6000	9.501	54.182	69.371	78.401

Appendix 3.18 THERMODYNAMIC PROPERTIES OF BEF GAS

T	C_P^0	$(H^0 - H_0^0)$	$-(F^0 - H_0^0)/T$	S_T^0
DEG-K	CAL/MOLE DEG-K	KCAL/MOLE	CAL/MOLE DEG-K	CAL/MOLE DEG-K
100	6.957	0.696	34.559	41.515
200	6.980	1.392	39.381	46.341
273.15	7.083	1.906	41.553	48.529
298.15	7.140	2.083	42.164	49.152
400	7.431	2.825	44.227	51.289
500	7.726	3.583	45.814	52.980
600	7.977	4.369	47.130	54.411
700	8.177	5.177	48.261	55.657
800	8.334	6.003	49.256	56.759
900	8.456	6.842	50.145	57.748
1000	8.554	7.693	50.951	58.644
1100	8.632	8.552	51.688	59.463
1200	8.696	9.419	52.368	60.217
1300	8.750	10.291	52.999	60.916
1400	8.795	11.169	53.588	61.566
1500	8.833	12.050	54.140	62.174
1600	8.867	12.935	54.660	62.745
1700	8.896	13.823	55.152	63.283
1800	8.922	14.714	55.618	63.793
1900	8.946	15.608	56.061	64.276
2000	8.967	16.503	56.483	64.735
2100	8.987	17.401	56.887	65.173
2200	9.005	18.301	57.273	65.592
2300	9.022	19.202	57.644	65.992
2400	9.037	20.105	57.999	66.377
2500	9.052	21.009	58.342	66.746
2600	9.066	21.915	58.672	67.101
2700	9.080	22.823	58.991	67.444
2800	9.093	23.731	59.298	67.774
2900	9.105	24.641	59.596	68.093
3000	9.117	25.552	59.885	68.402
3200	9.139	27.378	60.436	68.991
3400	9.161	29.208	60.955	69.546
3600	9.182	31.042	61.447	70.070
3800	9.201	32.881	61.914	70.567
4000	9.221	34.723	62.359	71.040
4200	9.239	36.569	62.783	71.490
4400	9.258	38.418	63.189	71.920
4600	9.276	40.272	63.577	72.332
4800	9.293	42.129	63.950	72.727
5000	9.311	43.989	64.309	73.107
5200	9.328	45.853	64.655	73.472
5400	9.345	47.720	64.988	73.825
5600	9.362	49.591	65.309	74.165
5800	9.379	51.465	65.620	74.494
6000	9.395	53.342	65.922	74.812

Appendix 3.19   THERMODYNAMIC PROPERTIES OF BEH   GAS

T	C_P^0	$(H^0 - H_0^0)$	$-(F^0 - H_0^0)/T$	S_T^0
DEG-K	CAL/MOLE DEG-K	KCAL/MOLE	CAL/MOLE DEG-K	CAL/MOLE DEG-K
100	6.961	0.696	27.667	34.626
200	6.967	1.392	32.491	39.452
273.15	6.977	1.902	34.661	41.625
298.15	6.985	2.077	35.271	42.236
400	7.060	2.791	37.320	44.298
500	7.205	3.504	38.879	45.887
600	7.393	4.234	40.161	47.217
700	7.593	4.983	41.253	48.372
800	7.785	5.752	42.209	49.398
900	7.959	6.539	43.060	50.326
1000	8.112	7.343	43.829	51.172
1100	8.246	8.161	44.533	51.952
1200	8.362	8.992	45.181	52.674
1300	8.463	9.833	45.784	53.348
1400	8.551	10.684	46.347	53.978
1500	8.629	11.543	46.876	54.571
1600	8.698	12.409	47.374	55.130
1700	8.759	13.282	47.846	55.659
1800	8.814	14.161	48.294	56.162
1900	8.864	15.045	48.721	56.639
2000	8.909	15.934	49.129	57.095
2100	8.951	16.827	49.518	57.531
2200	8.989	17.724	49.892	57.948
2300	9.025	18.624	50.251	58.349
2400	9.059	19.529	50.597	58.734
2500	9.090	20.436	50.930	59.104
2600	9.120	21.347	51.251	59.461
2700	9.148	22.260	51.561	59.806
2800	9.175	23.176	51.862	60.139
2900	9.200	24.095	52.153	60.461
3000	9.225	25.016	52.435	60.774
3200	9.272	26.866	52.975	61.371
3400	9.315	28.725	53.486	61.934
3600	9.357	30.592	53.970	62.468
3800	9.396	32.467	54.431	62.975
4000	9.435	34.350	54.870	63.458
4200	9.472	36.241	55.290	63.919
4400	9.507	38.139	55.692	64.360
4600	9.542	40.044	56.078	64.784
4800	9.577	41.956	56.450	65.190
5000	9.610	43.874	56.807	65.582
5200	9.644	45.800	57.152	65.960
5400	9.676	47.732	57.485	66.324
5600	9.709	49.670	57.807	66.677
5800	9.741	51.615	58.119	67.018
6000	9.772	53.567	58.421	67.349

Appendix 3.20 THERMODYNAMIC PROPERTIES OF BEH+ GAS

T	C_P^0	$(H^0 - H_0^0)$	$-(F^0 - H_0^0)/T$	S_T^0
DEG-K	CAL/MOLE DEG-K	KCAL/MOLE	CAL/MOLE DEG-K	CAL/MOLE DEG-K
100	6.955	0.696	26.193	33.148
200	6.965	1.392	31.019	37.979
273.15	6.972	1.902	33.189	40.151
298.15	6.977	2.076	33.798	40.762
400	7.030	2.789	35.846	42.818
500	7.144	3.497	37.404	44.398
600	7.307	4.219	38.682	45.714
700	7.490	4.959	39.770	46.854
800	7.674	5.718	40.720	47.867
900	7.845	6.494	41.566	48.781
1000	8.000	7.286	42.329	49.615
1100	8.138	8.093	43.027	50.384
1200	8.259	8.913	43.670	51.098
1300	8.365	9.744	44.268	51.763
1400	8.458	10.585	44.825	52.387
1500	8.540	11.435	45.349	52.973
1600	8.613	12.293	45.843	53.526
1700	8.678	13.158	46.311	54.051
1800	8.736	14.029	46.755	54.548
1900	8.789	14.905	47.177	55.022
2000	8.837	15.786	47.581	55.474
2100	8.881	16.672	47.967	55.906
2200	8.921	17.562	48.338	56.320
2300	8.958	18.456	48.693	56.718
2400	8.993	19.354	49.036	57.100
2500	9.025	20.255	49.366	57.468
2600	9.056	21.159	49.684	57.822
2700	9.084	22.066	49.992	58.164
2800	9.112	22.975	50.290	58.495
2900	9.137	23.888	50.578	58.815
3000	9.162	24.803	50.858	59.126
3200	9.209	26.640	51.393	59.718
3400	9.252	28.486	51.900	60.278
3600	9.293	30.341	52.380	60.808
3800	9.332	32.203	52.837	61.312
4000	9.369	34.073	53.273	61.791
4200	9.404	35.951	53.689	62.249
4400	9.438	37.835	54.089	62.687
4600	9.472	39.726	54.472	63.108
4800	9.504	41.624	54.840	63.512
5000	9.536	43.528	55.195	63.900
5200	9.567	45.438	55.537	64.275
5400	9.598	47.355	55.867	64.636
5600	9.628	49.277	56.187	64.986
5800	9.658	51.206	56.496	65.324
6000	9.688	53.141	56.796	65.652

Appendix 3.21 THERMODYNAMIC PROPERTIES OF BEO GAS

T	C_P^0	$(H^0 - H_0^0)$	$-(F^0 - H_0^0)/T$	S_T^0
DEG-K	CAL/MOLE DEG-K	KCAL/MOLE	CAL/MOLE DEG-K	CAL/MOLE DEG-K
100	6.957	0.696	32.637	39.593
200	6.965	1.392	37.459	44.416
273.15	7.014	1.902	39.628	46.593
298.15	7.046	2.078	40.238	47.208
400	7.254	2.806	42.292	49.306
500	7.510	3.544	43.864	50.952
600	7.757	4.307	45.164	52.343
700	7.969	5.094	46.278	53.555
800	8.145	5.900	47.256	54.631
900	8.287	6.722	48.131	55.599
1000	8.402	7.556	48.922	56.478
1100	8.497	8.401	49.646	57.284
1200	8.575	9.255	50.314	58.026
1300	8.640	10.116	50.934	58.715
1400	8.695	10.983	51.513	59.358
1500	8.741	11.855	52.056	59.959
1600	8.782	12.731	52.568	60.525
1700	8.817	13.611	53.052	61.058
1800	8.848	14.494	53.511	61.563
1900	8.876	15.380	53.947	62.042
2000	8.901	16.269	54.364	62.498
2100	8.924	17.160	54.761	62.933
2200	8.944	18.054	55.142	63.349
2300	8.963	18.949	55.508	63.747
2400	8.981	19.846	55.859	64.128
2500	8.997	20.745	56.197	64.495
2600	9.012	21.646	56.523	64.849
2700	9.027	22.548	56.838	65.189
2800	9.041	23.451	57.142	65.518
2900	9.054	24.356	57.436	65.835
3000	9.066	25.262	57.722	66.142
3200	9.089	27.077	58.266	66.728
3400	9.111	28.897	58.780	67.280
3600	9.132	30.722	59.267	67.801
3800	9.151	32.550	59.730	68.295
4000	9.170	34.382	60.170	68.765
4200	9.188	36.218	60.590	69.213
4400	9.205	38.057	60.991	69.641
4600	9.222	39.900	61.377	70.050
4800	9.239	41.746	61.746	70.443
5000	9.255	43.595	62.102	70.821
5200	9.271	45.448	62.444	71.184
5400	9.286	47.304	62.774	71.534
5600	9.302	49.162	63.093	71.872
5800	9.317	51.024	63.402	72.199
6000	9.332	52.889	63.700	72.515

Appendix 3.22   THERMODYNAMIC PROPERTIES OF BRCL GAS

T	C_P^0	$(H^0 - H_0^0)$	$-(F^0 - H_0^0)/T$	S_T^0
DEG-K	CAL/MOLE DEG-K	KCAL/MOLE	CAL/MOLE DEG-K	CAL/MOLE DEG-K
100	7.101	0.698	41.947	48.926
200	7.885	1.447	46.852	54.089
273.15	8.271	2.040	49.142	56.609
298.15	8.363	2.248	49.799	57.337
400	8.612	3.113	52.050	59.834
500	8.745	3.982	53.808	61.771
600	8.826	4.861	55.272	63.373
700	8.881	5.746	56.529	64.738
800	8.921	6.636	57.631	65.927
900	8.952	7.530	58.613	66.979
1000	8.977	8.426	59.497	67.924
1100	8.998	9.325	60.303	68.780
1200	9.017	10.226	61.042	69.564
1300	9.033	11.128	61.726	70.286
1400	9.049	12.033	62.362	70.956
1500	9.063	12.938	62.956	71.581
1600	9.077	13.845	63.513	72.167
1700	9.090	14.753	64.039	72.717
1800	9.102	15.663	64.535	73.237
1900	9.114	16.574	65.006	73.730
2000	9.126	17.486	65.454	74.197
2100	9.137	18.399	65.881	74.643
2200	9.149	19.313	66.289	75.068
2300	9.160	20.229	66.680	75.475
2400	9.171	21.145	67.055	75.865
2500	9.182	22.063	67.415	76.240
2600	9.193	22.982	67.761	76.600
2700	9.203	23.901	68.095	76.947
2800	9.214	24.822	68.417	77.282
2900	9.225	25.744	68.728	77.606
3000	9.235	26.667	69.030	77.919
3200	9.256	28.516	69.604	78.515
3400	9.277	30.370	70.145	79.077
3600	9.297	32.227	70.656	79.608
3800	9.318	34.089	71.140	80.111
4000	9.338	35.954	71.601	80.590
4200	9.359	37.824	72.040	81.046
4400	9.379	39.698	72.459	81.482
4600	9.399	41.576	72.861	81.899
4800	9.420	43.457	73.246	82.299
5000	9.440	45.343	73.616	82.684
5200	9.460	47.233	73.972	83.055
5400	9.480	49.127	74.315	83.412
5600	9.500	51.026	74.646	83.757
5800	9.521	52.928	74.966	84.091
6000	9.541	54.834	75.275	84.414

Appendix 3.23 THERMODYNAMIC PROPERTIES OF BRF GAS

T	C_p^0	$(H^0 - H_0^0)_T$	$-(F^0 - H_0^0)/T$	S_T^0
DEG-K	CAL/MOLE DEG-K	KCAL/MOLE	CAL/MOLE DEG-K	CAL/MOLE DEG-K
100	6.970	0.696	39.781	46.738
200	7.352	1.408	44.620	51.658
273.15	7.755	1.961	46.833	54.011
298.15	7.876	2.156	47.464	54.695
400	8.252	2.979	49.619	57.066
500	8.484	3.817	51.302	58.935
600	8.635	4.673	52.708	60.496
700	8.737	5.542	53.918	61.835
800	8.812	6.419	54.983	63.007
900	8.868	7.304	55.933	64.048
1000	8.912	8.193	56.792	64.985
1100	8.948	9.086	57.576	65.836
1200	8.979	9.982	58.297	66.616
1300	9.005	10.881	58.965	67.336
1400	9.029	11.783	59.587	68.004
1500	9.050	12.687	60.170	68.627
1600	9.070	13.593	60.717	69.212
1700	9.088	14.501	61.233	69.763
1800	9.105	15.411	61.721	70.283
1900	9.122	16.322	62.185	70.775
2000	9.137	17.235	62.626	71.244
2100	9.153	18.149	63.047	71.690
2200	9.167	19.065	63.450	72.116
2300	9.182	19.983	63.836	72.524
2400	9.196	20.902	64.206	72.915
2500	9.209	21.822	64.562	73.290
2600	9.223	22.744	64.904	73.652
2700	9.236	23.666	65.235	74.000
2800	9.249	24.591	65.554	74.336
2900	9.262	25.516	65.862	74.661
3000	9.275	26.443	66.161	74.975
3200	9.300	28.301	66.731	75.575
3400	9.325	30.163	67.268	76.139
3600	9.350	32.031	67.776	76.673
3800	9.375	33.903	68.257	77.179
4000	9.399	35.781	68.716	77.661
4200	9.423	37.663	69.153	78.120
4400	9.447	39.550	69.570	78.559
4600	9.471	41.442	69.970	78.979
4800	9.495	43.338	70.354	79.383
5000	9.519	45.240	70.723	79.771
5200	9.543	47.146	71.078	80.145
5400	9.566	49.057	71.421	80.505
5600	9.590	50.972	71.751	80.854
5800	9.614	52.893	72.071	81.191
6000	9.637	54.818	72.381	81.517

Appendix 3.24   THERMODYNAMIC PROPERTIES OF BR2 GAS

T	C_P^0	$(H^0 - H_0^0)/T$	$-(F^0 - H_0^0)/T$	S_T^0
DEG-K	CAL/MOLE DEG-K	KCAL/MOLE	CAL/MOLE DEG-K	CAL/MOLE DEG-K
100	7.385	0.705	42.793	49.841
200	8.268	1.493	47.804	55.270
273.15	8.554	2.110	50.171	57.895
298.15	8.616	2.324	50.851	58.647
400	8.775	3.211	53.176	61.204
500	8.857	4.093	54.986	63.172
600	8.908	4.981	56.489	64.791
700	8.944	5.874	57.776	66.167
800	8.970	6.770	58.901	67.363
900	8.992	7.668	59.901	68.421
1000	9.011	8.568	60.801	69.370
1100	9.027	9.470	61.620	70.229
1200	9.042	10.374	62.371	71.015
1300	9.056	11.279	63.064	71.740
1400	9.069	12.185	63.708	72.411
1500	9.082	13.092	64.309	73.038
1600	9.094	14.001	64.873	73.624
1700	9.106	14.911	65.404	74.176
1800	9.118	15.822	65.906	74.697
1900	9.129	16.735	66.382	75.190
2000	9.141	17.648	66.834	75.658
2100	9.152	18.563	67.265	76.105
2200	9.163	19.479	67.677	76.531
2300	9.174	20.396	68.071	76.938
2400	9.185	21.313	68.448	77.329
2500	9.196	22.232	68.811	77.704
2600	9.206	23.153	69.160	78.065
2700	9.217	24.074	69.496	78.413
2800	9.228	24.996	69.821	78.748
2900	9.238	25.919	70.134	79.072
3000	9.249	26.844	70.437	79.385
3200	9.270	28.696	71.016	79.983
3400	9.291	30.552	71.560	80.546
3600	9.312	32.412	72.074	81.077
3800	9.333	34.277	72.561	81.581
4000	9.354	36.146	73.024	82.061
4200	9.375	38.019	73.466	82.518
4400	9.396	39.896	73.887	82.954
4600	9.417	41.777	74.290	83.372
4800	9.438	43.662	74.677	83.774
5000	9.459	45.552	75.049	84.159
5200	9.479	47.446	75.406	84.531
5400	9.500	49.344	75.751	84.889
5600	9.521	51.246	76.084	85.235
5800	9.542	53.152	76.405	85.569
6000	9.563	55.063	76.716	85.893

281

Appendix 3.25 THERMODYNAMIC PROPERTIES OF CCL GAS

T	C_P^0	$(H^0 - H_0^0)$	$-(F^0 - H_0^0)/T$	S_T^0
DEG-K	CAL/MOLE DEG-K	KCAL/MOLE	CAL/MOLE DEG-K	CAL/MOLE DEG-K
100	6.959	0.696	37.873	44.830
200	7.129	1.397	42.700	49.685
273.15	7.433	1.929	44.888	51.951
298.15	7.543	2.116	45.508	52.606
400	7.937	2.906	47.616	54.881
500	8.212	3.714	49.255	56.683
600	8.401	4.545	50.623	58.198
700	8.532	5.392	51.800	59.504
800	8.626	6.250	52.836	60.650
900	8.695	7.117	53.762	61.670
1000	8.747	7.989	54.600	62.589
1100	8.787	8.866	55.365	63.424
1200	8.819	9.746	56.069	64.190
1300	8.845	10.629	56.721	64.897
1400	8.867	11.515	57.329	65.553
1500	8.885	12.403	57.898	66.166
1600	8.901	13.292	58.432	66.740
1700	8.914	14.183	58.937	67.280
1800	8.926	15.075	59.415	67.790
1900	8.937	15.968	59.869	68.273
2000	8.947	16.862	60.300	68.731
2100	8.955	17.757	60.712	69.168
2200	8.963	18.653	61.106	69.585
2300	8.971	19.550	61.484	69.983
2400	8.978	20.447	61.846	70.365
2500	8.984	21.345	62.194	70.732
2600	8.990	22.244	62.529	71.084
2700	8.996	23.143	62.852	71.424
2800	9.002	24.043	63.164	71.751
2900	9.007	24.944	63.466	72.067
3000	9.012	25.845	63.758	72.373
3200	9.022	27.648	64.315	72.954
3400	9.031	29.453	64.839	73.502
3600	9.039	31.260	65.335	74.018
3800	9.048	33.069	65.805	74.507
4000	9.056	34.879	66.252	74.971
4200	9.064	36.691	66.677	75.413
4400	9.071	38.505	67.084	75.835
4600	9.079	40.320	67.473	76.239
4800	9.086	42.136	67.847	76.625
5000	9.093	43.954	68.205	76.996
5200	9.101	45.774	68.550	77.353
5400	9.108	47.594	68.883	77.697
5600	9.115	49.417	69.204	78.028
5800	9.122	51.240	69.513	78.348
6000	9.128	53.065	69.813	78.657

THERMODYNAMIC PROPERTIES OF CF GAS

T	C_P^0	$(H^0 - H_0^0)$	$-(F^0 - H_0^0)/T$	S_T^0
DEG-K	CAL/MOLE DEG-K	KCAL/MOLE	CAL/MOLE DEG-K	CAL/MOLE DEG-K
100	6.957	0.696	36.335	43.292
200	6.976	1.392	41.158	48.117
273.15	7.066	1.905	43.328	50.302
298.15	7.118	2.082	43.939	50.923
400	7.394	2.820	46.000	53.051
500	7.684	3.575	47.584	54.733
600	7.937	4.356	48.897	56.157
700	8.142	5.160	50.024	57.396
800	8.303	5.983	51.016	58.495
900	8.431	6.820	51.902	59.480
1000	8.533	7.668	52.706	60.374
1100	8.615	8.526	53.440	61.191
1200	8.682	9.391	54.118	61.944
1300	8.739	10.262	54.747	62.641
1400	8.786	11.138	55.334	63.290
1500	8.827	12.019	55.885	63.898
1600	8.863	12.903	56.404	64.469
1700	8.894	13.791	56.895	65.007
1800	8.922	14.682	57.360	65.516
1900	8.947	15.576	57.802	65.999
2000	8.969	16.471	58.223	66.459
2100	8.990	17.369	58.626	66.897
2200	9.009	18.269	59.011	67.316
2300	9.027	19.171	59.381	67.716
2400	9.044	20.075	59.737	68.101
2500	9.060	20.980	60.079	68.471
2600	9.075	21.887	60.408	68.826
2700	9.089	22.795	60.726	69.169
2800	9.103	23.705	61.034	69.500
2900	9.116	24.616	61.331	69.819
3000	9.129	25.528	61.619	70.129
3200	9.153	27.356	62.170	70.719
3400	9.176	29.189	62.689	71.274
3600	9.198	31.026	63.181	71.799
3800	9.219	32.868	63.648	72.297
4000	9.240	34.714	64.092	72.771
4200	9.260	36.564	64.516	73.222
4400	9.279	38.418	64.922	73.653
4600	9.299	40.276	65.310	74.066
4800	9.317	42.137	65.684	74.462
5000	9.336	44.003	66.042	74.843
5200	9.354	45.872	66.388	75.209
5400	9.373	47.744	66.721	75.563
5600	9.391	49.621	67.043	75.904
5800	9.409	51.501	67.354	76.234
6000	9.426	53.384	67.656	76.553

Appendix 3.27   THERMODYNAMIC PROPERTIES OF CH   GAS

T	C_P^0	$(H^0 - H_0^0)$	$-(F^0 - H_0^0)/T$	S_T^0
DEG-K	CAL/MOLE DEG-K	KCAL/MOLE	CAL/MOLE DEG-K	CAL/MOLE DEG-K
100	6.955	0.696	29.158	36.113
200	6.963	1.392	33.983	40.943
273.15	6.967	1.901	36.153	43.114
298.15	6.968	2.076	36.762	43.724
400	6.982	2.786	38.808	45.773
500	7.025	3.486	40.363	47.335
600	7.106	4.192	41.635	48.622
700	7.223	4.908	42.714	49.726
800	7.361	5.637	43.653	50.699
900	7.508	6.381	44.485	51.575
1000	7.654	7.139	45.235	52.374
1100	7.794	7.911	45.918	53.110
1200	7.925	8.697	46.546	53.794
1300	8.045	9.496	47.128	54.433
1400	8.154	10.306	47.671	55.033
1500	8.253	11.127	48.181	55.599
1600	8.343	11.956	48.662	56.135
1700	8.424	12.795	49.116	56.643
1800	8.498	13.641	49.548	57.126
1900	8.565	14.494	49.959	57.588
2000	8.626	15.354	50.352	58.029
2100	8.682	16.219	50.727	58.451
2200	8.733	17.090	51.088	58.856
2300	8.781	17.966	51.434	59.245
2400	8.825	18.846	51.767	59.620
2500	8.866	19.731	52.089	59.981
2600	8.904	20.619	52.399	60.329
2700	8.940	21.511	52.699	60.666
2800	8.974	22.407	52.989	60.992
2900	9.006	23.306	53.271	61.307
3000	9.036	24.208	53.544	61.613
3200	9.092	26.021	54.067	62.198
3400	9.143	27.845	54.561	62.751
3600	9.191	29.678	55.031	63.275
3800	9.235	31.521	55.478	63.773
4000	9.277	33.372	55.905	64.248
4200	9.316	35.231	56.313	64.701
4400	9.354	37.099	56.704	65.136
4600	9.390	38.973	57.080	65.552
4800	9.425	40.854	57.441	65.953
5000	9.459	42.743	57.790	66.338
5200	9.491	44.638	58.126	66.710
5400	9.523	46.539	58.450	67.068
5600	9.554	48.447	58.764	67.415
5800	9.585	50.361	59.068	67.751
6000	9.615	52.281	59.363	68.077

Appendix 3.28 THERMODYNAMIC PROPERTIES OF CN GAS

T	C_P^0	$(H^0 - H_0^0)$	$-(F^0 - H_0^0)/T$	S_T^0
DEG-K	CAL/MOLE DEG-K	KCAL/MOLE	CAL/MOLE DEG-K	CAL/MOLE DEG-K
100	6.956	0.696	33.851	40.807
200	6.958	1.391	38.673	45.629
273.15	6.963	1.900	40.841	47.799
298.15	6.969	2.074	41.451	48.409
400	7.029	2.787	43.496	50.463
500	7.156	3.495	45.053	52.044
600	7.326	4.219	46.331	53.364
700	7.511	4.961	47.419	54.507
800	7.690	5.721	48.370	55.522
900	7.852	6.499	49.216	56.437
1000	7.995	7.291	49.981	57.272
1100	8.119	8.097	50.679	58.040
1200	8.225	8.914	51.322	58.751
1300	8.316	9.741	51.919	59.413
1400	8.395	10.577	52.477	60.032
1500	8.463	11.420	53.000	60.614
1600	8.522	12.269	53.493	61.162
1700	8.573	13.124	53.960	61.680
1800	8.618	13.984	54.402	62.171
1900	8.658	14.848	54.824	62.638
2000	8.693	15.715	55.226	63.083
2100	8.725	16.586	55.610	63.508
2200	8.753	17.460	55.978	63.915
2300	8.779	18.337	56.332	64.305
2400	8.802	19.216	56.672	64.679
2500	8.823	20.097	57.000	65.038
2600	8.843	20.980	57.315	65.385
2700	8.860	21.866	57.621	65.719
2800	8.877	22.753	57.916	66.041
2900	8.892	23.641	58.201	66.353
3000	8.906	24.531	58.478	66.655
3200	8.932	26.315	59.007	67.231
3400	8.955	28.104	59.507	67.773
3600	8.976	29.897	59.981	68.285
3800	8.995	31.694	60.431	68.771
4000	9.012	33.495	60.859	69.233
4200	9.028	35.299	61.269	69.673
4400	9.043	37.106	61.660	70.093
4600	9.057	38.916	62.036	70.496
4800	9.070	40.728	62.396	70.881
5000	9.083	42.544	62.743	71.252
5200	9.095	44.361	63.077	71.608
5400	9.107	46.182	63.400	71.952
5600	9.118	48.004	63.711	72.283
5800	9.129	49.829	64.012	72.603
6000	9.140	51.656	64.304	72.913

THERMODYNAMIC PROPERTIES OF CO GAS

T	C_P^0	$(H^0 - H_0^0)$	$-(F^0 - H_0^0)/T$	S_T^0
DEG-K	CAL/MOLE DEG-K	KCAL/MOLE	CAL/MOLE DEG-K	CAL/MOLE DEG-K
100	6.955	0.696	32.659	39.615
200	6.957	1.391	37.481	44.438
273.15	6.961	1.900	39.650	46.606
298.15	6.965	2.074	40.259	47.216
400	7.013	2.786	42.304	49.268
500	7.121	3.492	43.860	50.844
600	7.275	4.211	45.136	52.155
700	7.450	4.948	46.222	53.290
800	7.624	5.701	47.169	54.296
900	7.785	6.472	48.012	55.203
1000	7.930	7.258	48.773	56.031
1100	8.056	8.057	49.468	56.793
1200	8.166	8.868	50.108	57.499
1300	8.261	9.690	50.702	58.156
1400	8.344	10.520	51.257	58.772
1500	8.415	11.358	51.777	59.350
1600	8.477	12.203	52.268	59.895
1700	8.531	13.053	52.732	60.410
1800	8.579	13.909	53.172	60.899
1900	8.621	14.769	53.591	61.364
2000	8.659	15.633	53.991	61.808
2100	8.692	16.501	54.373	62.231
2200	8.722	17.372	54.740	62.636
2300	8.749	18.245	55.092	63.024
2400	8.774	19.121	55.430	63.397
2500	8.796	20.000	55.756	63.756
2600	8.817	20.881	56.070	64.101
2700	8.835	21.763	56.374	64.434
2800	8.853	22.648	56.668	64.756
2900	8.869	23.534	56.952	65.067
3000	8.884	24.421	57.227	65.368
3200	8.911	26.201	57.754	65.942
3400	8.934	27.985	58.252	66.483
3600	8.956	29.774	58.724	66.994
3800	8.975	31.568	59.172	67.479
4000	8.993	33.364	59.599	67.940
4200	9.009	35.164	60.006	68.379
4400	9.024	36.968	60.397	68.798
4600	9.038	38.774	60.771	69.200
4800	9.051	40.583	61.130	69.585
5000	9.064	42.394	61.476	69.955
5200	9.076	44.208	61.809	70.310
5400	9.088	46.025	62.130	70.653
5600	9.099	47.843	62.440	70.984
5800	9.109	49.664	62.740	71.303
6000	9.120	51.487	63.031	71.612

Appendix 3.30 THERMODYNAMIC PROPERTIES OF CO+ GAS

T	C_P^0	$(H^0 - H_0^0)_T$	$-(F^0 - H_0^0)_T/T$	S_T^0
DEG-K	CAL/MOLE DEG-K	KCAL/MOLE	CAL/MOLE DEG-K	CAL/MOLE DEG-K
100	6.955	0.696	32.613	39.569
200	6.957	1.391	37.435	44.391
273.15	6.961	1.900	39.604	46.560
298.15	6.964	2.074	40.213	47.170
400	7.007	2.785	42.258	49.221
500	7.108	3.491	43.813	50.795
600	7.257	4.209	45.089	52.103
700	7.427	4.943	46.174	53.235
800	7.599	5.694	47.120	54.238
900	7.760	6.462	47.962	55.142
1000	7.905	7.246	48.722	55.967
1100	8.033	8.043	49.415	56.727
1200	8.145	8.852	50.054	57.431
1300	8.241	9.671	50.647	58.087
1400	8.326	10.499	51.201	58.700
1500	8.399	11.336	51.720	59.277
1600	8.462	12.179	52.210	59.822
1700	8.518	13.028	52.673	60.336
1800	8.567	13.882	53.112	60.825
1900	8.611	14.741	53.530	61.289
2000	8.649	15.604	53.930	61.732
2100	8.684	16.471	54.311	62.155
2200	8.715	17.341	54.677	62.559
2300	8.743	18.214	55.028	62.947
2400	8.768	19.090	55.366	63.320
2500	8.792	19.968	55.691	63.678
2600	8.813	20.848	56.005	64.024
2700	8.832	21.730	56.308	64.357
2800	8.850	22.614	56.602	64.678
2900	8.867	23.500	56.885	64.989
3000	8.882	24.387	57.161	65.290
3200	8.910	26.167	57.687	65.864
3400	8.935	27.951	58.184	66.405
3600	8.957	29.741	58.655	66.916
3800	8.977	31.534	59.103	67.401
4000	8.995	33.331	59.529	67.862
4200	9.012	35.132	59.937	68.301
4400	9.028	36.936	60.326	68.721
4600	9.043	38.743	60.700	69.123
4800	9.057	40.553	61.059	69.508
5000	9.070	42.366	61.405	69.878
5200	9.082	44.181	61.737	70.234
5400	9.094	45.999	62.058	70.577
5600	9.106	47.819	62.369	70.908
5800	9.117	49.641	62.669	71.227
6000	9.128	51.466	62.959	71.537

Appendix 3.31 THERMODYNAMIC PROPERTIES OF CP^0 GAS

T	C_P^0	$(H^0 - H_0^0)$	$-(F^0 - H_0^0)/T$	S_T^0
DEG-K	CAL/MOLE DEG-K	KCAL/MOLE	CAL/MOLE DEG-K	CAL/MOLE DEG-K
100	6.957	0.696	37.067	44.023
200	6.981	1.392	41.889	48.848
273.15	7.090	1.906	44.061	51.038
298.15	7.149	2.084	44.672	51.661
400	7.446	2.827	46.736	53.802
500	7.741	3.586	48.324	55.496
600	7.989	4.373	49.642	56.930
700	8.184	5.182	50.774	58.177
800	8.335	6.008	51.769	59.280
900	8.453	6.848	52.660	60.269
1000	8.545	7.698	53.466	61.164
1100	8.619	8.556	54.204	61.982
1200	8.679	9.421	54.884	62.735
1300	8.729	10.292	55.515	63.432
1400	8.770	11.167	56.104	64.080
1500	8.805	12.046	56.656	64.686
1600	8.835	12.928	57.176	65.256
1700	8.861	13.813	57.667	65.792
1800	8.884	14.700	58.133	66.299
1900	8.905	15.589	58.575	66.780
2000	8.923	16.481	58.997	67.237
2100	8.940	17.374	59.400	67.673
2200	8.955	18.269	59.785	68.089
2300	8.969	19.165	60.155	68.488
2400	8.982	20.063	60.510	68.870
2500	8.994	20.961	60.852	69.237
2600	9.006	21.861	61.181	69.590
2700	9.016	22.762	61.499	69.930
2800	9.027	23.665	61.806	70.258
2900	9.036	24.568	62.103	70.575
3000	9.046	25.472	62.391	70.881
3200	9.063	27.283	62.940	71.466
3400	9.080	29.097	63.458	72.016
3600	9.095	30.915	63.948	72.535
3800	9.110	32.735	64.413	73.027
4000	9.124	34.558	64.855	73.495
4200	9.138	36.385	65.277	73.940
4400	9.151	38.214	65.681	74.366
4600	9.164	40.045	66.067	74.773
4800	9.177	41.879	66.438	75.163
5000	9.189	43.716	66.795	75.538
5200	9.201	45.555	67.138	75.899
5400	9.213	47.396	67.469	76.246
5600	9.225	49.240	67.788	76.581
5800	9.237	51.086	68.097	76.905
6000	9.249	52.935	68.396	77.219

THERMODYNAMIC PROPERTIES OF CS   GAS

T	C_P^0	$(H^0 - H_0^0)$	$-(F^0 - H_0^0)/T$	S_T^0
DEG-K	CAL/MOLE DEG-K	KCAL/MOLE	CAL/MOLE DEG-K	CAL/MOLE DEG-K
100	6.956	0.696	35.711	42.667
200	6.975	1.392	40.533	47.491
273.15	7.069	1.905	42.703	49.677
298.15	7.122	2.082	43.315	50.298
400	7.401	2.821	45.376	52.429
500	7.690	3.576	46.960	54.112
600	7.939	4.358	48.273	55.536
700	8.138	5.162	49.401	56.776
800	8.294	5.984	50.393	57.873
900	8.416	6.820	51.280	58.857
1000	8.513	7.666	52.083	59.749
1100	8.590	8.522	52.817	60.564
1200	8.653	9.384	53.495	61.315
1300	8.704	10.252	54.123	62.009
1400	8.748	11.125	54.710	62.656
1500	8.784	12.001	55.260	63.261
1600	8.815	12.881	55.778	63.829
1700	8.843	13.764	56.267	64.364
1800	8.867	14.650	56.731	64.870
1900	8.888	15.537	57.173	65.350
2000	8.907	16.427	57.593	65.806
2100	8.924	17.319	57.994	66.241
2200	8.939	18.212	58.379	66.657
2300	8.953	19.106	58.747	67.055
2400	8.967	20.002	59.102	67.436
2500	8.979	20.900	59.442	67.802
2600	8.990	21.798	59.771	68.155
2700	9.001	22.698	60.088	68.494
2800	9.011	23.598	60.394	68.822
2900	9.021	24.500	60.690	69.138
3000	9.030	25.402	60.976	69.444
3200	9.047	27.210	61.524	70.027
3400	9.063	29.021	62.041	70.576
3600	9.078	30.835	62.529	71.095
3800	9.093	32.653	62.993	71.586
4000	9.106	34.473	63.435	72.053
4200	9.119	36.295	63.856	72.497
4400	9.132	38.120	64.258	72.922
4600	9.145	39.948	64.644	73.328
4800	9.157	41.778	65.014	73.718
5000	9.169	43.611	65.369	74.092
5200	9.180	45.445	65.712	74.451
5400	9.192	47.283	66.042	74.798
5600	9.203	49.122	66.361	75.133
5800	9.214	50.964	66.669	75.456
6000	9.225	52.808	66.967	75.768

Appendix 3.33   THERMODYNAMIC PROPERTIES OF C2   GAS

T	C_P^0	$(H^0 - H_0^0)$	$-(F^0 - H_0^0)/T$	S_T^0
DEG-K	CAL/MOLE DEG-K	KCAL/MOLE	CAL/MOLE DEG-K	CAL/MOLE DEG-K
100	6.957	0.696	34.720	41.676
200	6.960	1.391	39.542	46.499
273.15	6.988	1.901	41.711	48.672
298.15	7.009	2.076	42.321	49.285
400	7.164	2.797	44.371	51.363
500	7.385	3.524	45.937	52.985
600	7.617	4.274	47.228	54.352
700	7.829	5.047	48.333	55.543
800	8.011	5.839	49.301	56.600
900	8.162	6.648	50.166	57.553
1000	8.288	7.471	50.949	58.420
1100	8.392	8.305	51.664	59.214
1200	8.478	9.149	52.325	59.948
1300	8.550	10.000	52.938	60.630
1400	8.611	10.858	53.510	61.266
1500	8.663	11.722	54.047	61.862
1600	8.708	12.591	54.553	62.422
1700	8.747	13.463	55.032	62.952
1800	8.782	14.340	55.486	63.453
1900	8.812	15.220	55.918	63.928
2000	8.839	16.102	56.330	64.381
2100	8.863	16.987	56.723	64.813
2200	8.885	17.875	57.101	65.226
2300	8.905	18.764	57.463	65.621
2400	8.924	19.656	57.810	66.000
2500	8.941	20.549	58.145	66.365
2600	8.956	21.444	58.468	66.716
2700	8.971	22.340	58.780	67.054
2800	8.985	23.238	59.081	67.381
2900	8.998	24.137	59.373	67.696
3000	9.010	25.038	59.656	68.002
3200	9.033	26.842	60.196	68.584
3400	9.054	28.651	60.705	69.132
3600	9.073	30.463	61.188	69.650
3800	9.091	32.280	61.646	70.141
4000	9.108	34.100	62.083	70.608
4200	9.125	35.923	62.500	71.053
4400	9.140	37.750	62.898	71.478
4600	9.155	39.579	63.280	71.884
4800	9.170	41.412	63.647	72.274
5000	9.184	43.247	63.999	72.649
5200	9.198	45.085	64.339	73.009
5400	9.211	46.926	64.667	73.357
5600	9.225	48.770	64.983	73.692
5800	9.238	50.616	65.289	74.016
6000	9.251	52.465	65.585	74.329

T	C_P^0	$(H^0 - H_0^0)$	$-(F^0 - H_0^0)/T$	S_T^0
DEG-K	CAL/MOLE DEG-K	KCAL/MOLE	CAL/MOLE DEG-K	CAL/MOLE DEG-K
100	7.258	0.701	42.092	49.105
200	8.180	1.477	47.058	54.443
273.15	8.543	2.090	49.401	57.052
298.15	8.628	2.304	50.074	57.803
400	8.861	3.196	52.384	60.375
500	9.000	4.090	54.189	62.368
600	9.099	4.995	55.693	64.018
700	9.179	5.909	56.986	65.427
800	9.247	6.830	58.119	66.657
900	9.309	7.758	59.130	67.750
1000	9.367	8.692	60.042	68.734
1100	9.422	9.631	60.873	69.629
1200	9.475	10.576	61.638	70.451
1300	9.527	11.526	62.345	71.212
1400	9.578	12.482	63.004	71.920
1500	9.628	13.442	63.621	72.582
1600	9.677	14.407	64.201	73.205
1700	9.726	15.377	64.748	73.793
1800	9.775	16.352	65.266	74.351
1900	9.824	17.332	65.758	74.880
2000	9.872	18.317	66.227	75.385
2100	9.920	19.307	66.675	75.868
2200	9.968	20.301	67.103	76.331
2300	10.016	21.300	67.514	76.775
2400	10.064	22.304	67.909	77.202
2500	10.112	23.313	68.289	77.614
2600	10.159	24.327	68.655	78.012
2700	10.207	25.345	69.009	78.396
2800	10.254	26.368	69.351	78.768
2900	10.302	27.396	69.682	79.129
3000	10.349	28.428	70.003	79.479
3200	10.444	30.508	70.616	80.150
3400	10.538	32.606	71.196	80.786
3600	10.633	34.723	71.745	81.391
3800	10.727	36.859	72.268	81.968
4000	10.822	39.014	72.767	82.521
4200	10.916	41.188	73.244	83.051
4400	11.011	43.381	73.702	83.561
4600	11.105	45.592	74.141	84.053
4800	11.199	47.823	74.564	84.527
5000	11.294	50.072	74.972	84.986
5200	11.388	52.340	75.366	85.431
5400	11.482	54.627	75.746	85.863
5600	11.576	56.933	76.115	86.282
5800	11.670	59.257	76.473	86.690
6000	11.765	61.601	76.820	87.087

Appendix 3.35 THERMODYNAMIC PROPERTIES OF CAF GAS

T	C_P^0	$(H^0 - H_0^0)$	$-(F^0 - H_0^0)/T$	S_T^0
DEG-K	CAL/MOLE DEG-K	KCAL/MOLE	CAL/MOLE DEG-K	CAL/MOLE DEG-K
100	6.990	0.696	39.820	46.781
200	7.511	1.417	44.673	51.760
273.15	7.931	1.983	46.907	54.166
298.15	8.046	2.183	47.545	54.866
400	8.384	3.021	49.730	57.282
500	8.580	3.870	51.436	59.175
600	8.703	4.734	52.861	60.751
700	8.786	5.609	54.087	62.100
800	8.845	6.491	55.163	63.277
900	8.890	7.378	56.124	64.321
1000	8.925	8.269	56.991	65.260
1100	8.954	9.163	57.782	66.112
1200	8.978	10.059	58.509	66.892
1300	8.999	10.958	59.182	67.612
1400	9.018	11.859	59.809	68.279
1500	9.035	12.762	60.394	68.902
1600	9.051	13.666	60.944	69.486
1700	9.066	14.572	61.463	70.035
1800	9.080	15.479	61.954	70.553
1900	9.093	16.388	62.420	71.045
2000	9.106	17.298	62.863	71.511
2100	9.118	18.209	63.285	71.956
2200	9.130	19.121	63.689	72.381
2300	9.142	20.035	64.076	72.787
2400	9.153	20.950	64.447	73.176
2500	9.165	21.866	64.804	73.550
2600	9.176	22.783	65.147	73.910
2700	9.186	23.701	65.478	74.256
2800	9.197	24.620	65.797	74.590
2900	9.208	25.540	66.106	74.913
3000	9.218	26.462	66.405	75.226
3200	9.239	28.307	66.975	75.821
3400	9.260	30.157	67.512	76.382
3600	9.280	32.011	68.020	76.912
3800	9.300	33.869	68.501	77.414
4000	9.320	35.731	68.959	77.892
4200	9.340	37.598	69.395	78.347
4400	9.360	39.468	69.812	78.782
4600	9.380	41.342	70.211	79.198
4800	9.400	43.220	70.594	79.598
5000	9.419	45.101	70.962	79.982
5200	9.439	46.987	71.316	80.352
5400	9.459	48.877	71.657	80.708
5600	9.478	50.771	71.987	81.053
5800	9.498	52.668	72.305	81.386
6000	9.517	54.570	72.613	81.708

THERMODYNAMIC PROPERTIES OF CAH GAS

T	C_P^0	$(H^0 - H_0^0)_T$	$-(F^0 - H_0^0)_T/T$	S_T^0
DEG-K	CAL/MOLE DEG-K	KCAL/MOLE	CAL/MOLE DEG-K	CAL/MOLE DEG-K
100	6.961	0.696	33.615	40.573
200	6.986	1.393	38.439	45.402
273.15	7.089	1.907	40.612	47.592
298.15	7.145	2.085	41.223	48.216
400	7.440	2.827	43.288	50.355
500	7.743	3.586	44.876	52.048
600	8.005	4.374	46.194	53.484
700	8.217	5.186	47.326	54.734
800	8.386	6.016	48.323	55.843
900	8.522	6.862	49.215	56.839
1000	8.631	7.720	50.023	57.743
1100	8.721	8.587	50.763	58.570
1200	8.797	9.463	51.446	59.332
1300	8.862	10.346	52.080	60.039
1400	8.918	11.235	52.672	60.697
1500	8.967	12.130	53.228	61.314
1600	9.011	13.029	53.752	61.894
1700	9.051	13.932	54.247	62.442
1800	9.087	14.839	54.717	62.960
1900	9.121	15.749	55.164	63.453
2000	9.152	16.663	55.590	63.921
2100	9.182	17.579	55.997	64.368
2200	9.210	18.499	56.388	64.796
2300	9.237	19.421	56.762	65.206
2400	9.262	20.346	57.122	65.600
2500	9.287	21.274	57.469	65.978
2600	9.311	22.204	57.803	66.343
2700	9.334	23.136	58.126	66.695
2800	9.357	24.071	58.438	67.035
2900	9.379	25.007	58.740	67.364
3000	9.401	25.946	59.033	67.682
3200	9.443	27.831	59.593	68.290
3400	9.484	29.724	60.122	68.864
3600	9.524	31.624	60.622	69.407
3800	9.563	33.533	61.098	69.923
4000	9.601	35.449	61.552	70.414
4200	9.639	37.374	61.985	70.884
4400	9.677	39.305	62.400	71.333
4600	9.714	41.244	62.798	71.764
4800	9.751	43.191	63.180	72.178
5000	9.788	45.145	63.548	72.577
5200	9.824	47.106	63.903	72.962
5400	9.860	49.074	64.245	73.333
5600	9.896	51.050	64.576	73.692
5800	9.932	53.033	64.897	74.040
6000	9.968	55.023	65.207	74.378

T	C_P^0	$(H^0 - H_0^0)$	$-(F^0 - H_0^0)/T$	S_T^0
DEG-K	CAL/MOLE DEG-K	KCAL/MOLE	CAL/MOLE DEG-K	CAL/MOLE DEG-K
100	6.964	0.696	37.641	44.598
200	7.262	1.403	42.474	49.489
273.15	7.638	1.948	44.677	51.809
298.15	7.757	2.140	45.304	52.483
400	8.147	2.952	47.441	54.821
500	8.398	3.780	49.108	56.668
600	8.563	4.628	50.500	58.214
700	8.676	5.491	51.699	59.543
800	8.758	6.363	52.754	60.707
900	8.819	7.242	53.696	61.743
1000	8.867	8.126	54.548	62.674
1100	8.905	9.015	55.326	63.521
1200	8.937	9.907	56.042	64.298
1300	8.965	10.802	56.705	65.014
1400	8.989	11.700	57.322	65.679
1500	9.010	12.600	57.901	66.300
1600	9.029	13.502	58.444	66.882
1700	9.047	14.405	58.957	67.430
1800	9.063	15.311	59.442	67.948
1900	9.078	16.218	59.903	68.438
2000	9.093	17.127	60.341	68.904
2100	9.107	18.037	60.760	69.348
2200	9.120	18.948	61.160	69.772
2300	9.133	19.861	61.543	70.178
2400	9.146	20.774	61.911	70.567
2500	9.158	21.690	62.265	70.941
2600	9.170	22.606	62.605	71.300
2700	9.182	23.524	62.934	71.646
2800	9.193	24.442	63.251	71.980
2900	9.204	25.362	63.558	72.303
3000	9.216	26.283	63.854	72.615
3200	9.238	28.129	64.421	73.211
3400	9.259	29.978	64.954	73.772
3600	9.280	31.832	65.459	74.301
3800	9.301	33.690	65.938	74.804
4000	9.322	35.553	66.393	75.281
4200	9.343	37.419	66.827	75.737
4400	9.363	39.290	67.242	76.172
4600	9.384	41.164	67.640	76.588
4800	9.404	43.043	68.021	76.988
5000	9.424	44.926	68.387	77.372
5200	9.444	46.813	68.740	77.742
5400	9.464	48.704	69.080	78.099
5600	9.484	50.598	69.408	78.444
5800	9.504	52.497	69.726	78.777
6000	9.524	54.400	70.033	79.100

Appendix 3.38   THERMODYNAMIC PROPERTIES OF CLF   GAS

T	C_P^0	$(H^0 - H_0^0)$	$-(F^0 - H_0^0)/T$	S_T^0
DEG-K	CAL/MOLE DEG-K	KCAL/MOLE	CAL/MOLE DEG-K	CAL/MOLE DEG-K
100	6.961	0.696	37.262	44.219
200	7.199	1.400	42.092	49.092
273.15	7.549	1.939	44.287	51.387
298.15	7.668	2.129	44.911	52.053
400	8.070	2.932	47.036	54.366
500	8.341	3.754	48.691	56.198
600	8.526	4.597	50.074	57.736
700	8.655	5.457	51.265	59.061
800	8.750	6.327	52.314	60.223
900	8.823	7.206	53.251	61.258
1000	8.880	8.091	54.099	62.191
1100	8.926	8.982	54.874	63.039
1200	8.966	9.876	55.587	63.818
1300	9.000	10.775	56.248	64.537
1400	9.030	11.676	56.864	65.205
1500	9.057	12.581	57.442	65.829
1600	9.082	13.488	57.984	66.414
1700	9.104	14.397	58.496	66.965
1800	9.126	15.308	58.982	67.486
1900	9.146	16.222	59.442	67.980
2000	9.166	17.138	59.881	68.450
2100	9.184	18.055	60.300	68.897
2200	9.202	18.974	60.700	69.325
2300	9.220	19.895	61.084	69.735
2400	9.237	20.818	61.453	70.127
2500	9.253	21.743	61.808	70.505
2600	9.270	22.669	62.149	70.868
2700	9.286	23.597	62.478	71.218
2800	9.301	24.526	62.797	71.556
2900	9.317	25.457	63.104	71.883
3000	9.332	26.389	63.402	72.199
3200	9.363	28.259	63.971	72.802
3400	9.393	30.135	64.507	73.371
3600	9.422	32.016	65.015	73.908
3800	9.452	33.904	65.497	74.419
4000	9.481	35.797	65.955	74.904
4200	9.509	37.696	66.392	75.367
4400	9.538	39.601	66.810	75.810
4600	9.567	41.511	67.211	76.235
4800	9.595	43.427	67.595	76.643
5000	9.623	45.349	67.965	77.035
5200	9.652	47.276	68.321	77.413
5400	9.680	49.210	68.665	77.778
5600	9.708	51.148	68.997	78.130
5800	9.736	53.093	69.318	78.471
6000	9.764	55.043	69.628	78.802

Appendix 3.39   THERMODYNAMIC PROPERTIES OF CLO GAS

T	C_P^0	$(H^0 - H_0^0)$	$-(F^0 - H_0^0)/T$	S_T^0
DEG-K	CAL/MOLE DEG-K	KCAL/MOLE	CAL/MOLE DEG-K	CAL/MOLE DEG-K
100	6.959	0.696	39.406	46.363
200	7.124	1.397	44.233	51.217
273.15	7.426	1.929	46.419	53.480
298.15	7.537	2.116	47.039	54.135
400	7.939	2.905	49.147	56.408
500	8.226	3.714	50.785	58.213
600	8.427	4.547	52.153	59.731
700	8.570	5.397	53.332	61.042
800	8.674	6.260	54.369	62.193
900	8.753	7.131	55.296	63.220
1000	8.815	8.010	56.136	64.145
1100	8.865	8.894	56.903	64.988
1200	8.906	9.782	57.609	65.761
1300	8.941	10.675	58.264	66.475
1400	8.971	11.570	58.874	67.139
1500	8.998	12.469	59.446	67.759
1600	9.022	13.370	59.984	68.340
1700	9.044	14.273	60.492	68.888
1800	9.064	15.179	60.973	69.406
1900	9.083	16.086	61.430	69.896
2000	9.101	16.995	61.865	70.362
2100	9.117	17.906	62.280	70.807
2200	9.134	18.819	62.677	71.231
2300	9.149	19.733	63.058	71.638
2400	9.164	20.648	63.424	72.027
2500	9.178	21.566	63.776	72.402
2600	9.192	22.484	64.114	72.762
2700	9.206	23.404	64.441	73.109
2800	9.220	24.325	64.757	73.444
2900	9.233	25.248	65.062	73.768
3000	9.246	26.172	65.357	74.081
3200	9.272	28.024	65.921	74.679
3400	9.296	29.881	66.453	75.242
3600	9.321	31.742	66.957	75.774
3800	9.345	33.609	67.434	76.278
4000	9.369	35.480	67.888	76.758
4200	9.393	37.356	68.322	77.216
4400	9.416	39.237	68.736	77.654
4600	9.439	41.123	69.133	78.073
4800	9.462	43.013	69.514	78.475
5000	9.485	44.908	69.880	78.862
5200	9.508	46.807	70.233	79.234
5400	9.531	48.711	70.573	79.593
5600	9.554	50.620	70.901	79.940
5800	9.576	52.533	71.219	80.276
6000	9.599	54.450	71.526	80.601

Appendix 3.40 THERMODYNAMIC PROPERTIES OF CL2 GAS

T	C_P	$(H^0 - H^0_0)$	$-(F^0 - H^0_0)/T$	S^0_T
DEG-K	CAL/MOLE DEG-K	KCAL/MOLE	CAL/MOLE DEG-K	CAL/MOLE DEG-K
100	7.000	0.696	38.163	45.124
200	7.567	1.421	43.021	50.127
273.15	7.990	1.991	45.263	52.552
298.15	8.103	2.192	45.904	53.256
400	8.432	3.036	48.099	55.688
500	8.620	3.889	49.813	57.592
600	8.739	4.758	51.245	59.174
700	8.820	5.636	52.477	60.528
800	8.878	6.521	53.559	61.710
900	8.923	7.411	54.524	62.758
1000	8.959	8.305	55.395	63.700
1100	8.989	9.203	56.190	64.556
1200	9.015	10.103	56.920	65.339
1300	9.038	11.006	57.596	66.061
1400	9.059	11.910	58.225	66.732
1500	9.078	12.817	58.813	67.358
1600	9.096	13.726	59.365	67.944
1700	9.113	14.636	59.886	68.496
1800	9.129	15.548	60.379	69.017
1900	9.145	16.462	60.847	69.511
2000	9.160	17.377	61.292	69.981
2100	9.174	18.294	61.717	70.428
2200	9.189	19.212	62.122	70.855
2300	9.203	20.132	62.511	71.264
2400	9.217	21.053	62.884	71.656
2500	9.230	21.975	63.242	72.033
2600	9.244	22.899	63.588	72.395
2700	9.257	23.824	63.920	72.744
2800	9.271	24.750	64.241	73.081
2900	9.284	25.678	64.552	73.406
3000	9.297	26.607	64.852	73.721
3200	9.323	28.469	65.426	74.322
3400	9.348	30.336	65.966	74.888
3600	9.374	32.208	66.476	75.423
3800	9.399	34.086	66.961	75.931
4000	9.424	35.968	67.421	76.413
4200	9.449	37.855	67.861	76.874
4400	9.474	39.748	68.280	77.314
4600	9.499	41.645	68.682	77.736
4800	9.524	43.547	69.068	78.140
5000	9.549	45.454	69.439	78.530
5200	9.573	47.367	69.796	78.905
5400	9.598	49.284	70.140	79.266
5600	9.623	51.206	70.472	79.616
5800	9.647	53.133	70.793	79.954
6000	9.672	55.065	71.104	80.282

T	C_P^0	$(H^0 - H_0^0)$	$-(F^0 - H_0^0)/T$	S_T^0
DEG-K	CAL/MOLE DEG-K	KCAL/MOLE	CAL/MOLE DEG-K	CAL/MOLE DEG-K
100	6.974	0.696	40.716	47.674
200	7.393	1.410	45.558	52.608
273.15	7.801	1.966	47.777	54.975
298.15	7.920	2.163	48.409	55.663
400	8.282	2.989	50.572	58.046
500	8.501	3.829	52.261	59.919
600	8.640	4.687	53.671	61.482
700	8.733	5.556	54.885	62.822
800	8.800	6.433	55.952	63.992
900	8.850	7.315	56.904	65.032
1000	8.888	8.202	57.764	65.966
1100	8.919	9.093	58.549	66.815
1200	8.945	9.986	59.271	67.592
1300	8.967	10.882	59.939	68.309
1400	8.987	11.779	60.561	68.974
1500	9.004	12.679	61.142	69.595
1600	9.019	13.580	61.689	70.177
1700	9.034	14.483	62.205	70.724
1800	9.047	15.387	62.692	71.241
1900	9.060	16.292	63.155	71.730
2000	9.072	17.199	63.596	72.195
2100	9.083	18.106	64.016	72.638
2200	9.094	19.015	64.417	73.061
2300	9.105	19.925	64.802	73.465
2400	9.115	20.836	65.171	73.853
2500	9.126	21.748	65.526	74.225
2600	9.136	22.661	65.867	74.583
2700	9.145	23.576	66.197	74.928
2800	9.155	24.491	66.515	75.261
2900	9.164	25.406	66.822	75.583
3000	9.174	26.323	67.119	75.893
3200	9.192	28.160	67.686	76.486
3400	9.210	30.000	68.220	77.044
3600	9.228	31.844	68.725	77.571
3800	9.245	33.691	69.204	78.070
4000	9.263	35.542	69.659	78.545
4200	9.280	37.396	70.093	78.997
4400	9.297	39.254	70.508	79.429
4600	9.314	41.115	70.905	79.843
4800	9.331	42.980	71.286	80.240
5000	9.348	44.848	71.651	80.621
5200	9.365	46.719	72.004	80.988
5400	9.382	48.594	72.343	81.342
5600	9.399	50.472	72.670	81.683
5800	9.415	52.353	72.987	82.013
6000	9.432	54.238	73.293	82.333

Appendix 3.42   THERMODYNAMIC PROPERTIES OF F2   GAS

T	C_P^0	$(H^0 - H_0^0)_T$	$-(F^0 - H_0^0)/T$	S_T^0
DEG-K	CAL/MOLE DEG-K	KCAL/MOLE	CAL/MOLE DEG-K	CAL/MOLE DEG-K
100	6.959	0.696	33.739	40.695
200	7.097	1.396	38.564	45.543
273.15	7.378	1.925	40.749	47.795
298.15	7.485	2.110	41.367	48.446
400	7.890	2.894	43.468	50.704
500	8.192	3.699	45.101	52.499
600	8.409	4.530	46.463	54.013
700	8.566	5.379	47.637	55.321
800	8.684	6.242	48.671	56.473
900	8.774	7.115	49.596	57.501
1000	8.846	7.996	50.434	58.430
1100	8.905	8.884	51.200	59.276
1200	8.955	9.777	51.906	60.053
1300	8.998	10.674	52.560	60.771
1400	9.036	11.576	53.171	61.440
1500	9.070	12.482	53.743	62.064
1600	9.101	13.390	54.282	62.651
1700	9.130	14.302	54.790	63.203
1800	9.157	15.216	55.272	63.726
1900	9.182	16.133	55.731	64.222
2000	9.206	17.053	56.167	64.693
2100	9.229	17.974	56.584	65.143
2200	9.252	18.898	56.983	65.573
2300	9.273	19.825	57.365	65.985
2400	9.294	20.753	57.733	66.380
2500	9.315	21.683	58.086	66.760
2600	9.335	22.616	58.427	67.125
2700	9.355	23.550	58.756	67.478
2800	9.374	24.487	59.073	67.818
2900	9.393	25.425	59.380	68.148
3000	9.412	26.365	59.678	68.467
3200	9.449	28.252	60.247	69.075
3400	9.486	30.145	60.783	69.649
3600	9.522	32.046	61.291	70.192
3800	9.557	33.954	61.773	70.708
4000	9.593	35.869	62.232	71.199
4200	9.628	37.791	62.670	71.668
4400	9.663	39.720	63.090	72.117
4600	9.697	41.656	63.491	72.547
4800	9.732	43.599	63.877	72.961
5000	9.766	45.549	64.249	73.358
5200	9.800	47.505	64.607	73.742
5400	9.835	49.469	64.952	74.113
5600	9.869	51.439	65.285	74.471
5800	9.903	53.416	65.608	74.818
6000	9.937	55.400	65.921	75.154

Appendix 3.43 THERMODYNAMIC PROPERTIES OF HBR GAS

T	C_P^0	$(H^0 - H_0^0)_T$	$-(F^0 - H_0^0)/T$	S_T^0
DEG-K	CAL/MOLE DEG-K	KCAL/MOLE	CAL/MOLE DEG-K	CAL/MOLE DEG-K
100	6.955	0.696	32.901	39.856
200	6.961	1.392	37.725	44.683
273.15	6.963	1.901	39.894	46.853
298.15	6.965	2.075	40.503	47.463
400	6.984	2.785	42.549	49.512
500	7.039	3.486	44.103	51.075
600	7.139	4.194	45.376	52.367
700	7.272	4.915	46.456	53.477
800	7.422	5.649	47.396	54.458
900	7.576	6.399	48.230	55.341
1000	7.724	7.164	48.982	56.147
1100	7.862	7.944	49.668	56.889
1200	7.988	8.736	50.299	57.579
1300	8.102	9.541	50.884	58.223
1400	8.204	10.356	51.430	58.827
1500	8.296	11.182	51.942	59.396
1600	8.377	12.015	52.425	59.934
1700	8.451	12.857	52.882	60.444
1800	8.516	13.705	53.315	60.929
1900	8.576	14.560	53.728	61.391
2000	8.630	15.420	54.123	61.833
2100	8.679	16.286	54.500	62.255
2200	8.723	17.156	54.862	62.660
2300	8.764	18.030	55.209	63.048
2400	8.802	18.908	55.544	63.422
2500	8.837	19.790	55.866	63.782
2600	8.869	20.676	56.177	64.129
2700	8.899	21.564	56.478	64.465
2800	8.928	22.455	56.769	64.789
2900	8.954	23.350	57.051	65.103
3000	8.979	24.246	57.325	65.407
3200	9.026	26.047	57.848	65.988
3400	9.068	27.856	58.343	66.536
3600	9.106	29.674	58.813	67.056
3800	9.142	31.499	59.260	67.549
4000	9.175	33.330	59.686	68.019
4200	9.207	35.169	60.094	68.467
4400	9.237	37.013	60.484	68.896
4600	9.265	38.863	60.859	69.307
4800	9.292	40.719	61.219	69.702
5000	9.319	42.580	61.566	70.082
5200	9.344	44.446	61.901	70.448
5400	9.369	46.318	62.224	70.801
5600	9.393	48.194	62.536	71.142
5800	9.417	50.075	62.839	71.472
6000	9.440	51.961	63.132	71.792

Appendix 3.44 THERMODYNAMIC PROPERTIES OF HCL GAS

T	C_P^0	$(H^0 - H_0^0)$	$-(F^0 - H_0^0)/T$	S_T^0
DEG-K	CAL/MOLE DEG-K	KCAL/MOLE	CAL/MOLE DEG-K	CAL/MOLE DEG-K
100	6.955	0.696	30.083	37.038
200	6.961	1.392	34.907	41.865
273.15	6.963	1.901	37.076	44.035
298.15	6.964	2.075	37.685	44.645
400	6.973	2.785	39.731	46.692
500	7.004	3.483	41.285	48.251
600	7.069	4.186	42.556	49.533
700	7.167	4.898	43.633	50.630
800	7.289	5.621	44.569	51.594
900	7.423	6.356	45.398	52.461
1000	7.560	7.105	46.144	53.250
1100	7.693	7.868	46.824	53.976
1200	7.819	8.644	47.448	54.651
1300	7.936	9.431	48.027	55.282
1400	8.043	10.230	48.567	55.874
1500	8.141	11.040	49.072	56.432
1600	8.230	11.858	49.549	56.961
1700	8.310	12.685	50.000	57.462
1800	8.383	13.520	50.428	57.939
1900	8.449	14.362	50.835	58.394
2000	8.510	15.210	51.224	58.829
2100	8.564	16.064	51.596	59.246
2200	8.615	16.923	51.953	59.645
2300	8.661	17.786	52.296	60.029
2400	8.704	18.655	52.626	60.399
2500	8.743	19.527	52.944	60.755
2600	8.779	20.403	53.251	61.098
2700	8.813	21.283	53.548	61.430
2800	8.845	22.166	53.835	61.752
2900	8.875	23.052	54.114	62.062
3000	8.903	23.941	54.384	62.364
3200	8.954	25.726	54.901	62.940
3400	9.000	27.522	55.390	63.484
3600	9.042	29.326	55.854	64.000
3800	9.081	31.139	56.296	64.490
4000	9.117	32.959	56.717	64.957
4200	9.150	34.785	57.120	65.402
4400	9.182	36.619	57.506	65.829
4600	9.212	38.458	57.877	66.237
4800	9.240	40.303	58.234	66.630
5000	9.267	42.154	58.577	67.008
5200	9.293	44.010	58.908	67.372
5400	9.319	45.871	59.228	67.723
5600	9.343	47.737	59.538	68.062
5800	9.367	49.608	59.838	68.391
6000	9.390	51.484	60.128	68.709

THERMODYNAMIC PROPERTIES OF HCL+ GAS

T	C_P^0	$(H^0 - H_0^0)$	$-(F^0 - H_0^0)/T$	S_T^0
DEG-K	CAL/MOLE DEG-K	KCAL/MOLE	CAL/MOLE DEG-K	CAL/MOLE DEG-K
100	6.955	0.696	32.966	39.922
200	6.962	1.392	37.791	44.749
273.15	6.965	1.901	39.960	46.920
298.15	6.966	2.075	40.569	47.530
400	6.985	2.785	42.615	49.579
500	7.041	3.486	44.170	51.142
600	7.140	4.195	45.443	52.434
700	7.273	4.915	46.522	53.545
800	7.424	5.650	47.463	54.526
900	7.579	6.400	48.297	55.409
1000	7.729	7.166	49.049	56.215
1100	7.869	7.946	49.735	56.959
1200	7.997	8.739	50.366	57.649
1300	8.113	9.545	50.951	58.294
1400	8.217	10.361	51.498	58.899
1500	8.311	11.188	52.010	59.469
1600	8.395	12.023	52.493	60.008
1700	8.470	12.867	52.951	60.519
1800	8.538	13.717	53.385	61.005
1900	8.600	14.574	53.798	61.469
2000	8.656	15.437	54.193	61.911
2100	8.706	16.305	54.570	62.335
2200	8.753	17.178	54.933	62.741
2300	8.796	18.055	55.281	63.131
2400	8.836	18.937	55.616	63.506
2500	8.873	19.822	55.939	63.867
2600	8.907	20.711	56.250	64.216
2700	8.939	21.604	56.552	64.553
2800	8.969	22.499	56.843	64.879
2900	8.998	23.398	57.126	65.194
3000	9.025	24.299	57.400	65.499
3200	9.075	26.109	57.924	66.083
3400	9.120	27.928	58.421	66.635
3600	9.163	29.757	58.892	67.157
3800	9.202	31.593	59.340	67.654
4000	9.239	33.437	59.768	68.127
4200	9.274	35.289	60.176	68.578
4400	9.307	37.147	60.568	69.011
4600	9.339	39.011	60.944	69.425
4800	9.370	40.882	61.306	69.823
5000	9.400	42.759	61.654	70.206
5200	9.428	44.642	61.991	70.576
5400	9.457	46.531	62.315	70.932
5600	9.484	48.425	62.629	71.276
5800	9.511	50.324	62.933	71.610
6000	9.538	52.229	63.228	71.933

THERMODYNAMIC PROPERTIES OF HF GAS

T	C_P^0	$(H^0 - H_0^0)/T$	$-(F^0 - H_0^0)/T$	S_T^0
DEG-K	CAL/MOLE DEG-K	KCAL/MOLE	CAL/MOLE DEG-K	CAL/MOLE DEG-K
100	6.955	0.696	26.949	33.904
200	6.961	1.392	31.772	38.731
273.15	6.963	1.901	33.941	40.901
298.15	6.964	2.075	34.551	41.510
400	6.967	2.784	36.596	43.557
500	6.972	3.481	38.150	45.112
600	6.986	4.179	39.419	46.385
700	7.015	4.879	40.493	47.464
800	7.063	5.583	41.425	48.403
900	7.129	6.292	42.247	49.239
1000	7.211	7.009	42.985	49.994
1100	7.303	7.735	43.654	50.685
1200	7.402	8.470	44.267	51.325
1300	7.504	9.215	44.833	51.922
1400	7.606	9.971	45.359	52.481
1500	7.705	10.736	45.852	53.010
1600	7.800	11.512	46.315	53.510
1700	7.891	12.296	46.752	53.986
1800	7.977	13.090	47.167	54.439
1900	8.058	13.891	47.561	54.873
2000	8.133	14.701	47.937	55.288
2100	8.204	15.518	48.297	55.686
2200	8.270	16.342	48.641	56.070
2300	8.331	17.172	48.973	56.438
2400	8.389	18.008	49.291	56.794
2500	8.442	18.849	49.598	57.138
2600	8.493	19.696	49.895	57.470
2700	8.540	20.548	50.181	57.791
2800	8.584	21.404	50.458	58.103
2900	8.625	22.264	50.727	58.405
3000	8.664	23.129	50.988	58.698
3200	8.735	24.869	51.488	59.259
3400	8.799	26.623	51.961	59.791
3600	8.857	28.388	52.410	60.295
3800	8.910	30.165	52.838	60.776
4000	8.958	31.952	53.246	61.234
4200	9.002	33.748	53.637	61.672
4400	9.043	35.552	54.012	62.092
4600	9.081	37.365	54.372	62.495
4800	9.117	39.185	54.718	62.882
5000	9.151	41.012	55.052	63.255
5200	9.184	42.845	55.375	63.614
5400	9.214	44.685	55.686	63.962
5600	9.244	46.531	55.988	64.297
5800	9.272	48.383	56.280	64.622
6000	9.299	50.240	56.564	64.937

T	C_P^0	$(H^0 - H_0^0)$	$-(F^0 - H_0^0)/T$	S_T^0
DEG-K	CAL/MOLE DEG-K	KCAL/MOLE	CAL/MOLE DEG-K	CAL/MOLE DEG-K
100	6.728	0.717	16.881	24.049
200	6.560	1.361	21.712	28.515
273.15	6.841	1.852	23.826	30.606
298.15	6.892	2.024	24.420	31.208
400	6.974	2.731	26.421	33.248
500	6.993	3.429	27.948	34.807
600	7.010	4.130	29.200	36.083
700	7.037	4.832	30.263	37.165
800	7.079	5.537	31.186	38.107
900	7.139	6.248	32.002	38.945
1000	7.215	6.966	32.735	39.701
1100	7.302	7.692	33.400	40.392
1200	7.397	8.426	34.010	41.032
1300	7.497	9.171	34.573	41.628
1400	7.599	9.926	35.097	42.187
1500	7.701	10.691	35.587	42.715
1600	7.801	11.466	36.049	43.215
1700	7.898	12.251	36.484	43.691
1800	7.991	13.045	36.897	44.145
1900	8.081	13.849	37.290	44.579
2000	8.168	14.662	37.665	44.996
2100	8.250	15.483	38.024	45.397
2200	8.330	16.312	38.368	45.782
2300	8.407	17.148	38.698	46.154
2400	8.481	17.993	39.017	46.514
2500	8.552	18.844	39.323	46.861
2600	8.621	19.703	39.620	47.198
2700	8.688	20.569	39.907	47.525
2800	8.753	21.441	40.184	47.842
2900	8.816	22.319	40.454	48.150
3000	8.878	23.204	40.715	48.450
3200	8.995	24.991	41.217	49.027
3400	9.105	26.802	41.693	49.575
3600	9.207	28.633	42.145	50.099
3800	9.301	30.484	42.577	50.599
4000	9.386	32.353	42.990	51.078
4200	9.461	34.237	43.386	51.538
4400	9.526	36.136	43.767	51.980
4600	9.582	38.047	44.133	52.405
4800	9.629	39.969	44.487	52.813
5000	9.667	41.898	44.828	53.207
5200	9.696	43.835	45.157	53.587
5400	9.717	45.776	45.476	53.953
5600	9.730	47.721	45.785	54.307
5800	9.737	49.668	46.085	54.649
6000	9.738	51.615	46.376	54.979

Appendix 3.48   THERMODYNAMIC PROPERTIES OF HE2   GAS

T	C_P^0	$(H^0 - H_0^0)$	$-(F^0 - H_0^0)/T$	S_T^0
DEG-K	CAL/MOLE DEG-K	KCAL/MOLE	CAL/MOLE DEG-K	CAL/MOLE DEG-K
100	6.961	0.696	24.820	31.778
200	6.967	1.392	29.644	36.605
273.15	6.985	1.902	31.814	38.778
298.15	7.000	2.077	32.424	39.391
400	7.117	2.795	34.474	41.462
500	7.307	3.516	36.037	43.069
600	7.527	4.258	37.325	44.421
700	7.742	5.021	38.424	45.597
800	7.937	5.805	39.387	46.644
900	8.106	6.608	40.247	47.589
1000	8.251	7.426	41.025	48.451
1100	8.375	8.257	41.737	49.243
1200	8.481	9.100	42.393	49.977
1300	8.573	9.953	43.003	50.659
1400	8.652	10.814	43.573	51.298
1500	8.721	11.683	44.108	51.897
1600	8.782	12.558	44.613	52.462
1700	8.837	13.439	45.090	52.996
1800	8.886	14.326	45.544	53.502
1900	8.931	15.216	45.975	53.984
2000	8.971	16.112	46.387	54.443
2100	9.009	17.011	46.781	54.882
2200	9.043	17.913	47.159	55.302
2300	9.076	18.819	47.522	55.704
2400	9.106	19.728	47.871	56.091
2500	9.135	20.640	48.207	56.464
2600	9.162	21.555	48.532	56.822
2700	9.188	22.473	48.845	57.169
2800	9.213	23.393	49.149	57.503
2900	9.237	24.315	49.442	57.827
3000	9.260	25.240	49.727	58.140
3200	9.304	27.096	50.272	58.739
3400	9.345	28.961	50.787	59.305
3600	9.385	30.834	51.275	59.840
3800	9.423	32.715	51.739	60.348
4000	9.460	34.603	52.182	60.833
4200	9.496	36.499	52.605	61.295
4400	9.531	38.402	53.010	61.738
4600	9.565	40.311	53.399	62.162
4800	9.599	42.228	53.773	62.570
5000	9.632	44.151	54.132	62.962
5200	9.665	46.080	54.479	63.341
5400	9.697	48.017	54.814	63.706
5600	9.729	49.959	55.138	64.059
5800	9.761	51.908	55.452	64.401
6000	9.793	53.864	55.756	64.733

Appendix 3.49   THERMODYNAMIC PROPERTIES OF KBR GAS

T	C_p^0	$(H^0 - H_0^0)/T$	$-(F^0 - H_0^0)/T$	S_T^0
DEG-K	CAL/MOLE DEG-K	KCAL/MOLE	CAL/MOLE DEG-K	CAL/MOLE DEG-K
100	7.936	0.726	43.293	50.556
200	8.637	1.563	48.513	56.328
273.15	8.803	2.202	50.988	59.048
298.15	8.837	2.422	51.697	59.821
400	8.930	3.327	54.113	62.432
500	8.983	4.223	55.984	64.431
600	9.022	5.124	57.533	66.072
700	9.054	6.027	58.855	67.465
800	9.081	6.934	60.008	68.676
900	9.107	7.844	61.032	69.747
1000	9.130	8.755	61.953	70.708
1100	9.153	9.670	62.789	71.579
1200	9.176	10.586	63.555	72.377
1300	9.198	11.505	64.262	73.112
1400	9.219	12.426	64.919	73.794
1500	9.241	13.349	65.532	74.431
1600	9.262	14.274	66.107	75.028
1700	9.283	15.201	66.649	75.590
1800	9.304	16.130	67.160	76.122
1900	9.325	17.062	67.645	76.625
2000	9.345	17.995	68.106	77.104
2100	9.366	18.931	68.546	77.560
2200	9.387	19.869	68.966	77.997
2300	9.407	20.808	69.367	78.414
2400	9.428	21.750	69.753	78.815
2500	9.448	22.694	70.123	79.200
2600	9.469	23.640	70.479	79.571
2700	9.489	24.588	70.823	79.929
2800	9.510	25.538	71.154	80.275
2900	9.530	26.490	71.474	80.609
3000	9.551	27.444	71.784	80.932
3200	9.592	29.358	72.376	81.550
3400	9.633	31.280	72.933	82.133
3600	9.673	33.211	73.459	82.684
3800	9.714	35.150	73.959	83.208
4000	9.755	37.097	74.434	83.708
4200	9.796	39.052	74.887	84.185
4400	9.836	41.015	75.320	84.641
4600	9.877	42.986	75.735	85.080
4800	9.918	44.966	76.133	85.501
5000	9.959	46.954	76.516	85.906
5200	9.999	48.949	76.884	86.298
5400	10.040	50.953	77.240	86.676
5600	10.081	52.965	77.584	87.042
5800	10.121	54.986	77.916	87.396
6000	10.162	57.014	78.238	87.740

Appendix 3.50   THERMODYNAMIC PROPERTIES OF KCL   GAS

T	C_P^0	$(H_T^0 - H_0^0)$	$-(F_T^0 - H_0^0)/T$	S_T^0
DEG-K	CAL/MOLE DEG-K	KCAL/MOLE	CAL/MOLE DEG-K	CAL/MOLE DEG-K
100	7.567	0.711	41.014	48.120
200	8.424	1.518	46.091	53.679
273.15	8.669	2.144	48.497	56.345
298.15	8.721	2.361	49.188	57.107
400	8.858	3.257	51.548	59.691
500	8.933	4.147	53.382	61.677
600	8.983	5.043	54.905	63.310
700	9.021	5.943	56.207	64.698
800	9.053	6.847	57.346	65.904
900	9.080	7.754	58.357	66.972
1000	9.105	8.663	59.267	67.930
1100	9.129	9.575	60.095	68.799
1200	9.151	10.489	60.854	69.594
1300	9.173	11.405	61.555	70.328
1400	9.194	12.323	62.206	71.008
1500	9.215	13.244	62.814	71.643
1600	9.235	14.166	63.385	72.239
1700	9.255	15.091	63.922	72.799
1800	9.275	16.017	64.430	73.329
1900	9.295	16.946	64.912	73.831
2000	9.315	17.876	65.370	74.308
2100	9.334	18.809	65.806	74.763
2200	9.354	19.743	66.224	75.198
2300	9.373	20.680	66.623	75.614
2400	9.393	21.618	67.006	76.013
2500	9.412	22.558	67.374	76.397
2600	9.431	23.500	67.728	76.767
2700	9.451	24.444	68.069	77.123
2800	9.470	25.390	68.399	77.467
2900	9.489	26.338	68.717	77.800
3000	9.508	27.288	69.026	78.122
3200	9.546	29.194	69.613	78.736
3400	9.585	31.107	70.167	79.316
3600	9.623	33.027	70.691	79.865
3800	9.661	34.956	71.188	80.387
4000	9.699	36.892	71.660	80.883
4200	9.737	38.835	72.111	81.357
4400	9.775	40.787	72.541	81.811
4600	9.813	42.745	72.954	82.246
4800	9.851	44.712	73.350	82.665
5000	9.889	46.686	73.731	83.068
5200	9.927	48.667	74.097	83.456
5400	9.965	50.657	74.451	83.832
5600	10.003	52.653	74.792	84.195
5800	10.041	54.658	75.123	84.546
6000	10.079	56.670	75.443	84.888

		0		0	0		0	0		0
T		C		(H	– H	)	-(F	-H)/T		S
		P		T	0		T	0		T

DEG-K	CAL/MOLE DEG-K	KCAL/MOLE	CAL/MOLE DEG-K	CAL/MOLE DEG-K
100	7.176	0.700	38.603	45.598
200	8.024	1.462	43.537	50.846
273.15	8.386	2.063	45.853	53.406
298.15	8.470	2.274	46.517	54.144
400	8.692	3.149	48.795	56.668
500	8.812	4.025	50.572	58.621
600	8.887	4.910	52.052	60.235
700	8.939	5.801	53.321	61.609
800	8.979	6.697	54.434	62.805
900	9.011	7.597	55.424	63.865
1000	9.038	8.499	56.316	64.816
1100	9.063	9.404	57.129	65.678
1200	9.085	10.312	57.875	66.468
1300	9.105	11.221	58.564	67.196
1400	9.125	12.133	59.205	67.871
1500	9.143	13.046	59.804	68.502
1600	9.161	13.962	60.366	69.092
1700	9.179	14.879	60.896	69.648
1800	9.196	15.797	61.397	70.173
1900	9.212	16.718	61.872	70.671
2000	9.229	17.640	62.324	71.144
2100	9.245	18.563	62.755	71.595
2200	9.261	19.489	63.166	72.025
2300	9.277	20.416	63.561	72.437
2400	9.293	21.344	63.939	72.832
2500	9.309	22.274	64.302	73.212
2600	9.324	23.206	64.652	73.577
2700	9.340	24.139	64.989	73.929
2800	9.356	25.074	65.314	74.269
2900	9.371	26.010	65.629	74.598
3000	9.386	26.948	65.933	74.916
3200	9.417	28.829	66.514	75.523
3400	9.448	30.715	67.061	76.095
3600	9.478	32.608	67.578	76.635
3800	9.509	34.506	68.068	77.149
4000	9.539	36.411	68.534	77.637
4200	9.569	38.322	68.979	78.103
4400	9.600	40.239	69.404	78.549
4600	9.630	42.162	69.811	78.977
4800	9.660	44.091	70.201	79.387
5000	9.690	46.026	70.577	79.782
5200	9.720	47.967	70.938	80.163
5400	9.751	49.914	71.287	80.530
5600	9.781	51.867	71.623	80.885
5800	9.811	53.826	71.949	81.229
6000	9.841	55.792	72.264	81.562

THERMODYNAMIC PROPERTIES OF KH   GAS

T	C_P^0	$(H^0 - H_0^0)$	$-(F^0 - H_0^0)/T$	S_T^0
DEG-K	CAL/MOLE DEG-K	KCAL/MOLE	CAL/MOLE DEG-K	CAL/MOLE DEG-K
100	6.964	0.696	32.616	39.575
200	7.070	1.396	37.443	44.421
273.15	7.317	1.921	39.625	46.658
298.15	7.418	2.105	40.242	47.304
400	7.818	2.882	42.337	49.541
500	8.135	3.680	43.961	51.321
600	8.370	4.506	45.316	52.826
700	8.545	5.352	46.484	54.130
800	8.679	6.214	47.513	55.280
900	8.783	7.087	48.434	56.309
1000	8.867	7.969	49.269	57.238
1100	8.937	8.860	50.033	58.087
1200	8.997	9.757	50.737	58.867
1300	9.049	10.659	51.390	59.589
1400	9.095	11.566	52.000	60.262
1500	9.137	12.478	52.572	60.891
1600	9.176	13.393	53.111	61.482
1700	9.212	14.313	53.620	62.039
1800	9.246	15.236	54.102	62.567
1900	9.278	16.162	54.561	63.067
2000	9.309	17.091	54.998	63.544
2100	9.338	18.024	55.416	63.999
2200	9.367	18.959	55.816	64.434
2300	9.395	19.897	56.200	64.851
2400	9.422	20.838	56.569	65.251
2500	9.449	21.782	56.924	65.637
2600	9.475	22.728	57.266	66.008
2700	9.501	23.677	57.597	66.366
2800	9.526	24.628	57.916	66.712
2900	9.552	25.582	58.225	67.047
3000	9.576	26.538	58.525	67.371
3200	9.625	28.458	59.097	67.990
3400	9.674	30.388	59.638	68.575
3600	9.721	32.328	60.150	69.130
3800	9.769	34.277	60.636	69.657
4000	9.816	36.235	61.100	70.159
4200	9.862	38.203	61.543	70.639
4400	9.908	40.180	61.967	71.099
4600	9.955	42.166	62.374	71.540
4800	10.000	44.162	62.764	71.965
5000	10.046	46.167	63.141	72.374
5200	10.092	48.180	63.503	72.769
5400	10.137	50.203	63.854	73.151
5600	10.183	52.235	64.192	73.520
5800	10.228	54.276	64.520	73.878
6000	10.274	56.327	64.838	74.226

Appendix 3.53   THERMODYNAMIC PROPERTIES OF K2   GAS

T	C_P^0	$(H^0 - H_0^0)$	$-(F^0 - H_0^0)/T$	S_T^0
DEG-K	CAL/MOLE DEG-K	KCAL/MOLE	CAL/MOLE DEG-K	CAL/MOLE DEG-K
100	8.723	0.793	41.994	49.923
200	8.969	1.681	47.663	56.066
273.15	9.038	2.339	50.309	58.873
298.15	9.057	2.566	51.060	59.666
400	9.121	3.491	53.608	62.336
500	9.177	4.406	55.565	64.378
600	9.230	5.327	57.178	66.056
700	9.281	6.252	58.550	67.482
800	9.332	7.183	59.746	68.725
900	9.382	8.119	60.806	69.827
1000	9.432	9.059	61.759	70.818
1100	9.482	10.005	62.624	71.719
1200	9.532	10.956	63.417	72.547
1300	9.581	11.911	64.149	73.312
1400	9.631	12.872	64.829	74.023
1500	9.680	13.838	65.464	74.690
1600	9.729	14.808	66.061	75.316
1700	9.779	15.783	66.623	75.907
1800	9.828	16.764	67.154	76.467
1900	9.878	17.749	67.659	77.000
2000	9.927	18.739	68.138	77.508
2100	9.976	19.734	68.596	77.994
2200	10.025	20.735	69.034	78.459
2300	10.075	21.740	69.454	78.906
2400	10.124	22.750	69.856	79.335
2500	10.173	23.764	70.244	79.750
2600	10.223	24.784	70.617	80.150
2700	10.272	25.809	70.978	80.536
2800	10.321	26.839	71.326	80.911
2900	10.370	27.873	71.662	81.274
3000	10.420	28.913	71.989	81.626
3200	10.518	31.006	72.612	82.302
3400	10.617	33.120	73.201	82.943
3600	10.715	35.253	73.760	83.552
3800	10.814	37.406	74.290	84.134
4000	10.912	39.579	74.797	84.691
4200	11.011	41.771	75.281	85.226
4400	11.109	43.983	75.744	85.741
4600	11.208	46.215	76.190	86.237
4800	11.306	48.466	76.619	86.716
5000	11.405	50.737	77.032	87.179
5200	11.503	53.028	77.431	87.628
5400	11.602	55.339	77.817	88.064
5600	11.700	57.669	78.190	88.488
5800	11.799	60.019	78.552	88.901
6000	11.897	62.388	78.904	89.302

THERMODYNAMIC PROPERTIES OF LIBR GAS

T	C_P^0	$(H^0 - H_0^0)_T$	$-(F^0 - H_0^0)/T$	S_T^0
DEG-K	CAL/MOLE DEG-K	KCAL/MOLE	CAL/MOLE DEG-K	CAL/MOLE DEG-K
100	6.997	0.696	38.501	45.463
200	7.549	1.420	43.358	50.458
273.15	7.975	1.989	45.597	52.877
298.15	8.090	2.189	46.237	53.581
400	8.428	3.032	48.429	56.010
500	8.626	3.886	50.142	57.914
600	8.752	4.755	51.573	59.498
700	8.838	5.635	52.804	60.854
800	8.902	6.522	53.886	62.039
900	8.952	7.415	54.852	63.090
1000	8.993	8.312	55.724	64.036
1100	9.027	9.213	56.519	64.894
1200	9.057	10.117	57.250	65.681
1300	9.084	11.024	57.927	66.407
1400	9.109	11.934	58.557	67.081
1500	9.132	12.846	59.146	67.710
1600	9.154	13.760	59.700	68.301
1700	9.175	14.677	60.223	68.856
1800	9.195	15.595	60.717	69.381
1900	9.215	16.516	61.186	69.879
2000	9.234	17.438	61.633	70.352
2100	9.252	18.363	62.059	70.803
2200	9.270	19.289	62.466	71.234
2300	9.288	20.217	62.856	71.646
2400	9.306	21.146	63.231	72.042
2500	9.323	22.078	63.591	72.422
2600	9.341	23.011	63.938	72.788
2700	9.358	23.946	64.272	73.141
2800	9.375	24.883	64.595	73.482
2900	9.392	25.821	64.907	73.811
3000	9.409	26.761	65.209	74.130
3200	9.442	28.646	65.786	74.738
3400	9.475	30.538	66.330	75.311
3600	9.508	32.436	66.844	75.854
3800	9.541	34.341	67.332	76.369
4000	9.574	36.252	67.796	76.859
4200	9.606	38.170	68.239	77.327
4400	9.639	40.095	68.662	77.774
4600	9.671	42.026	69.068	78.204
4800	9.703	43.963	69.457	78.616
5000	9.736	45.907	69.831	79.013
5200	9.768	47.858	70.192	79.395
5400	9.800	49.814	70.540	79.764
5600	9.832	51.778	70.875	80.121
5800	9.864	53.747	71.200	80.467
6000	9.897	55.723	71.515	80.802

Appendix 3.55   THERMODYNAMIC PROPERTIES OF LICL GAS

T	C_P^0	$(H^0 - H_0^0)_T$	$-(F^0 - H_0^0)/T$	S_T^0
DEG-K	CAL/MOLE DEG-K	KCAL/MOLE	CAL/MOLE DEG-K	CAL/MOLE DEG-K
100	6.973	0.696	36.135	43.094
200	7.365	1.409	40.976	48.019
273.15	7.768	1.962	43.191	50.376
298.15	7.888	2.158	43.823	51.061
400	8.258	2.982	45.980	53.435
500	8.483	3.820	47.664	55.304
600	8.628	4.676	49.071	56.864
700	8.726	5.544	50.282	58.202
800	8.796	6.420	51.347	59.372
900	8.848	7.302	52.297	60.411
1000	8.889	8.189	53.156	61.346
1100	8.922	9.080	53.940	62.194
1200	8.949	9.973	54.661	62.972
1300	8.973	10.870	55.328	63.689
1400	8.993	11.768	55.949	64.355
1500	9.012	12.668	56.531	64.976
1600	9.028	13.570	57.077	65.558
1700	9.044	14.474	57.592	66.106
1800	9.058	15.379	58.079	66.623
1900	9.072	16.285	58.542	67.113
2000	9.085	17.193	58.982	67.579
2100	9.097	18.102	59.402	68.023
2200	9.109	19.013	59.804	68.446
2300	9.121	19.924	60.189	68.851
2400	9.132	20.837	60.558	69.240
2500	9.143	21.751	60.912	69.613
2600	9.154	22.665	61.254	69.971
2700	9.164	23.581	61.583	70.317
2800	9.175	24.498	61.901	70.651
2900	9.185	25.416	62.209	70.973
3000	9.195	26.335	62.506	71.284
3200	9.215	28.176	63.073	71.878
3400	9.234	30.021	63.608	72.438
3600	9.254	31.870	64.113	72.966
3800	9.273	33.723	64.592	73.467
4000	9.292	35.579	65.048	73.943
4200	9.311	37.439	65.483	74.397
4400	9.329	39.303	65.898	74.830
4600	9.348	41.171	66.295	75.245
4800	9.366	43.043	66.676	75.644
5000	9.385	44.918	67.043	76.026
5200	9.403	46.797	67.395	76.395
5400	9.422	48.679	67.735	76.750
5600	9.440	50.565	68.064	77.093
5800	9.458	52.455	68.381	77.425
6000	9.476	54.348	68.687	77.746

Appendix 3.56 THERMODYNAMIC PROPERTIES OF LIF GAS

T	C_P^0	$(H^0 - H_T^0)$	$-(F_T^0 - H_0^0)/T$	S_T^0
DEG-K	CAL/MOLE DEG-K	KCAL/MOLE	CAL/MOLE DEG-K	CAL/MOLE DEG-K
100	6.960	0.696	33.108	40.066
200	7.100	1.396	37.935	44.915
273.15	7.382	1.925	40.119	47.168
298.15	7.489	2.111	40.738	47.819
400	7.891	2.895	42.840	50.078
500	8.189	3.700	44.473	51.872
600	8.401	4.530	45.835	53.385
700	8.554	5.378	47.009	54.692
800	8.667	6.239	48.043	55.842
900	8.753	7.111	48.968	56.868
1000	8.821	7.990	49.805	57.794
1100	8.877	8.875	50.570	58.638
1200	8.923	9.765	51.275	59.412
1300	8.962	10.659	51.929	60.128
1400	8.997	11.557	52.539	60.793
1500	9.028	12.458	53.110	61.415
1600	9.055	13.362	53.647	61.999
1700	9.081	14.269	54.155	62.549
1800	9.104	15.178	54.636	63.068
1900	9.126	16.090	55.093	63.561
2000	9.147	17.004	55.528	64.030
2100	9.167	17.919	55.943	64.477
2200	9.186	18.837	56.341	64.903
2300	9.205	19.757	56.722	65.312
2400	9.223	20.678	57.088	65.704
2500	9.240	21.601	57.441	66.081
2600	9.257	22.526	57.780	66.444
2700	9.274	23.453	58.107	66.794
2800	9.290	24.381	58.424	67.131
2900	9.306	25.311	58.730	67.457
3000	9.322	26.242	59.026	67.773
3200	9.353	28.109	59.592	68.376
3400	9.383	29.983	60.125	68.944
3600	9.413	31.863	60.630	69.481
3800	9.443	33.748	61.110	69.991
4000	9.472	35.640	61.566	70.476
4200	9.501	37.537	62.001	70.939
4400	9.530	39.440	62.418	71.381
4600	9.558	41.349	62.817	71.805
4800	9.587	43.264	63.200	72.213
5000	9.615	45.184	63.568	72.605
5200	9.643	47.110	63.923	72.982
5400	9.671	49.041	64.265	73.347
5600	9.699	50.978	64.596	73.699
5800	9.727	52.921	64.916	74.040
6000	9.755	54.869	65.225	74.370

Appendix 3.57   THERMODYNAMIC PROPERTIES OF LIH GAS

T	C_P^0	$(H^0 - H_0^0)$	$-(F^0 - H_0^0)/T$	S_T^0
DEG-K	CAL/MOLE DEG-K	KCAL/MOLE	CAL/MOLE DEG-K	CAL/MOLE DEG-K
100	6.964	0.696	26.225	33.185
200	6.984	1.393	31.051	38.016
273.15	7.060	1.906	33.224	40.202
298.15	7.106	2.083	33.835	40.822
400	7.364	2.819	35.896	42.944
500	7.656	3.570	37.478	44.619
600	7.922	4.350	38.790	46.039
700	8.146	5.153	39.916	47.278
800	8.330	5.978	40.906	48.378
900	8.479	6.818	41.792	49.368
1000	8.602	7.673	42.595	50.268
1100	8.705	8.538	43.331	51.093
1200	8.791	9.413	44.010	51.854
1300	8.866	10.296	44.641	52.561
1400	8.931	11.186	45.230	53.220
1500	8.989	12.082	45.784	53.838
1600	9.040	12.983	46.305	54.420
1700	9.088	13.890	46.799	54.969
1800	9.131	14.801	47.268	55.490
1900	9.171	15.716	47.713	55.985
2000	9.208	16.635	48.139	56.456
2100	9.244	17.557	48.546	56.906
2200	9.278	18.484	48.936	57.337
2300	9.310	19.413	49.310	57.750
2400	9.341	20.345	49.670	58.147
2500	9.371	21.281	50.017	58.529
2600	9.399	22.220	50.351	58.897
2700	9.428	23.161	50.674	59.253
2800	9.455	24.105	50.987	59.596
2900	9.482	25.052	51.290	59.928
3000	9.508	26.001	51.583	60.250
3200	9.559	27.908	52.144	60.865
3400	9.609	29.825	52.674	61.446
3600	9.658	31.752	53.177	61.997
3800	9.705	33.688	53.655	62.520
4000	9.752	35.634	54.111	63.019
4200	9.799	37.589	54.547	63.496
4400	9.845	39.553	54.964	63.953
4600	9.890	41.527	55.364	64.392
4800	9.935	43.509	55.749	64.814
5000	9.980	45.501	56.120	65.220
5200	10.025	47.501	56.478	65.613
5400	10.069	49.511	56.823	65.992
5600	10.113	51.529	57.157	66.359
5800	10.157	53.556	57.481	66.714
6000	10.201	55.592	57.794	67.059

Appendix 3.58 THERMODYNAMIC PROPERTIES OF LI2 GAS

T	C_P^0	$(H^0 - H_T^0)$	$-(F^0 - H_T^0)/T$	S_T^0
DEG-K	CAL/MOLE DEG-K	KCAL/MOLE	CAL/MOLE DEG-K	CAL/MOLE DEG-K
100	7.311	0.703	31.291	38.321
200	8.217	1.484	36.278	43.697
273.15	8.548	2.098	38.631	46.313
298.15	8.624	2.313	39.307	47.065
400	8.827	3.203	41.624	49.631
500	8.943	4.092	43.430	51.614
600	9.023	4.990	44.935	53.252
700	9.085	5.896	46.225	54.647
800	9.137	6.807	47.355	55.864
900	9.182	7.723	48.362	56.943
1000	9.224	8.643	49.269	57.912
1100	9.264	9.568	50.096	58.793
1200	9.302	10.496	50.855	59.601
1300	9.339	11.428	51.556	60.347
1400	9.374	12.364	52.209	61.041
1500	9.409	13.303	52.820	61.688
1600	9.444	14.245	53.393	62.297
1700	9.478	15.192	53.934	62.870
1800	9.512	16.141	54.446	63.413
1900	9.546	17.094	54.932	63.928
2000	9.580	18.050	55.394	64.419
2100	9.613	19.010	55.835	64.887
2200	9.646	19.973	56.256	65.335
2300	9.679	20.939	56.661	65.765
2400	9.712	21.909	57.049	66.177
2500	9.745	22.882	57.422	66.574
2600	9.778	23.858	57.781	66.957
2700	9.811	24.837	58.128	67.327
2800	9.844	25.820	58.463	67.684
2900	9.877	26.806	58.787	68.030
3000	9.909	27.795	59.101	68.366
3200	9.975	29.784	59.700	69.007
3400	10.040	31.785	60.265	69.614
3600	10.105	33.800	60.801	70.190
3800	10.170	35.827	61.309	70.738
4000	10.235	37.868	61.794	71.261
4200	10.300	39.921	62.257	71.762
4400	10.365	41.988	62.700	72.243
4600	10.430	44.067	63.125	72.705
4800	10.495	46.160	63.533	73.150
5000	10.560	48.265	63.927	73.580
5200	10.625	50.383	64.306	73.995
5400	10.690	52.515	64.672	74.397
5600	10.754	54.659	65.027	74.787
5800	10.819	56.817	65.370	75.166
6000	10.884	58.987	65.703	75.534

Appendix 3.59 THERMODYNAMIC PROPERTIES OF MGBR GAS

T	C_P^0	$(H^0 - H_0^0)$	$-(F^0 - H_0^0)/T$	S_T^0
DEG-K	CAL/MOLE DEG-K	KCAL/MOLE	CAL/MOLE DEG-K	CAL/MOLE DEG-K
100	7.234	0.701	42.804	49.812
200	8.105	1.471	47.761	55.117
273.15	8.442	2.078	50.092	57.698
298.15	8.517	2.290	50.761	58.441
400	8.716	3.168	53.054	60.975
500	8.821	4.046	54.841	62.932
600	8.886	4.931	56.328	64.546
700	8.930	5.822	57.602	65.920
800	8.964	6.717	58.718	67.115
900	8.991	7.615	59.711	68.172
1000	9.013	8.515	60.605	69.120
1100	9.033	9.417	61.419	69.980
1200	9.051	10.322	62.166	70.767
1300	9.068	11.228	62.856	71.492
1400	9.083	12.135	63.497	72.165
1500	9.098	13.044	64.096	72.792
1600	9.113	13.955	64.658	73.380
1700	9.127	14.867	65.187	73.933
1800	9.140	15.780	65.688	74.455
1900	9.153	16.695	66.162	74.949
2000	9.166	17.611	66.614	75.419
2100	9.179	18.528	67.044	75.867
2200	9.192	19.447	67.454	76.294
2300	9.205	20.366	67.848	76.703
2400	9.217	21.288	68.225	77.095
2500	9.230	22.210	68.587	77.471
2600	9.242	23.133	68.936	77.833
2700	9.254	24.058	69.272	78.183
2800	9.267	24.984	69.596	78.519
2900	9.279	25.912	69.910	78.845
3000	9.291	26.840	70.213	79.159
3200	9.315	28.701	70.791	79.760
3400	9.339	30.566	71.335	80.325
3600	9.363	32.436	71.850	80.860
3800	9.387	34.311	72.337	81.367
4000	9.411	36.191	72.801	81.849
4200	9.435	38.076	73.243	82.309
4400	9.459	39.965	73.665	82.748
4600	9.483	41.859	74.069	83.169
4800	9.506	43.758	74.457	83.573
5000	9.530	45.662	74.829	83.962
5200	9.554	47.570	75.188	84.336
5400	9.577	49.483	75.533	84.697
5600	9.601	51.401	75.867	85.046
5800	9.625	53.324	76.189	85.383
6000	9.649	55.251	76.501	85.710

Appendix 3.60　　THERMODYNAMIC PROPERTIES OF MGCL GAS

T	C_P	$(H_T - H_0)$	$-(F_T - H_0)/T$	S_T
DEG-K	CAL/MOLE DEG-K	KCAL/MOLE	CAL/MOLE DEG-K	CAL/MOLE DEG-K
100	7.074	0.697	40.348	47.322
200	7.822	1.442	45.241	52.449
273.15	8.221	2.030	47.521	54.951
298.15	8.319	2.236	48.175	55.675
400	8.584	3.099	50.415	58.161
500	8.729	3.965	52.164	60.094
600	8.818	4.843	53.623	61.694
700	8.879	5.728	54.876	63.058
800	8.923	6.618	55.974	64.247
900	8.958	7.512	56.953	65.300
1000	8.986	8.409	57.836	66.245
1100	9.010	9.309	58.640	67.102
1200	9.031	10.211	59.378	67.887
1300	9.050	11.115	60.061	68.611
1400	9.067	12.021	60.696	69.282
1500	9.084	12.928	61.289	69.908
1600	9.099	13.838	61.847	70.495
1700	9.114	14.748	62.372	71.047
1800	9.128	15.660	62.868	71.569
1900	9.142	16.574	63.339	72.062
2000	9.156	17.489	63.787	72.532
2100	9.169	18.405	64.215	72.979
2200	9.182	19.322	64.623	73.406
2300	9.195	20.241	65.013	73.814
2400	9.207	21.161	65.388	74.206
2500	9.220	22.083	65.749	74.582
2600	9.233	23.005	66.095	74.944
2700	9.245	23.929	66.430	75.292
2800	9.257	24.854	66.752	75.629
2900	9.269	25.781	67.064	75.954
3000	9.282	26.708	67.365	76.268
3200	9.306	28.567	67.941	76.868
3400	9.330	30.430	68.483	77.433
3600	9.353	32.299	68.995	77.967
3800	9.377	34.172	69.481	78.473
4000	9.401	36.050	69.942	78.955
4200	9.424	37.932	70.383	79.414
4400	9.448	39.819	70.803	79.853
4600	9.471	41.711	71.206	80.273
4800	9.495	43.608	71.592	80.677
5000	9.518	45.509	71.963	81.065
5200	9.542	47.415	72.321	81.439
5400	9.565	49.326	72.665	81.799
5600	9.588	51.241	72.997	82.148
5800	9.611	53.161	73.319	82.485
6000	9.635	55.086	73.630	82.811

317

Appendix 3.61 THERMODYNAMIC PROPERTIES OF MGF GAS

T	C_P^0	$(H^0 - H_0^0)$	$-(F^0 - H_0^0)/T$	S_T^0
DEG-K	CAL/MOLE DEG-K	KCAL/MOLE	CAL/MOLE DEG-K	CAL/MOLE DEG-K
100	6.965	0.696	37.962	44.920
200	7.283	1.404	42.797	49.818
273.15	7.666	1.951	45.002	52.145
298.15	7.786	2.144	45.630	52.821
400	8.172	2.958	47.772	55.167
500	8.416	3.788	49.442	57.019
600	8.577	4.639	50.837	58.568
700	8.686	5.502	52.039	59.899
800	8.765	6.375	53.096	61.064
900	8.824	7.254	54.040	62.100
1000	8.870	8.139	54.893	63.033
1100	8.907	9.028	55.672	63.880
1200	8.937	9.920	56.389	64.656
1300	8.963	10.815	57.053	65.372
1400	8.986	11.713	57.671	66.038
1500	9.006	12.613	58.250	66.658
1600	9.025	13.514	58.794	67.240
1700	9.042	14.417	59.307	67.788
1800	9.057	15.322	59.793	68.305
1900	9.072	16.229	60.254	68.795
2000	9.086	17.137	60.692	69.261
2100	9.099	18.046	61.111	69.704
2200	9.112	18.957	61.511	70.128
2300	9.124	19.868	61.895	70.533
2400	9.136	20.781	62.263	70.922
2500	9.148	21.696	62.617	71.295
2600	9.159	22.611	62.958	71.654
2700	9.171	23.527	63.286	72.000
2800	9.182	24.445	63.603	72.334
2900	9.192	25.364	63.910	72.656
3000	9.203	26.284	64.207	72.968
3200	9.224	28.126	64.773	73.563
3400	9.245	29.973	65.307	74.122
3600	9.265	31.824	65.811	74.651
3800	9.285	33.679	66.290	75.153
4000	9.305	35.538	66.745	75.630
4200	9.324	37.401	67.179	76.084
4400	9.344	39.268	67.594	76.518
4600	9.363	41.139	67.991	76.934
4800	9.383	43.013	68.372	77.333
5000	9.402	44.892	68.738	77.716
5200	9.421	46.774	69.090	78.085
5400	9.440	48.660	69.430	78.441
5600	9.459	50.550	69.758	78.785
5800	9.478	52.444	70.075	79.117
6000	9.497	54.341	70.382	79.439

Appendix 3.62   THERMODYNAMIC PROPERTIES OF MGH GAS

T	C_P^0	$(H - H_0^0)_T$	$-(F - H_0^0)_T/T$	S_T^0
DEG-K	CAL/MOLE DEG-K	KCAL/MOLE	CAL/MOLE DEG-K	CAL/MOLE DEG-K
100	6.961	0.696	31.569	38.527
200	6.974	1.392	36.393	43.355
273.15	7.033	1.904	38.564	45.536
298.15	7.071	2.081	39.175	46.153
400	7.298	2.811	41.232	48.260
500	7.573	3.555	42.808	49.918
600	7.835	4.326	44.113	51.323
700	8.061	5.121	45.233	52.548
800	8.249	5.937	46.216	53.637
900	8.404	6.769	47.096	54.618
1000	8.532	7.616	47.894	55.510
1100	8.639	8.475	48.624	56.329
1200	8.730	9.344	49.298	57.084
1300	8.807	10.221	49.924	57.786
1400	8.875	11.105	50.509	58.441
1500	8.935	11.995	51.059	59.056
1600	8.988	12.892	51.577	59.634
1700	9.036	13.793	52.067	60.180
1800	9.080	14.699	52.532	60.698
1900	9.121	15.609	52.975	61.190
2000	9.158	16.523	53.398	61.659
2100	9.194	17.440	53.802	62.107
2200	9.227	18.361	54.189	62.535
2300	9.259	19.286	54.561	62.946
2400	9.290	20.213	54.919	63.341
2500	9.319	21.144	55.263	63.721
2600	9.347	22.077	55.596	64.087
2700	9.374	23.013	55.917	64.440
2800	9.401	23.952	56.227	64.781
2900	9.427	24.893	56.528	65.112
3000	9.452	25.837	56.819	65.432
3200	9.501	27.732	57.377	66.043
3400	9.549	29.638	57.904	66.621
3600	9.595	31.552	58.403	67.168
3800	9.640	33.476	58.878	67.688
4000	9.685	35.408	59.331	68.183
4200	9.729	37.349	59.764	68.657
4400	9.772	39.299	60.179	69.111
4600	9.814	41.258	60.577	69.546
4800	9.857	43.225	60.959	69.965
5000	9.899	45.201	61.328	70.368
5200	9.940	47.185	61.683	70.757
5400	9.982	49.177	62.026	71.133
5600	10.023	51.177	62.358	71.496
5800	10.064	53.186	62.679	71.849
6000	10.105	55.203	62.990	72.191

Appendix 3.63   THERMODYNAMIC PROPERTIES OF MGH+ GAS

T	C_P^0	$(H^0 - H_0^0)$	$-(F^0 - H_0^0)/T$	S_T^0
DEG-K	CAL/MOLE DEG-K	KCAL/MOLE	CAL/MOLE DEG-K	CAL/MOLE DEG-K
100	6.960	0.696	30.001	36.958
200	6.968	1.392	34.824	41.785
273.15	6.997	1.903	36.994	43.960
298.15	7.018	2.078	37.605	44.574
400	7.176	2.800	39.656	46.656
500	7.402	3.528	41.224	48.280
600	7.644	4.281	42.517	49.651
700	7.868	5.056	43.623	50.847
800	8.063	5.853	44.594	51.910
900	8.229	6.668	45.461	52.870
1000	8.368	7.498	46.246	53.744
1100	8.486	8.341	46.965	54.548
1200	8.586	9.195	47.628	55.291
1300	8.672	10.058	48.244	55.981
1400	8.747	10.929	48.820	56.627
1500	8.812	11.807	49.361	57.232
1600	8.870	12.691	49.871	57.803
1700	8.922	13.581	50.354	58.342
1800	8.968	14.475	50.812	58.854
1900	9.011	15.374	51.248	59.340
2000	9.050	16.277	51.664	59.803
2100	9.087	17.184	52.062	60.245
2200	9.121	18.095	52.444	60.669
2300	9.153	19.008	52.811	61.075
2400	9.183	19.925	53.163	61.465
2500	9.211	20.845	53.503	61.841
2600	9.239	21.767	53.830	62.202
2700	9.265	22.692	54.147	62.552
2800	9.291	23.620	54.453	62.889
2900	9.315	24.551	54.750	63.216
3000	9.339	25.483	55.037	63.532
3200	9.385	27.356	55.587	64.136
3400	9.429	29.237	56.107	64.706
3600	9.471	31.127	56.600	65.246
3800	9.511	33.025	57.069	65.759
4000	9.551	34.932	57.515	66.248
4200	9.590	36.846	57.943	66.715
4400	9.628	38.768	58.352	67.162
4600	9.666	40.697	58.744	67.591
4800	9.703	42.634	59.121	68.003
5000	9.740	44.578	59.485	68.400
5200	9.776	46.530	59.835	68.783
5400	9.812	48.489	60.173	69.152
5600	9.848	50.455	60.500	69.510
5800	9.883	52.428	60.817	69.856
6000	9.919	54.408	61.124	70.192

THERMODYNAMIC PROPERTIES OF MGO GAS

T	C_P^0	$(H^0 - H_0^0)_T$	$-(F^0 - H_0^0)_T/T$	S_T^0
DEG-K	CAL/MOLE DEG-K	KCAL/MOLE	CAL/MOLE DEG-K	CAL/MOLE DEG-K
100	6.958	0.696	38.176	45.132
200	7.105	1.396	43.001	49.982
273.15	7.393	1.926	45.186	52.237
298.15	7.502	2.112	45.805	52.889
400	7.903	2.897	47.909	55.152
500	8.198	3.703	49.543	56.949
600	8.408	4.534	50.906	58.463
700	8.558	5.383	52.081	59.771
800	8.670	6.244	53.116	60.922
900	8.755	7.116	54.041	61.948
1000	8.822	7.995	54.879	62.874
1100	8.876	8.880	55.645	63.717
1200	8.921	9.770	56.350	64.492
1300	8.960	10.664	57.004	65.207
1400	8.994	11.561	57.614	65.872
1500	9.024	12.462	58.186	66.494
1600	9.051	13.366	58.723	67.077
1700	9.076	14.273	59.231	67.627
1800	9.099	15.181	59.712	68.146
1900	9.121	16.092	60.169	68.639
2000	9.141	17.005	60.604	69.107
2100	9.161	17.921	61.020	69.554
2200	9.180	18.838	61.418	69.980
2300	9.198	19.756	61.799	70.389
2400	9.215	20.677	62.165	70.780
2500	9.232	21.599	62.517	71.157
2600	9.249	22.524	62.857	71.519
2700	9.265	23.449	63.184	71.869
2800	9.281	24.376	63.500	72.206
2900	9.296	25.305	63.806	72.532
3000	9.312	26.236	64.102	72.847
3200	9.342	28.101	64.668	73.449
3400	9.372	29.973	65.201	74.017
3600	9.401	31.850	65.706	74.553
3800	9.430	33.733	66.185	75.062
4000	9.458	35.622	66.641	75.547
4200	9.487	37.516	67.076	76.009
4400	9.515	39.416	67.492	76.451
4600	9.543	41.322	67.891	76.874
4800	9.570	43.233	68.274	77.281
5000	9.598	45.150	68.642	77.672
5200	9.625	47.073	68.997	78.049
5400	9.653	49.000	69.339	78.413
5600	9.680	50.934	69.669	78.764
5800	9.707	52.872	69.989	79.105
6000	9.734	54.817	70.298	79.434

Appendix 3.65   THERMODYNAMIC PROPERTIES OF NF GAS

T	C_P^0	$(H^0 - H_0^0)$	$-(F^0 - H_0^0)/T$	S_T^0
DEG-K	CAL/MOLE DEG-K	KCAL/MOLE	CAL/MOLE DEG-K	CAL/MOLE DEG-K
100	6.961	0.696	35.920	42.878
200	7.124	1.397	40.747	47.733
273.15	7.426	1.929	42.935	49.996
298.15	7.537	2.116	43.555	50.651
400	7.942	2.905	45.663	52.925
500	8.235	3.715	47.301	54.731
600	8.441	4.549	48.670	56.252
700	8.589	5.401	49.849	57.565
800	8.698	6.266	50.887	58.719
900	8.782	7.140	51.815	59.748
1000	8.848	8.021	52.656	60.677
1100	8.902	8.909	53.424	61.523
1200	8.947	9.801	54.132	62.300
1300	8.986	10.698	54.788	63.017
1400	9.020	11.598	55.400	63.685
1500	9.051	12.502	55.973	64.308
1600	9.079	13.408	56.513	64.893
1700	9.104	14.318	57.022	65.444
1800	9.128	15.229	57.504	65.965
1900	9.151	16.143	57.963	66.459
2000	9.172	17.059	58.400	66.929
2100	9.193	17.978	58.816	67.377
2200	9.213	18.898	59.215	67.805
2300	9.232	19.820	59.598	68.215
2400	9.250	20.744	59.965	68.609
2500	9.268	21.670	60.318	68.987
2600	9.286	22.598	60.659	69.350
2700	9.304	23.527	60.987	69.701
2800	9.321	24.459	61.305	70.040
2900	9.338	25.392	61.612	70.367
3000	9.354	26.326	61.909	70.684
3200	9.387	28.200	62.476	71.289
3400	9.420	30.081	63.012	71.859
3600	9.451	31.968	63.518	72.398
3800	9.483	33.862	63.999	72.910
4000	9.514	35.761	64.457	73.397
4200	9.545	37.667	64.894	73.862
4400	9.575	39.579	65.312	74.307
4600	9.606	41.497	65.712	74.733
4800	9.636	43.422	66.097	75.143
5000	9.667	45.352	66.466	75.537
5200	9.697	47.288	66.823	75.917
5400	9.727	49.231	67.166	76.283
5600	9.757	51.179	67.498	76.637
5800	9.787	53.133	67.819	76.980
6000	9.817	55.094	68.130	77.313

Appendix 3.66   THERMODYNAMIC PROPERTIES OF NO   GAS

T	C_P^0	$(H^0 - H_0^0)_T$	$-(F^0 - H_0^0)/T$	S_T^0
DEG-K	CAL/MOLE DEG-K	KCAL/MOLE	CAL/MOLE DEG-K	CAL/MOLE DEG-K
100	6.956	0.696	35.870	42.825
200	6.958	1.391	40.691	47.648
273.15	6.968	1.901	42.860	49.817
298.15	6.978	2.075	43.469	50.428
400	7.067	2.789	45.516	52.489
500	7.228	3.504	47.075	54.082
600	7.425	4.236	48.357	55.417
700	7.625	4.989	49.450	56.577
800	7.808	5.761	50.407	57.607
900	7.970	6.550	51.259	58.537
1000	8.108	7.354	52.030	59.384
1100	8.226	8.171	52.734	60.162
1200	8.326	8.998	53.384	60.882
1300	8.410	9.835	53.986	61.552
1400	8.483	10.680	54.549	62.178
1500	8.545	11.531	55.078	62.765
1600	8.599	12.389	55.576	63.319
1700	8.646	13.251	56.047	63.841
1800	8.687	14.118	56.494	64.337
1900	8.723	14.988	56.919	64.807
2000	8.755	15.862	57.325	65.256
2100	8.784	16.739	57.713	65.684
2200	8.810	17.619	58.084	66.093
2300	8.834	18.501	58.441	66.485
2400	8.855	19.386	58.784	66.862
2500	8.875	20.272	59.115	67.223
2600	8.893	21.161	59.433	67.572
2700	8.910	22.051	59.741	67.908
2800	8.925	22.943	60.038	68.232
2900	8.940	23.836	60.326	68.546
3000	8.953	24.730	60.605	68.849
3200	8.978	26.524	61.139	69.428
3400	9.001	28.322	61.643	69.973
3600	9.021	30.124	62.120	70.488
3800	9.040	31.930	62.573	70.976
4000	9.058	33.740	63.005	71.440
4200	9.074	35.553	63.417	71.882
4400	9.089	37.369	63.812	72.305
4600	9.104	39.189	64.190	72.709
4800	9.118	41.011	64.553	73.097
5000	9.132	42.836	64.902	73.469
5200	9.145	44.664	65.239	73.828
5400	9.158	46.494	65.563	74.173
5600	9.170	48.327	65.877	74.507
5800	9.182	50.162	66.180	74.829
6000	9.194	52.000	66.473	75.140

Appendix 3.67   THERMODYNAMIC PROPERTIES OF NO+ GAS

T	C_P^0	$(H^0 - H_0^0)_T$	$-(F^0 - H_0^0)/T$	S_T^0
DEG-K	CAL/MOLE DEG-K	KCAL/MOLE	CAL/MOLE DEG-K	CAL/MOLE DEG-K
100	6.955	0.696	32.908	39.863
200	6.957	1.391	37.730	44.686
273.15	6.959	1.900	39.898	46.855
298.15	6.961	2.074	40.507	47.464
400	6.990	2.784	42.552	49.513
500	7.068	3.487	44.107	51.080
600	7.193	4.199	45.380	52.379
700	7.346	4.926	46.462	53.499
800	7.507	5.669	47.404	54.490
900	7.664	6.427	48.242	55.384
1000	7.809	7.201	48.998	56.199
1100	7.940	7.989	49.687	56.949
1200	8.055	8.789	50.321	57.645
1300	8.157	9.599	50.910	58.294
1400	8.246	10.420	51.459	58.902
1500	8.324	11.248	51.975	59.474
1600	8.392	12.084	52.461	60.013
1700	8.452	12.926	52.920	60.524
1800	8.505	13.774	53.356	61.008
1900	8.552	14.627	53.771	61.469
2000	8.594	15.484	54.167	61.909
2100	8.632	16.346	54.546	62.329
2200	8.665	17.211	54.909	62.732
2300	8.696	18.079	55.257	63.118
2400	8.723	18.950	55.593	63.488
2500	8.748	19.823	55.916	63.845
2600	8.771	20.699	56.227	64.188
2700	8.792	21.578	56.528	64.520
2800	8.812	22.458	56.819	64.840
2900	8.829	23.340	57.101	65.150
3000	8.846	24.224	57.375	65.449
3200	8.876	25.996	57.897	66.021
3400	8.902	27.774	58.391	66.560
3600	8.925	29.556	58.859	67.069
3800	8.946	31.344	59.304	67.553
4000	8.965	33.135	59.728	68.012
4200	8.982	34.929	60.133	68.450
4400	8.998	36.727	60.521	68.868
4600	9.013	38.529	60.892	69.268
4800	9.027	40.333	61.250	69.652
5000	9.040	42.139	61.593	70.021
5200	9.053	43.949	61.924	70.376
5400	9.065	45.761	62.243	70.718
5600	9.076	47.575	62.552	71.047
5800	9.087	49.391	62.851	71.366
6000	9.097	51.209	63.140	71.674

Appendix 3.68 THERMODYNAMIC PROPERTIES OF NS GAS

T	C_P^0	$(H^0 - H_0^0)_T$	$-(F^0 - H_0^0)/T$	S_T^0
DEG-K	CAL/MOLE DEG-K	KCAL/MOLE	CAL/MOLE DEG-K	CAL/MOLE DEG-K
100	6.957	0.696	38.715	45.671
200	6.984	1.392	43.537	50.497
273.15	7.101	1.906	45.709	52.688
298.15	7.163	2.085	46.321	53.313
400	7.468	2.829	48.386	55.459
500	7.766	3.591	49.975	57.158
600	8.013	4.381	51.295	58.597
700	8.206	5.192	52.430	59.847
800	8.356	6.021	53.427	60.953
900	8.472	6.862	54.320	61.944
1000	8.563	7.714	55.128	62.842
1100	8.636	8.574	55.867	63.662
1200	8.695	9.441	56.548	64.416
1300	8.744	10.313	57.181	65.114
1400	8.785	11.189	57.771	65.763
1500	8.820	12.070	58.324	66.370
1600	8.850	12.953	58.845	66.941
1700	8.876	13.840	59.337	67.478
1800	8.899	14.728	59.804	67.986
1900	8.920	15.619	60.247	68.468
2000	8.938	16.512	60.670	68.926
2100	8.955	17.407	61.073	69.362
2200	8.971	18.303	61.460	69.779
2300	8.985	19.201	61.830	70.178
2400	8.998	20.100	62.186	70.561
2500	9.011	21.001	62.528	70.928
2600	9.022	21.902	62.858	71.282
2700	9.034	22.805	63.177	71.623
2800	9.044	23.709	63.484	71.952
2900	9.054	24.614	63.782	72.269
3000	9.064	25.520	64.070	72.576
3200	9.082	27.334	64.620	73.162
3400	9.100	29.153	65.139	73.713
3600	9.116	30.974	65.630	74.234
3800	9.132	32.799	66.096	74.727
4000	9.147	34.627	66.539	75.196
4200	9.162	36.458	66.962	75.642
4400	9.176	38.292	67.366	76.069
4600	9.190	40.128	67.753	76.477
4800	9.204	41.968	68.125	76.868
5000	9.217	43.810	68.482	77.244
5200	9.231	45.655	68.826	77.606
5400	9.244	47.502	69.158	77.955
5600	9.257	49.352	69.478	78.291
5800	9.270	51.205	69.788	78.616
6000	9.283	53.060	70.087	78.931

Appendix 3.69   THERMODYNAMIC PROPERTIES OF N2   GAS

T	C_P^0	$(H_T^0 - H_0^0)$	$-(F_T^0 - H_0^0)/T$	S_T^0
DEG-K	CAL/MOLE DEG-K	KCAL/MOLE	CAL/MOLE DEG-K	CAL/MOLE DEG-K
100	6.955	0.696	31.203	38.159
200	6.957	1.391	36.025	42.981
273.15	6.959	1.900	38.193	45.150
298.15	6.961	2.074	38.803	45.760
400	6.991	2.784	40.848	47.808
500	7.070	3.487	42.402	49.376
600	7.196	4.200	43.676	50.675
700	7.351	4.927	44.757	51.796
800	7.513	5.670	45.700	52.788
900	7.670	6.430	46.538	53.682
1000	7.815	7.204	47.294	54.498
1100	7.945	7.992	47.984	55.249
1200	8.060	8.792	48.618	55.945
1300	8.161	9.603	49.207	56.595
1400	8.250	10.424	49.757	57.203
1500	8.327	11.253	50.273	57.775
1600	8.395	12.089	50.758	58.314
1700	8.455	12.932	51.218	58.825
1800	8.508	13.780	51.654	59.310
1900	8.554	14.633	52.069	59.771
2000	8.596	15.491	52.466	60.211
2100	8.633	16.352	52.844	60.631
2200	8.667	17.217	53.208	61.034
2300	8.697	18.085	53.556	61.420
2400	8.724	18.956	53.892	61.790
2500	8.749	19.830	54.215	62.147
2600	8.771	20.706	54.527	62.491
2700	8.792	21.584	54.828	62.822
2800	8.811	22.464	55.119	63.142
2900	8.829	23.347	55.401	63.452
3000	8.845	24.230	55.674	63.751
3200	8.875	26.002	56.197	64.323
3400	8.900	27.780	56.691	64.862
3600	8.923	29.562	57.159	65.371
3800	8.944	31.349	57.604	65.854
4000	8.963	33.140	58.028	66.313
4200	8.980	34.934	58.434	66.751
4400	8.995	36.731	58.821	67.169
4600	9.010	38.532	59.193	67.569
4800	9.024	40.335	59.550	67.953
5000	9.037	42.142	59.894	68.322
5200	9.049	43.950	60.225	68.676
5400	9.061	45.761	60.544	69.018
5600	9.072	47.574	60.853	69.348
5800	9.082	49.390	61.151	69.666
6000	9.093	51.207	61.440	69.975

Appendix 3.70   THERMODYNAMIC PROPERTIES OF N2+ GAS

T	C_P^0	$(H^0 - H_0^0)$	$-(F^0 - H_0^0)/T$	S_T^0
DEG-K	CAL/MOLE DEG-K	KCAL/MOLE	CAL/MOLE DEG-K	CAL/MOLE DEG-K
100	6.955	0.696	32.660	39.616
200	6.957	1.391	37.482	44.439
273.15	6.961	1.900	39.651	46.608
298.15	6.964	2.074	40.260	47.217
400	7.008	2.785	42.305	49.269
500	7.111	3.491	43.861	50.842
600	7.261	4.209	45.136	52.152
700	7.433	4.944	46.221	53.284
800	7.605	5.696	47.168	54.288
900	7.767	6.464	48.010	55.193
1000	7.912	7.248	48.770	56.019
1100	8.040	8.046	49.464	56.779
1200	8.151	8.856	50.103	57.483
1300	8.248	9.676	50.697	58.140
1400	8.332	10.505	51.250	58.754
1500	8.405	11.342	51.770	59.331
1600	8.469	12.186	52.260	59.876
1700	8.525	13.035	52.723	60.391
1800	8.574	13.890	53.163	60.880
1900	8.617	14.750	53.581	61.345
2000	8.656	15.614	53.981	61.788
2100	8.691	16.481	54.363	62.211
2200	8.722	17.352	54.729	62.616
2300	8.750	18.225	55.080	63.004
2400	8.775	19.102	55.418	63.377
2500	8.798	19.980	55.744	63.736
2600	8.820	20.861	56.058	64.081
2700	8.839	21.744	56.361	64.414
2800	8.857	22.629	56.654	64.736
2900	8.874	23.516	56.939	65.047
3000	8.890	24.404	57.214	65.348
3200	8.918	26.185	57.740	65.923
3400	8.943	27.971	58.238	66.465
3600	8.966	29.762	58.709	66.976
3800	8.986	31.557	59.157	67.462
4000	9.005	33.356	59.584	67.923
4200	9.022	35.159	59.992	68.363
4400	9.038	36.965	60.382	68.783
4600	9.053	38.774	60.756	69.185
4800	9.067	40.586	61.115	69.571
5000	9.081	42.401	61.461	69.941
5200	9.094	44.218	61.794	70.297
5400	9.106	46.038	62.115	70.641
5600	9.118	47.861	62.426	70.972
5800	9.130	49.685	62.726	71.292
6000	9.141	51.513	63.017	71.602

Appendix 3.71 THERMODYNAMIC PROPERTIES OF NABR GAS

T	C_P^0	$(H^0 - H_0^0)$	$-(F^0 - H_0^0)/T$	S_T^0
DEG-K	CAL/MOLE DEG-K	KCAL/MOLE	CAL/MOLE DEG-K	CAL/MOLE DEG-K
100	7.475	0.708	41.649	48.725
200	8.355	1.506	46.693	54.222
273.15	8.624	2.128	49.080	56.871
298.15	8.682	2.344	49.766	57.629
400	8.833	3.237	52.111	60.204
500	8.916	4.125	53.934	62.184
600	8.970	5.019	55.449	63.815
700	9.011	5.918	56.746	65.201
800	9.044	6.821	57.880	66.406
900	9.073	7.727	58.888	67.473
1000	9.098	8.636	59.795	68.430
1100	9.122	9.547	60.620	69.299
1200	9.145	10.460	61.377	70.093
1300	9.167	11.376	62.076	70.826
1400	9.188	12.293	62.725	71.506
1500	9.209	13.213	63.332	72.141
1600	9.229	14.135	63.902	72.736
1700	9.249	15.059	64.438	73.296
1800	9.269	15.985	64.945	73.825
1900	9.289	16.913	65.426	74.327
2000	9.308	17.843	65.883	74.804
2100	9.328	18.774	66.318	75.259
2200	9.347	19.708	66.735	75.693
2300	9.366	20.644	67.133	76.109
2400	9.385	21.581	67.516	76.508
2500	9.404	22.521	67.883	76.891
2600	9.423	23.462	68.237	77.261
2700	9.442	24.406	68.577	77.617
2800	9.461	25.351	68.906	77.960
2900	9.480	26.298	69.224	78.293
3000	9.499	27.247	69.532	78.614
3200	9.537	29.150	70.119	79.229
3400	9.575	31.061	70.672	79.808
3600	9.612	32.980	71.195	80.356
3800	9.650	34.906	71.691	80.877
4000	9.687	36.840	72.163	81.373
4200	9.725	38.781	72.613	81.846
4400	9.762	40.730	73.043	82.300
4600	9.800	42.686	73.455	82.734
4800	9.837	44.650	73.850	83.152
5000	9.875	46.621	74.230	83.555
5200	9.912	48.600	74.597	83.943
5400	9.949	50.586	74.950	84.317
5600	9.987	52.579	75.291	84.680
5800	10.024	54.581	75.621	85.031
6000	10.062	56.589	75.940	85.372

Appendix 3.72   THERMODYNAMIC PROPERTIES OF NACL GAS

T	C_P^0	$(H^0 - H_0^0)$	$-(F^0 - H_0^0)/T$	S_T^0
DEG-K	CAL/MOLE DEG-K	KCAL/MOLE	CAL/MOLE DEG-K	CAL/MOLE DEG-K
100	7.260	0.701	39.198	46.212
200	8.143	1.476	44.164	51.542
273.15	8.477	2.085	46.503	54.135
298.15	8.552	2.298	47.174	54.880
400	8.751	3.180	49.475	57.425
500	8.858	4.061	51.268	59.390
600	8.927	4.950	52.761	61.012
700	8.977	5.846	54.041	62.392
800	9.015	6.745	55.161	63.593
900	9.048	7.648	56.158	64.657
1000	9.076	8.555	57.057	65.611
1100	9.102	9.464	57.874	66.478
1200	9.125	10.375	58.625	67.271
1300	9.148	11.289	59.318	68.002
1400	9.169	12.204	59.963	68.681
1500	9.190	13.122	60.566	69.314
1600	9.210	14.042	61.131	69.908
1700	9.230	14.965	61.664	70.467
1800	9.250	15.889	62.168	70.995
1900	9.269	16.814	62.646	71.495
2000	9.288	17.742	63.100	71.971
2100	9.307	18.672	63.534	72.425
2200	9.326	19.604	63.948	72.858
2300	9.345	20.537	64.344	73.273
2400	9.363	21.473	64.725	73.672
2500	9.382	22.410	65.090	74.054
2600	9.400	23.349	65.442	74.422
2700	9.418	24.290	65.781	74.778
2800	9.437	25.233	66.109	75.120
2900	9.455	26.177	66.425	75.452
3000	9.473	27.124	66.731	75.773
3200	9.509	29.022	67.316	76.385
3400	9.546	30.927	67.867	76.963
3600	9.582	32.840	68.387	77.509
3800	9.618	34.760	68.881	78.028
4000	9.654	36.687	69.351	78.523
4200	9.690	38.622	69.799	78.995
4400	9.726	40.563	70.227	79.446
4600	9.762	42.512	70.638	79.879
4800	9.798	44.468	71.031	80.296
5000	9.833	46.431	71.410	80.696
5200	9.869	48.401	71.775	81.083
5400	9.905	50.379	72.126	81.456
5600	9.941	52.363	72.466	81.817
5800	9.977	54.355	72.795	82.166
6000	10.012	56.354	73.113	82.505

THERMODYNAMIC PROPERTIES OF NAF   GAS

T	C_P^0	$(H^0 - H_0^0)$	$-(F^0 - H_0^0)/T$	S_T^0
DEG-K	CAL/MOLE DEG-K	KCAL/MOLE	CAL/MOLE DEG-K	CAL/MOLE DEG-K
100	6.994	0.696	36.636	43.598
200	7.531	1.419	41.491	48.586
273.15	7.952	1.986	43.728	50.998
298.15	8.066	2.186	44.367	51.700
400	8.399	3.026	46.556	54.121
500	8.591	3.876	48.265	56.017
600	8.711	4.742	49.692	57.595
700	8.792	5.617	50.920	58.944
800	8.850	6.500	51.998	60.122
900	8.894	7.387	52.960	61.167
1000	8.928	8.278	53.828	62.106
1100	8.956	9.172	54.620	62.959
1200	8.980	10.069	55.348	63.739
1300	9.001	10.968	56.022	64.459
1400	9.019	11.869	56.648	65.126
1500	9.036	12.772	57.234	65.749
1600	9.052	13.676	57.785	66.333
1700	9.066	14.582	58.304	66.882
1800	9.080	15.490	58.795	67.401
1900	9.093	16.398	59.261	67.892
2000	9.106	17.308	59.705	68.359
2100	9.118	18.219	60.127	68.803
2200	9.130	19.132	60.531	69.228
2300	9.141	20.045	60.918	69.634
2400	9.153	20.960	61.290	70.023
2500	9.164	21.876	61.647	70.397
2600	9.175	22.793	61.990	70.756
2700	9.185	23.711	62.321	71.103
2800	9.196	24.630	62.641	71.437
2900	9.207	25.550	62.950	71.760
3000	9.217	26.471	63.249	72.072
3200	9.238	28.317	63.819	72.668
3400	9.258	30.166	64.356	73.229
3600	9.278	32.020	64.864	73.758
3800	9.298	33.878	65.345	74.260
4000	9.318	35.739	65.803	74.738
4200	9.338	37.605	66.239	75.193
4400	9.358	39.475	66.656	75.628
4600	9.378	41.348	67.056	76.044
4800	9.397	43.226	67.439	76.444
5000	9.417	45.107	67.806	76.828
5200	9.436	46.992	68.161	77.198
5400	9.456	48.881	68.502	77.554
5600	9.475	50.774	68.831	77.898
5800	9.494	52.671	69.150	78.231
6000	9.514	54.572	69.458	78.553

Appendix 3.74　　THERMODYNAMIC PROPERTIES OF NAH　GAS

T	C_P^0	$(H^0 - H_0^0)$	$-(F^0 - H_0^0)/T$	S_T^0
DEG-K	CAL/MOLE DEG-K	KCAL/MOLE	CAL/MOLE DEG-K	CAL/MOLE DEG-K
100	6.964	0.696	30.377	37.337
200	7.011	1.394	35.203	42.171
273.15	7.165	1.911	37.379	44.377
298.15	7.240	2.091	37.992	45.007
400	7.590	2.846	40.067	47.183
500	7.911	3.622	41.668	48.912
600	8.173	4.427	43.001	50.379
700	8.377	5.255	44.148	51.655
800	8.538	6.101	45.158	52.784
900	8.665	6.961	46.063	53.797
1000	8.768	7.833	46.883	54.716
1100	8.854	8.714	47.634	55.556
1200	8.927	9.603	48.326	56.329
1300	8.990	10.499	48.970	57.046
1400	9.046	11.401	49.571	57.715
1500	9.096	12.308	50.135	58.341
1600	9.142	13.220	50.666	58.929
1700	9.184	14.136	51.169	59.485
1800	9.223	15.057	51.646	60.011
1900	9.259	15.981	52.099	60.510
2000	9.294	16.909	52.532	60.986
2100	9.328	17.840	52.945	61.440
2200	9.360	18.774	53.341	61.875
2300	9.391	19.712	53.721	62.292
2400	9.421	20.652	54.087	62.692
2500	9.450	21.596	54.439	63.077
2600	9.479	22.542	54.778	63.448
2700	9.507	23.492	55.106	63.807
2800	9.534	24.444	55.423	64.153
2900	9.561	25.398	55.730	64.488
3000	9.588	26.356	56.027	64.813
3200	9.641	28.279	56.596	65.433
3400	9.692	30.212	57.133	66.019
3600	9.743	32.156	57.642	66.575
3800	9.793	34.109	58.127	67.103
4000	9.843	36.073	58.588	67.606
4200	9.892	38.046	59.029	68.088
4400	9.941	40.030	59.451	68.549
4600	9.989	42.023	59.857	68.992
4800	10.037	44.025	60.246	69.418
5000	10.085	46.037	60.621	69.829
5200	10.133	48.059	60.983	70.225
5400	10.181	50.091	61.333	70.609
5600	10.228	52.132	61.670	70.980
5800	10.276	54.182	61.998	71.339
6000	10.323	56.242	62.315	71.689

331

Appendix 3.75 THERMODYNAMIC PROPERTIES OF NAO GAS

T	C_P^0	$(H^0 - H_0^0)$	$-(F^0 - H_0^0)/T$	S_T^0
DEG-K	CAL/MOLE DEG-K	KCAL/MOLE	CAL/MOLE DEG-K	CAL/MOLE DEG-K
100	6.972	0.696	39.129	46.088
200	7.368	1.409	43.970	51.013
273.15	7.775	1.963	46.185	53.371
298.15	7.895	2.159	46.817	54.058
400	8.270	2.984	48.976	56.434
500	8.500	3.823	50.661	58.306
600	8.649	4.681	52.069	59.870
700	8.751	5.551	53.281	61.212
800	8.825	6.430	54.348	62.385
900	8.882	7.316	55.300	63.428
1000	8.927	8.206	56.160	64.366
1100	8.964	9.101	56.946	65.219
1200	8.995	9.999	57.668	66.000
1300	9.023	10.900	58.337	66.721
1400	9.047	11.803	58.960	67.391
1500	9.070	12.709	59.543	68.016
1600	9.090	13.617	60.091	68.602
1700	9.110	14.527	60.608	69.154
1800	9.128	15.439	61.098	69.675
1900	9.146	16.353	61.562	70.169
2000	9.162	17.268	62.004	70.638
2100	9.179	18.185	62.426	71.086
2200	9.195	19.104	62.830	71.513
2300	9.210	20.024	63.216	71.922
2400	9.225	20.946	63.587	72.314
2500	9.240	21.869	63.944	72.691
2600	9.255	22.794	64.287	73.054
2700	9.269	23.720	64.618	73.404
2800	9.284	24.648	64.938	73.741
2900	9.298	25.577	65.247	74.067
3000	9.312	26.507	65.547	74.382
3200	9.339	28.372	66.118	74.984
3400	9.367	30.243	66.656	75.551
3600	9.394	32.119	67.166	76.087
3800	9.421	34.000	67.649	76.596
4000	9.448	35.887	68.108	77.080
4200	9.474	37.779	68.546	77.542
4400	9.501	39.677	68.965	77.983
4600	9.527	41.580	69.367	78.406
4800	9.553	43.488	69.752	78.812
5000	9.580	45.401	70.122	79.202
5200	9.606	47.320	70.479	79.579
5400	9.632	49.243	70.823	79.942
5600	9.658	51.172	71.154	80.292
5800	9.684	53.106	71.475	80.632
6000	9.710	55.046	71.786	80.961

THERMODYNAMIC PROPERTIES OF NA2   GAS

T	C_P^0	$(H^0 - H_0^0)$	$-(F^0 - H_0^0)/T$	S_T^0
DEG-K	CAL/MOLE DEG-K	KCAL/MOLE	CAL/MOLE DEG-K	CAL/MOLE DEG-K
100	8.302	0.749	37.998	45.485
200	8.816	1.611	43.387	51.444
273.15	8.936	2.261	45.934	54.211
298.15	8.963	2.485	46.661	54.995
400	9.043	3.402	49.136	57.641
500	9.101	4.309	51.047	59.665
600	9.150	5.222	52.626	61.329
700	9.195	6.139	53.973	62.743
800	9.237	7.061	55.148	63.973
900	9.278	7.986	56.190	65.064
1000	9.319	8.916	57.127	66.044
1100	9.359	9.850	57.979	66.934
1200	9.399	10.788	58.759	67.750
1300	9.438	11.730	59.480	68.503
1400	9.477	12.676	60.150	69.204
1500	9.516	13.625	60.776	69.860
1600	9.555	14.579	61.363	70.475
1700	9.594	15.536	61.916	71.055
1800	9.633	16.498	62.439	71.605
1900	9.672	17.463	62.936	72.127
2000	9.711	18.432	63.408	72.624
2100	9.749	19.405	63.858	73.099
2200	9.788	20.382	64.288	73.553
2300	9.827	21.363	64.701	73.989
2400	9.865	22.347	65.097	74.408
2500	9.904	23.336	65.477	74.811
2600	9.942	24.328	65.844	75.201
2700	9.981	25.324	66.197	75.577
2800	10.020	26.324	66.539	75.940
2900	10.058	27.328	66.869	76.293
3000	10.097	28.336	67.189	76.634
3200	10.174	30.363	67.800	77.288
3400	10.251	32.406	68.376	77.907
3600	10.328	34.464	68.922	78.496
3800	10.405	36.537	69.441	79.056
4000	10.482	38.626	69.935	79.592
4200	10.559	40.730	70.407	80.105
4400	10.636	42.849	70.860	80.598
4600	10.713	44.984	71.293	81.072
4800	10.790	47.135	71.710	81.530
5000	10.868	49.301	72.112	81.972
5200	10.945	51.482	72.500	82.400
5400	11.022	53.678	72.874	82.814
5600	11.099	55.890	73.236	83.217
5800	11.176	58.118	73.587	83.607
6000	11.253	60.361	73.927	83.988

Appendix 3.77   THERMODYNAMIC PROPERTIES OF OH   GAS

T	C_p^0	$(H^0 - H_0^0)_T$	$-(F^0 - H_0^0)/T$	S_T^0
DEG-K	CAL/MOLE DEG-K	KCAL/MOLE	CAL/MOLE DEG-K	CAL/MOLE DEG-K
100	6.955	0.696	29.426	36.382
200	6.962	1.392	34.250	41.209
273.15	6.964	1.901	36.420	43.379
298.15	6.965	2.075	37.029	43.989
400	6.969	2.785	39.075	46.036
500	6.978	3.482	40.628	47.592
600	7.003	4.181	41.898	48.866
700	7.050	4.883	42.973	49.949
800	7.120	5.592	43.905	50.895
900	7.209	6.308	44.730	51.738
1000	7.312	7.034	45.469	52.503
1100	7.423	7.771	46.141	53.205
1200	7.536	8.518	46.757	53.856
1300	7.648	9.278	47.327	54.463
1400	7.756	10.048	47.857	55.034
1500	7.860	10.829	48.354	55.573
1600	7.957	11.620	48.821	56.083
1700	8.048	12.420	49.263	56.568
1800	8.132	13.229	49.681	57.031
1900	8.210	14.046	50.080	57.473
2000	8.283	14.871	50.460	57.896
2100	8.351	15.703	50.824	58.301
2200	8.413	16.541	51.173	58.691
2300	8.471	17.385	51.508	59.067
2400	8.525	18.235	51.830	59.428
2500	8.575	19.090	52.141	59.777
2600	8.622	19.950	52.442	60.115
2700	8.665	20.814	52.732	60.441
2800	8.706	21.683	53.013	60.757
2900	8.745	22.555	53.285	61.063
3000	8.781	23.432	53.549	61.360
3200	8.847	25.194	54.056	61.929
3400	8.907	26.970	54.535	62.467
3600	8.961	28.757	54.990	62.978
3800	9.010	30.554	55.423	63.463
4000	9.056	32.361	55.837	63.927
4200	9.098	34.176	56.233	64.370
4400	9.137	36.000	56.612	64.794
4600	9.175	37.831	56.977	65.201
4800	9.210	39.669	57.328	65.592
5000	9.243	41.515	57.666	65.969
5200	9.275	43.366	57.992	66.332
5400	9.305	45.224	58.308	66.682
5600	9.335	47.088	58.613	67.021
5800	9.363	48.958	58.908	67.349
6000	9.391	50.834	59.195	67.667

Appendix 3.78 THERMODYNAMIC PROPERTIES OF O2 GAS

T	C_P^0	$(H^0 - H_0^0)$	$-(F^0 - H_0^0)/T$	S_T^0
DEG-K	CAL/MOLE DEG-K	KCAL/MOLE	CAL/MOLE DEG-K	CAL/MOLE DEG-K
100	6.957	0.696	34.440	41.396
200	6.961	1.391	39.262	46.219
273.15	6.996	1.902	41.431	48.392
298.15	7.021	2.077	42.041	49.006
400	7.196	2.800	44.092	51.091
500	7.431	3.531	45.660	52.722
600	7.670	4.286	46.954	54.098
700	7.883	5.064	48.062	55.297
800	8.063	5.862	49.034	56.362
900	8.211	6.676	49.903	57.320
1000	8.332	7.503	50.689	58.192
1100	8.432	8.341	51.408	58.991
1200	8.515	9.189	52.071	59.728
1300	8.585	10.044	52.686	60.412
1400	8.643	10.905	53.261	61.051
1500	8.693	11.772	53.801	61.649
1600	8.736	12.644	54.309	62.211
1700	8.774	13.519	54.790	62.742
1800	8.807	14.398	55.245	63.245
1900	8.836	15.281	55.679	63.721
2000	8.862	16.165	56.093	64.175
2100	8.885	17.053	56.488	64.608
2200	8.907	17.942	56.866	65.022
2300	8.926	18.834	57.230	65.418
2400	8.944	19.728	57.579	65.799
2500	8.961	20.623	57.915	66.164
2600	8.976	21.520	58.239	66.516
2700	8.991	22.418	58.552	66.855
2800	9.004	23.318	58.854	67.182
2900	9.017	24.219	59.147	67.498
3000	9.029	25.121	59.431	67.804
3200	9.052	26.929	59.972	68.388
3400	9.073	28.742	60.484	68.937
3600	9.093	30.559	60.968	69.456
3800	9.111	32.379	61.428	69.949
4000	9.129	34.203	61.866	70.416
4200	9.145	36.030	62.283	70.862
4400	9.162	37.861	62.683	71.288
4600	9.177	39.695	63.066	71.696
4800	9.192	41.532	63.434	72.086
5000	9.207	43.372	63.788	72.462
5200	9.222	45.215	64.128	72.823
5400	9.236	47.061	64.457	73.172
5600	9.250	48.909	64.774	73.508
5800	9.263	50.760	65.081	73.833
6000	9.277	52.614	65.378	74.147

Appendix 3.79 THERMODYNAMIC PROPERTIES OF O2+ GAS

T	C_P^0	$(H^0 - H_T^0)$	$-(F^0 - H_T^0)/T$	S_T^0
DEG-K	CAL/MOLE DEG-K	KCAL/MOLE	CAL/MOLE DEG-K	CAL/MOLE DEG-K
100	6.956	0.696	34.723	41.679
200	6.958	1.391	39.545	46.501
273.15	6.970	1.901	41.713	48.671
298.15	6.980	2.075	42.323	49.282
400	7.077	2.790	44.370	51.345
500	7.245	3.506	45.930	52.941
600	7.448	4.240	47.213	54.280
700	7.650	4.995	48.307	55.443
800	7.835	5.770	49.265	56.477
900	7.996	6.561	50.119	57.409
1000	8.134	7.368	50.891	58.259
1100	8.251	8.188	51.597	59.040
1200	8.350	9.018	52.248	59.762
1300	8.435	9.857	52.852	60.434
1400	8.506	10.704	53.416	61.062
1500	8.568	11.558	53.946	61.651
1600	8.622	12.418	54.445	62.206
1700	8.668	13.282	54.917	62.730
1800	8.709	14.151	55.365	63.226
1900	8.746	15.024	55.791	63.698
2000	8.778	15.900	56.198	64.148
2100	8.807	16.779	56.587	64.577
2200	8.833	17.661	56.959	64.987
2300	8.857	18.546	57.317	65.380
2400	8.879	19.433	57.661	65.758
2500	8.899	20.322	57.992	66.120
2600	8.917	21.212	58.311	66.470
2700	8.934	22.105	58.620	66.807
2800	8.950	22.999	58.918	67.132
2900	8.965	23.895	59.207	67.446
3000	8.979	24.792	59.486	67.750
3200	9.005	26.591	60.021	68.331
3400	9.029	28.394	60.526	68.877
3600	9.050	30.202	61.005	69.394
3800	9.070	32.014	61.459	69.884
4000	9.089	33.830	61.892	70.350
4200	9.107	35.650	62.306	70.794
4400	9.124	37.473	62.701	71.218
4600	9.140	39.299	63.080	71.624
4800	9.155	41.129	63.444	72.013
5000	9.170	42.961	63.795	72.387
5200	9.185	44.797	64.132	72.747
5400	9.199	46.635	64.458	73.094
5600	9.213	48.476	64.772	73.429
5800	9.226	50.320	65.076	73.752
6000	9.240	52.167	65.371	74.065

THERMODYNAMIC PROPERTIES OF PF GAS

T	C_P^0	$(H^0 - H_0^0)_T$	$-(F^0 - H_0^0)/T_T$	S_T^0
DEG-K	CAL/MOLE DEG-K	KCAL/MOLE	CAL/MOLE DEG-K	CAL/MOLE DEG-K
100	6.957	0.696	39.039	45.995
200	7.070	1.395	43.863	50.837
273.15	7.324	1.921	46.044	53.075
298.15	7.425	2.105	46.661	53.721
400	7.815	2.882	48.755	55.959
500	8.111	3.679	50.379	57.737
600	8.324	4.501	51.734	59.235
700	8.476	5.341	52.900	60.530
800	8.588	6.195	53.926	61.670
900	8.673	7.058	54.844	62.687
1000	8.738	7.929	55.675	63.604
1100	8.789	8.805	56.434	64.439
1200	8.831	9.686	57.134	65.206
1300	8.866	10.571	57.782	65.914
1400	8.895	11.459	58.387	66.572
1500	8.920	12.350	58.953	67.187
1600	8.943	13.243	59.486	67.763
1700	8.962	14.139	59.989	68.306
1800	8.980	15.036	60.466	68.819
1900	8.996	15.935	60.918	69.305
2000	9.011	16.835	61.349	69.767
2100	9.025	17.737	61.760	70.207
2200	9.038	18.640	62.154	70.627
2300	9.050	19.544	62.531	71.029
2400	9.062	20.450	62.893	71.414
2500	9.073	21.357	63.242	71.784
2600	9.084	22.264	63.577	72.140
2700	9.094	23.173	63.901	72.483
2800	9.104	24.083	64.213	72.814
2900	9.114	24.994	64.515	73.134
3000	9.123	25.906	64.808	73.443
3200	9.141	27.732	65.366	74.032
3400	9.159	29.562	65.892	74.587
3600	9.176	31.396	66.390	75.111
3800	9.192	33.233	66.862	75.608
4000	9.209	35.073	67.311	76.080
4200	9.225	36.916	67.740	76.529
4400	9.240	38.763	68.149	76.959
4600	9.256	40.612	68.541	77.370
4800	9.271	42.465	68.917	77.764
5000	9.287	44.321	69.279	78.143
5200	9.302	46.180	69.627	78.507
5400	9.317	48.042	69.962	78.859
5600	9.332	49.907	70.286	79.198
5800	9.347	51.774	70.599	79.526
6000	9.362	53.645	70.902	79.843

T	C_P^0	$(H^0 - H_T^0)$	$-(F^0 - H_T^0)/T$	S_T^0
DEG-K	CAL/MOLE DEG-K	KCAL/MOLE	CAL/MOLE DEG-K	CAL/MOLE DEG-K
100	6.956	0.696	35.856	42.812
200	6.971	1.392	40.678	47.635
273.15	7.050	1.904	42.848	49.817
298.15	7.096	2.081	43.458	50.437
400	7.355	2.816	45.517	52.556
500	7.636	3.566	47.097	54.228
600	7.885	4.342	48.406	55.643
700	8.088	5.141	49.530	56.874
800	8.249	5.958	50.518	57.965
900	8.376	6.790	51.400	58.944
1000	8.477	7.632	52.200	59.832
1100	8.558	8.484	52.931	60.644
1200	8.623	9.343	53.605	61.392
1300	8.678	10.209	54.231	62.084
1400	8.723	11.079	54.816	62.729
1500	8.762	11.953	55.363	63.332
1600	8.795	12.831	55.879	63.899
1700	8.823	13.712	56.367	64.433
1800	8.848	14.595	56.829	64.938
1900	8.870	15.481	57.269	65.417
2000	8.890	16.369	57.688	65.872
2100	8.907	17.259	58.088	66.306
2200	8.923	18.151	58.471	66.721
2300	8.938	19.044	58.838	67.118
2400	8.951	19.938	59.191	67.499
2500	8.964	20.834	59.531	67.864
2600	8.975	21.731	59.858	68.216
2700	8.986	22.629	60.174	68.555
2800	8.997	23.528	60.479	68.882
2900	9.006	24.428	60.774	69.198
3000	9.015	25.329	61.060	69.503
3200	9.033	27.134	61.606	70.086
3400	9.049	28.942	62.121	70.634
3600	9.063	30.753	62.609	71.152
3800	9.077	32.568	63.072	71.642
4000	9.091	34.384	63.512	72.108
4200	9.104	36.204	63.932	72.552
4400	9.116	38.026	64.333	72.976
4600	9.128	39.850	64.718	73.381
4800	9.139	41.677	65.087	73.770
5000	9.151	43.506	65.442	74.143
5200	9.162	45.337	65.783	74.502
5400	9.173	47.171	66.113	74.848
5600	9.184	49.006	66.431	75.182
5800	9.194	50.844	66.738	75.504
6000	9.205	52.684	67.036	75.816

Appendix 3.82 THERMODYNAMIC PROPERTIES OF PO GAS

T	C_p^0	$(H^0 - H_0^0)$	$-(F^0 - H_0^0)/T$	S_T^0
DEG-K	CAL/MOLE DEG-K	KCAL/MOLE	CAL/MOLE DEG-K	CAL/MOLE DEG-K
100	6.957	0.696	38.804	45.760
200	6.982	1.392	43.626	50.585
273.15	7.094	1.906	45.797	52.775
298.15	7.154	2.084	46.409	53.399
400	7.454	2.828	48.473	55.542
500	7.750	3.588	50.062	57.238
600	7.997	4.376	51.380	58.674
700	8.191	5.186	52.513	59.922
800	8.341	6.013	53.510	61.025
900	8.457	6.853	54.401	62.015
1000	8.549	7.703	55.208	62.911
1100	8.622	8.562	55.946	63.729
1200	8.681	9.427	56.626	64.482
1300	8.730	10.298	57.258	65.179
1400	8.771	11.173	57.847	65.827
1500	8.805	12.052	58.399	66.434
1600	8.835	12.934	58.919	67.003
1700	8.861	13.819	59.411	67.539
1800	8.883	14.706	59.877	68.047
1900	8.903	15.595	60.319	68.527
2000	8.922	16.486	60.741	68.985
2100	8.938	17.379	61.144	69.420
2200	8.953	18.274	61.530	69.836
2300	8.967	19.170	61.900	70.235
2400	8.979	20.067	62.255	70.617
2500	8.991	20.966	62.597	70.983
2600	9.002	21.865	62.926	71.336
2700	9.013	22.766	63.244	71.676
2800	9.023	23.668	63.551	72.004
2900	9.032	24.571	63.848	72.321
3000	9.041	25.474	64.136	72.627
3200	9.058	27.284	64.685	73.211
3400	9.074	29.098	65.203	73.761
3600	9.089	30.914	65.693	74.280
3800	9.104	32.733	66.158	74.772
4000	9.117	34.555	66.600	75.239
4200	9.131	36.380	67.022	75.684
4400	9.144	38.208	67.426	76.109
4600	9.156	40.038	67.812	76.516
4800	9.169	41.870	68.183	76.906
5000	9.181	43.705	68.540	77.281
5200	9.193	45.543	68.883	77.641
5400	9.204	47.382	69.214	77.988
5600	9.216	49.224	69.533	78.323
5800	9.227	51.069	69.842	78.647
6000	9.239	52.915	70.140	78.960

Appendix 3.83 THERMODYNAMIC PROPERTIES OF P2 GAS

T	C_P^0	$(H^0 - H_0^0)$	$-(F^0 - H_0^0)/T$	S_T^0
DEG-K	CAL/MOLE DEG-K	KCAL/MOLE	CAL/MOLE DEG-K	CAL/MOLE DEG-K
100	6.960	0.696	37.323	44.279
200	7.195	1.400	42.152	49.151
273.15	7.540	1.939	44.347	51.444
298.15	7.657	2.129	44.970	52.110
400	8.050	2.930	47.094	54.418
500	8.311	3.748	48.747	56.244
600	8.485	4.589	50.128	57.776
700	8.604	5.444	51.317	59.093
800	8.690	6.309	52.362	60.248
900	8.752	7.181	53.297	61.275
1000	8.800	8.058	54.142	62.200
1100	8.838	8.940	54.913	63.041
1200	8.868	9.826	55.623	63.811
1300	8.893	10.714	56.280	64.522
1400	8.914	11.604	56.893	65.182
1500	8.933	12.497	57.466	65.797
1600	8.949	13.391	58.005	66.374
1700	8.963	14.286	58.514	66.917
1800	8.976	15.183	58.995	67.430
1900	8.987	16.081	59.452	67.916
2000	8.998	16.981	59.887	68.377
2100	9.008	17.881	60.301	68.816
2200	9.018	18.782	60.698	69.235
2300	9.027	19.685	61.078	69.636
2400	9.035	20.588	61.443	70.021
2500	9.043	21.492	61.793	70.390
2600	9.051	22.396	62.131	70.745
2700	9.059	23.302	62.456	71.086
2800	9.066	24.208	62.770	71.416
2900	9.073	25.115	63.074	71.734
3000	9.080	26.023	63.368	72.042
3200	9.093	27.840	63.928	72.628
3400	9.106	29.660	64.457	73.180
3600	9.119	31.482	64.956	73.701
3800	9.131	33.307	65.429	74.194
4000	9.143	35.135	65.879	74.663
4200	9.155	36.965	66.308	75.109
4400	9.167	38.797	66.718	75.536
4600	9.179	40.632	67.110	75.943
4800	9.190	42.469	67.487	76.334
5000	9.202	44.308	67.848	76.710
5200	9.213	46.149	68.196	77.071
5400	9.224	47.993	68.531	77.419
5600	9.235	49.839	68.854	77.754
5800	9.246	51.687	69.167	78.079
6000	9.258	53.537	69.469	78.392

Appendix 3.84   THERMODYNAMIC PROPERTIES OF PBBR GAS

T	C_P^0	$(H^0 - H_0^0)/T$	$-(F^0 - H_0^0)/T$	S_T^0
DEG-K	CAL/MOLE DEG-K	KCAL/MOLE	CAL/MOLE DEG-K	CAL/MOLE DEG-K
100	7.962	0.728	49.954	57.230
200	8.637	1.566	55.184	63.012
273.15	8.791	2.204	57.662	65.730
298.15	8.823	2.424	58.371	66.502
400	8.904	3.327	60.789	69.107
500	8.949	4.220	62.659	71.099
600	8.979	5.117	64.206	72.734
700	9.002	6.016	65.526	74.120
800	9.022	6.917	66.677	75.323
900	9.040	7.820	67.698	76.387
1000	9.056	8.725	68.615	77.340
1100	9.071	9.631	69.448	78.204
1200	9.086	10.539	70.211	78.994
1300	9.100	11.448	70.915	79.721
1400	9.114	12.359	71.569	80.396
1500	9.128	13.271	72.178	81.026
1600	9.141	14.184	72.750	81.615
1700	9.155	15.099	73.288	82.170
1800	9.168	16.015	73.796	82.693
1900	9.181	16.933	74.277	83.189
2000	9.194	17.852	74.735	83.661
2100	9.208	18.772	75.171	84.110
2200	9.221	19.693	75.587	84.538
2300	9.234	20.616	75.985	84.948
2400	9.247	21.540	76.367	85.342
2500	9.260	22.465	76.733	85.719
2600	9.273	23.392	77.086	86.083
2700	9.286	24.320	77.426	86.433
2800	9.298	25.249	77.753	86.771
2900	9.311	26.179	78.070	87.097
3000	9.324	27.111	78.376	87.413
3200	9.350	28.979	78.960	88.016
3400	9.376	30.851	79.510	88.584
3600	9.401	32.729	80.029	89.120
3800	9.427	34.612	80.521	89.629
4000	9.453	36.500	80.988	90.113
4200	9.478	38.393	81.434	90.575
4400	9.504	40.291	81.860	91.017
4600	9.530	42.195	82.267	91.440
4800	9.555	44.103	82.658	91.846
5000	9.581	46.017	83.033	92.236
5200	9.606	47.935	83.394	92.613
5400	9.632	49.859	83.743	92.976
5600	9.658	51.788	84.079	93.326
5800	9.683	53.722	84.403	93.666
6000	9.709	55.661	84.718	93.995

Appendix 3.85   THERMODYNAMIC PROPERTIES OF PBCL GAS

T	C_P^0	$(H^0 - H_0^0)$	$-(F^0 - H_0^0)/T$	S_T^0
DEG-K	CAL/MOLE DEG-K	KCAL/MOLE	CAL/MOLE DEG-K	CAL/MOLE DEG-K
100	7.459	0.707	47.875	54.945
200	8.333	1.503	52.913	60.429
273.15	8.599	2.124	55.296	63.071
298.15	8.656	2.339	55.980	63.826
400	8.801	3.229	58.319	66.393
500	8.877	4.114	60.138	68.366
600	8.925	5.004	61.649	69.989
700	8.958	5.898	62.941	71.367
800	8.984	6.795	64.071	72.565
900	9.005	7.695	65.075	73.624
1000	9.024	8.596	65.978	74.574
1100	9.041	9.499	66.799	75.435
1200	9.056	10.404	67.552	76.222
1300	9.071	11.311	68.247	76.948
1400	9.084	12.218	68.893	77.621
1500	9.098	13.128	69.496	78.248
1600	9.111	14.038	70.062	78.835
1700	9.123	14.950	70.594	79.388
1800	9.136	15.863	71.097	79.910
1900	9.148	16.777	71.574	80.404
2000	9.160	17.692	72.028	80.874
2100	9.172	18.609	72.460	81.321
2200	9.184	19.527	72.872	81.748
2300	9.196	20.446	73.267	82.156
2400	9.208	21.366	73.646	82.548
2500	9.219	22.287	74.009	82.924
2600	9.231	23.210	74.359	83.286
2700	9.243	24.133	74.696	83.635
2800	9.254	25.058	75.021	83.971
2900	9.266	25.984	75.336	84.296
3000	9.277	26.911	75.640	84.610
3200	9.300	28.769	76.219	85.210
3400	9.323	30.631	76.765	85.774
3600	9.346	32.498	77.280	86.308
3800	9.369	34.370	77.769	86.814
4000	9.392	36.246	78.233	87.295
4200	9.414	38.126	78.676	87.753
4400	9.437	40.012	79.098	88.192
4600	9.460	41.901	79.503	88.612
4800	9.482	43.795	79.891	89.015
5000	9.505	45.694	80.264	89.403
5200	9.528	47.597	80.622	89.776
5400	9.550	49.505	80.968	90.136
5600	9.573	51.418	81.302	90.484
5800	9.596	53.334	81.624	90.820
6000	9.618	55.256	81.936	91.146

Appendix 3.86　　THERMODYNAMIC PROPERTIES OF PBF GAS

T	C_P^0	$(H_T^0 - H_0^0)$	$-(F_T^0 - H_0^0)/T$	S_T^0
DEG-K	CAL/MOLE DEG-K	KCAL/MOLE	CAL/MOLE DEG-K	CAL/MOLE DEG-K
100	7.033	0.697	45.801	52.768
200	7.700	1.431	50.676	57.832
273.15	8.111	2.011	52.937	60.298
298.15	8.215	2.215	53.584	61.013
400	8.504	3.068	55.802	63.471
500	8.663	3.927	57.534	65.388
600	8.760	4.798	58.979	66.976
700	8.825	5.678	60.221	68.332
800	8.871	6.563	61.310	69.514
900	8.905	7.452	62.281	70.560
1000	8.932	8.343	63.157	71.500
1100	8.954	9.238	63.955	72.353
1200	8.973	10.134	64.687	73.132
1300	8.989	11.032	65.365	73.851
1400	9.003	11.932	65.995	74.518
1500	9.017	12.833	66.584	75.140
1600	9.029	13.735	67.137	75.722
1700	9.040	14.639	67.659	76.270
1800	9.051	15.543	68.152	76.787
1900	9.061	16.449	68.619	77.276
2000	9.071	17.355	69.064	77.741
2100	9.080	18.263	69.487	78.184
2200	9.090	19.171	69.892	78.607
2300	9.099	20.081	70.280	79.011
2400	9.108	20.991	70.652	79.398
2500	9.116	21.902	71.009	79.770
2600	9.125	22.814	71.353	80.128
2700	9.133	23.727	71.685	80.473
2800	9.142	24.641	72.005	80.805
2900	9.150	25.555	72.314	81.126
3000	9.158	26.471	72.613	81.436
3200	9.174	28.304	73.183	82.028
3400	9.190	30.141	73.720	82.584
3600	9.206	31.980	74.227	83.110
3800	9.222	33.823	74.708	83.608
4000	9.237	35.669	75.164	84.082
4200	9.253	37.518	75.600	84.533
4400	9.268	39.370	76.016	84.964
4600	9.284	41.225	76.414	85.376
4800	9.299	43.083	76.796	85.771
5000	9.314	44.945	77.162	86.151
5200	9.330	46.809	77.515	86.517
5400	9.345	48.677	77.855	86.869
5600	9.360	50.547	78.183	87.209
5800	9.375	52.421	78.500	87.538
6000	9.390	54.297	78.807	87.856

Appendix 3.87   THERMODYNAMIC PROPERTIES OF PBH   GAS

T	C_P^0	$(H^0 - H_0^0)$	$-(F^0 - H_0^0)/T$	S_T^0
DEG-K	CAL/MOLE DEG-K	KCAL/MOLE	CAL/MOLE DEG-K	CAL/MOLE DEG-K
100	6.960	0.696	39.537	46.495
200	6.969	1.392	44.361	51.321
273.15	7.015	1.903	46.531	53.499
298.15	7.045	2.079	47.142	54.114
400	7.245	2.806	49.196	56.210
500	7.501	3.543	50.768	57.854
600	7.756	4.306	52.068	59.244
700	7.981	5.093	53.181	60.457
800	8.171	5.901	54.159	61.536
900	8.329	6.726	55.034	62.507
1000	8.459	7.566	55.826	63.392
1100	8.569	8.417	56.551	64.203
1200	8.661	9.279	57.221	64.953
1300	8.740	10.149	57.843	65.650
1400	8.809	11.027	58.424	66.300
1500	8.869	11.911	58.969	66.910
1600	8.922	12.800	59.484	67.484
1700	8.970	13.695	59.970	68.026
1800	9.013	14.594	60.432	68.540
1900	9.053	15.497	60.872	69.028
2000	9.089	16.404	61.292	69.494
2100	9.124	17.315	61.693	69.938
2200	9.156	18.229	62.077	70.363
2300	9.186	19.146	62.446	70.771
2400	9.215	20.066	62.802	71.162
2500	9.242	20.989	63.144	71.539
2600	9.268	21.915	63.473	71.902
2700	9.294	22.843	63.792	72.252
2800	9.318	23.773	64.100	72.591
2900	9.342	24.706	64.399	72.918
3000	9.365	25.642	64.688	73.235
3200	9.410	27.519	65.241	73.841
3400	9.453	29.406	65.764	74.413
3600	9.495	31.300	66.260	74.955
3800	9.535	33.203	66.731	75.469
4000	9.575	35.114	67.180	75.959
4200	9.613	37.033	67.610	76.427
4400	9.652	38.960	68.021	76.875
4600	9.689	40.894	68.415	77.305
4800	9.727	42.835	68.794	77.718
5000	9.764	44.784	69.159	78.116
5200	9.800	46.741	69.511	78.500
5400	9.837	48.705	69.851	78.870
5600	9.873	50.675	70.179	79.229
5800	9.909	52.654	70.498	79.576
6000	9.944	54.639	70.806	79.912

THERMODYNAMIC PROPERTIES OF PBO GAS

T	C_P^0	$(H^0 - H_0^0)$	$-(F^0 - H_0^0)/T$	S_T^0
DEG-K	CAL/MOLE DEG-K	KCAL/MOLE	CAL/MOLE DEG-K	CAL/MOLE DEG-K
100	6.973	0.696	43.226	50.185
200	7.588	1.416	48.072	55.151
273.15	8.367	1.999	50.312	57.631
298.15	8.623	2.212	50.957	58.375
400	9.526	3.138	53.196	61.041
500	10.225	4.127	54.991	63.244
600	10.810	5.179	56.530	65.161
700	11.327	6.286	57.887	66.867
800	11.804	7.443	59.107	68.411
900	12.257	8.646	60.221	69.828
1000	12.693	9.894	61.248	71.142
1100	13.119	11.185	62.204	72.372
1200	13.537	12.517	63.100	73.531
1300	13.949	13.892	63.945	74.631
1400	14.358	15.307	64.746	75.680
1500	14.764	16.763	65.509	76.684
1600	15.168	18.260	66.238	77.650
1700	15.569	19.797	66.936	78.582
1800	15.970	21.374	67.609	79.483
1900	16.370	22.991	68.257	80.357
2000	16.768	24.648	68.883	81.207
2100	17.166	26.344	69.490	82.035
2200	17.563	28.081	70.078	82.842
2300	17.960	29.857	70.650	83.632
2400	18.357	31.673	71.207	84.405
2500	18.753	33.528	71.751	85.162
2600	19.149	35.423	72.281	85.905
2700	19.544	37.358	72.799	86.635
2800	19.940	39.332	73.306	87.353
2900	20.335	41.346	73.803	88.060
3000	20.730	43.399	74.289	88.756
3200	21.519	47.624	75.236	90.119
3400	22.309	52.007	76.151	91.447
3600	23.098	56.548	77.037	92.745
3800	23.886	61.246	77.897	94.015
4000	24.675	66.102	78.734	95.260
4200	25.463	71.116	79.550	96.483
4400	26.251	76.287	80.347	97.685
4600	27.039	81.616	81.127	98.870
4800	27.827	87.103	81.891	100.037
5000	28.615	92.747	82.640	101.189
5200	29.402	98.549	83.375	102.327
5400	30.190	104.508	84.098	103.451
5600	30.978	110.625	84.809	104.563
5800	31.765	116.899	85.509	105.664
6000	32.553	123.331	86.199	106.754

Appendix 3.89   THERMODYNAMIC PROPERTIES OF PBS   GAS

T	C_P^0	$(H^0 - H_0^0)$	$-(F^0 - H_0^0)/T$	S_T^0
DEG-K	CAL/MOLE DEG-K	KCAL/MOLE	CAL/MOLE DEG-K	CAL/MOLE DEG-K
100	7.122	0.698	44.824	51.807
200	7.928	1.452	49.737	56.995
273.15	8.307	2.047	52.035	59.528
298.15	8.396	2.256	52.694	60.259
400	8.634	3.124	54.953	62.764
500	8.761	3.994	56.716	64.705
600	8.839	4.875	58.185	66.310
700	8.891	5.761	59.446	67.677
800	8.930	6.653	60.551	68.867
900	8.960	7.547	61.535	69.920
1000	8.984	8.444	62.421	70.865
1100	9.005	9.344	63.228	71.723
1200	9.023	10.245	63.969	72.507
1300	9.040	11.148	64.654	73.230
1400	9.055	12.053	65.291	73.900
1500	9.070	12.959	65.886	74.526
1600	9.083	13.867	66.445	75.112
1700	9.096	14.776	66.971	75.663
1800	9.109	15.686	67.468	76.183
1900	9.121	16.598	67.940	76.676
2000	9.133	17.511	68.389	77.144
2100	9.145	18.424	68.816	77.590
2200	9.157	19.340	69.225	78.015
2300	9.168	20.256	69.616	78.423
2400	9.179	21.173	69.991	78.813
2500	9.190	22.092	70.351	79.188
2600	9.201	23.011	70.698	79.549
2700	9.212	23.932	71.033	79.896
2800	9.223	24.854	71.355	80.231
2900	9.234	25.777	71.667	80.555
3000	9.245	26.701	71.968	80.869
3200	9.267	28.552	72.543	81.466
3400	9.288	30.407	73.085	82.028
3600	9.309	32.267	73.597	82.560
3800	9.330	34.131	74.082	83.064
4000	9.351	35.999	74.543	83.543
4200	9.372	37.871	74.983	84.000
4400	9.393	39.748	75.402	84.436
4600	9.414	41.628	75.804	84.854
4800	9.435	43.513	76.190	85.255
5000	9.456	45.402	76.560	85.641
5200	9.477	47.296	76.917	86.012
5400	9.497	49.193	77.260	86.370
5600	9.518	51.095	77.592	86.716
5800	9.539	53.000	77.912	87.050
6000	9.560	54.910	78.222	87.374

Appendix 3.90   THERMODYNAMIC PROPERTIES OF PB2   GAS

T	C$_P^0$	(H^0 – H$_0^0$)	–(F^0 –H$_0^0$)/T	S$_T^0$
DEG–K	CAL/MOLE DEG–K	KCAL/MOLE	CAL/MOLE DEG–K	CAL/MOLE DEG–K
100	7.708	0.716	46.357	53.517
200	8.531	1.536	51.488	59.167
273.15	8.755	2.169	53.922	61.863
298.15	8.804	2.389	54.621	62.632
400	8.935	3.293	57.008	65.239
500	9.014	4.190	58.862	67.242
600	9.072	5.095	60.400	68.891
700	9.120	6.004	61.716	70.293
800	9.162	6.918	62.866	71.514
900	9.201	7.837	63.888	72.595
1000	9.238	8.758	64.808	73.566
1100	9.273	9.684	65.645	74.449
1200	9.308	10.613	66.413	75.257
1300	9.342	11.546	67.122	76.003
1400	9.375	12.481	67.781	76.697
1500	9.409	13.421	68.398	77.345
1600	9.442	14.363	68.976	77.953
1700	9.474	15.309	69.521	78.526
1800	9.507	16.258	70.037	79.069
1900	9.539	17.210	70.526	79.584
2000	9.572	18.166	70.991	80.074
2100	9.604	19.125	71.435	80.542
2200	9.636	20.087	71.859	80.989
2300	9.668	21.052	72.265	81.418
2400	9.700	22.020	72.655	81.830
2500	9.732	22.992	73.030	82.227
2600	9.764	23.967	73.391	82.609
2700	9.796	24.945	73.740	82.978
2800	9.828	25.926	74.076	83.335
2900	9.860	26.910	74.401	83.681
3000	9.892	27.898	74.716	84.016
3200	9.956	29.883	75.318	84.656
3400	10.020	31.880	75.885	85.262
3600	10.083	33.891	76.422	85.836
3800	10.147	35.914	76.932	86.383
4000	10.211	37.949	77.418	86.905
4200	10.274	39.998	77.881	87.405
4400	10.338	42.059	78.325	87.884
4600	10.401	44.133	78.751	88.345
4800	10.465	46.220	79.160	88.789
5000	10.528	48.319	79.554	89.218
5200	10.592	50.431	79.933	89.632
5400	10.655	52.556	80.300	90.033
5600	10.719	54.693	80.655	90.421
5800	10.782	56.843	80.998	90.799
6000	10.846	59.006	81.331	91.165

Appendix 3.91 THERMODYNAMIC PROPERTIES OF SO₂ GAS

T	C_p^0	$(H^0 - H_0^0)_T$	$-(F^0 - H_0^0)/T$	S_T^0
DEG-K	CAL/MOLE DEG-K	KCAL/MOLE	CAL/MOLE DEG-K	CAL/MOLE DEG-K
100	6.957	0.696	38.443	45.399
200	7.001	1.392	43.266	50.228
273.15	7.157	1.910	45.439	52.430
298.15	7.232	2.089	46.052	53.060
400	7.572	2.843	48.124	55.232
500	7.876	3.616	49.724	56.956
600	8.115	4.416	51.054	58.414
700	8.297	5.237	52.197	59.679
800	8.434	6.074	53.204	60.796
900	8.540	6.923	54.104	61.796
1000	8.622	7.781	54.919	62.700
1100	8.687	8.647	55.664	63.525
1200	8.740	9.518	56.351	64.283
1300	8.783	10.394	56.989	64.984
1400	8.819	11.274	57.584	65.637
1500	8.851	12.158	58.141	66.246
1600	8.877	13.044	58.666	66.818
1700	8.901	13.933	59.161	67.357
1800	8.921	14.824	59.631	67.867
1900	8.940	15.718	60.077	68.349
2000	8.957	16.612	60.502	68.808
2100	8.972	17.509	60.908	69.246
2200	8.986	18.407	61.297	69.664
2300	9.000	19.306	61.669	70.063
2400	9.012	20.207	62.027	70.447
2500	9.023	21.108	62.371	70.815
2600	9.034	22.011	62.703	71.169
2700	9.045	22.915	63.023	71.510
2800	9.055	23.820	63.332	71.839
2900	9.064	24.726	63.631	72.157
3000	9.074	25.633	63.920	72.465
3200	9.091	27.450	64.473	73.051
3400	9.108	29.270	64.994	73.602
3600	9.124	31.093	65.486	74.123
3800	9.139	32.919	65.954	74.617
4000	9.154	34.748	66.399	75.086
4200	9.168	36.580	66.824	75.533
4400	9.182	38.415	67.229	75.960
4600	9.196	40.253	67.618	76.368
4800	9.209	42.094	67.991	76.760
5000	9.223	43.937	68.349	77.136
5200	9.236	45.783	68.694	77.498
5400	9.249	47.631	69.026	77.847
5600	9.262	49.482	69.348	78.184
5800	9.274	51.336	69.658	78.509
6000	9.287	53.192	69.958	78.823

Appendix 3.92   THERMODYNAMIC PROPERTIES OF S2 GAS

T	C_P^0	$(H-H_T^0)$	$-(F-H_T^0)/T$	S_T^0
DEG-K	CAL/MOLE DEG-K	KCAL/MOLE	CAL/MOLE DEG-K	CAL/MOLE DEG-K
100	6.963	0.696	39.661	46.618
200	7.263	1.403	44.494	51.509
273.15	7.638	1.948	46.697	53.829
298.15	7.757	2.141	47.324	54.503
400	8.142	2.952	49.461	56.840
500	8.388	3.779	51.128	58.686
600	8.548	4.626	52.520	60.230
700	8.657	5.487	53.718	61.557
800	8.734	6.357	54.772	62.718
900	8.792	7.233	55.713	63.750
1000	8.835	8.115	56.564	64.679
1100	8.870	9.000	57.341	65.522
1200	8.898	9.888	58.055	66.296
1300	8.922	10.779	58.717	67.009
1400	8.942	11.673	59.333	67.671
1500	8.960	12.568	59.910	68.288
1600	8.975	13.464	60.452	68.867
1700	8.989	14.363	60.963	69.412
1800	9.002	15.262	61.447	69.926
1900	9.014	16.163	61.906	70.413
2000	9.025	17.065	62.343	70.875
2100	9.036	17.968	62.760	71.316
2200	9.045	18.872	63.158	71.737
2300	9.055	19.777	63.540	72.139
2400	9.064	20.683	63.906	72.524
2500	9.073	21.590	64.259	72.895
2600	9.081	22.498	64.598	73.251
2700	9.090	23.406	64.925	73.593
2800	9.098	24.316	65.240	73.924
2900	9.105	25.226	65.545	74.244
3000	9.113	26.137	65.840	74.552
3200	9.128	27.961	66.403	75.141
3400	9.143	29.788	66.934	75.695
3600	9.157	31.618	67.435	76.218
3800	9.172	33.451	67.911	76.713
4000	9.185	35.287	68.363	77.184
4200	9.199	37.125	68.793	77.633
4400	9.213	38.966	69.205	78.061
4600	9.226	40.810	69.599	78.471
4800	9.240	42.657	69.977	78.864
5000	9.253	44.506	70.340	79.241
5200	9.266	46.358	70.689	79.604
5400	9.279	48.213	71.026	79.954
5600	9.293	50.070	71.351	80.292
5800	9.306	51.930	71.665	80.618
6000	9.319	53.792	71.969	80.934

Appendix 3.93 THERMODYNAMIC PROPERTIES OF SIBR GAS

T	C_P^0	$(H^0 - H_0^0)$	$-(F^0 - H_0^0)/T$	S_T^0
DEG-K	CAL/MOLE DEG-K	KCAL/MOLE	CAL/MOLE DEG-K	CAL/MOLE DEG-K
100	7.127	0.698	44.312	51.297
200	7.937	1.453	49.228	56.491
273.15	8.313	2.048	51.528	59.026
298.15	8.401	2.257	52.187	59.758
400	8.636	3.126	54.448	62.264
500	8.761	3.997	56.212	64.205
600	8.838	4.877	57.682	65.810
700	8.889	5.763	58.943	67.177
800	8.927	6.654	60.048	68.366
900	8.956	7.548	61.032	69.419
1000	8.979	8.445	61.919	70.364
1100	9.000	9.344	62.726	71.221
1200	9.017	10.245	63.467	72.005
1300	9.033	11.148	64.152	72.727
1400	9.048	12.052	64.789	73.397
1500	9.062	12.957	65.384	74.022
1600	9.075	13.864	65.942	74.607
1700	9.087	14.772	66.468	75.158
1800	9.099	15.681	66.966	75.677
1900	9.111	16.592	67.437	76.170
2000	9.123	17.504	67.886	76.637
2100	9.134	18.416	68.313	77.083
2200	9.145	19.330	68.721	77.508
2300	9.156	20.245	69.112	77.915
2400	9.166	21.161	69.487	78.304
2500	9.177	22.079	69.847	78.679
2600	9.187	22.997	70.194	79.039
2700	9.198	23.916	70.528	79.386
2800	9.208	24.836	70.850	79.721
2900	9.218	25.758	71.162	80.044
3000	9.229	26.680	71.463	80.357
3200	9.249	28.528	72.038	80.953
3400	9.269	30.380	72.579	81.514
3600	9.289	32.236	73.090	82.045
3800	9.309	34.095	73.575	82.547
4000	9.329	35.959	74.036	83.025
4200	9.349	37.827	74.475	83.481
4400	9.369	39.699	74.894	83.916
4600	9.389	41.575	75.295	84.333
4800	9.409	43.455	75.680	84.733
5000	9.428	45.338	76.050	85.118
5200	9.448	47.226	76.406	85.488
5400	9.468	49.118	76.749	85.845
5600	9.488	51.013	77.080	86.190
5800	9.507	52.913	77.400	86.523
6000	9.527	54.816	77.710	86.846

Appendix 3.94 THERMODYNAMIC PROPERTIES OF SICL GAS

T	C_P^0	$(H_T^0 - H_0^0)$	$-(F_T^0 - H_0^0)/T$	S_T^0
DEG-K	CAL/MOLE DEG-K	KCAL/MOLE	CAL/MOLE DEG-K	CAL/MOLE DEG-K
100	7.014	0.696	41.871	48.834
200	7.629	1.426	46.736	53.865
273.15	8.048	2.000	48.987	56.309
298.15	8.157	2.203	49.631	57.018
400	8.466	3.051	51.836	59.463
500	8.639	3.907	53.559	61.372
600	8.746	4.776	54.997	62.958
700	8.818	5.655	56.233	64.311
800	8.869	6.539	57.318	65.493
900	8.908	7.428	58.286	66.540
1000	8.939	8.321	59.159	67.480
1100	8.964	9.216	59.955	68.333
1200	8.986	10.113	60.686	69.114
1300	9.005	11.013	61.362	69.834
1400	9.022	11.914	61.992	70.502
1500	9.037	12.817	62.580	71.125
1600	9.051	13.722	63.133	71.709
1700	9.065	14.627	63.653	72.258
1800	9.078	15.535	64.146	72.776
1900	9.090	16.443	64.613	73.267
2000	9.101	17.352	65.058	73.734
2100	9.113	18.263	65.481	74.178
2200	9.124	19.175	65.886	74.602
2300	9.135	20.088	66.274	75.008
2400	9.146	21.002	66.646	75.397
2500	9.156	21.917	67.004	75.771
2600	9.166	22.833	67.348	76.130
2700	9.177	23.750	67.680	76.476
2800	9.187	24.668	68.000	76.810
2900	9.197	25.588	68.309	77.133
3000	9.207	26.508	68.609	77.445
3200	9.226	28.351	69.180	78.039
3400	9.246	30.198	69.717	78.599
3600	9.265	32.049	70.226	79.128
3800	9.284	33.904	70.708	79.630
4000	9.303	35.763	71.166	80.106
4200	9.322	37.625	71.602	80.561
4400	9.341	39.492	72.019	80.995
4600	9.359	41.362	72.419	81.410
4800	9.378	43.235	72.802	81.809
5000	9.397	45.113	73.170	82.192
5200	9.415	46.994	73.524	82.561
5400	9.434	48.879	73.865	82.917
5600	9.453	50.768	74.195	83.260
5800	9.471	52.660	74.513	83.592
6000	9.490	54.556	74.821	83.914

Appendix 3.95   THERMODYNAMIC PROPERTIES OF SIF   GAS

T	C_P^0	$(H^0 - H_0^0)$	$-(F^0 - H_0^0)/T$	S_T^0
DEG-K	CAL/MOLE DEG-K	KCAL/MOLE	CAL/MOLE DEG-K	CAL/MOLE DEG-K
100	6.959	0.696	39.354	46.310
200	7.127	1.397	44.180	51.165
273.15	7.432	1.929	46.368	53.430
298.15	7.542	2.116	46.988	54.085
400	7.941	2.906	49.096	56.360
500	8.223	3.715	50.735	58.164
600	8.419	4.547	52.103	59.682
700	8.556	5.396	53.281	60.991
800	8.656	6.257	54.318	62.140
900	8.730	7.127	55.245	63.164
1000	8.788	8.003	56.084	64.087
1100	8.833	8.884	56.850	64.927
1200	8.871	9.769	57.556	65.697
1300	8.902	10.658	58.210	66.408
1400	8.928	11.549	58.819	67.069
1500	8.952	12.443	59.390	67.686
1600	8.972	13.340	59.927	68.264
1700	8.990	14.238	60.433	68.808
1800	9.007	15.138	60.913	69.323
1900	9.023	16.039	61.369	69.810
2000	9.037	16.942	61.802	70.273
2100	9.050	17.846	62.216	70.715
2200	9.063	18.752	62.612	71.136
2300	9.075	19.659	62.992	71.539
2400	9.087	20.567	63.356	71.926
2500	9.098	21.476	63.706	72.297
2600	9.109	22.387	64.044	72.654
2700	9.119	23.298	64.369	72.998
2800	9.129	24.210	64.683	73.330
2900	9.139	25.124	64.987	73.650
3000	9.149	26.038	65.281	73.960
3200	9.168	27.870	65.842	74.551
3400	9.186	29.705	66.371	75.107
3600	9.204	31.544	66.871	75.633
3800	9.222	33.387	67.345	76.131
4000	9.239	35.233	67.796	76.605
4200	9.256	37.082	68.227	77.056
4400	9.273	38.935	68.638	77.487
4600	9.289	40.791	69.032	77.899
4800	9.306	42.651	69.409	78.295
5000	9.322	44.514	69.772	78.675
5200	9.339	46.380	70.122	79.041
5400	9.355	48.249	70.459	79.394
5600	9.371	50.122	70.784	79.734
5800	9.387	51.998	71.098	80.064
6000	9.403	53.877	71.403	80.382

Appendix 3.96   THERMODYNAMIC PROPERTIES OF SIH GAS

T	C_P^0	$(H^0 - H_0^0)_T$	$-(F^0 - H_0^0)/T$	S_T^0
DEG-K	CAL/MOLE DEG-K	KCAL/MOLE	CAL/MOLE DEG-K	CAL/MOLE DEG-K
100	6.959	0.696	32.854	39.811
200	6.964	1.392	37.677	44.636
273.15	6.973	1.902	39.846	46.808
298.15	6.981	2.076	40.456	47.419
400	7.058	2.790	42.504	49.479
500	7.204	3.503	44.063	51.069
600	7.394	4.233	45.344	52.399
700	7.594	4.982	46.436	53.554
800	7.785	5.751	47.391	54.580
900	7.957	6.538	48.243	55.507
1000	8.109	7.342	49.012	56.354
1100	8.240	8.159	49.715	57.133
1200	8.354	8.989	50.364	57.855
1300	8.453	9.830	50.966	58.528
1400	8.540	10.679	51.529	59.157
1500	8.615	11.537	52.058	59.749
1600	8.682	12.402	52.556	60.307
1700	8.741	13.273	53.028	60.835
1800	8.794	14.150	53.475	61.337
1900	8.842	15.032	53.902	61.813
2000	8.886	15.919	54.309	62.268
2100	8.926	16.809	54.698	62.703
2200	8.963	17.704	55.072	63.119
2300	8.997	18.602	55.430	63.518
2400	9.029	19.503	55.775	63.901
2500	9.058	20.407	56.108	64.271
2600	9.086	21.315	56.429	64.626
2700	9.113	22.225	56.739	64.970
2800	9.138	23.137	57.039	65.302
2900	9.162	24.052	57.329	65.623
3000	9.185	24.970	57.611	65.934
3200	9.229	26.811	58.150	66.528
3400	9.270	28.661	58.659	67.089
3600	9.308	30.519	59.142	67.620
3800	9.345	32.384	59.602	68.124
4000	9.380	34.257	60.040	68.604
4200	9.414	36.136	60.459	69.063
4400	9.447	38.022	60.860	69.501
4600	9.479	39.915	61.245	69.922
4800	9.511	41.814	61.615	70.326
5000	9.542	43.719	61.971	70.715
5200	9.572	45.631	62.315	71.090
5400	9.602	47.548	62.647	71.452
5600	9.631	49.471	62.967	71.801
5800	9.661	51.401	63.278	72.140
6000	9.689	53.336	63.579	72.468

THERMODYNAMIC PROPERTIES OF SIN GAS

T	C_P^0	$(H^0 - H_0^0)$	$-(F^0 - H_0^0)/T$	S_T^0
DEG-K	CAL/MOLE DEG-K	KCAL/MOLE	CAL/MOLE DEG-K	CAL/MOLE DEG-K
100	6.957	0.696	37.181	44.137
200	6.995	1.392	42.003	48.965
273.15	7.139	1.908	44.176	51.163
298.15	7.210	2.088	44.789	51.792
400	7.540	2.839	46.859	53.956
500	7.843	3.608	48.455	55.672
600	8.085	4.405	49.782	57.124
700	8.270	5.223	50.923	58.385
800	8.411	6.058	51.927	59.499
900	8.520	6.905	52.824	60.496
1000	8.604	7.761	53.637	61.398
1100	8.672	8.625	54.381	62.222
1200	8.726	9.495	55.066	62.979
1300	8.771	10.370	55.702	63.679
1400	8.809	11.249	56.295	64.330
1500	8.841	12.132	56.852	64.939
1600	8.869	13.017	57.375	65.511
1700	8.893	13.905	57.870	66.049
1800	8.914	14.796	58.338	66.558
1900	8.933	15.688	58.784	67.041
2000	8.951	16.582	59.208	67.499
2100	8.967	17.478	59.614	67.936
2200	8.981	18.375	60.001	68.354
2300	8.994	19.274	60.373	68.753
2400	9.007	20.174	60.731	69.137
2500	9.019	21.076	61.074	69.504
2600	9.030	21.978	61.405	69.858
2700	9.040	22.882	61.725	70.199
2800	9.051	23.786	62.033	70.528
2900	9.060	24.692	62.332	70.846
3000	9.070	25.598	62.621	71.153
3200	9.087	27.414	63.172	71.739
3400	9.104	29.233	63.693	72.291
3600	9.120	31.055	64.185	72.812
3800	9.135	32.881	64.652	73.305
4000	9.150	34.709	65.097	73.774
4200	9.164	36.541	65.521	74.221
4400	9.178	38.375	65.926	74.647
4600	9.192	40.212	66.314	75.056
4800	9.206	42.052	66.686	75.447
5000	9.219	43.895	67.044	75.823
5200	9.232	45.740	67.389	76.185
5400	9.245	47.587	67.721	76.534
5600	9.258	49.438	68.042	76.870
5800	9.271	51.291	68.352	77.195
6000	9.283	53.146	68.652	77.510

Appendix 3.98   THERMODYNAMIC PROPERTIES OF SIO GAS

T	C_P^0	$(H^0 - H_0^0)$	$-(F^0 - H_0^0)/T$	S_T^0
DEG-K	CAL/MOLE DEG-K	KCAL/MOLE	CAL/MOLE DEG-K	CAL/MOLE DEG-K
100	6.956	0.696	35.953	42.909
200	6.980	1.392	40.775	47.734
273.15	7.088	1.906	42.946	49.923
298.15	7.146	2.084	43.558	50.546
400	7.441	2.826	45.621	52.686
500	7.735	3.585	47.209	54.379
600	7.982	4.371	48.526	55.812
700	8.177	5.180	49.658	57.058
800	8.328	6.005	50.653	58.160
900	8.445	6.844	51.543	59.148
1000	8.538	7.694	52.349	60.042
1100	8.611	8.551	53.086	60.860
1200	8.671	9.415	53.766	61.612
1300	8.720	10.285	54.396	62.308
1400	8.761	11.159	54.985	62.955
1500	8.795	12.037	55.536	63.561
1600	8.825	12.918	56.056	64.130
1700	8.851	13.802	56.547	64.666
1800	8.873	14.688	57.012	65.172
1900	8.893	15.576	57.454	65.652
2000	8.911	16.467	57.876	66.109
2100	8.927	17.359	58.278	66.544
2200	8.942	18.252	58.663	66.960
2300	8.956	19.147	59.033	67.358
2400	8.968	20.043	59.388	67.739
2500	8.980	20.941	59.729	68.105
2600	8.990	21.839	60.058	68.458
2700	9.001	22.739	60.376	68.797
2800	9.010	23.639	60.682	69.125
2900	9.019	24.541	60.979	69.441
3000	9.028	25.443	61.266	69.747
3200	9.045	27.250	61.815	70.330
3400	9.060	29.061	62.332	70.879
3600	9.074	30.874	62.821	71.397
3800	9.088	32.690	63.286	71.888
4000	9.101	34.509	63.727	72.355
4200	9.113	36.331	64.149	72.799
4400	9.126	38.155	64.552	73.223
4600	9.137	39.981	64.938	73.629
4800	9.149	41.810	65.308	74.018
5000	9.160	43.641	65.664	74.392
5200	9.171	45.474	66.007	74.752
5400	9.182	47.309	66.337	75.098
5600	9.193	49.147	66.656	75.432
5800	9.204	50.986	66.964	75.755
6000	9.214	52.828	67.262	76.067

Appendix 3.99 THERMODYNAMIC PROPERTIES OF SIO+ GAS

T	C_P^0	$(H^0 - H_T^0)$	$-(F^0 - H_T^0)/T$	S_T^0
DEG-K	CAL/MOLE DEG-K	KCAL/MOLE	CAL/MOLE DEG-K	CAL/MOLE DEG-K
100	6.960	0.696	37.327	44.284
200	7.153	1.398	42.155	49.145
273.15	7.480	1.933	44.345	51.422
298.15	7.596	2.121	44.967	52.082
400	8.009	2.917	47.082	54.374
500	8.300	3.733	48.728	56.195
600	8.505	4.574	50.104	57.727
700	8.653	5.433	51.289	59.050
800	8.763	6.304	52.334	60.213
900	8.849	7.184	53.268	61.250
1000	8.918	8.073	54.114	62.186
1100	8.975	8.968	54.887	63.039
1200	9.024	9.868	55.599	63.822
1300	9.068	10.772	56.260	64.546
1400	9.106	11.681	56.876	65.220
1500	9.142	12.593	57.454	65.849
1600	9.174	13.509	57.997	66.440
1700	9.205	14.428	58.510	66.997
1800	9.234	15.350	58.997	67.524
1900	9.262	16.275	59.459	68.024
2000	9.289	17.203	59.899	68.500
2100	9.315	18.133	60.319	68.954
2200	9.340	19.065	60.722	69.388
2300	9.364	20.001	61.108	69.804
2400	9.388	20.938	61.478	70.203
2500	9.412	21.878	61.835	70.586
2600	9.435	22.821	62.179	70.956
2700	9.458	23.765	62.511	71.312
2800	9.481	24.712	62.831	71.657
2900	9.503	25.661	63.141	71.990
3000	9.525	26.613	63.442	72.312
3200	9.569	28.522	64.015	72.929
3400	9.612	30.440	64.557	73.510
3600	9.655	32.367	65.070	74.061
3800	9.698	34.303	65.557	74.584
4000	9.740	36.246	66.021	75.082
4200	9.782	38.199	66.464	75.559
4400	9.824	40.159	66.888	76.015
4600	9.866	42.128	67.294	76.452
4800	9.908	44.106	67.684	76.873
5000	9.949	46.091	68.060	77.278
5200	9.990	48.085	68.422	77.669
5400	10.032	50.088	68.772	78.047
5600	10.073	52.098	69.110	78.413
5800	10.114	54.117	69.436	78.767
6000	10.155	56.144	69.753	79.111

THERMODYNAMIC PROPERTIES OF SIS GAS

T	C_P^0	$(H^0 - H_0^0)_T$	$-(F^0 - H_0^0)/T$	S_T^0
DEG-K	CAL/MOLE DEG-K	KCAL/MOLE	CAL/MOLE DEG-K	CAL/MOLE DEG-K
100	6.962	0.696	38.611	45.567
200	7.231	1.401	43.442	50.449
273.15	7.593	1.944	45.641	52.756
298.15	7.711	2.135	46.266	53.427
400	8.100	2.941	48.397	55.751
500	8.352	3.765	50.057	57.587
600	8.518	4.609	51.444	59.126
700	8.632	5.467	52.638	60.448
800	8.712	6.334	53.688	61.606
900	8.772	7.209	54.626	62.636
1000	8.817	8.088	55.474	63.562
1100	8.852	8.972	56.248	64.404
1200	8.881	9.858	56.961	65.176
1300	8.905	10.748	57.620	65.888
1400	8.925	11.639	58.235	66.548
1500	8.943	12.533	58.810	67.165
1600	8.958	13.428	59.350	67.742
1700	8.972	14.324	59.860	68.286
1800	8.985	15.222	60.342	68.799
1900	8.996	16.121	60.800	69.285
2000	9.007	17.021	61.236	69.747
2100	9.017	17.923	61.652	70.187
2200	9.026	18.825	62.050	70.606
2300	9.035	19.728	62.431	71.008
2400	9.044	20.632	62.796	71.393
2500	9.052	21.536	63.147	71.762
2600	9.060	22.442	63.485	72.117
2700	9.067	23.348	63.812	72.459
2800	9.075	24.255	64.126	72.789
2900	9.082	25.163	64.431	73.108
3000	9.089	26.072	64.725	73.416
3200	9.103	27.891	65.287	74.003
3400	9.116	29.713	65.816	74.555
3600	9.129	31.537	66.316	75.076
3800	9.141	33.364	66.790	75.570
4000	9.154	35.194	67.241	76.039
4200	9.166	37.026	67.671	76.486
4400	9.178	38.860	68.081	76.913
4600	9.190	40.697	68.474	77.321
4800	9.202	42.536	68.851	77.713
5000	9.214	44.378	69.213	78.089
5200	9.226	46.222	69.561	78.450
5400	9.238	48.068	69.897	78.799
5600	9.249	49.917	70.221	79.135
5800	9.261	51.768	70.534	79.459
6000	9.272	53.621	70.837	79.774

THERMODYNAMIC PROPERTIES OF SI2 GAS

T	C_P^0	$(H_T^0 - H_0^0)$	$-(F_T^0 - H_0^0)/T$	S_T^0
DEG-K	CAL/MOLE DEG-K	KCAL/MOLE	CAL/MOLE DEG-K	CAL/MOLE DEG-K
100	7.007	0.696	40.904	47.866
200	7.600	1.424	45.766	52.883
273.15	8.020	1.996	48.012	55.318
298.15	8.130	2.198	48.654	56.025
400	8.447	3.043	50.855	58.463
500	8.626	3.898	52.574	60.369
600	8.737	4.766	54.008	61.952
700	8.812	5.644	55.242	63.305
800	8.866	6.528	56.325	64.485
900	8.906	7.417	57.291	65.532
1000	8.938	8.309	58.163	66.472
1100	8.964	9.204	58.958	67.325
1200	8.987	10.102	59.688	68.106
1300	9.006	11.001	60.364	68.826
1400	9.024	11.903	60.992	69.494
1500	9.040	12.806	61.580	70.118
1600	9.055	13.711	62.132	70.701
1700	9.069	14.617	62.653	71.251
1800	9.082	15.524	63.145	71.770
1900	9.095	16.433	63.612	72.261
2000	9.107	17.343	64.056	72.728
2100	9.119	18.255	64.480	73.172
2200	9.130	19.167	64.885	73.597
2300	9.142	20.081	65.272	74.003
2400	9.153	20.995	65.644	74.392
2500	9.163	21.911	66.002	74.766
2600	9.174	22.828	66.346	75.126
2700	9.185	23.746	66.677	75.472
2800	9.195	24.665	66.997	75.806
2900	9.206	25.585	67.307	76.129
3000	9.216	26.506	67.606	76.441
3200	9.236	28.351	68.177	77.037
3400	9.256	30.201	68.715	77.597
3600	9.276	32.054	69.223	78.127
3800	9.296	33.911	69.705	78.629
4000	9.316	35.772	70.163	79.107
4200	9.335	37.638	70.600	79.562
4400	9.355	39.507	71.017	79.996
4600	9.374	41.379	71.417	80.413
4800	9.394	43.256	71.800	80.812
5000	9.413	45.137	72.168	81.196
5200	9.432	47.021	72.523	81.565
5400	9.452	48.910	72.864	81.922
5600	9.471	50.802	73.194	82.266
5800	9.490	52.698	73.513	82.598
6000	9.509	54.598	73.821	82.920

Appendix 3.102 THERMODYNAMIC PROPERTIES OF TICL GAS

T	C_P^0	$(H^0 - H_0^0)$	$-(F^0 - H_0^0)/T$	S_T^0
DEG-K	CAL/MOLE DEG-K	KCAL/MOLE	CAL/MOLE DEG-K	CAL/MOLE DEG-K
100	7.096	0.698	43.835	50.813
200	7.884	1.447	48.738	55.972
273.15	8.287	2.039	51.028	58.494
298.15	8.385	2.248	51.685	59.224
400	8.656	3.117	53.938	61.730
500	8.810	3.991	55.698	63.679
600	8.910	4.877	57.166	65.295
700	8.982	5.772	58.429	66.674
800	9.039	6.673	59.536	67.877
900	9.086	7.579	60.523	68.945
1000	9.127	8.490	61.414	69.904
1100	9.164	9.405	62.226	70.776
1200	9.199	10.323	62.972	71.575
1300	9.231	11.244	63.663	72.312
1400	9.262	12.169	64.306	72.998
1500	9.292	13.097	64.907	73.638
1600	9.322	14.028	65.471	74.238
1700	9.350	14.961	66.004	74.804
1800	9.378	15.898	66.508	75.340
1900	9.406	16.837	66.986	75.847
2000	9.433	17.779	67.441	76.331
2100	9.460	18.723	67.876	76.791
2200	9.487	19.671	68.291	77.232
2300	9.514	20.621	68.689	77.654
2400	9.540	21.573	69.071	78.060
2500	9.566	22.529	69.438	78.450
2600	9.593	23.487	69.792	78.826
2700	9.619	24.447	70.134	79.188
2800	9.645	25.410	70.463	79.538
2900	9.671	26.376	70.782	79.877
3000	9.697	27.345	71.091	80.206
3200	9.749	29.289	71.680	80.833
3400	9.800	31.244	72.236	81.426
3600	9.852	33.209	72.762	81.987
3800	9.903	35.185	73.262	82.521
4000	9.954	37.170	73.738	83.031
4200	10.006	39.166	74.192	83.517
4400	10.057	41.173	74.627	83.984
4600	10.108	43.189	75.043	84.432
4800	10.159	45.216	75.444	84.864
5000	10.210	47.253	75.829	85.279
5200	10.261	49.300	76.200	85.681
5400	10.312	51.357	76.558	86.069
5600	10.363	53.425	76.905	86.445
5800	10.414	55.502	77.240	86.809
6000	10.465	57.590	77.565	87.163

Appendix 3.103 THERMODYNAMIC PROPERTIES OF TIO GAS

T	C_P^0	$(H^0 - H_0^0)$	$-(F^0 - H_0^0)/T$	S_T^0
DEG-K	CAL/MOLE DEG-K	KCAL/MOLE	CAL/MOLE DEG-K	CAL/MOLE DEG-K
100	6.957	0.696	41.224	48.180
200	7.036	1.393	46.048	53.015
273.15	7.249	1.915	48.225	55.237
298.15	7.340	2.098	48.840	55.875
400	7.713	2.864	50.924	58.085
500	8.014	3.651	52.537	59.840
600	8.237	4.465	53.881	61.322
700	8.400	5.297	55.038	62.605
800	8.521	6.143	56.056	63.735
900	8.611	7.000	56.966	64.744
1000	8.681	7.865	57.790	65.655
1100	8.737	8.736	58.543	66.485
1200	8.781	9.612	59.237	67.247
1300	8.817	10.492	59.881	67.951
1400	8.848	11.375	60.481	68.606
1500	8.874	12.261	61.043	69.217
1600	8.896	13.150	61.572	69.791
1700	8.916	14.040	62.072	70.331
1800	8.933	14.933	62.545	70.841
1900	8.949	15.827	62.994	71.324
2000	8.963	16.723	63.422	71.784
2100	8.976	17.620	63.831	72.221
2200	8.988	18.518	64.222	72.639
2300	8.999	19.417	64.597	73.039
2400	9.010	20.318	64.957	73.422
2500	9.019	21.219	65.303	73.790
2600	9.029	22.121	65.636	74.144
2700	9.038	23.025	65.957	74.485
2800	9.046	23.929	66.268	74.814
2900	9.054	24.834	66.568	75.131
3000	9.062	25.740	66.859	75.439
3200	9.077	27.554	67.413	76.024
3400	9.092	29.371	67.936	76.575
3600	9.105	31.190	68.431	77.095
3800	9.119	33.013	68.900	77.587
4000	9.131	34.838	69.346	78.055
4200	9.144	36.665	69.771	78.501
4400	9.156	38.495	70.178	78.927
4600	9.168	40.328	70.567	79.334
4800	9.180	42.163	70.941	79.725
5000	9.192	44.000	71.300	80.100
5200	9.203	45.839	71.645	80.460
5400	9.215	47.681	71.978	80.808
5600	9.226	49.525	72.299	81.143
5800	9.237	51.372	72.610	81.467
6000	9.249	53.220	72.911	81.781

Appendix 3.104 THERMODYNAMIC PROPERTIES OF ZRCL GAS

T	C_P^0	$(H^0 - H_0^0)$	$-(F^0 - H_0^0)/T$	S_T^0
DEG-K	CAL/MOLE DEG-K	KCAL/MOLE	CAL/MOLE DEG-K	CAL/MOLE DEG-K
100	7.246	0.701	45.397	52.408
200	8.116	1.473	50.357	57.722
273.15	8.445	2.080	52.691	60.306
298.15	8.518	2.292	53.361	61.049
400	8.708	3.170	55.656	63.582
500	8.806	4.047	57.443	65.536
600	8.865	4.930	58.930	67.147
700	8.904	5.819	60.204	68.517
800	8.933	6.711	61.320	69.708
900	8.955	7.605	62.311	70.762
1000	8.973	8.502	63.204	71.706
1100	8.989	9.400	64.017	72.562
1200	9.003	10.299	64.762	73.345
1300	9.015	11.200	65.450	74.066
1400	9.026	12.102	66.090	74.734
1500	9.037	13.005	66.687	75.357
1600	9.047	13.910	67.247	75.941
1700	9.057	14.815	67.775	76.490
1800	9.066	15.721	68.274	77.008
1900	9.075	16.628	68.747	77.498
2000	9.084	17.536	69.196	77.964
2100	9.093	18.445	69.624	78.407
2200	9.101	19.355	70.033	78.830
2300	9.110	20.265	70.424	79.235
2400	9.118	21.176	70.800	79.623
2500	9.126	22.089	71.160	79.995
2600	9.135	23.002	71.507	80.354
2700	9.143	23.916	71.841	80.698
2800	9.151	24.830	72.163	81.031
2900	9.159	25.746	72.475	81.352
3000	9.167	26.662	72.776	81.663
3200	9.183	28.497	73.350	82.255
3400	9.199	30.335	73.890	82.812
3600	9.214	32.176	74.401	83.339
3800	9.230	34.021	74.884	83.837
4000	9.246	35.868	75.344	84.311
4200	9.261	37.719	75.782	84.762
4400	9.277	39.573	76.200	85.194
4600	9.292	41.430	76.600	85.606
4800	9.308	43.290	76.983	86.002
5000	9.323	45.153	77.352	86.382
5200	9.338	47.019	77.706	86.748
5400	9.354	48.888	78.048	87.101
5600	9.369	50.760	78.377	87.442
5800	9.385	52.636	78.695	87.771
6000	9.400	54.514	79.003	88.089

T	C_P	$(H-H^0_T)_0$	$-(F-H^0_T)_0/T$	S_T
DEG-K	CAL/MOLE DEG-K	KCAL/MOLE	CAL/MOLE DEG-K	CAL/MOLE DEG-K
100	6.958	0.696	42.587	49.543
200	7.082	1.395	47.411	54.387
273.15	7.361	1.923	49.594	56.633
298.15	7.472	2.108	50.212	57.282
400	7.904	2.892	52.311	59.540
500	8.238	3.700	53.942	61.342
600	8.485	4.536	55.306	62.867
700	8.670	5.395	56.483	64.189
800	8.813	6.269	57.520	65.357
900	8.927	7.156	58.450	66.402
1000	9.022	8.054	59.293	67.347
1100	9.103	8.960	60.065	68.211
1200	9.173	9.874	60.778	69.006
1300	9.237	10.795	61.439	69.743
1400	9.295	11.721	62.057	70.430
1500	9.349	12.654	62.637	71.073
1600	9.400	13.591	63.183	71.678
1700	9.449	14.534	63.700	72.249
1800	9.495	15.481	64.190	72.791
1900	9.540	16.433	64.656	73.305
2000	9.584	17.389	65.101	73.796
2100	9.626	18.349	65.526	74.264
2200	9.668	19.314	65.934	74.713
2300	9.709	20.283	66.325	75.144
2400	9.749	21.256	66.701	75.558
2500	9.789	22.233	67.063	75.956
2600	9.828	23.213	67.413	76.341
2700	9.867	24.198	67.750	76.713
2800	9.905	25.187	68.077	77.072
2900	9.944	26.179	68.393	77.421
3000	9.982	27.175	68.700	77.758
3200	10.057	29.179	69.286	78.405
3400	10.132	31.198	69.841	79.017
3600	10.206	33.232	70.367	79.598
3800	10.280	35.281	70.867	80.152
4000	10.354	37.344	71.345	80.681
4200	10.427	39.422	71.802	81.188
4400	10.500	41.515	72.240	81.675
4600	10.573	43.622	72.660	82.143
4800	10.645	45.744	73.065	82.595
5000	10.718	47.880	73.455	83.031
5200	10.790	50.031	73.831	83.452
5400	10.862	52.196	74.195	83.861
5600	10.935	54.376	74.547	84.257
5800	11.007	56.570	74.889	84.642
6000	11.079	58.778	75.220	85.017

APPENDIX 4

THERMODYNAMIC PROPERTIES OF SOME POLYATOMIC MOLECULES IN THE IDEAL GAS STATE

In this appendix we tabulate thermodynamic properties of polyatomic species which consist of elements in the first three rows of the periodic chart. This data was computed using molecular data listed in Tables (1.9) and (1.10). For a discussion of the method of calculation, read Section (1.4.1).

Appendix 4.1   THERMODYNAMIC PROPERTIES OF ALCLF2 GAS

T	C_P^0	$(H^0 - H_0^0)$	$-(F^0 - H_0^0)/T$	S_T^0
DEG-K	CAL/MOLE DEG-K	KCAL/MOLE	CAL/MOLE DEG-K	CAL/MOLE DEG-K
100	10.117	0.856	48.446	57.009
200	13.405	2.043	54.888	65.103
273.15	15.109	3.089	58.238	69.547
298.15	15.575	3.473	59.243	70.891
400	16.986	5.137	62.840	75.682
500	17.835	6.881	65.809	79.571
600	18.374	8.694	68.385	82.874
700	18.732	10.550	70.663	85.735
800	18.978	12.436	72.708	88.253
900	19.154	14.343	74.562	90.499
1000	19.283	16.266	76.259	92.524
1100	19.381	18.199	77.823	94.367
1200	19.457	20.141	79.273	96.057
1300	19.516	22.090	80.625	97.617
1400	19.564	24.044	81.891	99.065
1500	19.603	26.002	83.081	100.416
1600	19.635	27.964	84.205	101.682
1700	19.661	29.929	85.268	102.873
1800	19.684	31.896	86.278	103.998
1900	19.703	33.866	87.238	105.063
2000	19.719	35.837	88.155	106.074
2100	19.733	37.810	89.032	107.036
2200	19.746	39.783	89.871	107.954
2300	19.756	41.759	90.676	108.832
2400	19.766	43.735	91.451	109.673
2500	19.774	45.712	92.196	110.480
2600	19.781	47.689	92.914	111.256
2700	19.788	49.668	93.607	112.003
2800	19.794	51.647	94.277	112.723
2900	19.799	53.627	94.925	113.417
3000	19.804	55.607	95.553	114.089
3200	19.812	59.568	96.752	115.367
3400	19.819	63.532	97.882	116.568
3600	19.825	67.496	98.952	117.701
3800	19.830	71.461	99.968	118.773
4000	19.834	75.428	100.933	119.790
4200	19.837	79.395	101.855	120.758
4400	19.840	83.363	102.735	121.681
4600	19.843	87.331	103.578	122.563
4800	19.846	91.300	104.387	123.408
5000	19.848	95.269	105.164	124.218
5200	19.850	99.239	105.912	124.996
5400	19.851	103.209	106.633	125.746
5600	19.853	107.179	107.328	126.467
5800	19.854	111.150	108.000	127.164
6000	19.855	115.121	108.650	127.837

Appendix 4.2   THERMODYNAMIC PROPERTIES OF ALCLO GAS

T	C_P^0	$(H^0 - H_0^0)$	$-(F^0 - H_0^0)/T$	S_T^0
DEG-K	CAL/MOLE DEG-K	KCAL/MOLE	CAL/MOLE DEG-K	CAL/MOLE DEG-K
100	7.749	0.711	41.679	48.785
200	10.374	1.623	46.888	55.004
273.15	11.639	2.431	49.536	58.438
298.15	11.967	2.727	50.326	59.471
400	12.935	3.999	53.138	63.136
500	13.511	5.324	55.442	66.089
600	13.877	6.694	57.430	68.587
700	14.120	8.095	59.181	70.745
800	14.288	9.516	60.748	72.643
900	14.409	10.951	62.165	74.333
1000	14.498	12.396	63.459	75.856
1100	14.565	13.850	64.650	77.241
1200	14.617	15.309	65.753	78.510
1300	14.658	16.773	66.780	79.682
1400	14.691	18.240	67.741	80.770
1500	14.718	19.711	68.644	81.784
1600	14.740	21.184	69.495	82.735
1700	14.758	22.659	70.300	83.629
1800	14.774	24.135	71.064	84.473
1900	14.787	25.613	71.791	85.272
2000	14.798	27.092	72.485	86.031
2100	14.808	28.573	73.147	86.753
2200	14.816	30.054	73.781	87.442
2300	14.824	31.536	74.390	88.101
2400	14.830	33.019	74.974	88.732
2500	14.836	34.502	75.537	89.337
2600	14.841	35.986	76.079	89.919
2700	14.846	37.470	76.602	90.480
2800	14.850	38.955	77.107	91.020
2900	14.853	40.440	77.596	91.541
3000	14.857	41.926	78.069	92.044
3200	14.863	44.898	78.973	93.003
3400	14.867	47.871	79.825	93.905
3600	14.871	50.845	80.631	94.755
3800	14.875	53.819	81.396	95.559
4000	14.878	56.794	82.123	96.322
4200	14.880	59.770	82.817	97.048
4400	14.882	62.746	83.479	97.740
4600	14.884	65.723	84.114	98.401
4800	14.886	68.700	84.722	99.035
5000	14.887	71.677	85.307	99.643
5200	14.888	74.655	85.870	100.227
5400	14.890	77.633	86.412	100.789
5600	14.891	80.611	86.935	101.330
5800	14.892	83.589	87.441	101.853
6000	14.892	86.567	87.930	102.357

T	C_P^0	$(H^0 - H_0^0)$	$-(F^0 - H_0^0)/T$	S_T^0
DEG-K	CAL/MOLE DEG-K	KCAL/MOLE	CAL/MOLE DEG-K	CAL/MOLE DEG-K
100	9.674	0.858	48.860	57.438
200	11.464	1.922	55.132	64.740
273.15	12.262	2.792	58.221	68.441
298.15	12.459	3.101	59.124	69.524
400	13.000	4.400	62.269	73.269
500	13.292	5.716	64.772	76.205
600	13.467	7.055	66.887	78.645
700	13.578	8.407	68.719	80.730
800	13.652	9.769	70.336	82.548
900	13.705	11.137	71.784	84.159
1000	13.743	12.510	73.095	85.605
1100	13.771	13.885	74.293	86.916
1200	13.793	15.264	75.396	88.115
1300	13.810	16.644	76.417	89.220
1400	13.824	18.025	77.369	90.244
1500	13.835	19.408	78.259	91.198
1600	13.844	20.792	79.096	92.091
1700	13.851	22.177	79.886	92.931
1800	13.858	23.563	80.632	93.723
1900	13.863	24.949	81.341	94.472
2000	13.868	26.335	82.016	95.183
2100	13.872	27.722	82.659	95.860
2200	13.875	29.110	83.274	96.506
2300	13.878	30.497	83.863	97.122
2400	13.881	31.885	84.428	97.713
2500	13.883	33.273	84.970	98.280
2600	13.885	34.662	85.493	98.824
2700	13.887	36.050	85.996	99.348
2800	13.889	37.439	86.482	99.853
2900	13.890	38.828	86.952	100.341
3000	13.892	40.217	87.406	100.812
3200	13.894	42.996	88.272	101.708
3400	13.896	45.775	89.088	102.551
3600	13.897	48.554	89.858	103.345
3800	13.899	51.334	90.588	104.097
4000	13.900	54.114	91.281	104.809
4200	13.901	56.894	91.942	105.488
4400	13.902	59.674	92.572	106.134
4600	13.903	62.454	93.175	106.752
4800	13.903	65.235	93.753	107.344
5000	13.904	68.016	94.308	107.912
5200	13.904	70.797	94.842	108.457
5400	13.905	73.578	95.356	108.982
5600	13.905	76.359	95.852	109.487
5800	13.906	79.140	96.331	109.975
6000	13.906	81.921	96.793	110.447

Appendix 4.4　　THERMODYNAMIC PROPERTIES OF ALCL2F GAS

T	C_P	$(H^0 - H_T^0)$	$-(F^0 - H_T^0)/T$	S_T^0
DEG-K	CAL/MOLE DEG-K	KCAL/MOLE	CAL/MOLE DEG-K	CAL/MOLE DEG-K
100	11.012	0.899	50.149	59.138
200	14.362	2.180	56.985	67.887
273.15	15.971	3.294	60.560	72.617
298.15	16.391	3.698	61.631	74.034
400	17.607	5.435	65.450	79.038
500	18.302	7.234	68.580	83.048
600	18.731	9.087	71.281	86.426
700	19.010	10.975	73.657	89.335
800	19.199	12.886	75.779	91.887
900	19.334	14.813	77.698	94.157
1000	19.432	16.752	79.447	96.199
1100	19.506	18.699	81.056	98.055
1200	19.563	20.652	82.544	99.754
1300	19.607	22.611	83.929	101.322
1400	19.643	24.573	85.224	102.776
1500	19.672	26.539	86.440	104.133
1600	19.696	28.507	87.586	105.403
1700	19.716	30.478	88.669	106.598
1800	19.733	32.451	89.697	107.725
1900	19.747	34.425	90.674	108.792
2000	19.759	36.400	91.606	109.806
2100	19.769	38.376	92.495	110.770
2200	19.778	40.354	93.347	111.690
2300	19.786	42.332	94.164	112.569
2400	19.793	44.311	94.948	113.411
2500	19.799	46.291	95.703	114.219
2600	19.805	48.271	96.430	114.996
2700	19.810	50.251	97.132	115.744
2800	19.814	52.233	97.810	116.464
2900	19.818	54.214	98.465	117.160
3000	19.822	56.196	99.099	117.831
3200	19.828	60.161	100.311	119.111
3400	19.833	64.127	101.452	120.313
3600	19.837	68.094	102.532	121.447
3800	19.841	72.062	103.556	122.520
4000	19.844	76.031	104.530	123.537
4200	19.847	80.000	105.458	124.506
4400	19.849	83.969	106.345	125.429
4600	19.851	87.939	107.194	126.311
4800	19.853	91.910	108.008	127.156
5000	19.854	95.880	108.791	127.967
5200	19.856	99.851	109.543	128.745
5400	19.857	103.822	110.268	129.495
5600	19.858	107.794	110.968	130.217
5800	19.859	111.766	111.644	130.914
6000	19.860	115.737	112.297	131.587

Appendix 4.5   THERMODYNAMIC PROPERTIES OF ALCL3 GAS

T	C_P^0	$(H^0 - H_0^0)_T$	$-(F^0 - H_0^0)/T$	S_T^0
DEG-K	CAL/MOLE DEG-K	KCAL/MOLE	CAL/MOLE DEG-K	CAL/MOLE DEG-K
100	11.807	0.934	49.494	58.836
200	15.264	2.305	56.675	68.199
273.15	16.747	3.480	60.454	73.194
298.15	17.114	3.903	61.585	74.677
400	18.133	5.704	65.605	79.864
500	18.687	7.547	68.881	83.975
600	19.020	9.434	71.691	87.414
700	19.232	11.347	74.153	90.363
800	19.375	13.278	76.344	92.941
900	19.476	15.221	78.318	95.230
1000	19.549	17.172	80.113	97.286
1100	19.604	19.130	81.761	99.151
1200	19.646	21.092	83.282	100.859
1300	19.679	23.059	84.695	102.433
1400	19.705	25.028	86.015	103.892
1500	19.726	27.000	87.253	105.252
1600	19.744	28.973	88.418	106.526
1700	19.758	30.948	89.519	107.724
1800	19.770	32.925	90.562	108.853
1900	19.781	34.902	91.553	109.922
2000	19.790	36.881	92.497	110.937
2100	19.797	38.860	93.398	111.903
2200	19.804	40.840	94.260	112.824
2300	19.810	42.821	95.087	113.705
2400	19.815	44.802	95.880	114.548
2500	19.819	46.784	96.643	115.357
2600	19.823	48.766	97.378	116.134
2700	19.827	50.748	98.087	116.882
2800	19.830	52.731	98.771	117.604
2900	19.833	54.714	99.432	118.299
3000	19.836	56.698	100.073	118.972
3200	19.840	60.665	101.294	120.252
3400	19.844	64.634	102.445	121.455
3600	19.847	68.603	103.533	122.589
3800	19.849	72.573	104.564	123.663
4000	19.852	76.543	105.545	124.681
4200	19.854	80.513	106.480	125.649
4400	19.855	84.484	107.372	126.573
4600	19.857	88.455	108.226	127.456
4800	19.858	92.427	109.045	128.301
5000	19.859	96.398	109.832	129.111
5200	19.860	100.370	110.588	129.890
5400	19.861	104.343	111.317	130.640
5600	19.862	108.315	112.020	131.362
5800	19.863	112.287	112.699	132.059
6000	19.863	116.260	113.356	132.733

Appendix 4.6   THERMODYNAMIC PROPERTIES OF ALFO GAS

T	C_P^0	$(H^0 - H_0^0)$	$-(F^0 - H_0^0)/T$	S_T^0
DEG-K	CAL/MOLE DEG-K	KCAL/MOLE	CAL/MOLE DEG-K	CAL/MOLE DEG-K
100	7.116	0.698	39.728	46.705
200	8.839	1.485	44.668	52.095
273.15	10.271	2.186	47.066	55.068
298.15	10.692	2.448	47.776	55.986
400	12.018	3.609	50.304	59.328
500	12.846	4.856	52.394	62.105
600	13.381	6.169	54.217	64.498
700	13.740	7.526	55.838	66.590
800	13.989	8.913	57.300	68.442
900	14.167	10.322	58.632	70.100
1000	14.299	11.745	59.855	71.600
1100	14.399	13.180	60.986	72.968
1200	14.477	14.624	62.037	74.224
1300	14.538	16.075	63.020	75.385
1400	14.587	17.531	63.942	76.465
1500	14.627	18.992	64.811	77.472
1600	14.659	20.457	65.632	78.417
1700	14.687	21.924	66.411	79.307
1800	14.710	23.394	67.151	80.147
1900	14.729	24.866	67.856	80.943
2000	14.746	26.340	68.529	81.699
2100	14.761	27.815	69.174	82.419
2200	14.773	29.292	69.791	83.106
2300	14.784	30.770	70.385	83.763
2400	14.794	32.249	70.955	84.392
2500	14.803	33.728	71.505	84.996
2600	14.810	35.209	72.035	85.577
2700	14.817	36.690	72.547	86.136
2800	14.823	38.172	73.042	86.675
2900	14.829	39.655	73.521	87.195
3000	14.834	41.138	73.985	87.698
3200	14.842	44.106	74.873	88.656
3400	14.849	47.075	75.710	89.556
3600	14.855	50.045	76.503	90.405
3800	14.860	53.017	77.256	91.208
4000	14.864	55.989	77.973	91.970
4200	14.868	58.963	78.657	92.696
4400	14.871	61.936	79.311	93.387
4600	14.874	64.911	79.937	94.048
4800	14.877	67.886	80.539	94.681
5000	14.879	70.862	81.117	95.289
5200	14.881	73.838	81.673	95.872
5400	14.882	76.814	82.209	96.434
5600	14.884	79.791	82.727	96.975
5800	14.885	82.767	83.227	97.498
6000	14.887	85.745	83.712	98.002

Appendix 4.7 THERMODYNAMIC PROPERTIES OF ALF2 GAS

T	C_P^0	$(H^0 - H_0^0)/T$	$-(F^0 - H_0^0)/T$	S_T^0
DEG-K	CAL/MOLE DEG-K	KCAL/MOLE	CAL/MOLE DEG-K	CAL/MOLE DEG-K
100	8.466	0.807	44.738	52.804
200	9.777	1.719	50.481	59.075
273.15	10.678	2.468	53.224	62.259
298.15	10.952	2.738	54.022	63.206
400	11.842	3.902	56.803	66.558
500	12.419	5.117	59.032	69.266
600	12.799	6.379	60.935	71.567
700	13.057	7.673	62.599	73.560
800	13.238	8.988	64.081	75.316
900	13.368	10.319	65.418	76.883
1000	13.465	11.661	66.637	78.297
1100	13.538	13.011	67.756	79.584
1200	13.595	14.368	68.791	80.765
1300	13.640	15.729	69.755	81.855
1400	13.676	17.095	70.656	82.867
1500	13.705	18.464	71.502	83.811
1600	13.729	19.836	72.299	84.697
1700	13.750	21.210	73.053	85.530
1800	13.767	22.586	73.768	86.316
1900	13.781	23.963	74.448	87.061
2000	13.794	25.342	75.097	87.768
2100	13.804	26.722	75.716	88.441
2200	13.814	28.103	76.309	89.084
2300	13.822	29.485	76.878	89.698
2400	13.829	30.867	77.425	90.286
2500	13.835	32.251	77.951	90.851
2600	13.841	33.634	78.457	91.394
2700	13.846	35.019	78.946	91.916
2800	13.850	36.404	79.418	92.420
2900	13.855	37.789	79.875	92.906
3000	13.858	39.174	80.317	93.376
3200	13.865	41.947	81.162	94.270
3400	13.870	44.720	81.958	95.111
3600	13.874	47.495	82.711	95.904
3800	13.878	50.270	83.425	96.654
4000	13.881	53.046	84.104	97.366
4200	13.884	55.822	84.752	98.043
4400	13.886	58.599	85.371	98.689
4600	13.888	61.377	85.964	99.306
4800	13.890	64.154	86.532	99.898
5000	13.892	66.933	87.078	100.465
5200	13.893	69.711	87.604	101.009
5400	13.894	72.490	88.110	101.534
5600	13.896	75.269	88.598	102.039
5800	13.897	78.048	89.070	102.527
6000	13.898	80.828	89.527	102.998

Appendix 4.8   THERMODYNAMIC PROPERTIES OF ALF3 GAS

T	C_P^0	$(H^0 - H_0^0)_T$	$-(F^0 - H_0^0)/T$	S_T^0
DEG-K	CAL/MOLE DEG-K	KCAL/MOLE	CAL/MOLE DEG-K	CAL/MOLE DEG-K
100	9.184	0.822	44.499	52.718
200	12.312	1.903	50.572	60.087
273.15	14.086	2.871	53.687	64.198
298.15	14.596	3.230	54.621	65.454
400	16.210	4.805	57.975	69.986
500	17.238	6.481	60.760	73.722
600	17.912	8.240	63.194	76.928
700	18.368	10.056	65.360	79.726
800	18.686	11.909	67.314	82.200
900	18.916	13.790	69.093	84.415
1000	19.086	15.691	70.727	86.418
1100	19.215	17.606	72.238	88.243
1200	19.315	19.533	73.642	89.919
1300	19.395	21.468	74.955	91.469
1400	19.458	23.411	76.186	92.908
1500	19.510	25.359	77.346	94.253
1600	19.553	27.313	78.443	95.513
1700	19.589	29.270	79.482	96.700
1800	19.619	31.230	80.470	97.820
1900	19.644	33.193	81.411	98.882
2000	19.666	35.159	82.310	99.890
2100	19.685	37.126	83.171	100.850
2200	19.701	39.096	83.995	101.766
2300	19.716	41.067	84.787	102.642
2400	19.728	43.039	85.548	103.481
2500	19.740	45.012	86.282	104.287
2600	19.749	46.987	86.990	105.061
2700	19.758	48.962	87.673	105.807
2800	19.766	50.938	88.333	106.526
2900	19.773	52.915	88.973	107.219
3000	19.780	54.893	89.592	107.890
3200	19.791	58.850	90.776	109.167
3400	19.800	62.809	91.893	110.367
3600	19.808	66.770	92.952	111.499
3800	19.815	70.732	93.956	112.570
4000	19.820	74.696	94.912	113.586
4200	19.825	78.661	95.825	114.554
4400	19.829	82.626	96.697	115.476
4600	19.833	86.592	97.533	116.358
4800	19.836	90.559	98.335	117.202
5000	19.839	94.527	99.106	118.011
5200	19.842	98.495	99.848	118.790
5400	19.844	102.463	100.564	119.538
5600	19.846	106.432	101.254	120.260
5800	19.848	110.402	101.922	120.957
6000	19.849	114.371	102.568	121.630

Appendix 4.9   THERMODYNAMIC PROPERTIES OF O=AL-H GAS

T	C_P^0	$(H_T^0 - H_0^0)$	$-(F_T^0 - H_0^0)/T$	S_T^0
DEG-K	CAL/MOLE DEG-K	KCAL/MOLE	CAL/MOLE DEG-K	CAL/MOLE DEG-K
100	6.957	0.696	36.576	43.532
200	7.242	1.399	41.403	48.400
273.15	7.958	1.953	43.604	50.754
298.15	8.262	2.156	44.233	51.464
400	9.541	3.063	46.415	54.072
500	10.634	4.074	48.176	56.323
600	11.495	5.182	49.705	58.341
700	12.154	6.366	51.071	60.165
800	12.656	7.608	52.313	61.822
900	13.042	8.893	53.455	63.336
1000	13.342	10.213	54.513	64.726
1100	13.578	11.560	55.501	66.010
1200	13.767	12.927	56.427	67.199
1300	13.919	14.312	57.299	68.308
1400	14.043	15.710	58.122	69.344
1500	14.146	17.120	58.903	70.316
1600	14.232	18.539	59.645	71.232
1700	14.304	19.966	60.353	72.097
1800	14.366	21.399	61.028	72.917
1900	14.418	22.838	61.674	73.695
2000	14.464	24.283	62.294	74.435
2100	14.503	25.731	62.889	75.142
2200	14.537	27.183	63.462	75.818
2300	14.568	28.638	64.013	76.464
2400	14.594	30.096	64.545	77.085
2500	14.618	31.557	65.058	77.681
2600	14.639	33.020	65.555	78.255
2700	14.658	34.485	66.036	78.808
2800	14.675	35.952	66.501	79.341
2900	14.690	37.420	66.953	79.856
3000	14.704	38.889	67.392	80.355
3200	14.728	41.833	68.232	81.304
3400	14.748	44.780	69.027	82.198
3600	14.764	47.731	69.783	83.041
3800	14.778	50.686	70.502	83.840
4000	14.791	53.643	71.188	84.598
4200	14.801	56.602	71.844	85.320
4400	14.810	59.563	72.472	86.009
4600	14.818	62.526	73.075	86.668
4800	14.825	65.490	73.655	87.298
5000	14.831	68.456	74.213	87.904
5200	14.837	71.423	74.750	88.485
5400	14.842	74.391	75.269	89.046
5600	14.846	77.359	75.771	89.585
5800	14.850	80.329	76.257	90.106
6000	14.853	83.299	76.727	90.610

THERMODYNAMIC PROPERTIES OF ALOH GAS

T	C_P^0	$(H^0 - H_0^0)$	$-(F^0 - H_0^0)/T$	S_T^0
DEG-K	CAL/MOLE DEG-K	KCAL/MOLE	CAL/MOLE DEG-K	CAL/MOLE DEG-K
100	7.952	0.795	39.233	47.182
200	8.185	1.598	44.749	52.737
273.15	8.630	2.212	47.253	55.351
298.15	8.805	2.430	47.965	56.114
400	9.498	3.362	50.394	58.800
500	10.060	4.341	52.299	60.982
600	10.502	5.370	53.906	62.857
700	10.858	6.439	55.305	64.504
800	11.158	7.540	56.548	65.974
900	11.420	8.669	57.671	67.303
1000	11.652	9.823	58.696	68.519
1100	11.861	10.999	59.640	69.639
1200	12.048	12.195	60.517	70.680
1300	12.215	13.408	61.337	71.651
1400	12.365	14.637	62.106	72.562
1500	12.499	15.880	62.832	73.419
1600	12.619	17.137	63.520	74.230
1700	12.727	18.40-	64.172	74.998
1800	12.822	19.681	64.794	75.728
1900	12.908	20.968	65.388	76.424
2000	12.985	22.263	65.957	77.088
2100	13.055	23.565	66.502	77.723
2200	13.117	24.874	67.026	78.332
2300	13.173	26.188	67.530	78.916
2400	13.224	27.508	68.017	79.478
2500	13.270	28.833	68.486	80.019
2600	13.312	30.162	68.940	80.540
2700	13.350	31.495	69.379	81.043
2800	13.384	32.832	69.804	81.530
2900	13.416	34.172	70.216	82.000
3000	13.445	35.515	70.617	82.455
3200	13.496	38.209	71.384	83.324
3400	13.540	40.913	72.111	84.144
3600	13.577	43.625	72.801	84.919
3800	13.609	46.343	73.458	85.654
4000	13.636	49.068	74.086	86.353
4200	13.660	51.797	74.686	87.019
4400	13.682	54.532	75.261	87.655
4600	13.700	57.270	75.813	88.263
4800	13.717	60.012	76.344	88.847
5000	13.731	62.756	76.856	89.407
5200	13.744	65.504	77.349	89.946
5400	13.756	68.254	77.825	90.465
5600	13.766	71.006	78.285	90.965
5800	13.776	73.760	78.731	91.448
6000	13.784	76.517	79.163	91.915

Appendix 4.11   THERMODYNAMIC PROPERTIES OF O=AL-O-H GAS

T	C_P^0	$(H^0 - H_0^0)$	$-(F^0 - H_0^0)/T$	S_T^0
DEG-K	CAL/MOLE DEG-K	KCAL/MOLE	CAL/MOLE DEG-K	CAL/MOLE DEG-K
100	8.245	0.800	42.117	50.114
200	10.137	1.713	47.804	56.369
273.15	11.548	2.507	50.563	59.742
298.15	11.983	2.802	51.376	60.773
400	13.484	4.102	54.259	64.514
500	14.567	5.508	56.631	67.646
600	15.361	7.006	58.699	70.376
700	15.961	8.573	60.543	72.790
800	16.436	10.194	62.211	74.954
900	16.826	11.858	63.738	76.913
1000	17.155	13.557	65.146	78.703
1100	17.437	15.287	66.455	80.352
1200	17.682	17.043	67.677	81.880
1300	17.895	18.822	68.825	83.304
1400	18.082	20.621	69.907	84.637
1500	18.246	22.438	70.931	85.890
1600	18.391	24.270	71.904	87.072
1700	18.520	26.116	72.829	88.191
1800	18.633	27.974	73.712	89.253
1900	18.734	29.842	74.557	90.263
2000	18.824	31.720	75.367	91.227
2100	18.905	33.607	76.144	92.147
2200	18.977	35.501	76.892	93.028
2300	19.041	37.402	77.612	93.873
2400	19.100	39.309	78.306	94.685
2500	19.152	41.221	78.977	95.466
2600	19.200	43.139	79.626	96.218
2700	19.243	45.061	80.254	96.943
2800	19.283	46.988	80.863	97.644
2900	19.319	48.918	81.453	98.321
3000	19.352	50.851	82.026	98.977
3200	19.409	54.727	83.125	100.227
3400	19.458	58.614	84.166	101.406
3600	19.500	62.510	85.155	102.519
3800	19.536	66.414	86.097	103.574
4000	19.567	70.324	86.996	104.577
4200	19.594	74.240	87.856	105.532
4400	19.617	78.161	88.681	106.444
4600	19.638	82.087	89.472	107.317
4800	19.657	86.017	90.233	108.153
5000	19.673	89.949	90.966	108.956
5200	19.687	93.886	91.673	109.728
5400	19.700	97.824	92.355	110.471
5600	19.712	101.766	93.015	111.188
5800	19.723	105.709	93.654	111.880
6000	19.732	109.655	94.273	112.548

Appendix 4.12   THERMODYNAMIC PROPERTIES OF AL2C2 GAS

T	C$_P^0$	(H^0 – H$_0^0$)	–(F^0 –H$_0^0$)/T	S$_T^0$
DEG–K	CAL/MOLE DEG–K	KCAL/MOLE	CAL/MOLE DEG–K	CAL/MOLE DEG–K
100	11.202	0.882	42.232	51.051
200	14.220	2.170	49.008	59.858
273.15	15.463	3.259	52.557	64.487
298.15	15.791	3.650	53.616	65.856
400	16.840	5.314	57.366	70.652
500	17.594	7.038	60.419	74.495
600	18.179	8.828	63.044	77.757
700	18.640	10.670	65.353	80.595
800	19.005	12.552	67.418	83.109
900	19.296	14.468	69.289	85.365
1000	19.530	16.410	71.000	87.410
1100	19.718	18.373	72.578	89.281
1200	19.872	20.352	74.043	91.003
1300	19.998	22.346	75.410	92.599
1400	20.103	24.351	76.691	94.085
1500	20.190	26.366	77.898	95.475
1600	20.264	28.389	79.037	96.780
1700	20.327	30.418	80.118	98.011
1800	20.380	32.454	81.144	99.174
1900	20.427	34.494	82.123	100.277
2000	20.467	36.539	83.057	101.326
2100	20.502	38.587	83.951	102.326
2200	20.532	40.639	84.808	103.280
2300	20.559	42.694	85.631	104.193
2400	20.583	44.751	86.423	105.069
2500	20.604	46.810	87.186	105.910
2600	20.623	48.872	87.921	106.718
2700	20.640	50.935	88.632	107.497
2800	20.656	53.000	89.319	108.248
2900	20.669	55.066	89.985	108.973
3000	20.682	57.134	90.629	109.674
3200	20.704	61.272	91.862	111.009
3400	20.722	65.415	93.025	112.265
3600	20.737	69.561	94.127	113.450
3800	20.750	73.709	95.174	114.571
4000	20.761	77.861	96.171	115.636
4200	20.771	82.014	97.122	116.649
4400	20.779	86.169	98.032	117.616
4600	20.786	90.325	98.904	118.539
4800	20.793	94.483	99.740	119.424
5000	20.799	98.642	100.545	120.273
5200	20.804	102.803	101.319	121.089
5400	20.808	106.964	102.066	121.874
5600	20.812	111.126	102.787	122.631
5800	20.816	115.289	103.484	123.361
6000	20.819	119.452	104.158	124.067

T	C_P	$(H^0 - H_0^0)$	$-(F^0 - H_0^0)/T$	S_T^0
DEG-K	CAL/MOLE DEG-K	KCAL/MOLE	CAL/MOLE DEG-K	CAL/MOLE DEG-K
100	8.027	0.796	43.741	51.700
200	8.784	1.633	49.306	57.469
273.15	9.441	2.299	51.887	60.305
298.15	9.659	2.538	52.628	61.141
400	10.473	3.564	55.185	64.096
500	11.140	4.646	57.215	66.507
600	11.672	5.788	58.941	68.587
700	12.087	6.977	60.453	70.419
800	12.409	8.202	61.802	72.055
900	12.660	9.456	63.025	73.532
1000	12.857	10.732	64.144	74.876
1100	13.013	12.026	65.176	76.109
1200	13.139	13.334	66.136	77.247
1300	13.241	14.653	67.031	78.303
1400	13.324	15.982	67.872	79.287
1500	13.393	17.318	68.664	80.209
1600	13.451	18.660	69.413	81.075
1700	13.500	20.008	70.123	81.892
1800	13.542	21.360	70.799	82.665
1900	13.578	22.716	71.443	83.399
2000	13.609	24.075	72.058	84.096
2100	13.636	25.437	72.647	84.760
2200	13.659	26.802	73.213	85.395
2300	13.680	28.169	73.755	86.003
2400	13.698	29.538	74.278	86.586
2500	13.714	30.909	74.782	87.145
2600	13.729	32.281	75.268	87.683
2700	13.741	33.654	75.737	88.202
2800	13.753	35.029	76.191	88.702
2900	13.763	36.405	76.631	89.184
3000	13.773	37.782	77.057	89.651
3200	13.789	40.538	77.872	90.541
3400	13.803	43.297	78.642	91.377
3600	13.814	46.059	79.372	92.166
3800	13.824	48.823	80.065	92.913
4000	13.832	51.588	80.726	93.623
4200	13.840	54.356	81.356	94.298
4400	13.846	57.124	81.959	94.942
4600	13.851	59.894	82.537	95.557
4800	13.856	62.665	83.092	96.147
5000	13.860	65.436	83.625	96.713
5200	13.864	68.209	84.139	97.256
5400	13.868	70.982	84.635	97.780
5600	13.871	73.756	85.113	98.284
5800	13.873	76.530	85.576	98.771
6000	13.876	79.305	86.024	99.241

Appendix 4.14   THERMODYNAMIC PROPERTIES OF BBRCL2 GAS

T	C_P^0	$(H^0 - H_0^0)$	$-(F^0 - H_0^0)/T$	S_T^0
DEG-K	CAL/MOLE DEG-K	KCAL/MOLE	CAL/MOLE DEG-K	CAL/MOLE DEG-K
100	10.270	0.863	51.658	60.290
200	13.442	2.062	58.163	68.475
273.15	14.975	3.105	61.538	72.903
298.15	15.402	3.484	62.547	74.234
400	16.749	5.126	66.146	78.962
500	17.611	6.848	69.104	82.799
600	18.182	8.639	71.665	86.064
700	18.571	10.478	73.929	88.898
800	18.844	12.350	75.959	91.396
900	19.042	14.244	77.801	93.628
1000	19.189	16.156	79.486	95.642
1100	19.301	18.081	81.039	97.476
1200	19.387	20.015	82.480	99.160
1300	19.456	21.958	83.824	100.714
1400	19.511	23.906	85.082	102.158
1500	19.557	25.860	86.266	103.506
1600	19.594	27.817	87.384	104.769
1700	19.625	29.778	88.442	105.958
1800	19.651	31.742	89.446	107.081
1900	19.673	33.708	90.403	108.144
2000	19.692	35.677	91.315	109.153
2100	19.709	37.647	92.188	110.115
2200	19.723	39.618	93.023	111.032
2300	19.736	41.591	93.826	111.909
2400	19.747	43.565	94.597	112.749
2500	19.756	45.541	95.339	113.555
2600	19.765	47.517	96.055	114.330
2700	19.773	49.494	96.745	115.076
2800	19.780	51.471	97.413	115.796
2900	19.786	53.449	98.059	116.490
3000	19.792	55.428	98.685	117.161
3200	19.801	59.388	99.880	118.438
3400	19.809	63.349	101.007	119.639
3600	19.816	67.311	102.074	120.771
3800	19.822	71.275	103.086	121.843
4000	19.827	75.240	104.050	122.860
4200	19.831	79.206	104.969	123.827
4400	19.835	83.172	105.847	124.750
4600	19.838	87.140	106.688	125.632
4800	19.841	91.108	107.495	126.476
5000	19.843	95.076	108.271	127.286
5200	19.845	99.045	109.017	128.064
5400	19.847	103.014	109.737	128.813
5600	19.849	106.984	110.431	129.535
5800	19.851	110.954	111.102	130.232
6000	19.852	114.924	111.751	130.905

Appendix 4.15   THERMODYNAMIC PROPERTIES OF BBRF2 GAS

T	C_P^0	$(H^0 - H_0^0)$	$-(F^0 - H_0^0)/T$	S^0
DEG-K	CAL/MOLE DEG-K	KCAL/MOLE	CAL/MOLE DEG-K	CAL/MOLE DEG-K
100	8.742	0.811	48.417	56.523
200	11.472	1.823	54.315	63.431
273.15	13.043	2.722	57.283	67.250
298.15	13.492	3.054	58.168	68.412
400	14.997	4.509	61.326	72.598
500	16.088	6.066	63.936	76.068
600	16.896	7.717	66.215	79.076
700	17.496	9.438	68.245	81.728
800	17.944	11.211	70.081	84.095
900	18.283	13.023	71.759	86.229
1000	18.545	14.865	73.304	88.170
1100	18.749	16.730	74.738	89.947
1200	18.911	18.614	76.074	91.586
1300	19.041	20.512	77.327	93.105
1400	19.148	22.421	78.505	94.520
1500	19.235	24.340	79.617	95.844
1600	19.308	26.268	80.670	97.088
1700	19.369	28.202	81.671	98.260
1800	19.421	30.141	82.624	99.369
1900	19.465	32.086	83.533	100.420
2000	19.504	34.034	84.402	101.419
2100	19.537	35.986	85.236	102.372
2200	19.566	37.941	86.035	103.281
2300	19.591	39.899	86.804	104.152
2400	19.613	41.859	87.545	104.986
2500	19.633	43.822	88.258	105.787
2600	19.651	45.786	88.947	106.557
2700	19.667	47.752	89.614	107.299
2800	19.681	49.719	90.258	108.015
2900	19.694	51.688	90.882	108.706
3000	19.705	53.658	91.488	109.374
3200	19.725	57.601	92.646	110.646
3400	19.742	61.548	93.740	111.842
3600	19.756	65.497	94.777	112.971
3800	19.767	69.450	95.763	114.040
4000	19.778	73.404	96.703	115.054
4200	19.786	77.361	97.600	116.019
4400	19.794	81.319	98.458	116.940
4600	19.801	85.278	99.281	117.820
4800	19.806	89.239	100.071	118.662
5000	19.812	93.201	100.831	119.471
5200	19.816	97.164	101.563	120.248
5400	19.820	101.127	102.269	120.996
5600	19.824	105.092	102.951	121.717
5800	19.827	109.057	103.610	122.413
6000	19.830	113.022	104.248	123.085

Appendix 4.16 THERMODYNAMIC PROPERTIES OF BBR2CL GAS

T	C_P^0	$(H^0 - H_0^0)_T$	$-(F^0 - H_0^0)/T$	S_T^0
DEG-K	CAL/MOLE DEG-K	KCAL/MOLE	CAL/MOLE DEG-K	CAL/MOLE DEG-K
100	12.445	1.074	59.482	70.224
200	14.694	2.442	67.406	79.618
273.15	15.843	3.561	71.339	84.374
298.15	16.180	3.961	72.491	85.777
400	17.273	5.668	76.524	90.695
500	17.987	7.434	79.764	94.631
600	18.463	9.258	82.526	97.955
700	18.787	11.121	84.940	100.827
800	19.015	13.012	87.087	103.352
900	19.180	14.922	89.021	105.601
1000	19.302	16.847	90.782	107.629
1100	19.396	18.782	92.399	109.473
1200	19.468	20.725	93.893	111.164
1300	19.526	22.675	95.282	112.725
1400	19.572	24.630	96.581	114.173
1500	19.609	26.589	97.799	115.525
1600	19.640	28.551	98.947	116.792
1700	19.666	30.517	100.032	117.983
1800	19.688	32.484	101.061	119.108
1900	19.706	34.454	102.039	120.173
2000	19.722	36.426	102.971	121.184
2100	19.736	38.399	103.862	122.147
2200	19.748	40.373	104.714	123.065
2300	19.758	42.348	105.531	123.943
2400	19.768	44.324	106.316	124.784
2500	19.776	46.302	107.071	125.591
2600	19.783	48.280	107.798	126.367
2700	19.789	50.258	108.500	127.114
2800	19.795	52.237	109.177	127.834
2900	19.800	54.217	109.833	128.528
3000	19.805	56.198	110.467	129.200
3200	19.813	60.159	111.678	130.478
3400	19.820	64.123	112.820	131.680
3600	19.826	68.087	113.899	132.813
3800	19.830	72.053	114.923	133.885
4000	19.834	76.019	115.897	134.902
4200	19.838	79.987	116.825	135.870
4400	19.841	83.955	117.712	136.793
4600	19.844	87.923	118.561	137.675
4800	19.846	91.892	119.375	138.519
5000	19.848	95.861	120.157	139.329
5200	19.850	99.831	120.910	140.108
5400	19.852	103.801	121.635	140.857
5600	19.853	107.772	122.334	141.579
5800	19.854	111.743	123.010	142.276
6000	19.856	115.714	123.663	142.949

Appendix 4.17   THERMODYNAMIC PROPERTIES OF BBR2F GAS

T	C_P^0	$(H^0 - H_0^0)$	$-(F^0 - H_0^0)/T$	S^0
DEG-K	CAL/MOLE DEG-K	KCAL/MOLE	CAL/MOLE DEG-K	CAL/MOLE DEG-K
100	9.938	0.854	52.054	60.589
200	12.985	2.011	58.434	68.488
273.15	14.459	3.018	61.719	72.766
298.15	14.867	3.384	62.699	74.050
400	16.184	4.970	66.191	78.615
500	17.085	6.636	69.058	82.329
600	17.721	8.378	71.541	85.504
700	18.177	10.174	73.737	88.272
800	18.510	12.009	75.710	90.722
900	18.758	13.873	77.502	92.917
1000	18.946	15.759	79.145	94.903
1100	19.092	17.661	80.661	96.716
1200	19.207	19.576	82.069	98.383
1300	19.298	21.502	83.384	99.924
1400	19.373	23.435	84.617	101.357
1500	19.434	25.376	85.778	102.695
1600	19.484	27.322	86.875	103.951
1700	19.527	29.272	87.915	105.134
1800	19.563	31.227	88.903	106.251
1900	19.594	33.185	89.844	107.309
2000	19.620	35.145	90.743	108.315
2100	19.643	37.109	91.602	109.273
2200	19.663	39.074	92.426	110.187
2300	19.680	41.041	93.218	111.062
2400	19.695	43.010	93.979	111.900
2500	19.709	44.980	94.712	112.704
2600	19.721	46.952	95.419	113.477
2700	19.732	48.924	96.102	114.222
2800	19.742	50.898	96.762	114.939
2900	19.750	52.873	97.400	115.632
3000	19.758	54.848	98.019	116.302
3200	19.772	58.801	99.202	117.578
3400	19.783	62.757	100.319	118.777
3600	19.793	66.714	101.376	119.908
3800	19.801	70.674	102.380	120.978
4000	19.808	74.635	103.335	121.994
4200	19.814	78.597	104.247	122.961
4400	19.819	82.560	105.119	123.882
4600	19.824	86.524	105.954	124.763
4800	19.828	90.489	106.755	125.607
5000	19.831	94.455	107.526	126.417
5200	19.834	98.422	108.267	127.195
5400	19.837	102.389	108.982	127.943
5600	19.839	106.357	109.672	128.665
5800	19.842	110.325	110.339	129.361
6000	19.844	114.293	110.985	130.034

Appendix 4.18   THERMODYNAMIC PROPERTIES OF BBR3 GAS

T	C_P^0	$(H^0 - H_0^0)$	$-(F^0 - H_0^0)/T$	S_T^0
DEG-K	CAL/MOLE DEG-K	KCAL/MOLE	CAL/MOLE DEG-K	CAL/MOLE DEG-K
100	11.549	0.926	53.075	62.332
200	14.507	2.245	60.135	71.362
273.15	15.862	3.359	63.799	76.095
298.15	16.236	3.760	64.890	77.501
400	17.392	5.477	68.754	82.447
500	18.106	7.255	71.901	86.410
600	18.566	9.090	74.605	89.755
700	18.874	10.963	76.980	92.642
800	19.088	12.862	79.100	95.177
900	19.241	14.779	81.014	97.434
1000	19.354	16.709	82.759	99.468
1100	19.440	18.648	84.363	101.317
1200	19.506	20.596	85.848	103.011
1300	19.559	22.549	87.229	104.575
1400	19.601	24.507	88.520	106.026
1500	19.635	26.469	89.733	107.379
1600	19.663	28.434	90.876	108.647
1700	19.686	30.401	91.957	109.840
1800	19.706	32.371	92.982	110.966
1900	19.723	34.343	93.957	112.032
2000	19.737	36.316	94.886	113.044
2100	19.750	38.290	95.774	114.007
2200	19.760	40.265	96.623	114.926
2300	19.770	42.242	97.438	115.805
2400	19.778	44.219	98.221	116.646
2500	19.785	46.198	98.975	117.454
2600	19.792	48.176	99.700	118.230
2700	19.798	50.156	100.401	118.977
2800	19.803	52.136	101.077	119.697
2900	19.808	54.117	101.731	120.392
3000	19.812	56.097	102.364	121.064
3200	19.819	60.061	103.573	122.342
3400	19.825	64.025	104.713	123.544
3600	19.830	67.991	105.791	124.677
3800	19.835	71.957	106.814	125.750
4000	19.838	75.924	107.786	126.767
4200	19.841	79.892	108.713	127.735
4400	19.844	83.861	109.599	128.658
4600	19.847	87.830	110.447	129.540
4800	19.849	91.800	111.260	130.385
5000	19.851	95.770	112.042	131.195
5200	19.852	99.740	112.793	131.974
5400	19.854	103.710	113.518	132.723
5600	19.855	107.681	114.217	133.445
5800	19.856	111.652	114.892	134.142
6000	19.857	115.624	115.545	134.815

Appendix 4.19 THERMODYNAMIC PROPERTIES OF BClF GAS

T	C_P^0	$(H^0 - H_0^0)$	$-(F^0 - H_0^0)/T$	S_T^0
DEG-K	CAL/MOLE DEG-K	KCAL/MOLE	CAL/MOLE DEG-K	CAL/MOLE DEG-K
100	7.021	0.696	41.696	48.659
200	8.219	1.447	46.581	53.818
273.15	9.421	2.093	48.897	56.560
298.15	9.796	2.333	49.575	57.401
400	11.060	3.399	51.969	60.467
500	11.953	4.552	53.932	63.036
600	12.598	5.781	55.640	65.275
700	13.069	7.066	57.160	67.255
800	13.419	8.391	58.535	69.024
900	13.682	9.747	59.790	70.620
1000	13.884	11.126	60.947	72.073
1100	14.041	12.522	62.020	73.404
1200	14.166	13.933	63.020	74.631
1300	14.266	15.355	63.958	75.769
1400	14.348	16.785	64.840	76.829
1500	14.415	18.224	65.672	77.821
1600	14.471	19.668	66.461	78.754
1700	14.518	21.118	67.210	79.632
1800	14.558	22.571	67.924	80.463
1900	14.592	24.029	68.605	81.251
2000	14.621	25.490	69.256	82.001
2100	14.647	26.953	69.880	82.715
2200	14.669	28.419	70.479	83.397
2300	14.688	29.887	71.055	84.049
2400	14.706	31.357	71.609	84.675
2500	14.721	32.828	72.144	85.275
2600	14.734	34.301	72.660	85.853
2700	14.746	35.775	73.159	86.409
2800	14.757	37.250	73.642	86.946
2900	14.767	38.726	74.110	87.464
3000	14.776	40.203	74.563	87.964
3200	14.791	43.160	75.431	88.919
3400	14.804	46.120	76.251	89.816
3600	14.815	49.082	77.028	90.662
3800	14.824	52.045	77.767	91.463
4000	14.832	55.011	78.471	92.224
4200	14.838	57.978	79.143	92.948
4400	14.844	60.946	79.787	93.638
4600	14.849	63.916	80.403	94.298
4800	14.854	66.886	80.996	94.930
5000	14.858	69.857	81.565	95.537
5200	14.861	72.829	82.114	96.119
5400	14.864	75.802	82.643	96.680
5600	14.867	78.775	83.154	97.221
5800	14.870	81.748	83.648	97.743
6000	14.872	84.722	84.126	98.247

Appendix 4.20   THERMODYNAMIC PROPERTIES OF BCLF2 GAS

T	C_P^0	$(H^0 - H_0^0)$	$-(F^0 - H_0^0)/T$	S_T^0
DEG-K	CAL/MOLE DEG-K	KCAL/MOLE	CAL/MOLE DEG-K	CAL/MOLE DEG-K
100	8.431	0.803	46.250	54.284
200	10.907	1.766	52.026	60.857
273.15	12.541	2.626	54.894	64.508
298.15	13.020	2.946	55.747	65.627
400	14.639	4.358	58.796	69.691
500	15.815	5.884	61.323	73.091
600	16.684	7.511	63.537	76.055
700	17.327	9.213	65.516	78.677
800	17.808	10.971	67.310	81.024
900	18.172	12.771	68.954	83.143
1000	18.452	14.602	70.471	85.073
1100	18.670	16.459	71.880	86.842
1200	18.844	18.335	73.195	88.475
1300	18.983	20.227	74.430	89.989
1400	19.097	22.131	75.592	91.400
1500	19.191	24.045	76.690	92.721
1600	19.268	25.968	77.731	93.962
1700	19.334	27.899	78.721	95.132
1800	19.389	29.835	79.664	96.238
1900	19.437	31.776	80.564	97.288
2000	19.478	33.722	81.425	98.286
2100	19.513	35.672	82.251	99.237
2200	19.544	37.625	83.044	100.146
2300	19.571	39.580	83.806	101.015
2400	19.595	41.539	84.541	101.849
2500	19.617	43.499	85.249	102.649
2600	19.635	45.462	85.933	103.419
2700	19.652	47.426	86.595	104.160
2800	19.667	49.392	87.235	104.875
2900	19.681	51.360	87.855	105.566
3000	19.693	53.329	88.457	106.233
3200	19.715	57.269	89.608	107.505
3400	19.733	61.214	90.696	108.700
3600	19.748	65.162	91.728	109.829
3800	19.760	69.113	92.709	110.897
4000	19.771	73.066	93.644	111.911
4200	19.780	77.021	94.537	112.876
4400	19.789	80.978	95.392	113.796
4600	19.796	84.937	96.211	114.676
4800	19.802	88.896	96.998	115.518
5000	19.807	92.857	97.755	116.327
5200	19.812	96.819	98.485	117.104
5400	19.817	100.782	99.188	117.852
5600	19.820	104.746	99.868	118.572
5800	19.824	108.710	100.525	119.268
6000	19.827	112.676	101.161	119.940

T	C_P^0	$(H^0 - H_0^0)$	$-(F^0 - H_0^0)/T$	S_T^0
DEG-K	CAL/MOLE DEG-K	KCAL/MOLE	CAL/MOLE DEG-K	CAL/MOLE DEG-K
100	7.349	0.702	39.926	46.947
200	9.357	1.537	44.966	52.649
273.15	10.476	2.265	47.452	55.743
298.15	10.766	2.530	48.186	56.673
400	11.640	3.675	50.782	59.968
500	12.228	4.870	52.893	62.632
600	12.681	6.116	54.710	64.903
700	13.042	7.403	56.311	66.886
800	13.334	8.722	57.745	68.648
900	13.570	10.068	59.046	70.232
1000	13.762	11.435	60.238	71.672
1100	13.919	12.819	61.338	72.992
1200	14.048	14.217	62.361	74.208
1300	14.154	15.628	63.316	75.337
1400	14.243	17.048	64.212	76.389
1500	14.318	18.476	65.057	77.375
1600	14.381	19.911	65.857	78.301
1700	14.435	21.352	66.614	79.174
1800	14.481	22.798	67.335	80.001
1900	14.521	24.248	68.023	80.785
2000	14.556	25.702	68.680	81.531
2100	14.586	27.159	69.309	82.241
2200	14.612	28.619	69.912	82.921
2300	14.636	30.081	70.492	83.571
2400	14.657	31.546	71.050	84.194
2500	14.675	33.012	71.588	84.793
2600	14.692	34.481	72.107	85.369
2700	14.706	35.951	72.608	85.923
2800	14.720	37.422	73.093	86.458
2900	14.732	38.895	73.563	86.975
3000	14.743	40.368	74.019	87.475
3200	14.762	43.319	74.890	88.427
3400	14.778	46.273	75.713	89.322
3600	14.791	49.230	76.493	90.167
3800	14.802	52.189	77.233	90.967
4000	14.812	55.151	77.939	91.727
4200	14.821	58.114	78.613	92.450
4400	14.828	61.079	79.258	93.139
4600	14.834	64.045	79.876	93.799
4800	14.840	67.012	80.469	94.430
5000	14.845	69.981	81.040	95.036
5200	14.849	72.950	81.590	95.618
5400	14.853	75.921	82.120	96.179
5600	14.857	78.892	82.631	96.719
5800	14.860	81.863	83.126	97.241
6000	14.863	84.836	83.605	97.744

THERMODYNAMIC PROPERTIES OF BCL2 GAS

T	C_p^0	$(H^0 - H_0^0)$	$-(F^0 - H_0^0)/T$	S_T^0
DEG-K	CAL/MOLE DEG-K	KCAL/MOLE	CAL/MOLE DEG-K	CAL/MOLE DEG-K
100	8.244	0.800	45.689	53.686
200	9.816	1.702	51.366	59.877
273.15	10.722	2.455	54.090	63.078
298.15	10.974	2.726	54.884	64.028
400	11.785	3.888	57.654	67.374
500	12.329	5.095	59.875	70.066
600	12.705	6.348	61.769	72.349
700	12.969	7.633	63.425	74.329
800	13.160	8.940	64.899	76.074
900	13.299	10.263	66.229	77.632
1000	13.405	11.598	67.441	79.039
1100	13.486	12.943	68.554	80.321
1200	13.549	14.295	69.584	81.497
1300	13.600	15.652	70.543	82.583
1400	13.640	17.015	71.440	83.593
1500	13.674	18.380	72.282	84.535
1600	13.701	19.749	73.075	85.418
1700	13.724	21.120	73.826	86.250
1800	13.744	22.494	74.538	87.035
1900	13.761	23.869	75.216	87.778
2000	13.775	25.246	75.862	88.485
2100	13.787	26.624	76.479	89.157
2200	13.798	28.003	77.070	89.799
2300	13.807	29.384	77.637	90.412
2400	13.816	30.765	78.181	91.000
2500	13.823	32.147	78.705	91.564
2600	13.829	33.529	79.211	92.106
2700	13.835	34.912	79.698	92.628
2800	13.841	36.296	80.169	93.132
2900	13.845	37.681	80.624	93.617
3000	13.849	39.065	81.065	94.087
3200	13.857	41.836	81.907	94.981
3400	13.863	44.608	82.701	95.821
3600	13.868	47.381	83.452	96.614
3800	13.872	50.155	84.165	97.364
4000	13.876	52.930	84.843	98.075
4200	13.879	55.706	85.489	98.752
4400	13.882	58.482	86.107	99.398
4600	13.885	61.258	86.698	100.015
4800	13.887	64.035	87.266	100.606
5000	13.889	66.813	87.811	101.173
5200	13.890	69.591	88.335	101.718
5400	13.892	72.369	88.840	102.242
5600	13.893	75.148	89.328	102.747
5800	13.894	77.926	89.799	103.235
6000	13.895	80.705	90.255	103.706

Appendix 4.23 THERMODYNAMIC PROPERTIES OF BCL2F GAS

T	C_P^0	$(H^0 - H_0^0)$	$-(F^0 - H_0^0)/T$	S_T^0
DEG-K	CAL/MOLE DEG-K	KCAL/MOLE	CAL/MOLE DEG-K	CAL/MOLE DEG-K
100	9.078	0.821	48.058	56.263
200	12.034	1.881	54.089	63.494
273.15	13.656	2.823	57.160	67.497
298.15	14.115	3.171	58.079	68.713
400	15.614	4.689	61.361	73.083
500	16.650	6.305	64.075	76.685
600	17.384	8.009	66.441	79.790
700	17.911	9.775	68.547	82.511
800	18.296	11.587	70.446	84.929
900	18.583	13.431	72.178	87.102
1000	18.801	15.301	73.771	89.072
1100	18.970	17.190	75.245	90.872
1200	19.102	19.094	76.617	92.528
1300	19.208	21.009	77.900	94.062
1400	19.294	22.935	79.106	95.488
1500	19.365	24.868	80.243	96.822
1600	19.424	26.807	81.319	98.074
1700	19.473	28.752	82.340	99.253
1800	19.514	30.702	83.311	100.367
1900	19.550	32.655	84.236	101.423
2000	19.580	34.611	85.121	102.427
2100	19.607	36.571	85.968	103.383
2200	19.630	38.533	86.780	104.295
2300	19.650	40.497	87.561	105.168
2400	19.668	42.463	88.312	106.005
2500	19.683	44.430	89.036	106.808
2600	19.697	46.399	89.735	107.580
2700	19.710	48.370	90.409	108.324
2800	19.721	50.341	91.062	109.041
2900	19.731	52.314	91.694	109.733
3000	19.740	54.287	92.307	110.402
3200	19.756	58.237	93.478	111.677
3400	19.769	62.190	94.584	112.875
3600	19.780	66.145	95.632	114.005
3800	19.790	70.102	96.627	115.075
4000	19.798	74.061	97.575	116.090
4200	19.805	78.021	98.480	117.056
4400	19.811	81.982	99.346	117.978
4600	19.816	85.945	100.175	118.859
4800	19.820	89.909	100.971	119.702
5000	19.825	93.873	101.737	120.511
5200	19.828	97.838	102.474	121.289
5400	19.831	101.804	103.185	122.037
5600	19.834	105.771	103.871	122.759
5800	19.837	109.738	104.534	123.455
6000	19.839	113.706	105.176	124.127

Appendix 4.24   THERMODYNAMIC PROPERTIES OF BCL3 GAS

T	C_P^0	$(H^0 - H_0^0)$	$-(F^0 - H_0^0)/T$	S_T^0
DEG-K	CAL/MOLE DEG-K	KCAL/MOLE	CAL/MOLE DEG-K	CAL/MOLE DEG-K
100	9.724	0.841	47.524	55.938
200	12.866	1.982	53.807	63.714
273.15	14.462	2.984	57.049	67.973
298.15	14.912	3.351	58.019	69.259
400	16.354	4.948	61.486	73.857
500	17.299	6.634	64.346	77.614
600	17.935	8.398	66.832	80.828
700	18.374	10.214	69.036	83.628
800	18.684	12.068	71.018	86.103
900	18.910	13.949	72.819	88.317
1000	19.079	15.848	74.470	90.319
1100	19.208	17.763	75.995	92.143
1200	19.308	19.689	77.412	93.819
1300	19.388	21.624	78.734	95.368
1400	19.452	23.566	79.974	96.807
1500	19.504	25.514	81.142	98.151
1600	19.547	27.467	82.245	99.411
1700	19.583	29.423	83.290	100.597
1800	19.614	31.383	84.283	101.718
1900	19.640	33.346	85.228	102.779
2000	19.662	35.311	86.131	103.787
2100	19.681	37.278	86.995	104.747
2200	19.698	39.247	87.823	105.663
2300	19.713	41.218	88.618	106.539
2400	19.725	43.190	89.382	107.378
2500	19.737	45.163	90.118	108.183
2600	19.747	47.137	90.828	108.958
2700	19.756	49.112	91.513	109.703
2800	19.764	51.088	92.176	110.422
2900	19.771	53.065	92.817	111.115
3000	19.778	55.042	93.438	111.786
3200	19.789	58.999	94.625	113.062
3400	19.799	62.958	95.745	114.262
3600	19.807	66.918	96.806	115.394
3800	19.813	70.880	97.813	116.465
4000	19.819	74.844	98.771	117.482
4200	19.824	78.808	99.685	118.449
4400	19.828	82.773	100.559	119.371
4600	19.832	86.739	101.396	120.253
4800	19.835	90.706	102.200	121.097
5000	19.838	94.673	102.972	121.907
5200	19.841	98.641	103.715	122.685
5400	19.843	102.610	104.432	123.434
5600	19.845	106.579	105.123	124.155
5800	19.847	110.548	105.792	124.852
6000	19.849	114.517	106.438	125.525

Appendix 4.25 — THERMODYNAMIC PROPERTIES OF BFO GAS

T	C_P^0	$(H^0 - H_0^0)$	$-(F^0 - H_0^0)/T$	S_T^0
DEG-K	CAL/MOLE DEG-K	KCAL/MOLE	CAL/MOLE DEG-K	CAL/MOLE DEG-K
100	7.376	0.703	37.767	44.795
200	9.157	1.531	42.808	50.464
273.15	10.127	2.238	45.275	53.470
298.15	10.394	2.495	46.001	54.369
400	11.258	3.600	48.551	57.551
500	11.884	4.759	50.617	60.134
600	12.379	5.973	52.391	62.346
700	12.779	7.231	53.955	64.285
800	13.105	8.526	55.356	66.014
900	13.371	9.850	56.628	67.573
1000	13.588	11.199	57.795	68.994
1100	13.766	12.567	58.873	70.297
1200	13.913	13.951	59.876	71.502
1300	14.035	15.348	60.814	72.620
1400	14.137	16.757	61.695	73.664
1500	14.223	18.175	62.526	74.642
1600	14.296	19.601	63.312	75.563
1700	14.358	21.034	64.058	76.431
1800	14.411	22.472	64.769	77.253
1900	14.457	23.916	65.447	78.034
2000	14.498	25.364	66.095	78.777
2100	14.533	26.815	66.716	79.485
2200	14.564	28.270	67.312	80.162
2300	14.591	29.728	67.884	80.810
2400	14.615	31.188	68.436	81.431
2500	14.636	32.651	68.968	82.028
2600	14.656	34.115	69.481	82.603
2700	14.673	35.582	69.978	83.156
2800	14.689	37.050	70.458	83.690
2900	14.703	38.519	70.923	84.206
3000	14.715	39.990	71.374	84.704
3200	14.738	42.936	72.237	85.655
3400	14.756	45.885	73.053	86.549
3600	14.772	48.838	73.826	87.393
3800	14.785	51.794	74.562	88.192
4000	14.796	54.752	75.262	88.950
4200	14.806	57.712	75.931	89.672
4400	14.815	60.674	76.572	90.361
4600	14.822	63.638	77.186	91.020
4800	14.829	66.603	77.775	91.651
5000	14.835	69.569	78.343	92.257
5200	14.840	72.537	78.889	92.838
5400	14.845	75.505	79.416	93.399
5600	14.849	78.475	79.925	93.939
5800	14.852	81.445	80.418	94.460
6000	14.856	84.416	80.894	94.963

Appendix 4.26   THERMODYNAMIC PROPERTIES OF BF2 GAS

T	C_P^0	$(H^0 - H_0^0)$	$-(F^0 - H_0^0)/T$	S_T^0
DEG-K	CAL/MOLE DEG-K	KCAL/MOLE	CAL/MOLE DEG-K	CAL/MOLE DEG-K
100	6.960	0.696	38.211	45.166
200	7.434	1.407	43.045	50.078
273.15	8.322	1.982	45.266	52.520
298.15	8.659	2.194	45.906	53.264
400	9.956	3.143	48.136	55.994
500	10.986	4.193	49.946	58.331
600	11.777	5.333	51.520	60.408
700	12.377	6.542	52.925	62.270
800	12.834	7.803	54.200	63.954
900	13.186	9.105	55.370	65.487
1000	13.460	10.438	56.453	66.891
1100	13.676	11.795	57.462	68.184
1200	13.849	13.171	58.406	69.382
1300	13.989	14.564	59.293	70.496
1400	14.104	15.969	60.131	71.537
1500	14.199	17.384	60.924	72.514
1600	14.279	18.808	61.678	73.433
1700	14.346	20.239	62.395	74.300
1800	14.402	21.677	63.079	75.122
1900	14.451	23.119	63.734	75.902
2000	14.493	24.567	64.361	76.644
2100	14.530	26.018	64.963	77.352
2200	14.562	27.472	65.542	78.029
2300	14.590	28.930	66.099	78.677
2400	14.615	30.390	66.636	79.299
2500	14.637	31.853	67.154	79.896
2600	14.657	33.318	67.656	80.470
2700	14.674	34.784	68.140	81.024
2800	14.690	36.252	68.610	81.557
2900	14.704	37.722	69.066	82.073
3000	14.717	39.193	69.507	82.572
3200	14.739	42.139	70.354	83.522
3400	14.758	45.089	71.155	84.417
3600	14.773	48.042	71.916	85.261
3800	14.787	50.998	72.639	86.060
4000	14.798	53.956	73.329	86.818
4200	14.808	56.917	73.989	87.541
4400	14.816	59.879	74.621	88.230
4600	14.824	62.843	75.227	88.889
4800	14.830	65.809	75.809	89.520
5000	14.836	68.775	76.370	90.125
5200	14.841	71.743	76.910	90.707
5400	14.846	74.712	77.432	91.267
5600	14.850	77.681	77.936	91.807
5800	14.853	80.652	78.423	92.328
6000	14.857	83.623	78.895	92.832

Appendix 4.27   THERMODYNAMIC PROPERTIES OF BF3 GAS

T	C_P^0	$(H^0 - H_0^0)$	$-(F^0 - H_0^0)/T$	S_T^0
DEG-K	CAL/MOLE DEG-K	KCAL/MOLE	CAL/MOLE DEG-K	CAL/MOLE DEG-K
100	8.145	0.798	42.161	50.138
200	10.001	1.696	47.809	56.287
273.15	11.529	2.484	50.540	59.635
298.15	12.005	2.778	51.346	60.665
400	13.683	4.090	54.212	64.437
500	14.968	5.525	56.584	67.635
600	15.955	7.074	58.666	70.455
700	16.707	8.708	60.533	72.974
800	17.282	10.409	62.232	75.244
900	17.724	12.160	63.794	77.306
1000	18.068	13.951	65.241	79.192
1100	18.340	15.772	66.589	80.927
1200	18.557	17.617	67.852	82.533
1300	18.732	19.482	69.039	84.025
1400	18.876	21.362	70.160	85.419
1500	18.995	23.256	71.221	86.725
1600	19.094	25.160	72.229	87.954
1700	19.177	27.074	73.188	89.114
1800	19.248	28.996	74.104	90.213
1900	19.309	30.923	74.980	91.255
2000	19.362	32.857	75.818	92.247
2100	19.407	34.796	76.623	93.193
2200	19.447	36.738	77.397	94.096
2300	19.482	38.685	78.142	94.962
2400	19.513	40.635	78.860	95.791
2500	19.540	42.587	79.554	96.589
2600	19.565	44.543	80.224	97.355
2700	19.587	46.500	80.872	98.094
2800	19.606	48.460	81.500	98.807
2900	19.624	50.421	82.109	99.495
3000	19.640	52.385	82.699	100.161
3200	19.668	56.315	83.831	101.429
3400	19.691	60.251	84.901	102.622
3600	19.710	64.191	85.917	103.748
3800	19.726	68.135	86.884	104.815
4000	19.740	72.082	87.806	105.827
4200	19.753	76.031	88.687	106.790
4400	19.763	79.983	89.531	107.709
4600	19.772	83.936	90.341	108.588
4800	19.781	87.892	91.119	109.430
5000	19.788	91.849	91.868	110.237
5200	19.794	95.807	92.589	111.014
5400	19.800	99.766	93.285	111.761
5600	19.805	103.727	93.958	112.481
5800	19.809	107.688	94.609	113.176
6000	19.813	111.650	95.239	113.848

Appendix 4.28 THERMODYNAMIC PROPERTIES OF BHO2 GAS

T	C_P^0	$(H^0 - H_0^0)_T$	$-(F_T^0 - H_0^0)/T$	S_T^0
DEG-K	CAL/MOLE DEG-K	KCAL/MOLE	CAL/MOLE DEG-K	CAL/MOLE DEG-K
100	7.984	0.795	39.625	47.578
200	8.816	1.627	45.175	53.308
273.15	9.766	2.306	47.753	56.195
298.15	10.094	2.554	48.497	57.064
400	11.366	3.648	51.091	60.212
500	12.466	4.841	53.187	62.869
600	13.402	6.136	55.000	65.227
700	14.189	7.517	56.616	67.354
800	14.851	8.969	58.081	69.293
900	15.414	10.483	59.427	71.075
1000	15.895	12.050	60.675	72.725
1100	16.311	13.660	61.841	74.260
1200	16.672	15.310	62.937	75.695
1300	16.986	16.993	63.971	77.042
1400	17.260	18.706	64.950	78.311
1500	17.501	20.444	65.881	79.510
1600	17.713	22.205	66.769	80.647
1700	17.901	23.986	67.617	81.726
1800	18.066	25.784	68.430	82.754
1900	18.214	27.599	69.210	83.735
2000	18.345	29.427	69.960	84.673
2100	18.462	31.267	70.682	85.571
2200	18.567	33.119	71.378	86.432
2300	18.661	34.980	72.051	87.260
2400	18.746	36.850	72.701	88.056
2500	18.822	38.729	73.331	88.822
2600	18.892	40.615	73.941	89.562
2700	18.955	42.507	74.533	90.276
2800	19.012	44.405	75.107	90.967
2900	19.065	46.309	75.666	91.635
3000	19.112	48.218	76.209	92.282
3200	19.197	52.049	77.253	93.518
3400	19.268	55.896	78.244	94.684
3600	19.329	59.756	79.188	95.787
3800	19.381	63.627	80.090	96.834
4000	19.426	67.508	80.952	97.829
4200	19.465	71.397	81.778	98.778
4400	19.500	75.294	82.572	99.684
4600	19.530	79.197	83.335	100.551
4800	19.557	83.105	84.070	101.383
5000	19.581	87.019	84.778	102.182
5200	19.602	90.938	85.463	102.951
5400	19.621	94.860	86.124	103.691
5600	19.638	98.786	86.764	104.405
5800	19.654	102.715	87.384	105.094
6000	19.668	106.647	87.986	105.760

THERMODYNAMIC PROPERTIES OF BH3 GAS

T	C_p^0	$(H^0 - H_0^0)$	$-(F^0 - H_0^0)/T$	S_T^0
DEG-K	CAL/MOLE DEG-K	KCAL/MOLE	CAL/MOLE DEG-K	CAL/MOLE DEG-K
100	7.949	0.795	28.480	36.429
200	7.981	1.590	33.990	41.942
273.15	8.166	2.180	36.472	44.452
298.15	8.283	2.385	37.171	45.172
400	9.030	3.264	39.541	47.701
500	10.048	4.216	41.389	49.821
600	11.161	5.276	42.958	51.751
700	12.240	6.447	44.344	53.554
800	13.221	7.721	45.602	55.254
900	14.079	9.087	46.765	56.862
1000	14.816	10.533	47.851	58.384
1100	15.443	12.047	48.875	59.827
1200	15.975	13.618	49.845	61.194
1300	16.426	15.239	50.769	62.491
1400	16.810	16.901	51.650	63.723
1500	17.138	18.599	52.494	64.894
1600	17.419	20.327	53.304	66.009
1700	17.661	22.082	54.083	67.072
1800	17.870	23.858	54.833	68.088
1900	18.053	25.655	55.557	69.059
2000	18.212	27.468	56.255	69.989
2100	18.352	29.296	56.931	70.881
2200	18.476	31.138	57.584	71.738
2300	18.585	32.991	58.218	72.562
2400	18.683	34.855	58.832	73.355
2500	18.770	36.727	59.428	74.119
2600	18.848	38.608	60.008	74.857
2700	18.918	40.497	60.571	75.570
2800	18.981	42.392	61.119	76.259
2900	19.039	44.293	61.653	76.926
3000	19.091	46.199	62.173	77.572
3200	19.182	50.027	63.174	78.807
3400	19.258	53.871	64.128	79.973
3600	19.322	57.729	65.039	81.075
3800	19.377	61.599	65.911	82.121
4000	19.424	65.479	66.747	83.117
4200	19.464	69.368	67.549	84.065
4400	19.500	73.265	68.320	84.972
4600	19.531	77.168	69.063	85.839
4800	19.558	81.077	69.780	86.671
5000	19.582	84.991	70.472	87.470
5200	19.604	88.910	71.140	88.238
5400	19.623	92.832	71.787	88.978
5600	19.640	96.759	72.414	89.692
5800	19.656	100.688	73.022	90.382
6000	19.670	104.621	73.612	91.048

Appendix 4.30 THERMODYNAMIC PROPERTIES OF B(OH)3 GAS

T	C$_P^0$	(H^0 – H$_0^0$)	–(F^0 –H$_0^0$)/T	S$_T^0$
DEG-K	CAL/MOLE DEG-K	KCAL/MOLE	CAL/MOLE DEG-K	CAL/MOLE DEG-K
100	10.033	0.859	45.689	54.274
200	13.446	2.029	52.107	62.252
273.15	16.140	3.111	55.452	66.841
298.15	17.040	3.526	56.468	68.293
400	20.357	5.436	60.191	73.780
500	22.954	7.607	63.400	78.613
600	24.981	10.007	66.306	82.985
700	26.596	12.589	68.977	86.962
800	27.923	15.317	71.456	90.602
900	29.040	18.167	73.772	93.957
1000	29.996	21.120	75.948	97.068
1100	30.821	24.161	78.001	99.966
1200	31.538	27.280	79.946	102.679
1300	32.162	30.466	81.794	105.229
1400	32.707	33.710	83.554	107.633
1500	33.185	37.005	85.236	109.906
1600	33.604	40.345	86.846	112.061
1700	33.973	43.724	88.390	114.110
1800	34.298	47.138	89.873	116.061
1900	34.586	50.582	91.301	117.923
2000	34.842	54.054	92.677	119.704
2100	35.070	57.550	94.005	121.410
2200	35.274	61.067	95.288	123.046
2300	35.457	64.604	96.529	124.618
2400	35.621	68.158	97.731	126.131
2500	35.769	71.728	98.897	127.588
2600	35.902	75.311	100.027	128.993
2700	36.023	78.908	101.126	130.351
2800	36.133	82.516	102.193	131.663
2900	36.233	86.134	103.231	132.932
3000	36.325	89.762	104.242	134.162
3200	36.485	97.044	106.186	136.512
3400	36.621	104.354	108.036	138.728
3600	36.736	111.690	109.799	140.825
3800	36.835	119.048	111.485	142.814
4000	36.921	126.424	113.099	144.705
4200	36.995	133.815	114.648	146.508
4400	37.060	141.221	116.135	148.231
4600	37.117	148.639	117.567	149.880
4800	37.168	156.067	118.946	151.460
5000	37.212	163.505	120.277	152.979
5200	37.252	170.952	121.563	154.439
5400	37.288	178.406	122.807	155.845
5600	37.320	185.867	124.012	157.202
5800	37.349	193.334	125.179	158.512
6000	37.375	200.806	126.311	159.779

Appendix 4.31   THERMODYNAMIC PROPERTIES OF B2O2 GAS

T	C_P^0	$(H^0 - H_0^0)_T$	$-(F_T^0 - H_0^0)/T$	S_T^0
DEG-K	CAL/MOLE DEG-K	KCAL/MOLE	CAL/MOLE DEG-K	CAL/MOLE DEG-K
100	8.028	0.719	38.801	45.995
200	10.970	1.671	44.118	52.475
273.15	12.668	2.539	46.863	56.159
298.15	13.133	2.862	47.690	57.289
400	14.600	4.279	50.670	61.367
500	15.645	5.793	53.155	64.742
600	16.478	7.401	55.336	67.671
700	17.161	9.084	57.287	70.264
800	17.722	10.829	59.057	72.593
900	18.183	12.625	60.680	74.708
1000	18.560	14.463	62.181	76.644
1100	18.871	16.335	63.578	78.428
1200	19.128	18.235	64.885	80.082
1300	19.341	20.159	66.114	81.621
1400	19.520	22.102	67.274	83.061
1500	19.670	24.062	68.372	84.413
1600	19.798	26.036	69.415	85.687
1700	19.907	28.021	70.408	86.891
1800	20.001	30.017	71.355	88.031
1900	20.082	32.021	72.262	89.115
2000	20.152	34.033	73.130	90.147
2100	20.214	36.051	73.964	91.131
2200	20.268	38.075	74.766	92.073
2300	20.316	40.104	75.538	92.975
2400	20.358	42.138	76.283	93.841
2500	20.396	44.176	77.002	94.672
2600	20.430	46.217	77.697	95.473
2700	20.460	48.262	78.370	96.245
2800	20.487	50.309	79.022	96.989
2900	20.512	52.359	79.654	97.709
3000	20.534	54.411	80.267	98.404
3200	20.573	58.522	81.443	99.731
3400	20.606	62.640	82.556	100.979
3600	20.633	66.764	83.612	102.158
3800	20.657	70.893	84.618	103.274
4000	20.677	75.027	85.577	104.334
4200	20.694	79.164	86.495	105.343
4400	20.709	83.304	87.374	106.306
4600	20.722	87.447	88.217	107.227
4800	20.734	91.593	89.028	108.109
5000	20.744	95.741	89.808	108.956
5200	20.753	99.890	90.560	109.770
5400	20.761	104.042	91.286	110.553
5600	20.768	108.195	91.988	111.308
5800	20.775	112.349	92.667	112.037
6000	20.781	116.505	93.324	112.742

Appendix 4.32 THERMODYNAMIC PROPERTIES OF B2O3 GAS

T	C_P^0	$(H^0 - H_0^0)_T$	$-(F^0 - H_0^0)/T$	S_T^0
DEG-K	CAL/MOLE DEG-K	KCAL/MOLE	CAL/MOLE DEG-K	CAL/MOLE DEG-K
100	8.429	0.805	45.931	53.985
200	10.137	1.726	51.670	60.301
273.15	11.836	2.529	54.449	63.707
298.15	12.433	2.832	55.271	64.770
400	14.722	4.218	58.207	68.751
500	16.630	5.788	60.671	72.248
600	18.196	7.532	62.869	75.423
700	19.464	9.418	64.873	78.327
800	20.483	11.417	66.724	80.995
900	21.303	13.508	68.448	83.456
1000	21.965	15.672	70.064	85.736
1100	22.502	17.896	71.586	87.856
1200	22.942	20.169	73.025	89.833
1300	23.305	22.482	74.390	91.684
1400	23.607	24.828	75.688	93.423
1500	23.860	27.202	76.926	95.060
1600	24.074	29.599	78.108	96.607
1700	24.256	32.016	79.240	98.072
1800	24.412	34.449	80.325	99.463
1900	24.546	36.897	81.367	100.787
2000	24.663	39.358	82.370	102.049
2100	24.765	41.829	83.336	103.255
2200	24.854	44.310	84.268	104.409
2300	24.933	46.800	85.168	105.516
2400	25.003	49.297	86.038	106.578
2500	25.065	51.800	86.880	107.600
2600	25.121	54.310	87.696	108.584
2700	25.171	56.824	88.487	109.533
2800	25.215	59.343	89.255	110.450
2900	25.256	61.867	90.002	111.335
3000	25.293	64.395	90.727	112.192
3200	25.356	69.460	92.120	113.826
3400	25.409	74.536	93.443	115.365
3600	25.454	79.623	94.701	116.819
3800	25.492	84.718	95.902	118.196
4000	25.525	89.819	97.050	119.505
4200	25.553	94.927	98.149	120.751
4400	25.578	100.041	99.204	121.940
4600	25.599	105.158	100.217	123.078
4800	25.618	110.280	101.192	124.167
5000	25.635	115.406	102.132	125.214
5200	25.650	120.534	103.040	126.219
5400	25.663	125.665	103.916	127.188
5600	25.675	130.799	104.764	128.121
5800	25.686	135.935	105.585	129.022
6000	25.695	141.074	106.381	129.893

THERMODYNAMIC PROPERTIES OF BEBR2 GAS

T	C_P	$(H - H_T^0)$	$-(F_T^0 - H_0^0)/T$	S_T^0
DEG-K	CAL/MOLE DEG-K	KCAL/MOLE	CAL/MOLE DEG-K	CAL/MOLE DEG-K
100	7.386	0.703	44.990	52.019
200	9.409	1.543	50.044	57.758
273.15	10.534	2.275	52.540	60.867
298.15	10.836	2.542	53.278	61.803
400	11.789	3.697	55.887	65.130
500	12.451	4.911	58.014	67.835
600	12.945	6.182	59.848	70.151
700	13.318	7.496	61.468	72.176
800	13.603	8.842	62.921	73.974
900	13.822	10.214	64.240	75.589
1000	13.994	11.605	65.449	77.055
1100	14.130	13.012	66.566	78.395
1200	14.239	14.430	67.604	79.629
1300	14.327	15.859	68.573	80.773
1400	14.399	17.295	69.483	81.837
1500	14.459	18.738	70.340	82.833
1600	14.509	20.187	71.151	83.767
1700	14.551	21.640	71.919	84.648
1800	14.587	23.097	72.650	85.481
1900	14.618	24.557	73.346	86.271
2000	14.645	26.020	74.011	87.021
2100	14.668	27.486	74.648	87.736
2200	14.688	28.954	75.258	88.419
2300	14.706	30.423	75.845	89.072
2400	14.721	31.895	76.409	89.699
2500	14.735	33.368	76.953	90.300
2600	14.748	34.842	77.477	90.878
2700	14.759	36.317	77.984	91.435
2800	14.769	37.794	78.474	91.972
2900	14.778	39.271	78.948	92.490
3000	14.786	40.749	79.408	92.991
3200	14.800	43.708	80.287	93.946
3400	14.812	46.669	81.117	94.844
3600	14.822	49.632	81.904	95.690
3800	14.830	52.597	82.651	96.492
4000	14.837	55.564	83.362	97.253
4200	14.843	58.532	84.041	97.977
4400	14.849	61.501	84.690	98.668
4600	14.853	64.472	85.312	99.328
4800	14.857	67.443	85.909	99.960
5000	14.861	70.415	86.484	100.567
5200	14.864	73.387	87.037	101.150
5400	14.867	76.360	87.570	101.711
5600	14.870	79.334	88.085	102.251
5800	14.872	82.308	88.582	102.773
6000	14.874	85.283	89.064	103.277

THERMODYNAMIC PROPERTIES OF BEC2 GAS

T	C_P^0	$(H^0 - H_0^0)$	$-(F^0 - H_0^0)/T$	S_T^0
DEG-K	CAL/MOLE DEG-K	KCAL/MOLE	CAL/MOLE DEG-K	CAL/MOLE DEG-K
100	7.213	0.700	34.917	41.912
200	8.796	1.498	39.893	47.383
273.15	9.765	2.179	42.299	50.275
298.15	10.041	2.426	43.005	51.142
400	10.959	3.498	45.483	54.228
500	11.646	4.630	47.491	56.751
600	12.193	5.823	49.220	58.924
700	12.634	7.065	50.746	60.838
800	12.990	8.347	52.116	62.549
900	13.279	9.661	53.363	64.097
1000	13.513	11.001	54.508	65.508
1100	13.704	12.362	55.567	66.805
1200	13.860	13.740	56.554	68.005
1300	13.990	15.133	57.479	69.119
1400	14.099	16.537	58.348	70.160
1500	14.189	17.952	59.168	71.136
1600	14.266	19.375	59.945	72.054
1700	14.332	20.805	60.683	72.921
1800	14.388	22.241	61.386	73.742
1900	14.437	23.682	62.057	74.521
2000	14.479	25.128	62.699	75.263
2100	14.516	26.578	63.314	75.970
2200	14.548	28.031	63.905	76.646
2300	14.577	29.487	64.473	77.294
2400	14.602	30.946	65.020	77.915
2500	14.625	32.408	65.548	78.511
2600	14.645	33.871	66.058	79.085
2700	14.663	35.337	66.551	79.638
2800	14.679	36.804	67.028	80.172
2900	14.694	38.273	67.490	80.687
3000	14.707	39.743	67.938	81.186
3200	14.730	42.686	68.796	82.135
3400	14.750	45.635	69.607	83.029
3600	14.766	48.586	70.376	83.873
3800	14.780	51.541	71.108	84.671
4000	14.792	54.498	71.805	85.430
4200	14.802	57.457	72.471	86.152
4400	14.811	60.419	73.109	86.841
4600	14.819	63.382	73.720	87.499
4800	14.826	66.346	74.308	88.130
5000	14.832	69.312	74.873	88.735
5200	14.837	72.279	75.417	89.317
5400	14.842	75.247	75.943	89.877
5600	14.846	78.216	76.450	90.417
5800	14.850	81.185	76.941	90.938
6000	14.854	84.156	77.416	91.442

Appendix 4.35   THERMODYNAMIC PROPERTIES OF BECLBR GAS

T	C_p^0	$(H^0 - H_0^0)$	$-(F^0 - H_0^0)/T$	S_T^0
DEG-K	CAL/MOLE DEG-K	KCAL/MOLE	CAL/MOLE DEG-K	CAL/MOLE DEG-K
100	8.655	0.739	44.454	51.849
200	11.140	1.745	49.995	58.722
273.15	12.105	2.598	52.836	62.347
298.15	12.356	2.904	53.679	63.419
400	13.129	4.205	56.655	67.166
500	13.616	5.544	59.065	70.152
600	13.939	6.922	61.128	72.665
700	14.160	8.328	62.934	74.831
800	14.315	9.752	64.543	76.733
900	14.428	11.190	65.993	78.426
1000	14.512	12.637	67.314	79.950
1100	14.576	14.091	68.526	81.337
1200	14.625	15.551	69.648	82.607
1300	14.665	17.016	70.690	83.779
1400	14.697	18.484	71.664	84.867
1500	14.722	19.955	72.579	85.882
1600	14.744	21.429	73.440	86.833
1700	14.762	22.904	74.255	87.727
1800	14.777	24.381	75.027	88.572
1900	14.790	25.859	75.761	89.371
2000	14.801	27.339	76.461	90.130
2100	14.810	28.819	77.129	90.852
2200	14.818	30.301	77.768	91.541
2300	14.825	31.783	78.382	92.200
2400	14.832	33.266	78.971	92.831
2500	14.837	34.749	79.537	93.437
2600	14.842	36.233	80.083	94.019
2700	14.847	37.718	80.610	94.579
2800	14.851	39.202	81.118	95.119
2900	14.854	40.688	81.610	95.640
3000	14.858	42.173	82.086	96.144
3200	14.863	45.145	82.995	97.103
3400	14.868	48.119	83.852	98.004
3600	14.872	51.093	84.662	98.854
3800	14.875	54.067	85.430	99.658
4000	14.878	57.043	86.161	100.422
4200	14.880	60.019	86.857	101.148
4400	14.883	62.995	87.523	101.840
4600	14.884	65.972	88.160	102.501
4800	14.886	68.949	88.771	103.135
5000	14.887	71.926	89.357	103.743
5200	14.889	74.904	89.922	104.327
5400	14.890	77.881	90.466	104.888
5600	14.891	80.860	90.991	105.430
5800	14.892	83.838	91.498	105.953
6000	14.893	86.816	91.988	106.457

Appendix 4.36   THERMODYNAMIC PROPERTIES OF BECL2 GAS

T	C_p^0	$(H^0 - H_0^0)_T$	$-(F^0 - H_0^0)/T$	S_T^0
DEG-K	CAL/MOLE DEG-K	KCAL/MOLE	CAL/MOLE DEG-K	CAL/MOLE DEG-K
100	7.407	0.703	40.799	47.830
200	9.706	1.558	45.872	53.664
273.15	10.985	2.318	48.404	56.890
298.15	11.328	2.597	49.157	57.867
400	12.382	3.808	51.834	61.355
500	13.055	5.083	54.030	64.195
600	13.507	6.412	55.931	66.618
700	13.819	7.779	57.612	68.725
800	14.042	9.173	59.120	70.586
900	14.204	10.586	60.488	72.250
1000	14.326	12.013	61.740	73.753
1100	14.419	13.450	62.895	75.123
1200	14.492	14.896	63.967	76.381
1300	14.550	16.348	64.968	77.543
1400	14.596	17.805	65.905	78.623
1500	14.635	19.267	66.787	79.631
1600	14.666	20.732	67.619	80.577
1700	14.692	22.200	68.408	81.467
1800	14.715	23.670	69.157	82.307
1900	14.734	25.143	69.870	83.103
2000	14.750	26.617	70.551	83.860
2100	14.764	28.093	71.202	84.580
2200	14.776	29.570	71.826	85.267
2300	14.787	31.048	72.425	85.924
2400	14.796	32.527	73.000	86.553
2500	14.805	34.007	73.555	87.157
2600	14.812	35.488	74.089	87.738
2700	14.819	36.970	74.605	88.297
2800	14.825	38.452	75.104	88.836
2900	14.830	39.934	75.586	89.357
3000	14.835	41.418	76.054	89.860
3200	14.843	44.386	76.947	90.817
3400	14.850	47.355	77.789	91.717
3600	14.856	50.325	78.587	92.566
3800	14.861	53.297	79.344	93.370
4000	14.865	56.270	80.065	94.132
4200	14.869	59.243	80.752	94.857
4400	14.872	62.217	81.409	95.549
4600	14.875	65.192	82.038	96.210
4800	14.877	68.167	82.642	96.843
5000	14.879	71.143	83.222	97.451
5200	14.881	74.119	83.781	98.034
5400	14.883	77.095	84.319	98.596
5600	14.884	80.072	84.839	99.137
5800	14.886	83.049	85.341	99.660
6000	14.887	86.026	85.827	100.164

Appendix 4.37   THERMODYNAMIC PROPERTIES OF BEFBR GAS

T	C_P^0	$(H^0 - H_T^0)$	$-(F^0 - H_T^0)/T$	S_T^0
DEG-K	CAL/MOLE DEG-K	KCAL/MOLE	CAL/MOLE DEG-K	CAL/MOLE DEG-K
100	7.945	0.716	42.744	49.901
200	10.506	1.650	48.023	56.273
273.15	11.536	2.459	50.710	59.713
298.15	11.797	2.751	51.508	60.735
400	12.606	3.996	54.332	64.323
500	13.154	5.286	56.626	67.198
600	13.546	6.622	58.596	69.633
700	13.829	7.992	60.327	71.743
800	14.038	9.385	61.873	73.604
900	14.194	10.797	63.270	75.267
1000	14.313	12.223	64.546	76.769
1100	14.405	13.659	65.720	78.138
1200	14.478	15.103	66.808	79.394
1300	14.537	16.554	67.822	80.556
1400	14.584	18.010	68.770	81.635
1500	14.623	19.471	69.662	82.642
1600	14.656	20.935	70.503	83.587
1700	14.683	22.402	71.299	84.477
1800	14.706	23.871	72.055	85.316
1900	14.725	25.343	72.774	86.112
2000	14.742	26.816	73.460	86.868
2100	14.757	28.291	74.116	87.588
2200	14.770	29.768	74.744	88.274
2300	14.781	31.245	75.346	88.931
2400	14.791	32.724	75.926	89.560
2500	14.799	34.203	76.483	90.164
2600	14.807	35.684	77.020	90.745
2700	14.814	37.165	77.539	91.304
2800	14.820	38.646	78.041	91.843
2900	14.826	40.129	78.525	92.363
3000	14.831	41.611	78.995	92.866
3200	14.840	44.579	79.892	93.823
3400	14.847	47.547	80.738	94.723
3600	14.853	50.517	81.539	95.572
3800	14.858	53.489	82.299	96.375
4000	14.863	56.461	83.022	97.137
4200	14.867	59.434	83.712	97.863
4400	14.870	62.407	84.371	98.554
4600	14.873	65.382	85.002	99.215
4800	14.875	68.356	85.607	99.848
5000	14.878	71.332	86.189	100.456
5200	14.880	74.307	86.749	101.039
5400	14.882	77.284	87.289	101.601
5600	14.883	80.260	87.810	102.142
5800	14.885	83.237	88.313	102.664
6000	14.886	86.214	88.800	103.169

Appendix 4.38 THERMODYNAMIC PROPERTIES OF BEFCL GAS

T	C_P^0	$(H^0 - H_0^0)_T$	$-(F^0 - H_0^0)/T$	S_T^0
DEG-K	CAL/MOLE DEG-K	KCAL/MOLE	CAL/MOLE DEG-K	CAL/MOLE DEG-K
100	6.988	0.696	40.393	47.352
200	8.016	1.434	45.258	52.427
273.15	9.259	2.066	47.547	55.109
298.15	9.667	2.302	48.216	55.938
400	11.072	3.362	50.580	58.985
500	12.049	4.521	52.525	61.568
600	12.729	5.762	54.225	63.828
700	13.207	7.060	55.742	65.828
800	13.551	8.399	57.117	67.616
900	13.803	9.767	58.374	69.227
1000	13.993	11.158	59.534	70.692
1100	14.139	12.565	60.610	72.033
1200	14.254	13.984	61.614	73.268
1300	14.344	15.414	62.555	74.413
1400	14.418	16.853	63.441	75.478
1500	14.478	18.298	64.277	76.475
1600	14.527	19.748	65.069	77.411
1700	14.569	21.203	65.821	78.293
1800	14.604	22.662	66.537	79.127
1900	14.634	24.123	67.221	79.917
2000	14.660	25.588	67.875	80.669
2100	14.682	27.055	68.501	81.384
2200	14.701	28.525	69.102	82.068
2300	14.718	29.996	69.680	82.722
2400	14.733	31.468	70.237	83.349
2500	14.746	32.942	70.773	83.950
2600	14.758	34.417	71.291	84.529
2700	14.769	35.894	71.792	85.086
2800	14.778	37.371	72.277	85.623
2900	14.787	38.849	72.746	86.142
3000	14.794	40.328	73.201	86.643
3200	14.807	43.289	74.071	87.599
3400	14.818	46.251	74.893	88.497
3600	14.828	49.216	75.673	89.344
3800	14.835	52.182	76.414	90.146
4000	14.842	55.150	77.120	90.907
4200	14.848	58.119	77.794	91.631
4400	14.853	61.089	78.438	92.322
4600	14.857	64.060	79.056	92.983
4800	14.861	67.032	79.650	93.615
5000	14.864	70.004	80.221	94.222
5200	14.867	72.978	80.771	94.805
5400	14.870	75.951	81.301	95.366
5600	14.873	78.926	81.813	95.907
5800	14.875	81.900	82.308	96.429
6000	14.877	84.875	82.787	96.933

Appendix 4.39 THERMODYNAMIC PROPERTIES OF BEF2 GAS

T	C_P^0	$(H^0 - H_0^0)$	$-(F^0 - H_0^0)/T$	S_T^0
DEG-K	CAL/MOLE DEG-K	KCAL/MOLE	CAL/MOLE DEG-K	CAL/MOLE DEG-K
100	6.971	0.696	37.076	44.033
200	7.702	1.419	41.923	49.017
273.15	8.757	2.020	44.175	51.570
298.15	9.124	2.244	44.828	52.353
400	10.452	3.243	47.120	55.228
500	11.447	4.340	48.991	57.672
600	12.185	5.524	50.621	59.828
700	12.730	6.771	52.076	61.749
800	13.138	8.065	53.395	63.477
900	13.448	9.395	54.604	65.043
1000	13.686	10.753	55.720	66.473
1100	13.873	12.131	56.758	67.787
1200	14.021	13.526	57.729	69.000
1300	14.140	14.934	58.640	70.127
1400	14.238	16.353	59.498	71.179
1500	14.318	17.781	60.310	72.164
1600	14.385	19.216	61.080	73.090
1700	14.441	20.658	61.813	73.964
1800	14.488	22.104	62.511	74.791
1900	14.529	23.555	63.178	75.575
2000	14.564	25.010	63.817	76.322
2100	14.595	26.468	64.429	77.033
2200	14.622	27.929	65.018	77.713
2300	14.645	29.392	65.584	78.363
2400	14.665	30.858	66.129	78.987
2500	14.684	32.325	66.656	79.586
2600	14.700	33.794	67.164	80.162
2700	14.715	35.265	67.656	80.717
2800	14.728	36.737	68.132	81.252
2900	14.739	38.211	68.593	81.769
3000	14.750	39.685	69.041	82.269
3200	14.768	42.637	69.898	83.222
3400	14.784	45.592	70.708	84.118
3600	14.797	48.550	71.477	84.963
3800	14.807	51.511	72.208	85.763
4000	14.817	54.473	72.905	86.523
4200	14.825	57.437	73.571	87.246
4400	14.832	60.403	74.208	87.936
4600	14.838	63.370	74.819	88.596
4800	14.843	66.338	75.407	89.227
5000	14.848	69.307	75.972	89.833
5200	14.852	72.277	76.516	90.416
5400	14.856	75.248	77.041	90.976
5600	14.859	78.220	77.549	91.517
5800	14.863	81.192	78.039	92.038
6000	14.865	84.165	78.514	92.542

Appendix 4.40 THERMODYNAMIC PROPERTIES OF CCL4 GAS

T	C_P^0	$(H^0 - H_0^0)$	$-(F^0 - H_0^0)/T$	S_T^0
DEG-K	CAL/MOLE DEG-K	KCAL/MOLE	CAL/MOLE DEG-K	CAL/MOLE DEG-K
100	11.457	0.889	48.223	57.112
200	16.913	2.332	55.236	66.896
273.15	19.427	3.667	59.140	72.564
298.15	20.088	4.161	60.338	74.294
400	22.037	6.315	64.708	80.496
500	23.179	8.581	68.385	85.546
600	23.893	10.937	71.612	89.840
700	24.361	13.351	74.488	93.561
800	24.682	15.804	77.081	96.836
900	24.910	18.284	79.441	99.757
1000	25.077	20.784	81.606	102.390
1100	25.204	23.298	83.606	104.787
1200	25.301	25.824	85.464	106.984
1300	25.378	28.358	87.199	109.012
1400	25.439	30.899	88.825	110.895
1500	25.489	33.445	90.355	112.652
1600	25.530	35.996	91.801	114.299
1700	25.564	38.551	93.170	115.847
1800	25.593	41.109	94.471	117.309
1900	25.617	43.669	95.710	118.694
2000	25.638	46.232	96.892	120.008
2100	25.656	48.797	98.023	121.260
2200	25.672	51.363	99.107	122.454
2300	25.686	53.931	100.147	123.595
2400	25.698	56.501	101.147	124.689
2500	25.708	59.071	102.109	125.738
2600	25.718	61.642	103.038	126.746
2700	25.726	64.214	103.934	127.717
2800	25.734	66.787	104.800	128.653
2900	25.740	69.361	105.638	129.556
3000	25.747	71.935	106.450	130.429
3200	25.757	77.086	108.001	132.091
3400	25.766	82.238	109.465	133.652
3600	25.773	87.392	110.850	135.125
3800	25.779	92.547	112.164	136.519
4000	25.785	97.704	113.416	137.841
4200	25.789	102.861	114.609	139.100
4400	25.793	108.019	115.750	140.299
4600	25.797	113.178	116.842	141.446
4800	25.800	118.338	117.890	142.544
5000	25.803	123.498	118.898	143.597
5200	25.805	128.659	119.867	144.609
5400	25.807	133.820	120.802	145.583
5600	25.809	138.982	121.704	146.522
5800	25.811	144.144	122.575	147.428
6000	25.812	149.306	123.418	148.303

403

Appendix 4.41 THERMODYNAMIC PROPERTIES OF CF2 GAS

T	C_P^0	$(H^0 - H_0^0)_T$	$-(F^0 - H_0^0)/T$	S_T^0
DEG-K	CAL/MOLE DEG-K	KCAL/MOLE	CAL/MOLE DEG-K	CAL/MOLE DEG-K
100	7.961	0.795	40.358	48.308
200	8.376	1.607	45.885	53.918
273.15	8.972	2.240	48.411	56.613
298.15	9.199	2.467	49.133	57.409
400	10.124	3.452	51.613	60.243
500	10.909	4.505	53.579	62.589
600	11.528	5.628	55.255	64.635
700	11.999	6.806	56.727	66.449
800	12.355	8.024	58.046	68.076
900	12.628	9.274	59.243	69.548
1000	12.838	10.548	60.342	70.889
1100	13.002	11.840	61.357	72.121
1200	13.133	13.147	62.302	73.258
1300	13.238	14.466	63.186	74.314
1400	13.324	15.794	64.017	75.298
1500	13.395	17.130	64.800	76.220
1600	13.454	18.473	65.541	77.086
1700	13.503	19.821	66.244	77.903
1800	13.545	21.173	66.914	78.676
1900	13.581	22.529	67.552	79.410
2000	13.612	23.889	68.163	80.107
2100	13.639	25.252	68.747	80.772
2200	13.662	26.617	69.309	81.407
2300	13.683	27.984	69.848	82.015
2400	13.701	29.353	70.367	82.598
2500	13.717	30.724	70.868	83.157
2600	13.731	32.097	71.351	83.695
2700	13.744	33.470	71.818	84.214
2800	13.756	34.845	72.269	84.714
2900	13.766	36.221	72.707	85.197
3000	13.775	37.599	73.131	85.664
3200	13.791	40.355	73.942	86.553
3400	13.805	43.115	74.709	87.390
3600	13.816	45.877	75.436	88.179
3800	13.826	48.641	76.126	88.926
4000	13.834	51.407	76.784	89.636
4200	13.841	54.175	77.412	90.311
4400	13.847	56.944	78.013	90.955
4600	13.853	59.714	78.589	91.571
4800	13.857	62.485	79.143	92.160
5000	13.861	65.256	79.675	92.726
5200	13.865	68.029	80.187	93.270
5400	13.868	70.803	80.682	93.793
5600	13.871	73.577	81.159	94.298
5800	13.874	76.351	81.620	94.784
6000	13.876	79.126	82.067	95.255

Appendix 4.42   THERMODYNAMIC PROPERTIES OF CF2O GAS

T	C_P^0	$(H^0 - H_0^0)$	$-(F^0 - H_0^0)/T$	S_T^0
DEG-K	CAL/MOLE DEG-K	KCAL/MOLE	CAL/MOLE DEG-K	CAL/MOLE DEG-K
100	8.004	0.796	43.973	51.929
200	9.297	1.647	49.544	57.778
273.15	10.793	2.381	52.178	60.896
298.15	11.294	2.657	52.950	61.863
400	13.089	3.903	55.686	65.443
500	14.455	5.283	57.951	68.517
600	15.498	6.783	59.944	71.249
700	16.297	8.374	61.738	73.701
800	16.915	10.036	63.374	75.919
900	17.397	11.753	64.882	77.940
1000	17.778	13.512	66.282	79.794
1100	18.081	15.306	67.589	81.503
1200	18.327	17.127	68.815	83.087
1300	18.527	18.970	69.970	84.562
1400	18.692	20.831	71.062	85.942
1500	18.829	22.707	72.098	87.236
1600	18.945	24.596	73.082	88.455
1700	19.042	26.495	74.021	89.606
1800	19.126	28.404	74.917	90.697
1900	19.197	30.320	75.775	91.733
2000	19.259	32.243	76.598	92.720
2100	19.313	34.172	77.388	93.661
2200	19.361	36.106	78.149	94.560
2300	19.402	38.044	78.881	95.422
2400	19.439	39.986	79.588	96.248
2500	19.472	41.931	80.270	97.043
2600	19.501	43.880	80.930	97.807
2700	19.527	45.831	81.569	98.543
2800	19.551	47.785	82.188	99.254
2900	19.572	49.741	82.788	99.940
3000	19.591	51.700	83.371	100.604
3200	19.624	55.621	84.488	101.870
3400	19.652	59.549	85.546	103.060
3600	19.675	63.482	86.550	104.184
3800	19.695	67.419	87.507	105.248
4000	19.712	71.360	88.419	106.259
4200	19.727	75.304	89.292	107.221
4400	19.740	79.250	90.128	108.139
4600	19.751	83.199	90.930	109.017
4800	19.761	87.151	91.701	109.858
5000	19.769	91.104	92.444	110.665
5200	19.777	95.058	93.160	111.440
5400	19.784	99.014	93.851	112.187
5600	19.790	102.972	94.518	112.906
5800	19.796	106.930	95.165	113.601
6000	19.801	110.890	95.790	114.272

Appendix 4.43 THERMODYNAMIC PROPERTIES OF CF3 GAS

T	C_P^0	$(H^0 - H_0^0)$	$-(F^0 - H_0^0)/T$	S_T^0
DEG-K	CAL/MOLE DEG-K	KCAL/MOLE	CAL/MOLE DEG-K	CAL/MOLE DEG-K
100	8.153	0.798	43.773	51.751
200	10.084	1.700	49.426	57.926
273.15	11.665	2.497	52.168	61.308
298.15	12.157	2.794	52.978	62.351
400	13.889	4.124	55.865	66.176
500	15.195	5.582	58.259	69.422
600	16.178	7.153	60.362	72.283
700	16.913	8.809	62.251	74.835
800	17.467	10.529	63.970	77.132
900	17.887	12.298	65.550	79.214
1000	18.212	14.103	67.013	81.116
1100	18.467	15.938	68.376	82.865
1200	18.669	17.795	69.651	84.480
1300	18.831	19.670	70.850	85.981
1400	18.964	21.560	71.982	87.382
1500	19.073	23.462	73.052	88.694
1600	19.164	25.374	74.069	89.928
1700	19.241	27.295	75.036	91.092
1800	19.306	29.222	75.959	92.194
1900	19.362	31.156	76.842	93.239
2000	19.409	33.094	77.686	94.234
2100	19.451	35.037	78.497	95.182
2200	19.487	36.984	79.276	96.087
2300	19.519	38.935	80.026	96.954
2400	19.547	40.888	80.749	97.786
2500	19.572	42.844	81.447	98.584
2600	19.594	44.802	82.121	99.352
2700	19.614	46.763	82.772	100.092
2800	19.632	48.725	83.404	100.806
2900	19.648	50.689	84.016	101.495
3000	19.662	52.654	84.610	102.161
3200	19.687	56.589	85.747	103.431
3400	19.708	60.529	86.822	104.625
3600	19.726	64.472	87.843	105.752
3800	19.741	68.419	88.814	106.819
4000	19.753	72.369	89.740	107.832
4200	19.764	76.320	90.624	108.796
4400	19.774	80.274	91.471	109.716
4600	19.782	84.230	92.284	110.595
4800	19.789	88.187	93.065	111.437
5000	19.796	92.146	93.816	112.245
5200	19.802	96.105	94.540	113.021
5400	19.807	100.066	95.238	113.769
5600	19.811	104.028	95.913	114.489
5800	19.816	107.991	96.565	115.184
6000	19.819	111.954	97.197	115.856

THERMODYNAMIC PROPERTIES OF CF4 GAS

T	C_P^0	$(H^0 - H_0^0)_T$	$-(F^0 - H_0^0)/T$	S_T^0
DEG-K	CAL/MOLE DEG-K	KCAL/MOLE	CAL/MOLE DEG-K	CAL/MOLE DEG-K
100	8.304	0.800	42.907	50.910
200	11.322	1.767	48.654	57.487
273.15	13.816	2.688	51.552	61.391
298.15	14.595	3.043	52.429	62.635
400	17.308	4.674	55.637	67.322
500	19.295	6.509	58.390	71.409
600	20.745	8.515	60.870	75.062
700	21.803	10.645	63.136	78.343
800	22.583	12.866	65.225	81.308
900	23.169	15.155	67.164	84.004
1000	23.615	17.496	68.973	86.469
1100	23.962	19.875	70.668	88.736
1200	24.236	22.286	72.262	90.834
1300	24.455	24.721	73.767	92.782
1400	24.633	27.175	75.191	94.602
1500	24.779	29.646	76.542	96.306
1600	24.901	32.130	77.828	97.909
1700	25.003	34.626	79.054	99.422
1800	25.089	37.130	80.226	100.854
1900	25.163	39.643	81.348	102.212
2000	25.226	42.162	82.423	103.505
2100	25.281	44.688	83.457	104.737
2200	25.329	47.218	84.451	105.914
2300	25.371	49.753	85.409	107.041
2400	25.408	52.292	86.333	108.121
2500	25.440	54.835	87.225	109.159
2600	25.470	57.380	88.088	110.158
2700	25.496	59.929	88.924	111.119
2800	25.519	62.479	89.733	112.047
2900	25.540	65.032	90.518	112.943
3000	25.559	67.587	91.280	113.809
3200	25.592	72.702	92.740	115.460
3400	25.619	77.824	94.123	117.012
3600	25.642	82.950	95.435	118.477
3800	25.662	88.080	96.685	119.864
4000	25.678	93.214	97.877	121.181
4200	25.693	98.351	99.017	122.434
4400	25.705	103.491	100.109	123.629
4600	25.716	108.633	101.156	124.772
4800	25.726	113.778	102.163	125.867
5000	25.734	118.924	103.132	126.917
5200	25.742	124.071	104.067	127.927
5400	25.748	129.220	104.969	128.898
5600	25.754	134.371	105.840	129.835
5800	25.760	139.522	106.683	130.739
6000	25.765	144.675	107.500	131.612

THERMODYNAMIC PROPERTIES OF CHF3 GAS

T	C_P^0	$(H^0 - H_0^0)/T$	$-(F^0 - H_0^0)/T$	S_T^0
DEG-K	CAL/MOLE DEG-K	KCAL/MOLE	CAL/MOLE DEG-K	CAL/MOLE DEG-K
100	8.100	0.797	44.345	52.314
200	9.853	1.683	49.971	58.386
273.15	11.586	2.466	52.680	61.710
298.15	12.195	2.764	53.481	62.751
400	14.573	4.129	56.350	66.673
500	16.551	5.689	58.768	70.145
600	18.122	7.426	60.932	73.307
700	19.353	9.302	62.909	76.197
800	20.326	11.288	64.738	78.847
900	21.105	13.360	66.443	81.288
1000	21.738	15.504	68.042	83.546
1100	22.259	17.704	69.548	85.643
1200	22.692	19.953	70.971	87.599
1300	23.055	22.240	72.322	89.430
1400	23.361	24.562	73.606	91.150
1500	23.622	26.911	74.830	92.771
1600	23.846	29.285	75.999	94.302
1700	24.039	31.679	77.119	95.754
1800	24.206	34.092	78.193	97.133
1900	24.352	36.520	79.225	98.446
2000	24.479	38.961	80.217	99.698
2100	24.592	41.415	81.174	100.895
2200	24.691	43.879	82.096	102.042
2300	24.780	46.353	82.988	103.141
2400	24.858	48.835	83.849	104.197
2500	24.929	51.324	84.684	105.214
2600	24.992	53.820	85.492	106.193
2700	25.049	56.323	86.277	107.137
2800	25.100	58.830	87.038	108.049
2900	25.147	61.342	87.778	108.930
3000	25.190	63.859	88.497	109.784
3200	25.264	68.905	89.879	111.412
3400	25.326	73.964	91.191	112.945
3600	25.379	79.035	92.440	114.394
3800	25.424	84.115	93.632	115.768
4000	25.462	89.204	94.772	117.073
4200	25.496	94.299	95.864	118.316
4400	25.525	99.402	96.911	119.503
4600	25.551	104.509	97.919	120.638
4800	25.573	109.622	98.888	121.726
5000	25.593	114.738	99.823	122.770
5200	25.611	119.859	100.725	123.774
5400	25.627	124.983	101.596	124.741
5600	25.641	130.109	102.440	125.674
5800	25.654	135.239	103.256	126.574
6000	25.666	140.371	104.048	127.443

Appendix 4.46   THERMODYNAMIC PROPERTIES OF CH2 GAS

T	C_P^0	$(H^0 - H_0^0)$	$-(F^0 - H_0^0)/T$	S_T^0
DEG-K	CAL/MOLE DEG-K	KCAL/MOLE	CAL/MOLE DEG-K	CAL/MOLE DEG-K
100	7.949	0.795	29.712	37.661
200	7.956	1.590	35.222	43.171
273.15	8.006	2.173	37.700	45.657
298.15	8.040	2.374	38.397	46.359
400	8.258	3.203	40.743	48.750
500	8.552	4.043	42.537	50.623
600	8.888	4.915	44.020	52.212
700	9.248	5.821	45.292	53.609
800	9.617	6.765	46.412	54.868
900	9.981	7.745	47.416	56.021
1000	10.330	8.760	48.331	57.091
1100	10.655	9.810	49.173	58.091
1200	10.954	10.891	49.956	59.031
1300	11.225	12.000	50.689	59.919
1400	11.468	13.135	51.378	60.760
1500	11.686	14.293	52.030	61.559
1600	11.880	15.471	52.650	62.319
1700	12.054	16.668	53.240	63.045
1800	12.208	17.881	53.804	63.738
1900	12.346	19.109	54.345	64.402
2000	12.469	20.350	54.864	65.039
2100	12.580	21.602	55.363	65.650
2200	12.679	22.865	55.844	66.237
2300	12.768	24.138	56.308	66.803
2400	12.848	25.419	56.757	67.348
2500	12.920	26.707	57.191	67.874
2600	12.986	28.002	57.612	68.382
2700	13.046	29.304	58.020	68.873
2800	13.100	30.611	58.416	69.349
2900	13.150	31.924	58.801	69.809
3000	13.195	33.241	59.175	70.256
3200	13.275	35.888	59.895	71.110
3400	13.342	38.550	60.578	71.917
3600	13.399	41.224	61.230	72.681
3800	13.449	43.909	61.852	73.407
4000	13.491	46.603	62.447	74.098
4200	13.528	49.306	63.018	74.757
4400	13.561	52.015	63.566	75.387
4600	13.589	54.730	64.093	75.991
4800	13.615	57.450	64.601	76.569
5000	13.637	60.175	65.091	77.126
5200	13.657	62.905	65.564	77.661
5400	13.675	65.638	66.021	78.177
5600	13.691	68.375	66.465	78.674
5800	13.706	71.114	66.894	79.155
6000	13.719	73.857	67.310	79.620

409

Appendix 4.47 THERMODYNAMIC PROPERTIES OF CH3 GAS

T	C_P^0	$(H^0 - H_0^0)$	$-(F^0 - H_0^0)/T$	S_T^0
DEG-K	CAL/MOLE DEG-K	KCAL/MOLE	CAL/MOLE DEG-K	CAL/MOLE DEG-K
100	7.949	0.795	29.302	37.251
200	7.961	1.590	34.812	42.762
273.15	8.066	2.175	37.292	45.255
298.15	8.143	2.378	37.990	45.965
400	8.678	3.232	40.346	48.425
500	9.438	4.136	42.168	50.440
600	10.290	5.122	43.698	52.235
700	11.155	6.195	45.037	53.887
800	11.990	7.352	46.241	55.431
900	12.770	8.591	47.344	56.889
1000	13.483	9.904	48.368	58.272
1100	14.126	11.285	49.329	59.588
1200	14.699	12.727	50.236	60.842
1300	15.207	14.223	51.099	62.039
1400	15.656	15.766	51.921	63.183
1500	16.052	17.352	52.709	64.277
1600	16.401	18.975	53.465	65.324
1700	16.709	20.631	54.192	66.328
1800	16.982	22.316	54.893	67.291
1900	17.223	24.026	55.570	68.216
2000	17.438	25.760	56.225	69.105
2100	17.629	27.513	56.859	69.960
2200	17.800	29.285	57.473	70.784
2300	17.953	31.073	58.069	71.579
2400	18.090	32.875	58.648	72.346
2500	18.214	34.690	59.211	73.087
2600	18.326	36.517	59.759	73.804
2700	18.427	38.355	60.292	74.497
2800	18.519	40.202	60.811	75.169
2900	18.603	42.058	61.317	75.820
3000	18.679	43.922	61.811	76.452
3200	18.813	47.672	62.765	77.662
3400	18.926	51.446	63.675	78.806
3600	19.023	55.242	64.546	79.891
3800	19.105	59.055	65.381	80.922
4000	19.177	62.883	66.183	81.903
4200	19.238	66.725	66.954	82.841
4400	19.293	70.578	67.696	83.737
4600	19.340	74.441	68.413	84.596
4800	19.382	78.313	69.104	85.420
5000	19.419	82.194	69.773	86.212
5200	19.453	86.081	70.420	86.974
5400	19.482	89.974	71.047	87.709
5600	19.509	93.874	71.654	88.418
5800	19.533	97.778	72.244	89.103
6000	19.555	101.687	72.817	89.765

Appendix 4.48 THERMODYNAMIC PROPERTIES OF CH4 GAS

T	C_P^0	$(H^0 - H_0^0)_T$	$-(F^0 - H_0^0)/T$	S_T^0
DEG-K	CAL/MOLE DEG-K	KCAL/MOLE	CAL/MOLE DEG-K	CAL/MOLE DEG-K
100	7.949	0.795	27.767	35.716
200	8.001	1.591	33.277	41.232
273.15	8.320	2.186	35.762	43.763
298.15	8.518	2.396	36.464	44.500
400	9.680	3.319	38.857	47.154
500	11.076	4.356	40.751	49.462
600	12.483	5.534	42.383	51.607
700	13.814	6.850	43.847	53.632
800	15.042	8.293	45.192	55.558
900	16.158	9.854	46.446	57.396
1000	17.160	11.521	47.630	59.151
1100	18.052	13.283	48.754	60.829
1200	18.842	15.128	49.827	62.434
1300	19.538	17.048	50.857	63.971
1400	20.150	19.033	51.846	65.441
1500	20.688	21.075	52.800	66.850
1600	21.162	23.168	53.721	68.201
1700	21.579	25.306	54.611	69.497
1800	21.947	27.483	55.473	70.741
1900	22.273	29.694	56.308	71.936
2000	22.563	31.936	57.118	73.086
2100	22.820	34.205	57.905	74.193
2200	23.050	36.499	58.670	75.260
2300	23.256	38.815	59.414	76.290
2400	23.441	41.150	60.138	77.283
2500	23.608	43.502	60.843	78.244
2600	23.758	45.871	61.530	79.173
2700	23.894	48.253	62.200	80.072
2800	24.018	50.649	62.854	80.943
2900	24.131	53.057	63.493	81.788
3000	24.233	55.475	64.116	82.608
3200	24.413	60.340	65.321	84.178
3400	24.565	65.238	66.475	85.662
3600	24.695	70.165	67.580	87.070
3800	24.805	75.115	68.641	88.408
4000	24.901	80.086	69.662	89.683
4200	24.984	85.075	70.644	90.900
4400	25.057	90.079	71.592	92.064
4600	25.121	95.097	72.506	93.180
4800	25.177	100.127	73.390	94.250
5000	25.227	105.167	74.245	95.279
5200	25.271	110.217	75.073	96.269
5400	25.311	115.275	75.876	97.223
5600	25.347	120.341	76.655	98.145
5800	25.379	125.414	77.412	99.035
6000	25.409	130.493	78.147	99.896

THERMODYNAMIC PROPERTIES OF C2F2 GAS

T	C_P^0	$(H^0 - H_0^0)_T$	$-(F^0 - H_0^0)/T$	S_T^0
DEG-K	CAL/MOLE DEG-K	KCAL/MOLE	CAL/MOLE DEG-K	CAL/MOLE DEG-K
100	9.420	0.766	39.452	47.116
200	12.755	1.893	45.326	54.790
273.15	14.203	2.882	48.442	58.993
298.15	14.595	3.242	49.380	60.254
400	15.864	4.797	52.739	64.731
500	16.775	6.431	55.512	68.374
600	17.479	8.145	57.922	71.497
700	18.036	9.922	60.061	74.235
800	18.481	11.748	61.988	76.673
900	18.840	13.615	63.744	78.872
1000	19.130	15.514	65.358	80.872
1100	19.367	17.439	66.853	82.707
1200	19.562	19.386	68.246	84.401
1300	19.724	21.351	69.549	85.973
1400	19.858	23.330	70.776	87.440
1500	19.971	25.322	71.933	88.814
1600	20.067	27.324	73.029	90.106
1700	20.149	29.335	74.069	91.325
1800	20.219	31.353	75.060	92.479
1900	20.280	33.378	76.006	93.574
2000	20.333	35.409	76.911	94.615
2100	20.379	37.445	77.778	95.608
2200	20.419	39.484	78.610	96.557
2300	20.455	41.528	79.410	97.466
2400	20.487	43.575	80.181	98.337
2500	20.515	45.626	80.924	99.174
2600	20.540	47.678	81.641	99.979
2700	20.563	49.733	82.335	100.755
2800	20.583	51.791	83.006	101.503
2900	20.602	53.850	83.657	102.226
3000	20.618	55.911	84.287	102.924
3200	20.648	60.038	85.494	104.256
3400	20.672	64.170	86.635	105.508
3600	20.692	68.306	87.717	106.691
3800	20.710	72.447	88.745	107.810
4000	20.725	76.590	89.725	108.873
4200	20.738	80.736	90.661	109.884
4400	20.749	84.885	91.557	110.849
4600	20.759	89.036	92.416	111.772
4800	20.767	93.188	93.241	112.655
5000	20.775	97.342	94.035	113.503
5200	20.782	101.498	94.799	114.318
5400	20.788	105.655	95.537	115.102
5600	20.793	109.813	96.249	115.859
5800	20.798	113.972	96.938	116.588
6000	20.803	118.132	97.605	117.293

THERMODYNAMIC PROPERTIES OF COS GAS

T	C_P^0	$(H^0 - H_0^0)_T$	$-(F^0 - H_0^0)_T/T$	S_T^0
DEG-K	CAL/MOLE DEG-K	KCAL/MOLE	CAL/MOLE DEG-K	CAL/MOLE DEG-K
100	7.077	0.697	39.397	46.369
200	8.476	1.467	44.313	51.647
273.15	9.592	2.129	46.665	54.460
298.15	9.915	2.373	47.355	55.314
400	10.955	3.439	49.785	58.383
500	11.682	4.573	51.764	60.910
600	12.241	5.770	53.474	63.091
700	12.688	7.017	54.988	65.013
800	13.053	8.305	56.350	66.732
900	13.353	9.626	57.592	68.287
1000	13.601	10.974	58.733	69.707
1100	13.807	12.345	59.791	71.013
1200	13.980	13.734	60.777	72.222
1300	14.126	15.140	61.701	73.347
1400	14.250	16.559	62.571	74.399
1500	14.358	17.989	63.393	75.386
1600	14.451	19.430	64.172	76.315
1700	14.532	20.879	64.912	77.194
1800	14.604	22.336	65.618	78.027
1900	14.669	23.800	66.292	78.818
2000	14.726	25.269	66.937	79.572
2100	14.778	26.745	67.556	80.292
2200	14.826	28.225	68.151	80.980
2300	14.869	29.710	68.723	81.640
2400	14.910	31.199	69.274	82.274
2500	14.947	32.691	69.807	82.883
2600	14.982	34.188	70.321	83.470
2700	15.014	35.688	70.819	84.036
2800	15.045	37.191	71.300	84.583
2900	15.074	38.697	71.768	85.111
3000	15.101	40.205	72.221	85.623
3200	15.153	43.231	73.089	86.599
3400	15.201	46.266	73.911	87.519
3600	15.245	49.311	74.692	88.389
3800	15.287	52.364	75.435	89.215
4000	15.326	55.425	76.143	90.000
4200	15.364	58.495	76.821	90.748
4400	15.401	61.571	77.471	91.464
4600	15.436	64.655	78.094	92.149
4800	15.471	67.746	78.693	92.807
5000	15.504	70.843	79.271	93.439
5200	15.537	73.947	79.827	94.048
5400	15.569	77.058	80.365	94.635
5600	15.601	80.175	80.885	95.202
5800	15.632	83.298	81.388	95.750
6000	15.663	86.428	81.876	96.280

Appendix 4.51   THERMODYNAMIC PROPERTIES OF   CO2 GAS

T	C_P^0	$(H^0 - H_0^0)$	$-(F^0 - H_0^0)/T$	S_T^0
DEG-K	CAL/MOLE DEG-K	KCAL/MOLE	CAL/MOLE DEG-K	CAL/MOLE DEG-K
100	6.981	0.696	35.791	42.749
200	7.733	1.423	40.645	47.760
273.15	8.592	2.020	42.902	50.297
298.15	8.872	2.238	43.554	51.062
400	9.872	3.195	45.827	53.815
500	10.659	4.223	47.659	56.105
600	11.303	5.322	49.237	58.107
700	11.836	6.480	50.634	59.891
800	12.282	7.686	51.894	61.501
900	12.654	8.934	53.044	62.970
1000	12.965	10.215	54.105	64.320
1100	13.226	11.525	55.091	65.568
1200	13.446	12.859	56.013	66.729
1300	13.632	14.213	56.879	67.812
1400	13.791	15.584	57.697	68.829
1500	13.927	16.970	58.471	69.785
1600	14.045	18.369	59.207	70.688
1700	14.146	19.779	59.908	71.542
1800	14.235	21.198	60.577	72.353
1900	14.314	22.626	61.217	73.125
2000	14.383	24.060	61.831	73.861
2100	14.445	25.502	62.421	74.564
2200	14.500	26.949	62.988	75.238
2300	14.549	28.402	63.535	75.883
2400	14.594	29.859	64.062	76.504
2500	14.635	31.320	64.572	77.100
2600	14.672	32.786	65.065	77.675
2700	14.706	34.255	65.542	78.229
2800	14.738	35.727	66.005	78.765
2900	14.767	37.202	66.454	79.282
3000	14.794	38.680	66.890	79.783
3200	14.843	41.644	67.726	80.740
3400	14.886	44.617	68.518	81.641
3600	14.924	47.598	69.271	82.493
3800	14.959	50.586	69.989	83.301
4000	14.990	53.581	70.673	84.069
4200	15.019	56.582	71.329	84.801
4400	15.046	59.589	71.957	85.500
4600	15.072	62.600	72.561	86.170
4800	15.096	65.617	73.141	86.812
5000	15.118	68.639	73.701	87.428
5200	15.140	71.664	74.240	88.022
5400	15.161	74.694	74.761	88.593
5600	15.180	77.729	75.265	89.145
5800	15.200	80.767	75.753	89.678
6000	15.218	83.808	76.226	90.194

Appendix 4.52   THERMODYNAMIC PROPERTIES OF   CS2 GAS

T	C_P^0	$(H^0 - H_0^0)_T$	$-(F^0 - H_0^0)/T$	S_T^0
DEG-K	CAL/MOLE DEG-K	KCAL/MOLE	CAL/MOLE DEG-K	CAL/MOLE DEG-K
100	7.404	0.703	39.975	47.008
200	9.457	1.547	45.037	52.770
273.15	10.591	2.282	47.540	55.896
298.15	10.895	2.551	48.280	56.837
400	11.856	3.713	50.900	60.182
500	12.531	4.934	53.036	62.903
600	13.039	6.213	54.879	65.235
700	13.428	7.538	56.508	67.276
800	13.729	8.896	57.969	69.089
900	13.966	10.281	59.297	70.721
1000	14.154	11.688	60.514	72.202
1100	14.306	13.111	61.639	73.559
1200	14.432	14.548	62.685	74.809
1300	14.537	15.997	63.663	75.968
1400	14.625	17.455	64.581	77.049
1500	14.702	18.921	65.446	78.061
1600	14.768	20.395	66.265	79.012
1700	14.827	21.875	67.041	79.909
1800	14.880	23.360	67.780	80.758
1900	14.927	24.851	68.484	81.564
2000	14.970	26.345	69.158	82.330
2100	15.009	27.844	69.802	83.062
2200	15.046	29.347	70.421	83.761
2300	15.080	30.854	71.016	84.430
2400	15.112	32.363	71.588	85.073
2500	15.143	33.876	72.140	85.690
2600	15.171	35.392	72.673	86.285
2700	15.199	36.910	73.188	86.858
2800	15.225	38.431	73.686	87.411
2900	15.250	39.955	74.168	87.946
3000	15.275	41.481	74.636	88.463
3200	15.322	44.541	75.532	89.451
3400	15.366	47.610	76.378	90.381
3600	15.409	50.687	77.181	91.260
3800	15.450	53.773	77.944	92.095
4000	15.490	56.867	78.671	92.888
4200	15.528	59.969	79.366	93.645
4400	15.567	63.079	80.032	94.368
4600	15.604	66.196	80.670	95.061
4800	15.641	69.320	81.284	95.726
5000	15.677	72.452	81.875	96.365
5200	15.713	75.591	82.444	96.980
5400	15.748	78.737	82.993	97.574
5600	15.784	81.890	83.524	98.148
5800	15.819	85.050	84.038	98.702
6000	15.853	88.218	84.536	99.239

Appendix 4.53 THERMODYNAMIC PROPERTIES OF C2H2 GAS

T	C_P^0	$(H^0 - H_0^0)$	$-(F^0 - H_0^0)/T$	S_T^0
DEG-K	CAL/MOLE DEG-K	KCAL/MOLE	CAL/MOLE DEG-K	CAL/MOLE DEG-K
100	7.014	0.696	32.040	39.002
200	8.505	1.457	36.931	44.214
273.15	10.061	2.137	39.277	47.099
298.15	10.531	2.394	39.971	48.001
400	12.045	3.549	42.449	51.322
500	13.079	4.808	44.511	54.127
600	13.872	6.157	46.323	56.584
700	14.537	7.578	47.948	58.773
800	15.125	9.062	49.427	60.754
900	15.656	10.601	50.787	62.566
1000	16.139	12.191	52.050	64.241
1100	16.576	13.827	53.230	65.800
1200	16.972	15.505	54.339	67.260
1300	17.327	17.220	55.386	68.632
1400	17.644	18.969	56.379	69.928
1500	17.928	20.748	57.324	71.156
1600	18.182	22.554	58.225	72.321
1700	18.408	24.383	59.087	73.430
1800	18.609	26.234	59.913	74.488
1900	18.790	28.105	60.707	75.499
2000	18.951	29.992	61.471	76.467
2100	19.096	31.894	62.207	77.395
2200	19.226	33.810	62.918	78.287
2300	19.343	35.739	63.605	79.144
2400	19.449	37.679	64.270	79.969
2500	19.545	39.628	64.914	80.765
2600	19.631	41.587	65.538	81.534
2700	19.710	43.554	66.145	82.276
2800	19.782	45.529	66.734	82.994
2900	19.848	47.511	67.306	83.689
3000	19.908	49.499	67.864	84.363
3200	20.014	53.491	68.936	85.652
3400	20.104	57.503	69.955	86.868
3600	20.180	61.532	70.927	88.019
3800	20.246	65.574	71.856	89.112
4000	20.303	69.629	72.745	90.152
4200	20.352	73.695	73.597	91.144
4400	20.396	77.770	74.417	92.092
4600	20.434	81.853	75.205	92.999
4800	20.468	85.943	75.965	93.869
5000	20.498	90.040	76.698	94.706
5200	20.525	94.142	77.406	95.510
5400	20.549	98.250	78.091	96.285
5600	20.570	102.362	78.754	97.033
5800	20.590	106.478	79.397	97.755
6000	20.607	110.597	80.020	98.453

Appendix 4.54 THERMODYNAMIC PROPERTIES OF C2H4 GAS

T	C_P^0	$(H^0 - H_0^0)$	$-(F^0 - H_0^0)/T$	S^0
DEG-K	CAL/MOLE DEG-K	KCAL/MOLE	CAL/MOLE DEG-K	CAL/MOLE DEG-K
100	7.952	0.795	35.181	43.131
200	8.463	1.605	40.703	48.730
273.15	9.715	2.266	43.239	51.536
298.15	10.263	2.516	43.972	52.410
400	12.684	3.684	46.553	55.762
500	14.933	5.067	48.705	58.839
600	16.887	6.660	50.638	61.739
700	18.571	8.435	52.421	64.471
800	20.035	10.367	54.090	67.049
900	21.316	12.436	55.667	69.484
1000	22.440	14.625	57.165	71.790
1100	23.424	16.919	58.594	73.976
1200	24.287	19.306	59.963	76.052
1300	25.042	21.773	61.278	78.026
1400	25.704	24.311	62.542	79.907
1500	26.283	26.911	63.760	81.700
1600	26.792	29.566	64.935	83.413
1700	27.240	32.268	66.070	85.051
1800	27.635	35.012	67.169	86.620
1900	27.985	37.793	68.232	88.123
2000	28.295	40.607	69.263	89.567
2100	28.570	43.451	70.263	90.954
2200	28.817	46.321	71.234	92.289
2300	29.037	49.213	72.178	93.575
2400	29.235	52.127	73.095	94.815
2500	29.413	55.060	73.988	96.012
2600	29.574	58.009	74.858	97.169
2700	29.720	60.974	75.705	98.288
2800	29.852	63.953	76.531	99.371
2900	29.973	66.944	77.337	100.421
3000	30.083	69.947	78.123	101.439
3200	30.275	75.983	79.642	103.387
3400	30.438	82.055	81.093	105.227
3600	30.576	88.157	82.483	106.971
3800	30.695	94.284	83.816	108.627
4000	30.797	100.434	85.096	110.204
4200	30.886	106.602	86.328	111.709
4400	30.964	112.787	87.514	113.148
4600	31.032	118.987	88.659	114.526
4800	31.092	125.199	89.764	115.848
5000	31.146	131.423	90.833	117.118
5200	31.193	137.657	91.868	118.340
5400	31.236	143.900	92.870	119.519
5600	31.274	150.151	93.842	120.655
5800	31.309	156.410	94.786	121.753
6000	31.340	162.675	95.703	122.815

Appendix 4.55   THERMODYNAMIC PROPERTIES OF C2N2 GAS

T	C_p^0	$(H^0 - H_0^0)$	$-(F^0 - H_0^0)/T$	S_T^0
DEG-K	CAL/MOLE DEG-K	KCAL/MOLE	CAL/MOLE DEG-K	CAL/MOLE DEG-K
100	8.756	0.745	38.240	45.688
200	11.721	1.778	43.840	52.729
273.15	13.189	2.692	46.758	56.614
298.15	13.579	3.027	47.634	57.786
400	14.779	4.475	50.768	61.957
500	15.619	5.997	53.355	65.349
600	16.305	7.594	55.602	68.259
700	16.898	9.255	57.596	70.818
800	17.412	10.971	59.395	73.108
900	17.855	12.735	61.035	75.185
1000	18.234	14.540	62.547	77.087
1100	18.556	16.380	63.949	78.840
1200	18.829	18.249	65.259	80.467
1300	19.062	20.144	66.488	81.983
1400	19.261	22.061	67.646	83.403
1500	19.431	23.995	68.741	84.738
1600	19.577	25.946	69.781	85.997
1700	19.703	27.910	70.770	87.188
1800	19.812	29.886	71.714	88.317
1900	19.907	31.872	72.616	89.391
2000	19.991	33.867	73.481	90.414
2100	20.064	35.870	74.310	91.391
2200	20.129	37.880	75.108	92.326
2300	20.186	39.895	75.876	93.222
2400	20.238	41.917	76.617	94.082
2500	20.283	43.943	77.332	94.910
2600	20.325	45.973	78.024	95.706
2700	20.361	48.008	78.693	96.474
2800	20.395	50.045	79.341	97.215
2900	20.425	52.086	79.970	97.931
3000	20.453	54.130	80.580	98.624
3200	20.500	58.226	81.750	99.945
3400	20.541	62.330	82.857	101.190
3600	20.574	66.442	83.909	102.365
3800	20.603	70.559	84.910	103.478
4000	20.628	74.683	85.865	104.535
4200	20.650	78.811	86.778	105.542
4400	20.669	82.942	87.653	106.503
4600	20.685	87.078	88.492	107.422
4800	20.700	91.216	89.300	108.303
5000	20.712	95.358	90.077	109.148
5200	20.724	99.501	90.826	109.961
5400	20.734	103.647	91.549	110.743
5600	20.743	107.795	92.248	111.497
5800	20.751	111.944	92.925	112.226
6000	20.759	116.095	93.580	112.929

Appendix 4.56   THERMODYNAMIC PROPERTIES OF C3 GAS

T	C_P^0	$(H^0 - H_0^0)$	$-(F^0 - H_0^0)/T$	S_T^0
DEG-K	CAL/MOLE DEG-K	KCAL/MOLE	CAL/MOLE DEG-K	CAL/MOLE DEG-K
100	7.009	0.696	38.277	45.239
200	8.031	1.439	43.152	50.349
273.15	9.029	2.064	45.446	53.002
298.15	9.343	2.294	46.114	53.807
400	10.430	3.303	48.454	56.711
500	11.251	4.389	50.353	59.131
600	11.895	5.547	51.996	61.241
700	12.405	6.763	53.453	63.115
800	12.810	8.025	54.768	64.798
900	13.134	9.323	55.968	66.327
1000	13.394	10.649	57.075	67.724
1100	13.605	12.000	58.102	69.011
1200	13.778	13.369	59.062	70.203
1300	13.920	14.754	59.962	71.311
1400	14.037	16.152	60.810	72.347
1500	14.136	17.561	61.612	73.319
1600	14.220	18.979	62.372	74.234
1700	14.291	20.405	63.096	75.099
1800	14.351	21.837	63.786	75.917
1900	14.404	23.275	64.445	76.695
2000	14.449	24.717	65.076	77.435
2100	14.489	26.164	65.681	78.141
2200	14.524	27.615	66.263	78.815
2300	14.554	29.069	66.823	79.462
2400	14.582	30.526	67.363	80.082
2500	14.606	31.985	67.883	80.677
2600	14.627	33.447	68.387	81.251
2700	14.647	34.910	68.873	81.803
2800	14.664	36.376	69.345	82.336
2900	14.680	37.843	69.802	82.851
3000	14.694	39.312	70.245	83.349
3200	14.719	42.253	71.094	84.298
3400	14.739	45.199	71.897	85.191
3600	14.757	48.149	72.659	86.034
3800	14.772	51.102	73.384	86.832
4000	14.784	54.057	74.076	87.590
4200	14.795	57.015	74.737	88.312
4400	14.805	59.975	75.370	89.000
4600	14.813	62.937	75.977	89.659
4800	14.821	65.901	76.560	90.289
5000	14.827	68.865	77.121	90.894
5200	14.833	71.831	77.662	91.476
5400	14.838	74.799	78.184	92.036
5600	14.843	77.767	78.689	92.576
5800	14.847	80.736	79.177	93.097
6000	14.851	83.705	79.649	93.600

Appendix 4.57   THERMODYNAMIC PROPERTIES OF C3H6 GAS

T	C_P^0	$(H^0 - H_0^0)$	$-(F^0 - H_0^0)/T$	S_T^0
DEG-K	CAL/MOLE DEG-K	KCAL/MOLE	CAL/MOLE DEG-K	CAL/MOLE DEG-K
100	9.351	0.841	41.349	49.762
200	11.696	1.888	47.486	56.926
273.15	14.046	2.826	50.558	60.903
298.15	14.970	3.188	51.479	62.173
400	18.962	4.915	54.838	67.127
500	22.688	7.001	57.763	71.766
600	25.957	9.437	60.469	76.198
700	28.779	12.178	63.020	80.417
800	31.220	15.181	65.447	84.423
900	33.335	18.411	67.769	88.225
1000	35.171	21.838	69.996	91.835
1100	36.763	25.437	72.139	95.263
1200	38.145	29.184	74.203	98.523
1300	39.344	33.060	76.194	101.625
1400	40.386	37.048	78.117	104.579
1500	41.294	41.133	79.976	107.397
1600	42.087	45.303	81.774	110.088
1700	42.781	49.547	83.516	112.661
1800	43.391	53.856	85.204	115.124
1900	43.928	58.222	86.841	117.485
2000	44.404	62.639	88.431	119.750
2100	44.825	67.101	89.974	121.927
2200	45.201	71.603	91.474	124.021
2300	45.536	76.140	92.934	126.038
2400	45.837	80.709	94.354	127.983
2500	46.107	85.307	95.737	129.859
2600	46.351	89.930	97.084	131.672
2700	46.571	94.576	98.398	133.426
2800	46.771	99.243	99.679	135.123
2900	46.953	103.930	100.930	136.768
3000	47.119	108.633	102.151	138.362
3200	47.409	118.087	104.511	141.413
3400	47.653	127.594	106.767	144.295
3600	47.861	137.146	108.928	147.024
3800	48.038	146.736	111.002	149.617
4000	48.192	156.359	112.995	152.085
4200	48.325	166.011	114.913	154.440
4400	48.441	175.688	116.761	156.690
4600	48.543	185.387	118.544	158.846
4800	48.633	195.105	120.267	160.914
5000	48.713	204.839	121.933	162.901
5200	48.784	214.589	123.546	164.813
5400	48.848	224.352	125.108	166.655
5600	48.905	234.128	126.624	168.433
5800	48.956	243.914	128.096	170.150
6000	49.003	253.710	129.525	171.810

THERMODYNAMIC PROPERTIES OF   CLCN GAS

T	C_P^0	$(H^0 - H_0^0)_T$	$-(F^0 - H_0^0)/T$	S_T^0
DEG-K	CAL/MOLE DEG-K	KCAL/MOLE	CAL/MOLE DEG-K	CAL/MOLE DEG-K
100	7.468	0.705	39.525	46.574
200	9.433	1.552	44.607	52.368
273.15	10.453	2.282	47.115	55.470
298.15	10.718	2.547	47.855	56.397
400	11.509	3.682	50.461	59.666
500	12.031	4.860	52.573	62.294
600	12.436	6.084	54.384	64.524
700	12.772	7.345	55.974	66.467
800	13.058	8.637	57.395	68.192
900	13.300	9.955	58.683	69.744
1000	13.505	11.296	59.860	71.156
1100	13.678	12.655	60.947	72.452
1200	13.824	14.031	61.956	73.648
1300	13.948	15.419	62.899	74.760
1400	14.053	16.820	63.784	75.798
1500	14.143	18.229	64.617	76.770
1600	14.219	19.648	65.406	77.686
1700	14.286	21.073	66.154	78.550
1800	14.343	22.504	66.865	79.368
1900	14.393	23.941	67.544	80.145
2000	14.436	25.383	68.193	80.884
2100	14.474	26.828	68.814	81.589
2200	14.508	28.277	69.410	82.263
2300	14.538	29.730	69.983	82.909
2400	14.564	31.185	70.535	83.528
2500	14.588	32.643	71.066	84.123
2600	14.609	34.102	71.580	84.696
2700	14.628	35.564	72.076	85.248
2800	14.645	37.028	72.556	85.780
2900	14.661	38.493	73.021	86.294
3000	14.675	39.960	73.471	86.791
3200	14.699	42.897	74.334	87.739
3400	14.719	45.839	75.149	88.631
3600	14.736	48.785	75.921	89.473
3800	14.750	51.733	76.656	90.270
4000	14.762	54.685	77.356	91.027
4200	14.773	57.638	78.024	91.747
4400	14.782	60.594	78.663	92.435
4600	14.789	63.551	79.277	93.092
4800	14.796	66.509	79.865	93.722
5000	14.802	69.469	80.432	94.326
5200	14.807	72.430	80.978	94.906
5400	14.812	75.392	81.504	95.465
5600	14.815	78.355	82.012	96.004
5800	14.819	81.318	82.504	96.524
6000	14.822	84.282	82.979	97.026

Appendix 4.59 THERMODYNAMIC PROPERTIES OF CLFMG GAS

T	C_P^0	$(H^0 - H_T^0)$	$-(F^0 - H_T^0)/T$	S_T^0
DEG-K	CAL/MOLE DEG-K	KCAL/MOLE	CAL/MOLE DEG-K	CAL/MOLE DEG-K
100	7.519	0.705	42.011	49.060
200	10.333	1.598	47.144	55.132
273.15	11.817	2.412	49.760	58.590
298.15	12.184	2.712	50.545	59.641
400	13.199	4.010	53.354	63.379
500	13.747	5.360	55.669	66.389
600	14.073	6.752	57.673	68.926
700	14.281	8.171	59.440	71.112
800	14.421	9.606	61.021	73.029
900	14.519	11.053	62.452	74.733
1000	14.590	12.509	63.758	76.267
1100	14.643	13.971	64.959	77.660
1200	14.684	15.437	66.072	78.936
1300	14.716	16.907	67.107	80.113
1400	14.742	18.380	68.076	81.204
1500	14.762	19.855	68.985	82.222
1600	14.779	21.332	69.843	83.175
1700	14.793	22.811	70.653	84.072
1800	14.805	24.291	71.423	84.918
1900	14.815	25.772	72.154	85.718
2000	14.824	27.254	72.852	86.479
2100	14.831	28.737	73.518	87.202
2200	14.838	30.220	74.156	87.892
2300	14.843	31.704	74.767	88.552
2400	14.848	33.189	75.355	89.184
2500	14.853	34.674	75.920	89.790
2600	14.857	36.160	76.465	90.373
2700	14.860	37.645	76.991	90.933
2800	14.863	39.132	77.498	91.474
2900	14.866	40.618	77.989	91.995
3000	14.868	42.105	78.464	92.499
3200	14.873	45.079	79.372	93.459
3400	14.876	48.054	80.227	94.361
3600	14.879	51.029	81.036	95.211
3800	14.882	54.006	81.804	96.016
4000	14.884	56.982	82.534	96.779
4200	14.886	59.959	83.230	97.506
4400	14.888	62.937	83.894	98.198
4600	14.889	65.914	84.531	98.860
4800	14.890	68.892	85.141	99.494
5000	14.891	71.870	85.727	100.101
5200	14.892	74.849	86.292	100.686
5400	14.893	77.827	86.835	101.248
5600	14.894	80.806	87.360	101.789
5800	14.895	83.785	87.866	102.312
6000	14.895	86.764	88.356	102.817

Appendix 4.60   THERMODYNAMIC PROPERTIES OF CLFPB GAS

T	C_P^0	$(H^0 - H_0^0)$	$-(F^0 - H_0^0)/T$	S_T^0
DEG-K	CAL/MOLE DEG-K	KCAL/MOLE	CAL/MOLE DEG-K	CAL/MOLE DEG-K
100	9.738	0.812	41.591	49.715
200	12.316	1.929	47.706	57.354
273.15	13.266	2.869	50.846	61.348
298.15	13.482	3.203	51.776	62.519
400	14.045	4.608	55.049	66.569
500	14.332	6.029	57.681	69.738
600	14.498	7.471	59.915	72.367
700	14.602	8.926	61.858	74.610
800	14.671	10.390	63.577	76.565
900	14.719	11.860	65.118	78.295
1000	14.753	13.333	66.515	79.848
1100	14.779	14.810	67.792	81.255
1200	14.799	16.289	68.968	82.542
1300	14.814	17.770	70.059	83.727
1400	14.827	19.252	71.075	84.826
1500	14.836	20.735	72.026	85.849
1600	14.845	22.219	72.920	86.807
1700	14.851	23.704	73.764	87.707
1800	14.857	25.189	74.562	88.556
1900	14.862	26.675	75.320	89.359
2000	14.866	28.162	76.041	90.122
2100	14.870	29.648	76.729	90.847
2200	14.873	31.135	77.387	91.539
2300	14.875	32.623	78.016	92.200
2400	14.878	34.110	78.621	92.833
2500	14.880	35.598	79.201	93.441
2600	14.882	37.086	79.760	94.024
2700	14.883	38.575	80.299	94.586
2800	14.885	40.063	80.819	95.127
2900	14.886	41.552	81.322	95.650
3000	14.887	43.040	81.808	96.154
3200	14.889	46.018	82.735	97.115
3400	14.891	48.996	83.607	98.018
3600	14.893	51.974	84.432	98.869
3800	14.894	54.953	85.213	99.674
4000	14.895	57.932	85.955	100.438
4200	14.896	60.911	86.663	101.165
4400	14.896	63.890	87.338	101.858
4600	14.897	66.869	87.983	102.520
4800	14.898	69.849	88.602	103.154
5000	14.898	72.829	89.197	103.763
5200	14.899	75.808	89.768	104.347
5400	14.899	78.788	90.319	104.909
5600	14.899	81.768	90.850	105.451
5800	14.900	84.748	91.362	105.974
6000	14.900	87.728	91.858	106.479

Appendix 4.61   THERMODYNAMIC PROPERTIES OF CLF3 GAS

T	C_P^0	$(H^0 - H_0^0)$	$-(F^0 - H_0^0)/T$	S_T^0
DEG-K	CAL/MOLE DEG-K	KCAL/MOLE	CAL/MOLE DEG-K	CAL/MOLE DEG-K
100	9.395	0.829	46.360	54.649
200	13.059	1.957	52.535	62.318
273.15	15.030	2.988	55.758	66.698
298.15	15.549	3.371	56.732	68.037
400	17.056	5.038	60.242	72.838
500	17.920	6.791	63.163	76.745
600	18.452	8.611	65.710	80.062
700	18.799	10.475	67.970	82.935
800	19.035	12.367	70.002	85.461
900	19.202	14.280	71.847	87.713
1000	19.324	16.206	73.537	89.743
1100	19.416	18.143	75.095	91.589
1200	19.487	20.089	76.541	93.282
1300	19.542	22.040	77.890	94.844
1400	19.587	23.997	79.153	96.294
1500	19.623	25.957	80.342	97.647
1600	19.653	27.921	81.463	98.914
1700	19.677	29.888	82.525	100.106
1800	19.698	31.857	83.534	101.232
1900	19.716	33.827	84.493	102.297
2000	19.731	35.800	85.409	103.309
2100	19.744	37.773	86.284	104.272
2200	19.755	39.748	87.123	105.191
2300	19.765	41.724	87.928	106.069
2400	19.774	43.701	88.701	106.910
2500	19.782	45.679	89.446	107.718
2600	19.788	47.658	90.164	108.494
2700	19.795	49.637	90.857	109.241
2800	19.800	51.617	91.526	109.961
2900	19.805	53.597	92.174	110.656
3000	19.809	55.578	92.801	111.327
3200	19.817	59.540	93.999	112.606
3400	19.823	63.504	95.130	113.807
3600	19.829	67.469	96.199	114.941
3800	19.833	71.436	97.214	116.013
4000	19.837	75.403	98.179	117.030
4200	19.840	79.370	99.100	117.998
4400	19.843	83.339	99.980	118.921
4600	19.846	87.307	100.823	119.803
4800	19.848	91.277	101.632	120.648
5000	19.850	95.247	102.409	121.458
5200	19.851	99.217	103.157	122.237
5400	19.853	103.187	103.877	122.986
5600	19.854	107.158	104.573	123.708
5800	19.856	111.129	105.245	124.405
6000	19.857	115.100	105.894	125.078

Appendix 4.62 THERMODYNAMIC PROPERTIES OF CLH3SI GAS

T	C_P^0	$(H^0 - H_0^0)_T$	$-(F^0 - H_0^0)/T$	S_T^0
DEG-K	CAL/MOLE DEG-K	KCAL/MOLE	CAL/MOLE DEG-K	CAL/MOLE DEG-K
100	8.020	0.796	41.696	49.653
200	9.581	1.659	47.281	55.576
273.15	11.424	2.427	49.948	58.833
298.15	12.047	2.720	50.736	59.860
400	14.309	4.066	53.562	63.728
500	16.103	5.590	55.940	67.120
600	17.576	7.276	58.063	70.191
700	18.800	9.097	59.999	72.995
800	19.817	11.029	61.787	75.574
900	20.662	13.055	63.453	77.958
1000	21.363	15.157	65.016	80.173
1100	21.945	17.323	66.488	82.237
1200	22.431	19.543	67.882	84.168
1300	22.838	21.807	69.205	85.980
1400	23.180	24.108	70.465	87.685
1500	23.471	26.441	71.667	89.294
1600	23.718	28.801	72.817	90.817
1700	23.931	31.184	73.918	92.262
1800	24.114	33.586	74.976	93.635
1900	24.273	36.006	75.993	94.943
2000	24.411	38.440	76.972	96.192
2100	24.532	40.887	77.916	97.386
2200	24.639	43.346	78.827	98.529
2300	24.734	45.815	79.707	99.627
2400	24.818	48.292	80.559	100.681
2500	24.893	50.778	81.385	101.696
2600	24.960	53.271	82.185	102.674
2700	25.020	55.770	82.961	103.617
2800	25.075	58.274	83.715	104.528
2900	25.124	60.784	84.448	105.408
3000	25.168	63.299	85.161	106.261
3200	25.246	68.341	86.531	107.888
3400	25.311	73.397	87.833	109.420
3600	25.366	78.464	89.073	110.869
3800	25.413	83.542	90.257	112.241
4000	25.453	88.629	91.389	113.546
4200	25.487	93.723	92.474	114.789
4400	25.518	98.824	93.515	115.975
4600	25.544	103.930	94.517	117.110
4800	25.567	109.041	95.481	118.198
5000	25.588	114.157	96.410	119.242
5200	25.606	119.276	97.308	120.246
5400	25.623	124.399	98.176	121.212
5600	25.637	129.525	99.015	122.144
5800	25.650	134.654	99.828	123.044
6000	25.662	139.785	100.617	123.914

Appendix 4.63 — THERMODYNAMIC PROPERTIES OF CLO2 GAS

T	C_P^0	$(H^0 - H_0^0)$	$-(F^0 - H_0^0)/T$	S_T^0
DEG-K	CAL/MOLE DEG-K	KCAL/MOLE	CAL/MOLE DEG-K	CAL/MOLE DEG-K
100	8.078	0.797	43.840	51.809
200	8.970	1.646	49.429	57.660
273.15	9.733	2.330	52.038	60.568
298.15	9.992	2.577	52.789	61.432
400	10.942	3.644	55.394	64.505
500	11.656	4.776	57.476	67.028
600	12.174	5.969	59.253	69.201
700	12.546	7.206	60.813	71.108
800	12.818	8.475	62.208	72.801
900	13.019	9.767	63.471	74.323
1000	13.172	11.077	64.626	75.703
1100	13.289	12.400	65.691	76.964
1200	13.381	13.734	66.680	78.125
1300	13.455	15.076	67.602	79.199
1400	13.514	16.425	68.466	80.198
1500	13.563	17.779	69.280	81.132
1600	13.603	19.137	70.048	82.009
1700	13.637	20.499	70.777	82.835
1800	13.666	21.864	71.468	83.615
1900	13.690	23.232	72.127	84.355
2000	13.711	24.602	72.756	85.057
2100	13.729	25.974	73.358	85.727
2200	13.745	27.348	73.935	86.366
2300	13.759	28.723	74.489	86.977
2400	13.771	30.100	75.022	87.563
2500	13.782	31.477	75.535	88.125
2600	13.791	32.856	76.029	88.666
2700	13.800	34.235	76.507	89.187
2800	13.808	35.616	76.969	89.689
2900	13.814	36.997	77.416	90.173
3000	13.821	38.379	77.849	90.642
3200	13.831	41.144	78.677	91.534
3400	13.840	43.911	79.458	92.373
3600	13.848	46.680	80.198	93.164
3800	13.854	49.450	80.900	93.913
4000	13.860	52.222	81.569	94.624
4200	13.865	54.994	82.206	95.300
4400	13.869	57.767	82.816	95.945
4600	13.872	60.542	83.401	96.562
4800	13.875	63.316	83.962	97.152
5000	13.878	66.092	84.501	97.719
5200	13.881	68.867	85.020	98.263
5400	13.883	71.644	85.520	98.787
5600	13.885	74.421	86.003	99.292
5800	13.886	77.198	86.469	99.779
6000	13.888	79.975	86.921	100.250

Appendix 4.64   THERMODYNAMIC PROPERTIES OF CLPBBR GAS

T	C_P^0	$(H^0 - H_0^0)$	$-(F^0 - H_0^0)/T$	S_T^0
DEG-K	CAL/MOLE DEG-K	KCAL/MOLE	CAL/MOLE DEG-K	CAL/MOLE DEG-K
100	11.338	0.888	45.181	54.063
200	13.596	2.159	51.987	62.781
273.15	14.150	3.176	55.484	67.113
298.15	14.262	3.532	56.512	68.357
400	14.535	5.000	60.091	72.592
500	14.665	6.461	62.929	75.850
600	14.736	7.931	65.313	78.531
700	14.780	9.407	67.368	80.806
800	14.809	10.887	69.174	82.782
900	14.829	12.369	70.784	84.527
1000	14.843	13.852	72.238	86.090
1100	14.854	15.337	73.563	87.506
1200	14.862	16.823	74.779	88.798
1300	14.868	18.309	75.904	89.988
1400	14.873	19.796	76.950	91.090
1500	14.877	21.284	77.927	92.117
1600	14.880	22.772	78.844	93.077
1700	14.883	24.260	79.708	93.979
1800	14.885	25.748	80.525	94.830
1900	14.887	27.237	81.299	95.635
2000	14.889	28.726	82.035	96.398
2100	14.890	30.215	82.737	97.125
2200	14.892	31.704	83.407	97.818
2300	14.893	33.193	84.048	98.480
2400	14.894	34.683	84.662	99.113
2500	14.895	36.172	85.253	99.721
2600	14.895	37.661	85.820	100.306
2700	14.896	39.151	86.367	100.868
2800	14.897	40.641	86.895	101.409
2900	14.897	42.130	87.405	101.932
3000	14.898	43.620	87.897	102.437
3200	14.898	46.600	88.836	103.399
3400	14.899	49.579	89.720	104.302
3600	14.900	52.559	90.554	105.154
3800	14.900	55.539	91.344	105.959
4000	14.901	58.519	92.094	106.723
4200	14.901	61.499	92.808	107.450
4400	14.901	64.480	93.489	108.144
4600	14.901	67.460	94.141	108.806
4800	14.902	70.440	94.765	109.440
5000	14.902	73.421	95.364	110.049
5200	14.902	76.401	95.941	110.633
5400	14.902	79.381	96.495	111.195
5600	14.902	82.362	97.030	111.737
5800	14.903	85.342	97.546	112.260
6000	14.903	88.323	98.045	112.766

Appendix 4.65   THERMODYNAMIC PROPERTIES OF CLPBO GAS

T	C_P^0	$(H^0 - H_0^0)$	$-(F^0 - H_0^0)/T$	S_T^0
DEG-K	CAL/MOLE DEG-K	KCAL/MOLE	CAL/MOLE DEG-K	CAL/MOLE DEG-K
100	9.632	0.806	42.311	50.375
200	11.878	1.895	48.355	57.830
273.15	12.798	2.800	51.428	61.679
298.15	13.029	3.123	52.336	62.810
400	13.691	4.487	55.524	66.741
500	14.065	5.876	58.087	69.839
600	14.294	7.295	60.267	72.425
700	14.443	8.732	62.166	74.641
800	14.545	10.182	63.849	76.577
900	14.617	11.640	65.360	78.294
1000	14.669	13.105	66.732	79.837
1100	14.708	14.574	67.988	81.237
1200	14.739	16.046	69.146	82.518
1300	14.763	17.521	70.221	83.699
1400	14.782	18.999	71.223	84.794
1500	14.797	20.478	72.162	85.814
1600	14.810	21.958	73.046	86.769
1700	14.821	23.439	73.880	87.668
1800	14.830	24.922	74.669	88.515
1900	14.837	26.405	75.419	89.317
2000	14.844	27.889	76.134	90.078
2100	14.849	29.374	76.815	90.803
2200	14.854	30.859	77.467	91.494
2300	14.858	32.345	78.091	92.154
2400	14.862	33.831	78.690	92.786
2500	14.865	35.317	79.266	93.393
2600	14.868	36.804	79.821	93.976
2700	14.871	38.291	80.356	94.537
2800	14.873	39.778	80.872	95.078
2900	14.875	41.266	81.371	95.600
3000	14.877	42.753	81.853	96.105
3200	14.881	45.729	82.774	97.065
3400	14.883	48.705	83.642	97.967
3600	14.886	51.682	84.462	98.818
3800	14.887	54.660	85.239	99.623
4000	14.889	57.637	85.977	100.386
4200	14.891	60.615	86.681	101.113
4400	14.892	63.593	87.352	101.806
4600	14.893	66.572	87.995	102.468
4800	14.894	69.551	88.612	103.101
5000	14.895	72.529	89.204	103.709
5200	14.895	75.508	89.773	104.294
5400	14.896	78.488	90.321	104.856
5600	14.897	81.467	90.850	105.397
5800	14.897	84.446	91.361	105.920
6000	14.898	87.426	91.854	106.425

Appendix **4.66**   THERMODYNAMIC PROPERTIES OF CL2H2SI GAS

T	C_P^0	$(H^0 - H_0^0)$	$-(F^0 - H_0^0)/T$	S_T^0
DEG-K	CAL/MOLE DEG-K	KCAL/MOLE	CAL/MOLE DEG-K	CAL/MOLE DEG-K
100	9.183	0.835	47.669	56.017
200	11.896	1.877	53.749	63.136
273.15	14.148	2.832	56.817	67.184
298.15	14.831	3.194	57.740	68.453
400	17.079	4.826	61.080	73.145
500	18.650	6.616	63.901	77.134
600	19.837	8.543	66.405	80.643
700	20.774	10.575	68.667	83.774
800	21.531	12.692	70.734	86.599
900	22.148	14.877	72.642	89.172
1000	22.655	17.118	74.415	91.533
1100	23.073	19.405	76.071	93.712
1200	23.420	21.730	77.627	95.735
1300	23.710	24.087	79.093	97.622
1400	23.954	26.471	80.480	99.388
1500	24.161	28.877	81.797	101.048
1600	24.336	31.302	83.049	102.613
1700	24.487	33.743	84.244	104.093
1800	24.617	36.198	85.386	105.496
1900	24.729	38.666	86.480	106.830
2000	24.827	41.144	87.529	108.101
2100	24.913	43.631	88.538	109.315
2200	24.989	46.126	89.509	110.475
2300	25.056	48.628	90.445	111.588
2400	25.115	51.137	91.348	112.655
2500	25.168	53.651	92.221	113.682
2600	25.216	56.170	93.066	114.670
2700	25.259	58.694	93.884	115.622
2800	25.297	61.222	94.677	116.542
2900	25.332	63.753	95.446	117.430
3000	25.363	66.288	96.193	118.289
3200	25.418	71.367	97.626	119.928
3400	25.464	76.455	98.984	121.470
3600	25.503	81.552	100.274	122.927
3800	25.536	86.656	101.503	124.307
4000	25.564	91.766	102.676	125.617
4200	25.589	96.881	103.798	126.865
4400	25.610	102.001	104.874	128.056
4600	25.629	107.125	105.907	129.195
4800	25.645	112.253	106.900	130.286
5000	25.660	117.383	107.857	131.333
5200	25.673	122.517	108.779	132.340
5400	25.685	127.652	109.670	133.309
5600	25.695	132.790	110.531	134.243
5800	25.704	137.930	111.364	135.145
6000	25.713	143.072	112.171	136.017

Appendix 4.67 THERMODYNAMIC PROPERTIES OF CL2LI2 GAS

T	C_P^0	$(H_T^0 - H_0^0)$	$-(F_T^0 - H_0^0)/T$	S_T^0
DEG-K	CAL/MOLE DEG-K	KCAL/MOLE	CAL/MOLE DEG-K	CAL/MOLE DEG-K
100	9.465	0.826	45.430	53.688
200	13.731	1.998	51.650	61.639
273.15	15.701	3.080	54.958	66.234
298.15	16.188	3.479	55.963	67.630
400	17.543	5.204	59.589	72.598
500	18.283	6.998	62.603	76.599
600	18.728	8.850	65.224	79.975
700	19.012	10.738	67.544	82.885
800	19.204	12.650	69.624	85.437
900	19.339	14.577	71.510	87.707
1000	19.437	16.516	73.233	89.750
1100	19.510	18.464	74.821	91.606
1200	19.567	20.418	76.291	93.306
1300	19.611	22.377	77.661	94.874
1400	19.647	24.340	78.943	96.329
1500	19.675	26.306	80.148	97.685
1600	19.699	28.275	81.284	98.956
1700	19.719	30.246	82.359	100.151
1800	19.735	32.218	83.379	101.278
1900	19.749	34.193	84.350	102.346
2000	19.761	36.168	85.275	103.359
2100	19.771	38.145	86.159	104.323
2200	19.780	40.122	87.006	105.243
2300	19.788	42.101	87.818	106.123
2400	19.795	44.080	88.598	106.965
2500	19.801	46.060	89.349	107.773
2600	19.806	48.040	90.073	108.550
2700	19.811	50.021	90.771	109.297
2800	19.815	52.002	91.446	110.018
2900	19.819	53.984	92.098	110.713
3000	19.823	55.966	92.730	111.385
3200	19.829	59.931	93.936	112.665
3400	19.834	63.897	95.074	113.867
3600	19.838	67.865	96.150	115.001
3800	19.841	71.832	97.170	116.074
4000	19.844	75.801	98.141	117.091
4200	19.847	79.770	99.067	118.060
4400	19.849	83.740	99.951	118.983
4600	19.851	87.710	100.798	119.865
4800	19.853	91.680	101.610	120.710
5000	19.855	95.651	102.391	121.521
5200	19.856	99.622	103.141	122.300
5400	19.857	103.593	103.865	123.049
5600	19.858	107.565	104.563	123.771
5800	19.859	111.537	105.238	124.468
6000	19.860	115.509	105.890	125.141

Appendix 4.68   THERMODYNAMIC PROPERTIES OF CL2MG GAS

T	C_P^0	$(H-H_0^0)_T$	$-(F-H_0^0)_T/T$	S_T^0
DEG-K	CAL/MOLE DEG-K	KCAL/MOLE	CAL/MOLE DEG-K	CAL/MOLE DEG-K
100	8.547	0.732	42.266	49.586
200	11.603	1.756	47.781	56.562
273.15	12.763	2.651	50.660	60.367
298.15	13.033	2.974	51.522	61.497
400	13.754	4.342	54.584	65.440
500	14.131	5.738	57.077	68.553
600	14.352	7.163	59.212	71.151
700	14.491	8.606	61.080	73.374
800	14.585	10.060	62.741	75.316
900	14.650	11.522	64.235	77.038
1000	14.697	12.989	65.594	78.584
1100	14.732	14.461	66.840	79.986
1200	14.759	15.936	67.990	81.269
1300	14.780	17.413	69.057	82.452
1400	14.797	18.892	70.054	83.548
1500	14.811	20.372	70.988	84.569
1600	14.822	21.854	71.867	85.525
1700	14.831	23.336	72.697	86.424
1800	14.839	24.820	73.483	87.272
1900	14.846	26.304	74.230	88.075
2000	14.852	27.789	74.942	88.836
2100	14.856	29.274	75.621	89.561
2200	14.861	30.760	76.270	90.252
2300	14.864	32.247	76.893	90.913
2400	14.868	33.733	77.490	91.545
2500	14.870	35.220	78.064	92.152
2600	14.873	36.707	78.618	92.736
2700	14.875	38.195	79.151	93.297
2800	14.877	39.682	79.666	93.838
2900	14.879	41.170	80.164	94.360
3000	14.881	42.658	80.645	94.865
3200	14.884	45.635	81.564	95.825
3400	14.886	48.612	82.430	96.728
3600	14.888	51.589	83.248	97.578
3800	14.890	54.567	84.024	98.383
4000	14.891	57.545	84.761	99.147
4200	14.892	60.523	85.464	99.874
4400	14.893	63.502	86.134	100.567
4600	14.894	66.480	86.776	101.229
4800	14.895	69.459	87.392	101.863
5000	14.896	72.439	87.983	102.471
5200	14.897	75.418	88.551	103.055
5400	14.897	78.397	89.099	103.617
5600	14.898	81.377	89.627	104.159
5800	14.898	84.356	90.138	104.682
6000	14.898	87.336	90.631	105.187

Appendix 4.69 THERMODYNAMIC PROPERTIES OF CL2O GAS

T	C_P^0	$(H^0 - H_0^0)$	$-(F^0 - H_0^0)/T$	S_T^0
DEG-K	CAL/MOLE DEG-K	KCAL/MOLE	CAL/MOLE DEG-K	CAL/MOLE DEG-K
100	8.390	0.804	45.282	53.325
200	9.696	1.708	50.998	59.540
273.15	10.585	2.451	53.724	62.697
298.15	10.855	2.719	54.516	63.635
400	11.743	3.873	57.276	66.958
500	12.331	5.078	59.489	69.646
600	12.726	6.333	61.377	71.931
700	12.997	7.619	63.029	73.914
800	13.188	8.929	64.502	75.663
900	13.326	10.255	65.830	77.225
1000	13.429	11.593	67.041	78.634
1100	13.508	12.940	68.154	79.918
1200	13.569	14.294	69.184	81.096
1300	13.617	15.654	70.143	82.184
1400	13.656	17.017	71.040	83.195
1500	13.688	18.385	71.882	84.138
1600	13.714	19.755	72.676	85.022
1700	13.736	21.127	73.427	85.854
1800	13.754	22.502	74.139	86.640
1900	13.770	23.878	74.817	87.384
2000	13.784	25.256	75.463	88.091
2100	13.795	26.635	76.081	88.764
2200	13.805	28.015	76.672	89.406
2300	13.814	29.396	77.239	90.020
2400	13.822	30.777	77.784	90.608
2500	13.829	32.160	78.308	91.172
2600	13.835	33.543	78.813	91.715
2700	13.840	34.927	79.301	92.237
2800	13.845	36.311	79.772	92.740
2900	13.850	37.696	80.227	93.226
3000	13.854	39.081	80.669	93.696
3200	13.860	41.853	81.511	94.590
3400	13.866	44.625	82.305	95.430
3600	13.871	47.399	83.057	96.223
3800	13.875	50.174	83.770	96.973
4000	13.878	52.949	84.448	97.685
4200	13.881	55.725	85.094	98.362
4400	13.884	58.502	85.712	99.008
4600	13.886	61.279	86.304	99.625
4800	13.888	64.056	86.871	100.216
5000	13.890	66.834	87.417	100.783
5200	13.892	69.612	87.941	101.328
5400	13.893	72.391	88.447	101.852
5600	13.894	75.169	88.935	102.358
5800	13.895	77.948	89.406	102.845
6000	13.896	80.727	89.862	103.316

Appendix 4.70 THERMODYNAMIC PROPERTIES OF CL2PB GAS

T	C_P^0	$(H^0 - H_0^0)$	$-(F^0 - H_0^0)/T$	S_T^0
DEG-K	CAL/MOLE DEG-K	KCAL/MOLE	CAL/MOLE DEG-K	CAL/MOLE DEG-K
100	10.734	0.927	52.648	61.922
200	12.593	2.109	59.493	70.037
273.15	13.132	3.052	62.878	74.053
298.15	13.245	3.382	63.864	75.208
400	13.524	4.747	67.277	79.145
500	13.658	6.107	69.964	82.178
600	13.733	7.477	72.214	84.676
700	13.780	8.853	74.150	86.796
800	13.810	10.232	75.848	88.639
900	13.831	11.614	77.362	90.266
1000	13.846	12.998	78.726	91.724
1100	13.857	14.383	79.969	93.045
1200	13.866	15.770	81.109	94.251
1300	13.872	17.156	82.164	95.361
1400	13.877	18.544	83.143	96.389
1500	13.882	19.932	84.059	97.347
1600	13.885	21.320	84.918	98.243
1700	13.888	22.709	85.726	99.085
1800	13.891	24.098	86.491	99.878
1900	13.893	25.487	87.215	100.630
2000	13.894	26.876	87.904	101.342
2100	13.896	28.266	88.560	102.020
2200	13.897	29.656	89.187	102.667
2300	13.898	31.045	89.786	103.284
2400	13.899	32.435	90.361	103.876
2500	13.900	33.825	90.913	104.443
2600	13.901	35.215	91.444	104.989
2700	13.902	36.605	91.956	105.513
2800	13.902	37.996	92.449	106.019
2900	13.903	39.386	92.925	106.507
3000	13.903	40.776	93.386	106.978
3200	13.904	43.557	94.264	107.875
3400	13.905	46.338	95.089	108.718
3600	13.906	49.119	95.869	109.513
3800	13.906	51.900	96.607	110.265
4000	13.907	54.682	97.308	110.978
4200	13.907	57.463	97.975	111.657
4400	13.907	60.244	98.612	112.304
4600	13.908	63.026	99.221	112.922
4800	13.908	65.807	99.804	113.514
5000	13.908	68.589	100.364	114.082
5200	13.908	71.371	100.902	114.627
5400	13.909	74.152	101.420	115.152
5600	13.909	76.934	101.920	115.658
5800	13.909	79.716	102.402	116.146
6000	13.909	82.498	102.868	116.617

Appendix 4.71 THERMODYNAMIC PROPERTIES OF CL2SI GAS

T	C_P^0	$(H^0 - H_0^0)$	$-(F^0 - H_0^0)/T$	S_T^0
DEG-K	CAL/MOLE DEG-K	KCAL/MOLE	CAL/MOLE DEG-K	CAL/MOLE DEG-K
100	9.107	0.831	47.205	55.511
200	10.966	1.837	53.227	62.412
273.15	11.919	2.677	56.183	65.982
298.15	12.157	2.978	57.049	67.036
400	12.813	4.253	60.079	70.710
500	13.167	5.553	62.505	73.611
600	13.378	6.881	64.563	76.032
700	13.511	8.226	66.353	78.105
800	13.601	9.582	67.938	79.915
900	13.664	10.946	69.359	81.521
1000	13.709	12.314	70.649	82.963
1100	13.744	13.687	71.829	84.272
1200	13.770	15.063	72.916	85.469
1300	13.790	16.441	73.925	86.572
1400	13.807	17.821	74.865	87.594
1500	13.820	19.202	75.746	88.547
1600	13.831	20.585	76.574	89.440
1700	13.840	21.968	77.356	90.278
1800	13.847	23.353	78.096	91.070
1900	13.854	24.738	78.799	91.818
2000	13.859	26.123	79.468	92.529
2100	13.864	27.510	80.106	93.206
2200	13.868	28.896	80.716	93.851
2300	13.872	30.283	81.301	94.467
2400	13.875	31.671	81.862	95.058
2500	13.878	33.058	82.401	95.624
2600	13.880	34.446	82.920	96.168
2700	13.882	35.834	83.420	96.692
2800	13.884	37.223	83.903	97.197
2900	13.886	38.611	84.370	97.684
3000	13.888	40.000	84.822	98.155
3200	13.891	42.778	85.684	99.052
3400	13.893	45.556	86.495	99.894
3600	13.895	48.335	87.262	100.688
3800	13.896	51.114	87.988	101.439
4000	13.898	53.893	88.679	102.152
4200	13.899	56.673	89.337	102.830
4400	13.900	59.453	89.965	103.477
4600	13.901	62.233	90.566	104.095
4800	13.902	65.013	91.142	104.686
5000	13.902	67.794	91.695	105.254
5200	13.903	70.574	92.227	105.799
5400	13.904	73.355	92.740	106.324
5600	13.904	76.136	93.234	106.830
5800	13.905	78.917	93.711	107.317
6000	13.905	81.698	94.173	107.789

Appendix 4.72 THERMODYNAMIC PROPERTIES OF CL3HSI GAS

T	C_p^0	$(H^0 - H_0^0)$	$-(F^0 - H_0^0)/T$	S_T^0
DEG-K	CAL/MOLE DEG-K	KCAL/MOLE	CAL/MOLE DEG-K	CAL/MOLE DEG-K
100	11.161	0.899	50.464	59.455
200	15.211	2.225	57.359	68.485
273.15	17.518	3.426	61.041	73.585
298.15	18.155	3.872	62.159	75.147
400	20.094	5.828	66.206	80.776
500	21.314	7.902	69.595	85.399
600	22.161	10.078	72.567	89.364
700	22.789	12.327	75.219	92.830
800	23.274	14.631	77.617	95.906
900	23.659	16.979	79.805	98.670
1000	23.968	19.361	81.819	101.180
1100	24.220	21.771	83.685	103.476
1200	24.427	24.203	85.423	105.593
1300	24.599	26.655	87.051	107.555
1400	24.743	29.122	88.582	109.383
1500	24.864	31.603	90.026	111.095
1600	24.967	34.094	91.394	112.703
1700	25.055	36.595	92.692	114.219
1800	25.130	39.105	93.928	115.653
1900	25.196	41.621	95.108	117.014
2000	25.253	44.144	96.236	118.308
2100	25.302	46.671	97.317	119.541
2200	25.346	49.204	98.354	120.719
2300	25.385	51.741	99.351	121.847
2400	25.420	54.281	100.311	122.928
2500	25.450	56.824	101.236	123.966
2600	25.478	59.371	102.130	124.965
2700	25.502	61.920	102.994	125.927
2800	25.525	64.471	103.829	126.855
2900	25.545	67.025	104.639	127.751
3000	25.563	69.580	105.424	128.617
3200	25.595	74.696	106.925	130.268
3400	25.621	79.817	108.345	131.820
3600	25.643	84.944	109.690	133.285
3800	25.663	90.075	110.969	134.672
4000	25.679	95.209	112.187	135.989
4200	25.693	100.346	113.351	137.242
4400	25.705	105.486	114.464	138.438
4600	25.716	110.628	115.531	139.581
4800	25.726	115.772	116.556	140.676
5000	25.734	120.918	117.542	141.726
5200	25.741	126.066	118.492	142.735
5400	25.748	131.215	119.408	143.707
5600	25.754	136.365	120.293	144.643
5800	25.759	141.516	121.148	145.547
6000	25.764	146.669	121.976	146.421

Appendix 4.73 THERMODYNAMIC PROPERTIES OF CL3ZR GAS

T	C_P^0	$(H^0 - H_0^0)$	$-(F^0 - H_0^0)/T$	S_T^0
DEG-K	CAL/MOLE DEG-K	KCAL/MOLE	CAL/MOLE DEG-K	CAL/MOLE DEG-K
100	12.814	0.969	54.148	63.837
200	16.827	2.483	61.756	74.170
273.15	18.042	3.763	65.839	79.617
298.15	18.302	4.218	67.062	81.208
400	18.952	6.119	71.392	86.690
500	19.268	8.032	74.893	90.956
600	19.447	9.968	77.873	94.487
700	19.557	11.919	80.466	97.493
800	19.630	13.879	82.762	100.110
900	19.680	15.844	84.820	102.425
1000	19.716	17.814	86.686	104.500
1100	19.743	19.787	88.393	106.381
1200	19.764	21.762	89.964	108.100
1300	19.780	23.740	91.421	109.682
1400	19.792	25.718	92.778	111.149
1500	19.803	27.698	94.049	112.514
1600	19.811	29.679	95.244	113.793
1700	19.818	31.660	96.370	114.994
1800	19.824	33.642	97.437	116.127
1900	19.829	35.625	98.449	117.199
2000	19.833	37.608	99.412	118.216
2100	19.837	39.592	100.331	119.184
2200	19.840	41.575	101.209	120.107
2300	19.843	43.560	102.050	120.989
2400	19.845	45.544	102.857	121.833
2500	19.847	47.529	103.632	122.643
2600	19.849	49.513	104.378	123.422
2700	19.851	51.498	105.098	124.171
2800	19.852	53.484	105.792	124.893
2900	19.854	55.469	106.463	125.590
3000	19.855	57.454	107.111	126.263
3200	19.857	61.425	108.349	127.544
3400	19.859	65.397	109.514	128.748
3600	19.860	69.369	110.614	129.883
3800	19.862	73.341	111.657	130.957
4000	19.863	77.314	112.648	131.976
4200	19.864	81.286	113.591	132.945
4400	19.864	85.259	114.492	133.869
4600	19.865	89.232	115.354	134.752
4800	19.866	93.205	116.180	135.598
5000	19.866	97.178	116.973	136.409
5200	19.867	101.151	117.736	137.188
5400	19.867	105.125	118.470	137.938
5600	19.867	109.098	119.178	138.660
5800	19.868	113.072	119.862	139.357
6000	19.868	117.045	120.523	140.031

Appendix 4.74   THERMODYNAMIC PROPERTIES OF CL4PB GAS

T	C_P^0	$(H^0 - H_0^0)$	$-(F^0 - H_0^0)/T$	S_T^0
DEG-K	CAL/MOLE DEG-K	KCAL/MOLE	CAL/MOLE DEG-K	CAL/MOLE DEG-K
100	19.240	1.342	55.594	69.015
200	23.427	3.521	66.346	83.950
273.15	24.446	5.277	72.106	91.424
298.15	24.652	5.890	73.817	93.574
400	25.155	8.430	79.823	100.899
500	25.393	10.959	84.622	106.540
600	25.525	13.505	88.674	111.183
700	25.606	16.062	92.178	115.124
800	25.659	18.626	95.265	118.547
900	25.695	21.194	98.023	121.571
1000	25.722	23.764	100.515	124.280
1100	25.741	26.338	102.789	126.732
1200	25.756	28.912	104.879	128.973
1300	25.767	31.489	106.813	131.035
1400	25.777	34.066	108.612	132.945
1500	25.784	36.644	110.294	134.723
1600	25.790	39.223	111.873	136.388
1700	25.795	41.802	113.362	137.951
1800	25.799	44.382	114.769	139.426
1900	25.803	46.962	116.104	140.821
2000	25.806	49.542	117.373	142.144
2100	25.809	52.123	118.583	143.404
2200	25.811	54.704	119.739	144.604
2300	25.813	57.285	120.845	145.752
2400	25.815	59.866	121.906	146.850
2500	25.816	62.448	122.925	147.904
2600	25.817	65.030	123.905	148.917
2700	25.819	67.611	124.850	149.891
2800	25.820	70.193	125.761	150.830
2900	25.821	72.775	126.641	151.736
3000	25.822	75.358	127.492	152.611
3200	25.823	80.522	129.115	154.278
3400	25.824	85.687	130.641	155.843
3600	25.826	90.852	132.083	157.320
3800	25.826	96.017	133.448	158.716
4000	25.827	101.182	134.745	160.041
4200	25.828	106.348	135.980	161.301
4400	25.828	111.513	137.158	162.502
4600	25.829	116.679	138.285	163.650
4800	25.829	121.845	139.365	164.750
5000	25.830	127.011	140.402	165.804
5200	25.830	132.177	141.399	166.817
5400	25.830	137.343	142.358	167.792
5600	25.831	142.509	143.283	168.731
5800	25.831	147.675	144.177	169.638
6000	25.831	152.841	145.040	170.514

Appendix 4.75   THERMODYNAMIC PROPERTIES OF CL4SI GAS

T	C_P^0	$(H^0 - H_T^0)$	$-(F^0 - H_T^0)/T$	S_T^0
DEG-K	CAL/MOLE DEG-K	KCAL/MOLE	CAL/MOLE DEG-K	CAL/MOLE DEG-K
100	13.652	0.993	49.912	59.839
200	18.848	2.644	57.858	71.078
273.15	21.089	4.111	62.260	77.310
298.15	21.644	4.645	63.601	79.182
400	23.191	6.937	68.440	85.782
500	24.033	9.302	72.453	91.056
600	24.539	11.732	75.932	95.486
700	24.861	14.203	79.004	99.295
800	25.079	16.701	81.753	102.629
900	25.231	19.217	84.240	105.593
1000	25.342	21.746	86.511	108.257
1100	25.426	24.285	88.600	110.677
1200	25.489	26.830	90.533	112.892
1300	25.539	29.382	92.332	114.934
1400	25.579	31.938	94.015	116.828
1500	25.612	34.498	95.596	118.594
1600	25.638	37.060	97.085	120.248
1700	25.661	39.625	98.494	121.803
1800	25.679	42.192	99.830	123.270
1900	25.695	44.761	101.101	124.659
2000	25.708	47.331	102.312	125.977
2100	25.720	49.902	103.469	127.232
2200	25.730	52.475	104.576	128.429
2300	25.739	55.048	105.639	129.573
2400	25.747	57.623	106.659	130.668
2500	25.753	60.198	107.640	131.719
2600	25.760	62.773	108.586	132.730
2700	25.765	65.350	109.498	133.702
2800	25.770	67.926	110.380	134.639
2900	25.774	70.504	111.232	135.543
3000	25.778	73.081	112.057	136.417
3200	25.785	78.237	113.632	138.081
3400	25.790	83.395	115.117	139.644
3600	25.795	88.554	116.521	141.119
3800	25.799	93.713	117.852	142.514
4000	25.803	98.873	119.119	143.837
4200	25.806	104.034	120.326	145.096
4400	25.808	109.195	121.479	146.296
4600	25.810	114.357	122.583	147.444
4800	25.812	119.520	123.642	148.542
5000	25.814	124.682	124.660	149.596
5200	25.816	129.845	125.638	150.608
5400	25.817	135.008	126.581	151.583
5600	25.818	140.172	127.491	152.522
5800	25.819	145.336	128.370	153.428
6000	25.820	150.500	129.220	154.303

Appendix 4.76   THERMODYNAMIC PROPERTIES OF CL4TI GAS

T	C_P^0	$(H^0 - H_0^0)$	$-(F^0 - H_0^0)/T$	S_T^0
DEG-K	CAL/MOLE DEG-K	KCAL/MOLE	CAL/MOLE DEG-K	CAL/MOLE DEG-K
100	15.829	1.134	51.492	62.834
200	20.521	2.976	60.532	75.412
273.15	22.396	4.552	65.447	82.112
298.15	22.835	5.117	66.929	84.092
400	24.003	7.509	72.212	90.986
500	24.608	9.9+3	76.528	96.413
600	24.961	12.423	80.229	100.934
700	25.183	14.931	83.470	104.799
800	25.330	17.457	86.351	108.172
900	25.433	19.995	88.945	111.162
1000	25.508	22.543	91.303	113.846
1100	25.564	25.096	93.465	116.280
1200	25.606	27.655	95.460	118.506
1300	25.639	30.217	97.313	120.557
1400	25.666	32.783	99.042	122.458
1500	25.687	35.350	100.663	124.230
1600	25.705	37.920	102.188	125.888
1700	25.720	40.491	103.628	127.447
1800	25.732	43.064	104.993	128.917
1900	25.742	45.638	106.289	130.309
2000	25.751	48.212	107.523	131.629
2100	25.759	50.788	108.701	132.886
2200	25.766	53.364	109.828	134.084
2300	25.771	55.941	110.908	135.230
2400	25.777	58.518	111.944	136.327
2500	25.781	61.096	112.941	137.379
2600	25.785	63.674	113.900	138.390
2700	25.789	66.253	114.825	139.364
2800	25.792	68.832	115.719	140.302
2900	25.795	71.412	116.582	141.207
3000	25.797	73.991	117.418	142.081
3200	25.802	79.151	119.012	143.746
3400	25.805	84.312	120.513	145.311
3600	25.809	89.473	121.932	146.786
3800	25.811	94.635	123.277	148.181
4000	25.813	99.798	124.556	149.505
4200	25.815	104.961	125.774	150.765
4400	25.817	110.124	126.938	151.966
4600	25.819	115.287	128.051	153.113
4800	25.820	120.451	129.118	154.212
5000	25.821	125.615	130.143	155.266
5200	25.822	130.780	131.129	156.279
5400	25.823	135.944	132.079	157.253
5600	25.824	141.109	132.995	158.193
5800	25.824	146.273	133.879	159.099
6000	25.825	151.438	134.735	159.974

Appendix 4.77 THERMODYNAMIC PROPERTIES OF CL4ZR GAS

T	C_P^0	$(H^0 - H_0^0)$	$-(F^0 - H_0^0)/T$	S_T^0
DEG-K	CAL/MOLE DEG-K	KCAL/MOLE	CAL/MOLE DEG-K	CAL/MOLE DEG-K
100	17.250	1.270	53.749	66.450
200	21.498	3.230	63.714	79.864
273.15	23.100	4.867	69.009	86.827
298.15	23.464	5.449	70.589	88.866
400	24.409	7.893	76.178	95.910
500	24.888	10.360	80.693	101.414
600	25.163	12.864	84.538	105.978
700	25.335	15.389	87.885	109.870
800	25.449	17.929	90.850	113.261
900	25.528	20.478	93.510	116.264
1000	25.585	23.034	95.923	118.956
1100	25.628	25.595	98.129	121.397
1200	25.660	28.159	100.162	123.628
1300	25.686	30.727	102.048	125.683
1400	25.706	33.296	103.805	127.588
1500	25.723	35.868	105.450	129.362
1600	25.736	38.441	106.997	131.022
1700	25.747	41.015	108.457	132.583
1800	25.756	43.590	109.838	134.055
1900	25.764	46.166	111.150	135.448
2000	25.771	48.743	112.398	136.769
2100	25.777	51.320	113.589	138.027
2200	25.782	53.898	114.727	139.226
2300	25.787	56.477	115.817	140.372
2400	25.790	59.055	116.863	141.470
2500	25.794	61.635	117.869	142.523
2600	25.797	64.214	118.837	143.534
2700	25.800	66.794	119.770	144.508
2800	25.802	69.374	120.670	145.446
2900	25.804	71.954	121.540	146.352
3000	25.806	74.535	122.382	147.227
3200	25.810	79.696	123.987	148.892
3400	25.812	84.859	125.499	150.457
3600	25.815	90.021	126.927	151.933
3800	25.817	95.185	128.280	153.328
4000	25.818	100.348	129.566	154.653
4200	25.820	105.512	130.790	155.912
4400	25.821	110.676	131.960	157.114
4600	25.822	115.840	133.079	158.261
4800	25.823	121.005	134.151	159.360
5000	25.824	126.170	135.181	160.415
5200	25.825	131.335	136.171	161.427
5400	25.826	136.500	137.124	162.402
5600	25.826	141.665	138.044	163.341
5800	25.827	146.830	138.932	164.248
6000	25.827	151.995	139.791	165.123

THERMODYNAMIC PROPERTIES OF HCN GAS

T	C_P^0	$(H^0 - H_0^0)_T$	$-(F_T^0 - H_0^0)/T$	S_T^0
DEG-K	CAL/MOLE DEG-K	KCAL/MOLE	CAL/MOLE DEG-K	CAL/MOLE DEG-K
100	6.972	0.696	33.067	40.024
200	7.585	1.416	37.912	44.990
273.15	8.338	1.998	40.151	47.466
298.15	8.578	2.210	40.795	48.206
400	9.386	3.127	43.030	50.846
500	9.986	4.096	44.815	53.008
600	10.485	5.121	46.340	54.874
700	10.926	6.191	47.679	56.524
800	11.328	7.305	48.879	58.009
900	11.694	8.456	49.970	59.365
1000	12.028	9.642	50.973	60.615
1100	12.330	10.860	51.902	61.776
1200	12.601	12.107	52.771	62.860
1300	12.845	13.380	53.587	63.879
1400	13.063	14.675	54.356	64.839
1500	13.258	15.992	55.086	65.747
1600	13.433	17.326	55.779	66.608
1700	13.590	18.678	56.441	67.427
1800	13.731	20.044	57.073	68.208
1900	13.858	21.423	57.679	68.954
2000	13.973	22.815	58.260	69.668
2100	14.077	24.218	58.820	70.352
2200	14.172	25.630	59.359	71.009
2300	14.259	27.052	59.880	71.641
2400	14.338	28.482	60.382	72.250
2500	14.411	29.919	60.869	72.836
2600	14.479	31.364	61.340	73.403
2700	14.541	32.815	61.797	73.951
2800	14.599	34.272	62.241	74.481
2900	14.654	35.734	62.672	74.994
3000	14.704	37.202	63.091	75.491
3200	14.797	40.153	63.896	76.443
3400	14.879	43.120	64.661	77.343
3600	14.953	46.103	65.389	78.196
3800	15.020	49.101	66.085	79.006
4000	15.082	52.111	66.750	79.778
4200	15.139	55.133	67.388	80.515
4400	15.193	58.167	68.001	81.221
4600	15.243	61.210	68.591	81.897
4800	15.291	64.264	69.159	82.547
5000	15.336	67.327	69.707	83.172
5200	15.379	70.398	70.236	83.774
5400	15.420	73.478	70.749	84.356
5600	15.460	76.566	71.245	84.917
5800	15.499	79.662	71.725	85.460
6000	15.536	82.765	72.192	85.986

Appendix 4.79 THERMODYNAMIC PROPERTIES OF H2O GAS

T	C_P^0	$(H - H_0^0)_T$	$-(F - H_0^0)_T/T$	S_T^0
DEG-K	CAL/MOLE DEG-K	KCAL/MOLE	CAL/MOLE DEG-K	CAL/MOLE DEG-K
100	8.386	0.816	28.568	36.723
200	7.952	1.590	33.936	41.885
273.15	7.981	2.172	36.414	44.367
298.15	8.003	2.372	37.110	45.066
400	8.163	3.194	39.452	47.438
500	8.396	4.022	41.240	49.284
600	8.662	4.875	42.713	50.838
700	8.943	5.755	43.973	52.194
800	9.236	6.664	45.077	53.407
900	9.536	7.602	46.065	54.512
1000	9.838	8.571	46.962	55.533
1100	10.137	9.570	47.785	56.484
1200	10.426	10.598	48.547	57.379
1300	10.703	11.655	49.259	58.224
1400	10.963	12.738	49.929	59.027
1500	11.206	13.847	50.561	59.792
1600	11.432	14.979	51.161	60.523
1700	11.641	16.133	51.732	61.222
1800	11.834	17.307	52.278	61.893
1900	12.012	18.499	52.801	62.538
2000	12.175	19.708	53.304	63.158
2100	12.325	20.934	53.787	63.756
2200	12.464	22.173	54.254	64.332
2300	12.591	23.426	54.704	64.889
2400	12.709	24.691	55.140	65.428
2500	12.818	25.967	55.562	65.949
2600	12.919	27.254	55.971	66.453
2700	13.013	28.551	56.368	66.943
2800	13.100	29.857	56.754	67.418
2900	13.182	31.171	57.130	67.879
3000	13.258	32.493	57.496	68.327
3200	13.396	35.159	58.200	69.187
3400	13.518	37.850	58.870	70.003
3600	13.627	40.565	59.511	70.779
3800	13.726	43.300	60.123	71.518
4000	13.815	46.055	60.711	72.224
4200	13.896	48.826	61.275	72.901
4400	13.971	51.613	61.819	73.549
4600	14.040	54.414	62.342	74.171
4800	14.105	57.228	62.848	74.770
5000	14.165	60.055	63.336	75.347
5200	14.222	62.894	63.809	75.904
5400	14.276	65.744	64.267	76.442
5600	14.328	68.605	64.711	76.962
5800	14.377	71.475	65.142	77.465
6000	14.424	74.355	65.561	77.954

Appendix 4.80 THERMODYNAMIC PROPERTIES OF H2S GAS

T	C_P^0	$(H^0 - H_0^0)/T$	$-(F^0 - H_0^0)/T$	S_T^0
DEG-K	CAL/MOLE DEG-K	KCAL/MOLE	CAL/MOLE DEG-K	CAL/MOLE DEG-K
100	7.949	0.795	32.446	40.395
200	7.978	1.590	37.956	45.908
273.15	8.104	2.178	40.437	48.411
298.15	8.170	2.381	41.136	49.123
400	8.509	3.230	43.494	51.569
500	8.900	4.100	45.309	53.509
600	9.321	5.011	46.817	55.169
700	9.755	5.965	48.117	56.638
800	10.182	6.962	49.267	57.969
900	10.587	8.000	50.303	59.192
1000	10.961	9.078	51.249	60.327
1100	11.300	10.192	52.123	61.388
1200	11.604	11.337	52.937	62.385
1300	11.874	12.511	53.700	63.324
1400	12.114	13.711	54.420	64.213
1500	12.327	14.933	55.101	65.056
1600	12.517	16.176	55.748	65.858
1700	12.685	17.436	56.366	66.622
1800	12.836	18.712	56.956	67.352
1900	12.971	20.003	57.522	68.049
2000	13.093	21.306	58.065	68.718
2100	13.203	22.621	58.587	69.359
2200	13.304	23.946	59.091	69.976
2300	13.395	25.281	59.577	70.569
2400	13.479	26.625	60.047	71.141
2500	13.557	27.977	60.502	71.693
2600	13.628	29.336	60.943	72.226
2700	13.694	30.702	61.370	72.742
2800	13.756	32.075	61.786	73.241
2900	13.814	33.453	62.189	73.725
3000	13.868	34.838	62.581	74.194
3200	13.968	37.621	63.335	75.092
3400	14.057	40.424	64.052	75.942
3600	14.139	43.244	64.735	76.748
3800	14.214	46.079	65.388	77.514
4000	14.283	48.929	66.013	78.245
4200	14.348	51.792	66.612	78.943
4400	14.409	54.668	67.188	79.612
4600	14.467	57.555	67.742	80.254
4800	14.522	60.454	68.276	80.871
5000	14.575	63.364	68.792	81.465
5200	14.626	66.284	69.290	82.037
5400	14.676	69.214	69.773	82.590
5600	14.723	72.154	70.240	83.125
5800	14.770	75.104	70.693	83.642
6000	14.816	78.062	71.134	84.144

Appendix 4.81 THERMODYNAMIC PROPERTIES OF NO2 GAS

T	C_p^0	$(H^0 - H_0^0)$	$-(F^0 - H_0^0)/T$	S_T^0
DEG-K	CAL/MOLE DEG-K	KCAL/MOLE	CAL/MOLE DEG-K	CAL/MOLE DEG-K
100	7.954	0.795	40.434	48.383
200	8.230	1.600	45.953	53.952
273.15	8.691	2.218	48.462	56.582
298.15	8.875	2.438	49.176	57.351
400	9.670	3.382	51.615	60.069
500	10.419	4.387	53.536	62.309
600	11.063	5.462	55.164	64.268
700	11.590	6.595	56.592	66.014
800	12.012	7.776	57.870	67.590
900	12.350	8.995	59.031	69.025
1000	12.622	10.244	60.097	70.341
1100	12.842	11.518	61.084	71.555
1200	13.023	12.811	62.004	72.680
1300	13.173	14.121	62.866	73.729
1400	13.300	15.445	63.677	74.710
1500	13.407	16.781	64.444	75.631
1600	13.500	18.126	65.171	76.499
1700	13.580	19.480	65.861	77.320
1800	13.651	20.842	66.520	78.099
1900	13.714	22.210	67.149	78.838
2000	13.770	23.585	67.751	79.543
2100	13.821	24.964	68.329	80.216
2200	13.867	26.348	68.884	80.860
2300	13.909	27.737	69.418	81.478
2400	13.948	29.130	69.933	82.071
2500	13.984	30.527	70.430	82.641
2600	14.018	31.927	70.910	83.190
2700	14.049	33.330	71.375	83.719
2800	14.079	34.737	71.825	84.231
2900	14.107	36.146	72.261	84.725
3000	14.134	37.558	72.685	85.204
3200	14.185	40.390	73.496	86.118
3400	14.231	43.232	74.264	86.979
3600	14.275	46.082	74.993	87.794
3800	14.316	48.941	75.688	88.567
4000	14.355	51.809	76.350	89.302
4200	14.393	54.683	76.984	90.004
4400	14.429	57.566	77.591	90.674
4600	14.465	60.455	78.174	91.316
4800	14.499	63.351	78.734	91.932
5000	14.533	66.255	79.274	92.525
5200	14.566	69.164	79.795	93.096
5400	14.598	72.081	80.298	93.646
5600	14.630	75.004	80.784	94.177
5800	14.661	77.933	81.255	94.691
6000	14.692	80.868	81.711	95.189

Appendix 4.82 THERMODYNAMIC PROPERTIES OF N2O GAS

T	C_P^0	$(H^0 - H_0^0)_T$	$-(F^0 - H_0^0)/T$	S_T^0
DEG-K	CAL/MOLE DEG-K	KCAL/MOLE	CAL/MOLE DEG-K	CAL/MOLE DEG-K
100	7.016	0.696	37.025	43.988
200	8.035	1.441	41.904	49.108
273.15	8.950	2.063	44.199	51.751
298.15	9.230	2.290	44.866	52.547
400	10.201	3.282	47.197	55.401
500	10.955	4.341	49.080	57.761
600	11.574	5.468	50.701	59.815
700	12.089	6.652	52.136	61.639
800	12.517	7.883	53.428	63.282
900	12.875	9.153	54.608	64.778
1000	13.173	10.456	55.694	66.150
1100	13.422	11.786	56.703	67.418
1200	13.632	13.139	57.646	68.595
1300	13.810	14.512	58.531	69.694
1400	13.962	15.901	59.365	70.723
1500	14.093	17.303	60.155	71.691
1600	14.206	18.719	60.905	72.604
1700	14.304	20.144	61.618	73.468
1800	14.390	21.579	62.300	74.288
1900	14.467	23.022	62.951	75.068
2000	14.535	24.472	63.576	75.812
2100	14.596	25.929	64.176	76.523
2200	14.651	27.391	64.753	77.203
2300	14.702	28.859	65.308	77.855
2400	14.747	30.331	65.844	78.482
2500	14.789	31.808	66.362	79.085
2600	14.828	33.289	66.862	79.666
2700	14.864	34.774	67.347	80.226
2800	14.898	36.262	67.817	80.767
2900	14.929	37.753	68.272	81.291
3000	14.958	39.247	68.715	81.797
3200	15.013	42.245	69.563	82.764
3400	15.062	45.252	70.367	83.676
3600	15.106	48.269	71.130	84.538
3800	15.148	51.295	71.857	85.356
4000	15.187	54.328	72.552	86.134
4200	15.223	57.369	73.217	86.876
4400	15.258	60.417	73.854	87.585
4600	15.291	63.472	74.466	88.264
4800	15.322	66.533	75.054	88.915
5000	15.353	69.601	75.621	89.541
5200	15.383	72.674	76.168	90.144
5400	15.411	75.754	76.697	90.725
5600	15.440	78.839	77.208	91.286
5800	15.467	81.930	77.703	91.828
6000	15.494	85.026	78.182	92.353

Appendix 4.83 THERMODYNAMIC PROPERTIES OF SO2 GAS

T	C_P^0	$(H_T^0 - H_0^0)$	$-(F_T^0 - H_0^0)/T$	S_T^0
DEG-K	CAL/MOLE DEG-K	KCAL/MOLE	CAL/MOLE DEG-K	CAL/MOLE DEG-K
100	8.013	0.796	41.975	49.933
200	8.695	1.628	47.533	55.671
273.15	9.313	2.286	50.103	58.472
298.15	9.529	2.521	50.839	59.296
400	10.392	3.536	53.378	62.219
500	11.129	4.614	55.392	64.620
600	11.719	5.757	57.107	66.703
700	12.175	6.953	58.612	68.545
800	12.527	8.189	59.959	70.195
900	12.800	9.456	61.180	71.687
1000	13.015	10.747	62.300	73.047
1100	13.188	12.058	63.335	74.296
1200	13.328	13.384	64.297	75.450
1300	13.443	14.722	65.196	76.521
1400	13.540	16.072	66.041	77.521
1500	13.623	17.430	66.838	78.458
1600	13.694	18.796	67.592	79.340
1700	13.757	20.168	68.308	80.172
1800	13.812	21.547	68.989	80.960
1900	13.861	22.931	69.639	81.708
2000	13.905	24.319	70.261	82.420
2100	13.945	25.711	70.856	83.099
2200	13.982	27.108	71.427	83.749
2300	14.017	28.508	71.977	84.371
2400	14.049	29.911	72.506	84.969
2500	14.079	31.318	73.016	85.543
2600	14.107	32.727	73.508	86.095
2700	14.133	34.139	73.984	86.628
2800	14.159	35.553	74.445	87.143
2900	14.183	36.971	74.892	87.640
3000	14.207	38.390	75.325	88.121
3200	14.251	41.236	76.153	89.040
3400	14.293	44.090	76.937	89.905
3600	14.332	46.953	77.680	90.723
3800	14.370	49.823	78.387	91.499
4000	14.407	52.701	79.062	92.237
4200	14.442	55.586	79.706	92.941
4400	14.477	58.478	80.323	93.613
4600	14.511	61.376	80.915	94.258
4800	14.544	64.282	81.484	94.876
5000	14.576	67.194	82.031	95.470
5200	14.609	70.112	82.559	96.043
5400	14.640	73.037	83.069	96.594
5600	14.672	75.969	83.562	97.127
5800	14.703	78.906	84.038	97.643
6000	14.734	81.850	84.500	98.142

AUTHOR INDEX

SUBJECT INDEX

A

Ac (actinium), 7, 11
Acetphenone, resonance energy, 121
Acoustical vibrations, 80
Adiabatic flame temperature, 151–154
Adiabatic process, definition, 150
Ag (silver), 7, 10
Al (aluminum):
  atomic energy levels, 17
  atomic weight, 7
  dissociation energy, 117
  electronic configuration, 10
  heat content, 88
  heat of formation, 113, 117
  ionization potential, 102
  thermal functions, 90
  thermodynamic properties, App. 2.1
AlBr, 32, App. 3.1
AlC, 32

AlCl, 32, App. 3.2
AlClF$_2$ (aluminum chlorodifluoride), 62, App. 4.1
AlClO (aluminum oxychloride), 62, App. 4.2
AlCl$_2$ (aluminum dichloride), 62, App. 4.3
AlCl$_2$F (aluminum dichlorofluoride), 62, App. 4.4
AlCl$_3$ (aluminum trichloride), 62, 88, App. 4.5
AlF, 32, 117, App. 3.3
AlFO (aluminum oxyfluoride), 62, App. 4.6
AlF$_2$ (aluminum difluoride), 42, 62, 117, App. 4.7
AlF$_3$ (aluminum trifluoride):
  dissociation energy, 117
  heat content, 88
  heat of formation, 117
  molecular constants, 62
  symmetry numbers, 42

452

T